D0008296

OUR NATURAL RESOURCES AND THEIR CONSERVATION

Photo by Gabriel Moulin, San Francisco

AMONG THE REDWOODS OF CALIFORNIA
Forest conservation was the initial movement in resource conservation.

Our Natural Resources and Their Conservation

A. E. PARKINS
George Peabody College for Teachers

J. R. WHITAKER
University of Wisconsin

EDITORS

CONTRIBUTORS

WALLACE W. ATWOOD
O. E. BAKER
NELS BENGTSON
H. H. BENNETT
RALPH BROWN
ROBERT M. BROWN
LOYAL DURAND, JR.
W. H. HAAS
H. C. HANSON
ELLSWORTH HUNTINGTON
GEORGE J. MILLER
A. E. PARKINS
EDWARD C. PROPHET
GEORGE T. RENNER
V. E. SHELFORD
GUY-HAROLD SMITH
J. RUSSELL SMITH
HELEN M. STRONG
S. S. VISHER
J. R. WHITAKER
FRANK WILLIAMS
LOUIS WOLFANGER

NEW YORK
JOHN WILEY & SONS, INC.
LONDON: CHAPMAN & HALL, LIMITED
1936

Printed in the U. S. A.

THE HADDON CRAFTSMEN, INC.
CAMDEN, N. J.

PREFACE

Conservation seeks to insure to society the maximum benefit from the use of our natural resources. It involves the making of inventories, efforts at preservation, the discovery and prompt employment of methods of more efficient use, and the renewal and even restoration of resources. As a local, state, or national program, it is predicated on the assumption that earth-resources, and the materials prepared from them, are vital elements in man's well-being, contributing both to the satisfaction of his material wants and to his so-called "higher needs"; on the fact that, in occupying any region, man tends to destroy the natural resources on which his very existence depends; and on the conviction that man has it within his power to retard or to stop the destruction of resources, or even to restore certain of them, provided that he wills to do so.

Conservation of natural resources is a timely field of action in the United States. The occupation of this continent has been accompanied by an unprecedented destruction of the natural landscape. Moreover, as the nation comes of age and the limits of its resources and the character of its needs begin to appear more fully, the necessity for greater care in the utilization and renewal of resources becomes impressive indeed. The movement is a timely one, also, because the period of reckless spending, which continued unabated through the first decades of this century, has not as yet been carried to the point of national bankruptcy. There is still time for making community, state, and nation among the best of places in which to live. It may be noted, too, that this awakening of the nation to the problems growing out of the "gutting of a continent" is in line with a world-wide concern regarding the material bases of national well-being—a concern prompted in part by the rise of barriers to international intercourse and in part by the impossibility today of solving the problem of the exhaustion of resources by expanding to unoccupied lands or to those inhabited by primitive, exploitable peoples.

Conservational programs involve both short-time and long-time views, and both governmental and private action. A forest fire may work great havoc in a few hours, yet to produce a saw log may require a century. Governmental direction is clearly required in protecting migratory wildlife, but without public cooperation there would need to be a game warden for nearly every hunter. Both the immediate and the distant future are of vital concern; and in practically every phase of the work there are tasks which private individuals must shoulder and others which require social cooperation through governmental agencies.

The objectives of conservation vary with the nature of the resources and the uses being made of them. For certain lands, such as the western ranges, the forms of ownership and management may need alteration. Some resources, water power among them, may well be put promptly to use, for they are relatively permanent even though limited. The biotic or life resources—forests, grasses, and wild animal life—can and should be renewed, or even restored in large measure to their original condition. Resources like the soil and ground water are easily damaged by use, but commonly need not be, if proper precautions are taken. Reclamation through irrigation or drainage may be necessary to enable some lands to contribute to the national welfare. Certain resources, and articles made from them, are destroyed by natural processes unless such action is restrained by man—examples are the decay of wood, the rusting of iron, and the damage done by insects and fungi to biotic resources. Some resources may be used to protect others—as the galvanizing of iron with zinc; and certain ones, such as copper, may be used over and over again. In the preparation of some resources, great care must be exercised to reduce the losses involved in the process. Where the utilization of one resource may destroy others, a judicious compromise is required. Certain resources exist in such limited amounts in our country—zinc, lead, petroleum, and others—that their efficient use becomes a matter of grave national concern, whereas others, being very abundant or renewable, should be substituted wherever feasible for those that are less abundant or non-renewable.

It is evident that conservation as here defined is a field of vast national import, and of such magnitude and range as to depend on the cooperation of nearly everyone. Contributions to theory and practice may be made by the layman and the scientist, by the philosopher and the practical man of affairs, by the social scientist and the natural scientist. In one way or another, each of the natural and social sciences can give, indeed is giving, some assistance, directly or indirectly.

The contributions of geography to the field of conservation have been both theoretical and practical. In the mid-nineteenth century, George P. Marsh formulated a general framework of a theory in his book entitled *Man and Nature, or Physical Geography as Modified by*

Human Action; and before and since the publication of this book studies in systematic and regional geography have helped to build up our knowledge of our natural resources and the problems arising from their exploitation. Geographers have also taken an active part in the practical application of their viewpoint and techniques to problems faced by the nation. Moreover, they have been doing most of the teaching of conservation, as a subject or field, in our colleges and also at elementary and secondary levels of instruction. The rising generation is learning largely through geography teachers and textbooks about the aims and practices of conservation. These facts are not meant, in any sense, to imply that teaching in this field is exclusively the function of geography, but are set forth as essential to an understanding of the background and purposes of this book, which is prepared, for the most part, by geographers.

The plan of cooperative authorship by persons each writing about one field is open to a number of valid criticisms: the treatment of each phase cannot meet the detailed needs of students specializing in that particular subdivision; uniformity of style is sacrificed; some duplication of material is well-nigh unavoidable; and individual opinions may be contradictory—a situation almost certain to arise in any survey which presents policies for the future as well as facts about the past and present. These criticisms are not entirely derogatory, however. Variety of style may be an asset, not a liability; occasional duplication is not likely to make the book less teachable; inequality of treatment may reflect differences in the progress made in the several phases of the work as well as differences in authorship; and conflicts of opinion present an opportunity for the exercise of the reader's judgment. In brief, this volume is a symposium, written by scientists each of whom for many years has worked and thought in the field of which he writes. If it exhibits the shortcomings, it also shares in the favorable features, of a symposium.

Some positive advantages of the plan may well be called to mind. It provides for a general survey of the entire field—a major need in furthering the educational section of the conservational program. It makes possible a timeliness of content, both in terms of principles and of problems, which would be difficult of attainment except through joint authorship. It is far more authoritative than the work of any one man could be—save for the very few who have given decades of study to the field as a whole. It combines the viewpoints and contributions of the administrator, field worker, theorist, and teacher. It furnishes materials written for the intelligent student and the general reader rather than the specialist. Moreover, it provides a common philosophical background for the elementary student of the subject.

Particular attention is given throughout the book to the extent and distribution of our natural resources and to their service in regional and national development. Each problem discussed is viewed as the outgrowth of natural and cultural conditions in specific parts of our country; emphasis is placed on both the natural and the human factors involved in the genesis of current problems; and each problem is viewed not in isolation but in its relation to other problems associated with it. The central purpose is to give a balanced, concrete view of resources and problems in their actual setting as a part of the organic units concerned, whether regions, states, or the nation. Such a survey must depend, quite obviously, on contributions from somewhat specialized fields, like geology, forestry, agriculture, and engineering, as well as from the more general fields, such as geography, economics, and history—a fact clearly set forth in the bibliographies. The debt to those who have worked out a synthesis of the entire field—notably to Charles R. Van Hise (1851-1918)—is also evident.

The arrangement of the parts and chapters followed in this volume is for the most part logical, yet in some measure purely arbitrary. Since the material presented in each major division (designated as Part I, Part II, etc.) is relatively complete within itself, it is not necessary in teaching to follow the order here used. Good teaching demands that the dominating interests of students and teachers in the various regions of our country be considered in determining the order of presentation. Tradition has to a certain degree dictated the list of major topics selected for discussion—the ones that have for the last quarter of a century received attention in our colleges and schools. A few new topics which represent developments within the last decade or so have been added to the traditional list.

The authors and editors (who also are authors) acknowledge with gratitude their great dependence on the publications of the federal and state departments, bureaus, offices, and services from which so much of the source material has been derived. We wish also to thank the various organizations, private and public, that have supplied us many of the illustrations.

A. E. Parkins
J. R. Whitaker
Editors

CONTENTS

OUR NATURAL RESOURCES AND THEIR CONSERVATION

PART I

CHAPTER I

THE CONSERVATION MOVEMENT IN AMERICA

BY WALLACE W. ATWOOD
Clark University

THE GROWTH OF THE CONSERVATION MOVEMENT

During the Pioneer Days. Most of those who established this nation and most of those vigorous pioneers who cooperated in the remarkable national development as the frontier moved westward across the Appalachians, through the interior plains, and, in time, to the Pacific Ocean, helped themselves lavishly and were guilty of extravagant and wasteful use of the resources provided by nature, in what is now the domain of the United States. They proceeded for nearly three hundred years on the theory that the resources of this land were inexhaustible. It was a perfectly natural reaction for frontiersmen in a wilderness region so vast that they knew of no limitations. Even today settlers in the frontier zones of Canada and Alaska seldom restrain themselves from appropriating for their own use anything which nature has made available.

The American pioneers found extensive areas of fertile soils. Much of the land was clothed with magnificent forests of mixed hardwood and softwood trees, and there was an abundance of fish and wild game. The length of the growing season and the amount and distribution of rainfall throughout much of the land were adequate for agriculture. Vast supplies of fuel and of useful metals were discovered. Excellent harbors were available on each of the coastlines, and several large navigable rivers provided highways of travel far into the interior. Many of the smaller streams had steep gradients and were so frequently interrupted by falls or rapids that they simplified the problem of utilizing water power in the development of manufacturing industries. Nature had provided almost ideal natural conditions for human occupancy, and the chief concern of the pioneers was the utilization of the natural wealth in order that they might produce goods or money for the maintenance of their lives, for the building of homes, and for the development of new industries.

The Great Wastefulness. When forests were cleared away to provide farm lands, huge logs of birch, beech, oak, walnut, maple, hickory, pine, and hemlock were piled up and burned. Many trees were unnecessarily bled to death in order to produce naval stores. Soils were overcropped, pasture lands over-grazed, fish and game ruthlessly destroyed. Hunters in hiding were known to kill hundreds of elk or moose, as the animals were migrating from one feeding ground to another, and take but a small souvenir from each carcass in order to demonstrate to their associates their own great skill and prowess. Later, in the mining of coal, great columns of the black fuel were left and but a fraction of the most salable of that resource was taken from the ground. Then the mines were allowed to collapse or fill with water, making further exploration and development unprofitable. For many years great torches burned day and night in western Pennsylvania, where natural gas had been released from the ground by those who were drilling for oil. The complete loss of that most ideal of all natural fuels was shameful. A state geologist of West Virginia once said that the natural gas being wasted in his state alone was equivalent to dumping a freight carload of coal into the ocean every minute, day and night, year in and year out. The great torches now burning in the mid-continental oil and gas fields demonstrate that some problems of conservation have not yet been solved.

Early Signs of Appreciation. Nevertheless, a few examples of an appreciation of the importance of conservation and wiser use of the natural resources are recorded in the history of the early days of the nation. By 1670, certain of the towns of Massachusetts were becoming "much straitened for building timber," and before another one hundred years had passed, the larger cities such as Boston and Philadelphia were experiencing a shortage in the easily available timber resources. In 1681 William Penn signed an ordinance which required that, in clearing land, one acre in every five should be left in trees. He may be thought of as one of the first in public life who recognized the importance of preserving some of our forests and thus providing fuel and timber for the future.

There is one curious example of an incipient national idea of conservation which took form in 1828 when President John Quincy Adams, recognizing the importance of live-oak timber in the construction of battleships for our Navy, established a naval station in the live-oak region of Pensacola, Florida. He also had a survey made of the supply of live-oak near the coasts of Georgia, Florida, and North Carolina. He withdrew 30,000 acres of land where the live-oak flourished on the Island of Santa Rosa, which is across the bay from the new Pensacola Naval Station, and there provided for the planting and cultivation of live-oak trees. Thus, in the early part of the nineteenth century, a president of the United States, in some degree recognizing the importance of conservation, established a national reservation and inaugurated careful, if not scientific, forestry. This project was abandoned, however, during the immediately succeeding administration of Andrew Jackson.

Scientists Recognize Importance of Conservation. As the decades of the nineteenth century passed, more and more of the scientific men of the nation recognized that we were rapidly depleting certain of our natural resources, and that among those resources some were not replaceable. In 1873 a memorial was prepared and presented to Congress by the American Association for the Advancement of Science, to be reinforced in 1890 by another statement, urging upon the Congress of the United States the importance of passing laws which should lead to the conservation of our natural resources. Since 1897, the National Academy of Sciences has taken an active part in promoting an appreciation of the increasing necessity for conservation.

American Forestry Association Organized. In 1875 a group of citizens came together in Chicago and organized the American Forestry Association with the purpose of promoting publicly an appreciation of scientific forestry and timber culture. This was the first well-organized movement to influence national public sentiment in America. Congress soon authorized the Department of Agriculture to appoint a forestry agent, and Dr. Franklin B. Hough of Lowell, Massachusetts, who had been identified with various projects for the protection of forests, was selected for that position. When Carl Schurz, the German immigrant, became Secretary of the Interior in 1877, he used his influence in support of the scientific care of the forests and was one of the first to recommend the establishment of federal forest reservations.

The First National Forest. The American Forestry Association continued its efforts to influence public sentiment in favor of the establishment of national forests and the conservation of our timber reserves, but not until 1891 did Congress pass an act giving the president authority to withdraw areas of the public domain as forest reserves. In the year immediately following, President Harrison created the Yellowstone National Park Timberland Reserve in northwestern Wyoming. Two hundred and seventy-two years had passed since the landing of the Pilgrims before the first national forest was established. Before President Harrison's term of office expired, however, he had set

Courtesy of American Forestry Association

Fig. 1. Franklin B. Hough, First Forestry Agent in the United States Department of Agriculture—Appointed 1876.

Courtesy of American Forestry Association

Fig. 2. Carl Schurz, the Forest-minded Secretary of the Interior—1877-1881.

aside 13,000,000 acres as forest reservations, and President Cleveland, who followed President Harrison in office, withdrew 21,000,000 additional acres from the national domain and placed them in the forest reserve system. All these forest lands set aside by Presidents Harrison and Cleveland were in the western part of the United States.

Plans for the administration of our national forests were but slowly worked out. In 1898, Gifford Pinchot, who had been a conspicuous figure in all movements looking toward forest conservation, was appointed head of a Division of Forestry in the Department of Agriculture. Strangely enough, however, the national forests remained for several years in the Department of the Interior, and thus the government foresters were separated from the national forests and had no authority in the administration of those reservations.

Theodore Roosevelt Enters the Scene. Not until Theodore Roosevelt entered upon his presidency in 1901 was the nation truly aroused to the importance of conservation. With his great enthusiasm and energy he used his voice, his pen, and his official influence to

Courtesy of American Forestry Association

FIG. 3. Major J. W. Powell, Author of "Lands of the Arid Region," Director of the United States Geologic Survey (1881-1894).

Courtesy of American Forestry Association

FIG. 4. Gifford Pinchot, Chief Forester for President Theodore Roosevelt, and a Pioneer and Enthusiastic Supporter of the Conservation Movement in America.

awaken the nation to an appreciation of the waste that was going on and the responsibility we should assume for the wise use of our resources. After numerous attempts he finally succeeded in placing the national forests under the direction of the Bureau of Forestry in the Department of Agriculture. There they have remained to this day. This was accomplished by an act of Congress passed February 1, 1905.

Theodore Roosevelt was determined to carry forward the conservation movement, and during his administration he increased the forest reservations to more than 100,000,000 acres. He roused the enmity of the land grabbers and many pioneer settlers who were trying to gain control of larger and larger amounts of the forested lands, or of lands containing other very valuable natural resources. In 1907 a western senator proposed an amendment to the appropriation bill prohibiting the president from setting aside any more national forests in the six states of California, Washington, Oregon, Idaho, Wyoming, and Montana. The amendment was passed, but before it went into effect, Theodore Roosevelt, who had already received reports from the forest service as to the desirable lands in those states which should be added to the national forests, withdrew 16,000,000 more acres from the public domain and placed them in the national forests. In his own characteristic way he remarked: "The opponents of the forest service turned handsprings in their wrath."

Thus the birth of the idea of conservation was slow and painful. Many opposed any curtailment of their liberties in the use of whatever nature had provided, or any restraint in the wasteful and lavish appropriation of those natural resources for their own profit.

The White House Conference. Each year President Theodore Roosevelt became more and more determined to promote the cause of conservation. When the suggestion was made to him that a White House conference be held to which the governors of all states and territories should be invited, he acted promptly and sent out the invitations. On May 13, 1908, he called to order in the East Room of the White House a conference which, in some respects, was unique in the history of this nation. He had present the vice-president of the United States, seven members of the cabinet, nine justices of the Supreme Court, many members of Congress, the governors of thirty-four states, representatives of each of the other twelve states, the governors of all the territories, including Alaska, Hawaii, and the Philippine Islands, the president of the board of commissioners of the District of Columbia, representatives of sixty-eight national societies, and many special guests. Also, members of the Inland Waterways Commission were present.

In opening the White House Conference, President Theodore Roosevelt presented in a remarkable address his convictions, and those which the scientists had come to hold through the preceding decades, of the importance of conserving our national resources. He emphasized the value to the nation of the proper use of the great variety of gifts which nature had bestowed upon this nation. After this speech, many of the scientific men present gave equally strong addresses, and several of the governors and eminent citizens stated their conviction that the conference was of supreme importance to the nation. Among the papers presented some dealt with the mineral resources, others with conservation of soils, waterways, water power, and water supply. The care and preservation of the national forests commanded a large amount of attention. Jointly, the speakers presented facts which were actually startling to all present and to all those who read the public statements relative to the conference. The governors of the several states were so impressed with the importance of the problems presented at this conference that they drew up a set of supporting resolutions, and many of them resolved, upon their return to their respective capitals, to appoint state commissions on conservation. This was the first time in the history of the United States of America that the governors of the several states had been called together in Washington to consider a problem of national welfare.

The National Conservation Commission. Immediately after the White House Conference, President Theodore Roosevelt appointed a national conservation commission. This commission consisted of forty-nine prominent citizens; about one-third were engaged in politics, one-third in industries, and one-third in scientific work. Gifford Pinchot was made the chairman. The commission was charged with making an inventory of existing available natural resources. It was directed to report as to the portion of those resources which had been utilized and exhausted, the rate of increase in the consumption of those resources, and the length of time they might be expected to last if the then rate of increase in use continued. This inventory was presented to the governors of the states at a meeting held on December 8, 1908, and, with their endorsement, was presented to the president on January 11, 1909.

North American and World Conferences. President Theodore Roosevelt's ideas of conservation continued to expand, and his enthusiasm for this subject led to his calling the North American Conservation Conference, to which he invited representatives from Canada, Newfoundland, and Mexico. This conference was called to order on February 18, 1909. Again the broad principles of conservation were presented and received general and enthusiastic approval.

But this movement was not enough to satisfy the energetic president. He desired to impress the entire world with the importance of conservation of natural resources, and to point out the significance of the conservation of natural resources in the various countries, not only to countries in which such resources were found, but to all nations. He called upon the powers of the world to meet at The Hague to consider the conservation of natural resources of the entire earth.

Vast Areas Withdrawn from Entry. During Theodore Roosevelt's administration the secretary of the interior was James R. Garfield, and through him the administration withdrew from private entry large areas of public land to be held until the resources within those areas could be thoroughly studied. They included lands where coal was known to be beneath the surface, where petroleum or natural gas was likely to be present, where phosphate rock was known to exist, and where it was believed important potash deposits were present. Other areas bordering streams were withdrawn anticipating a need of water-power sites. Altogether 234,000,000 acres of land were withdrawn from private entry during this one administration. In 1911 Congress passed a bill which provided for the purchase by the government of privately owned lands that had been approved by the Bureau of Forestry as appropriate and desirable additions to the national forests. This has made possible the establishment of national forests in the eastern half of the country where most of the land had passed into private ownership before the idea of conservation was born.

Theodore Roosevelt was commended by members of all parties for his services in the cause of conservation of our natural resources and for convincing the public of the necessity of this program. Some immediately placed him among the greatest statesmen of this nation; some even pronounced him one of the greatest statesmen of any nation of any time. Certain it is that a movement which had been very slow in taking form in the United States received, within a few years, a tremendous impetus due to the dynamic influence of Presidents Benjamin Harrison, Grover Cleveland, and Theodore Roosevelt.

Dr. Van Hise's Book Appears. Soon after the White House conference closed and after the publication of the report of the National Conservation Commission, Charles Richard Van Hise, then president of the University of Wisconsin and long a member of the United States Geological Survey and a member of the White House Conference, prepared and presented a series of lectures on the conservation of our natural resources before the students and faculty of the University of Wisconsin. In 1910 he published, in revised form, the lectures which he had delivered at the University, and for twenty-five years his volume, *The Conservation of Natural Resources in the United States,* has served as the most concise and authoritative statement of the situation which the United States had faced in the care and use of its natural resources. This book has been the basis for many courses of instruction in the colleges and universities of this country and has been instrumental in developing public appreciation of the problems involved in the conservation of natural resources.

The Conservation Movement Checked. Even with a strong public opinion aroused in favor of conservation and with various commissions appointed in the different states to study the problem, President Theodore Roosevelt was forced to meet keen disappointment. Bills which he helped to formulate and had introduced into Congress to provide for the necessary expenses of the National Conservation Commission were defeated. Congress, furthermore, prohibited the several departments of the government from serving such a commission and from making further inventories or special studies of the natural resources of the country. There was sufficient opposition from those who believed that the resources should be free for exploitation to prevent further progressive movements by the administration. The same opposition held over and was effective during the administration of President Taft, preventing Congress during that period from promoting any measures which would further the cause of conservation.

SOME RECENT PHASES OF THE CONSERVATION MOVEMENT

Public Sentiment Aroused. The opposition which had thus appeared in Congress persuaded a number of public-spirited citizens to organize the National Conservation Association. The honorary president of this association, when formed in 1909, was Charles W. Eliot, then president of Harvard University. The active president was Gifford Pinchot. Throughout the nation various societies were organized for the promotion of a greater interest in conservation. Many societies appointed committees on conservation. Lecturers were called for, and many scientific men, educators, and public-spirited citizens throughout the nation contributed in this effort to arouse favorable public opinion. The American Forestry Association undertook active support of the program, and that organization, throughout its history, has been very effective in educating the American people to the importance of care of our forests and the possibility of producing a forest crop adequate for all our needs.

The National Parks. The birth of the national park idea occurred in 1869, while a little party of explorers were sitting about a campfire in northwestern Wyoming. The men in that party were working out plans for apportioning among themselves, under the homestead or settlement laws, the different portions of that weird wonderland where they were in camp, when a Montana lawyer, Cornelius Hedges, proposed instead that the entire area should be preserved by the government for all the people. The men all agreed, and upon emerging from the wilderness, hastened to Helena where they drew up the bill, which in 1872, when passed by Congress, established Yellowstone National Park. Eighteen years later Congress established the Yosemite, the

Courtesy of American Forestry Association

Fig. 5. Stephen T. Mather, on Inspection Trip in Glacier National Park.

Mather was the first director of the National Park Service. He established high standards and a firm foundation for a great public service.

Sequoia, and the General Grant National Parks. These were followed by Mount Rainier National Park in 1899, and Crater Lake in 1902. Little by little the national park movement has grown and has spread eastward, until today there are several such parks in the central and eastern portion of the country. There are in all 24 national parks, one national historical park, 11 national military parks, and 67 national monuments. The national monuments are areas of scientific or historic significance, but they do not have the superb grandeur or great natural interest that should characterize a national park.

The National Park Service. As the conservation movement developed and the desire for national parks became well established, it became necessary to form the National Park Service. This was done in April, 1917, when Franklin K. Lane, then Secretary of the Interior, secured funds for this purpose from Congress and appointed Stephen T. Mather, who had been assistant secretary of the interior, as the first director of the National Park Service. To Mr. Mather, who served during the twelve formative years of that Service, and who gave enthusiastically of his personal resources, his energy, and finally his health, are due the highest praise and credit for the administration of these wonderland reservations. When Mr. Mather took charge, Secretary Lane issued to him the following statement, which has been called the "Magna Charta of the National Parks":

> The administration policy to which the new service will adhere is based on three broad principles: First, that the National Parks must be maintained in absolutely unimpaired form for the use of future generations as well as those of our own time; second, that they are set apart for the use, observation, health and pleasure of the people; and, third, that the national interest must dictate all decisions affecting public or private enterprise in the parks. Every activity of the service is subordinate to the duties imposed upon it to faithfully preserve the parks for posterity in essentially their natural state. . . . You should not permit the leasing of park lands for summer homes. . . . Every opportunity should be afforded the public, wherever possible, to enjoy the national parks in the manner that best satisfies the individual tastes. . . . All outdoor sports which may be maintained consistently with the observation of the safeguards thrown around the national parks by law will be heartily indorsed and aided wherever possible. The educational as well as the recreational use of the national parks should be encouraged in every practicable way. . . . Low-priced camps operated by concessionaires should be maintained, as well as comfortable and even luxurious hotels wherever the volume of travel warrants the establishment of these classes of accommodations. . . . You should encourage all movements looking to outdoor living. . . . The national park system as now constituted should not be lowered in standard, dignity, and prestige by the inclusion of areas which express in less than the highest terms the particular class or kind of exhibit which they represent.

The National Parks Association. In 1919 the National Parks Association came into existence, and that organization has persistently worked for the preservation of all the superb natural wonderlands of this country that are especially valuable for scientific, educational, or inspirational purposes. The Association has endeavored to prevent any substandard areas from being included in the national parks, and it has always opposed measures which would allow the use of the natural resources within the parks for private gain. The National Parks Association has tried to develop throughout the nation an enthusiastic appreciation of the parks and a desire on the part of all visitors to preserve, as far as possible, the primitive beauty of these areas. It has directly promoted the educational program now well organized in the national parks.

Many Organizations Cooperate. As the conservation movement gained still greater momentum, the Izaak Walton League and the Audubon Societies took up the cause and contributed their influence in support of the conservation of wildlife. Women's clubs throughout the country called for speakers and appointed committees on conservation. State park commissions were set up, and an enthusiasm for national monuments and national historic sites appeared among many of these organizations. In California an organization called the "Save the Redwoods League" came into existence, and, as a private society, it has accomplished a remarkable piece of work in the repurchase of vast areas where the primitive beauty and grandeur of the redwood groves are being preserved. Those magnificent forests, located near the coast north of San Francisco, with trees 1,200 to 1,500 years old, 10 to 15 feet in diameter, and nearly 300 feet tall, cannot be matched for beauty anywhere in the world.

United States Geological Survey Assists. In connection with the movement for the wise use or conservation of our natural resources the United States Geological Survey has played a very important part. Members of that Survey are charged with the classification of public lands with respect to mineral wealth, water power, and agricultural values. The facts regarding the national domain are made available in Survey publications. The wholesale fraud which was practiced in some parts of the country previous to 1905, through acquiring, as if for farming purposes, under the homestead laws, lands which actually contained valuable fuels or other mineral resources beneath the surface, had to be stopped. Drastic action was necessary to prevent looting of the nation's treasures. The Geological Survey is also the government's guardian of power sites, and more than 6,000,000 acres of public lands are now included in power-site reserves. Some idea of the extent of the vast resources on the surface and below the surface of the earth, held by the United States, may be obtained from the following table, published by the United States Government in 1931.

TABLE 1

NATURAL RESOURCES, SURFACE AND SUBSURFACE, HELD BY THE UNITED STATES

	Acres
Areas in national forests (net)	135,971,883
All minerals reserved (stock-raising homestead entries)	56,134,312
Areas patented with reservation to the U. S. for oil, gas, phosphate, nitrate, potash, or asphaltic minerals	1,571,743
Areas patented with reservation of coal in United States	14,522,906
All minerals reserved in patented lands other than stock-raising homesteads	77,273
Lands certified to states with coal or other mineral reserved	617,815
National parks	5,935,912
National monuments	130,599
Gold, silver, and quicksilver reserved to the U. S. in patented Spanish and Mexican land grants (estimated)	2,040,881
Indian lands owned or controlled by the U. S.	70,993,326
Specific withdrawals:	
Coal lands	29,825,444
Oil lands	5,183,096
Oil shale (specific)	156,147
Oil shale (general, estimated)	4,000,000
Phosphate	2,004,765
Potash	9,411,939
Power sites	6,587,865
Public water	419,339
Reservoir sites	254,050
Helium	12,255
Reservoir sites (Arizona, New Mexico, and Oregon)	1,074,550
Reclamation	19,034,330
Miscellaneous	7,668,627

The Rental or Royalty Basis. Individual citizens are not prevented from developing the resources in the lands held by the nation. Congress has provided that certain resources may be developed on a royalty basis and that some lands may be leased or rented. By leasing the coal lands alone, half a million dollars in royalties came in during the single year 1930. In that same year $4,000,000 was paid to the United States Treasury for oil and gas royalties and $1,500,000 as additional royalties on petroleum reserves. It is possible for individuals, by paying a rental charge, to establish summer homes in the national forests and for ranchmen to arrange, on a payment basis, for the pasturage of livestock in these forests, or for lumbermen to engage in the marketing of mature trees which have been selected by the foresters and marked for cutting.

Conservation does not interfere with private ownerships which have been established. It does not call for, or justify, any confiscation of personal or real property. The principles of conservation do not interfere with the acquiring by individuals of property rights from one another. Our national conservation policy, however, may prevent individuals from acquiring more of the public lands.

Conservation by Wilbur and Du Puy. In 1931 Ray Lyman Wilbur, who was secretary of the interior during the administration of President Herbert Hoover, prepared and published, with the help of William Atherton Du Puy, a volume in which he presented a summary of the various conservation projects supervised by the Department of

Courtesy of National Park Service

FIG. 6. Clean-up Work of the CCC, along the East Side of Jackson Lake.
The Tetons in the distance are in the Grand Teton National Park.

the Interior. This volume presents in a very interesting style many of the national problems in conservation, and it undoubtedly has assisted in maintaining a favorable public opinion for the work which the government is doing in the field of conservation.

Franklin D. Roosevelt Enters the Scene. On March 4, 1933, when Franklin D. Roosevelt was inagurated President of the United States, the nation was in the midst of a terrible depression. During the three preceding years millions of men and women had been thrown out of employment, and the savings of many families had been exhausted. Many of these men had graduated from high schools and colleges and could not find work. Among the emergency plans made to provide employment and give relief to those in need, several were in the field of conservation. Civilian Conservation Camps were established in the national forests where hundreds of thousands of young men were given wholesome outdoor occupation. They were put to work on various types of forestry. Trails, fire lanes, and highways were constructed. In many of the forests dead timber and débris were cleared away, and in burnt-over areas replanting was undertaken on a large scale.

Several million dollars was provided for the study of soil erosion, and several areas were selected for intensive experimentation, in the hope that methods would be discovered or invented which farmers might use to prevent the loss of soils. Special plans were made to maintain the fertility of the soils in areas of good croplands and to allow the poorer marginal lands to revert to grassland. If the latter plans can be successfully carried out it is hoped that devastating dust storms during periods of drought may be avoided or at least greatly diminished. The Tennessee Valley Authority, financed by large appropriations by Congress, undertook the construction of a number of reservoirs in the valley of the Tennessee, which should help to prevent floods and make a large amount of water power available. That organization has drawn up extensive plans for the conservation of soils and forests and is working on others for the utilization of all lands within the area under study.

The National Resources Board was appointed by the president, charged with the responsibility of taking another inventory of the natural resources of the nation, and the National Planning Board was appointed, the program of which includes some of the problems of conservation.

THE CONSERVATION PROBLEM TODAY

Each Year Forests Are Burned. According to Forest Service reports there are, on the average, more than 156,000 forest fires annually, and 90 per cent of them are avoidable. These figures are based on the average for the years 1926 to 1930. On the average these fires burn over more than 141,000,000 acres of land. They have contributed, furthermore, to the unproductive nature of 81,000,000 acres of land formerly forested which nature, apparently, cannot reforest without assistance. The destruction of forests on watersheds has caused dangerous runoffs and floods, and has prevented the hillsides from holding the water which would otherwise have been available for streams or, possibly, for irrigation purposes later in the season. From experiments conducted in California, the eroded material from burned-over areas was found to be 2,300 times as great as from unburned areas. The destruction to life and property due to floods in the lowlands bordering streams that rise in deforested areas is beyond calculation. The forest fires that are started intentionally and those that are caused by the carelessness of campers, or by those who throw lighted cigarettes from the saddle while on the trail, are disgraceful.

Pasture Lands Are Over-grazed. In extensive areas of the semiarid and arid portions of the west, where stock-raising homesteads were established, we now find ruined fences and abandoned homes, standing as pitiful evidence of human errors. Settlers have been guilty repeatedly of over-grazing lands and thus making them entirely unfit for grazing or greatly reducing their stock-carrying power. Today 50 per cent of the sheep and 16 per cent of the cattle are raised in the public lands states, and most of them are pastured on the public domain. With the consequent removal of the forage cover, both stream and wind erosion have greatly increased.

Mr. E. A. Sherman of the Forest Service said:

> This is the way deserts start. Excessive grazing, which destroys the protective vegetative cover and permits the ground to be trampled into dust, and the plowing of naturally well-sodded grazing lands for grain crops make it easy for the wind to whip away the dry soil and develop into a destructive dust storm. Wind erosion on the plains is like water erosion in states farther east in its power to destroy rich land in a few years and to transform broad stretches of country into devastated badlands.

Soil Is Lost. It is asserted that erosion is costing the American farmers at least $200,000,000 annually. Large quantities of plant food are taken by the streams each year to the sea. Rich topsoil in the cotton belt has been known to be washed away at the rate of 23 tons per acre during a 5-inch rainfall. Mr. Bennett (see Chapter IV), one of the experts on soil-erosion problems, reports that erosion of a 2 per cent slope amounted to 40 tons of soil material per acre, with a 27-inch annual rainfall. He points out that more than 40 tons of soil per acre was washed away during a single rainy period in northeastern Kansas. The destruction of the sod, in many places, has led not only to disastrous erosion, but also to the silting up of costly irrigation works and irrigation reservoirs with what is often the best of soils. Both overgrazing and deforestation are very definitely related to the problem of soil conservation. It is estimated that 15,000,000 acres of formerly tilled soils have been totally destroyed by erosion in the United States and that approximately 864,000,000 acres have been affected by destructive gullying. Soil erosion has become one of the vital problems to many farmers and therefore to the nation. In some places the deepening of gullies has lowered the water table and caused the desiccation of the effective soil which was supporting the plant life. An almost immediate decline in the wheat or the corn yield per acre results from such desiccation.

Wildlife Requires Protection. The preservation of animal life presents many difficult and obscure problems. The more beautiful and more conspicuous animals and flowering plants catch the eye of the hunters; they go first. When a plant species which certain animals need is removed, the fauna dependent upon it goes also. Birds, mammals, and insects that dwell in or on its bark or among its foliage must disappear. When a forest is removed, animal life numbering hundreds, possibly thousands, of species, is likely to go. The elimination of the troublesome coyote would probably complicate the rodent situation and it might make conditions worse rather than better. Over-fishing, or fishing at the wrong times of the year, threatens the fish food supply. The prevention of salmon from migrating from the sea up the fresh-water streams during the spawning season is intolerable. The pollution of waters in the industrial areas, especially in New York and Illinois, presents problems in the conservation of fish. Oyster beds have been seriously affected by pollution. The fight against alligators in Florida resulted in a decreased supply of fish. "This was entirely contrary to expectation. The alligators were found to prey mostly upon turtles which fed largely on fish eggs."

The conservation of the fur seals of the north Pacific involves international relationships. It is being accomplished by a treaty between Canada, Japan, and the United States. The drainage of large swamp areas, which in many cases has not proved as profitable for farmers as was expected, has reduced the area where waterfowl could stop during periods of migration. The over-production of game has brought on peculiar problems, as in the Kaibab National Forest which borders the Grand Canyon in northern Arizona. There the deer were protected until they multiplied and were so numerous that sufficient forage was not available. The deer in some sections of Pennsylvania have so increased as to become a pest. Adjustment of wildlife to an ever-changing environment is thus seen to be exceedingly difficult. The transfer of plant and animal species by man to different habitats is dangerous, at present, because of our imperfect knowledge of ecology. The problems of conservation are so intimately interrelated and so exceedingly complex that we have only begun to solve them.

Wise Reclamation of Lands Not Easy. With the very best of intentions the national government has undertaken many large reclamation projects, and, by establishing reservoirs and building canals through which the waters are taken to arid or semiarid lands, the frontier of the deserts has been pushed back and floods have been prevented. Some of these projects have been financed in part from federal water licenses, from royalties derived from mineral leases, and from rentals from potassium deposits.

But many irrigation projects end in disaster. Farmers cannot afford to cultivate the lands and pay the necessary costs for irrigation unless the marketing conditions and prices for their crops are such as to yield a fair profit. The over-watering of the land, in several sections, has resulted in the saturation of the soil with alkalis which prevent crops from growing, and in those places expensive plans are sometimes undertaken to rinse the soils and remove the excess of alkali. Each individual farmer should learn how his particular soil and his particular crops should be irrigated. It should be remembered, also, that irrigation agriculture may be but temporary. Few places in the world are as fortunate as the valley of the Nile, where irrigation has been successfully carried on through centuries of time. There natural conditions are peculiarly favorable. Those lands have their periods of flooding and drying which alternate regularly. After all our efforts in the reclamation of arid lands, the total value of crops grown on irrigated lands included in these projects is only three-fourths of one per cent of the total crop value of the nation.

Modern Conservation Has Many Phases. As our ideas of conservation have developed we have seen them expand to include not only the care of the forests and wonderlands, but also the preservation of certain recreational and historic sites, the maintenance of the fertility of soils, the prevention of soil erosion, the careful mining of metals and of fuels, the protection of wildlife, including the fish of the fresh waters and of the salt waters near the continent, the preservation of primitive beauty in the landscape, and finally, the conservation of the human life and culture of the nation. Public opinion has become so favorable to the ideas of conservation that many projects are represented by their promoters to be in the field of conservation in order to secure popular support for those projects.

Its True Meaning. Conservation does not mean restriction from all use; it means the elimination of waste in the use of our natural resources. Conservation has been well defined as *wise use*. The supporters

"We May Need Some of That Some Time"

Courtesy Better Homes and Gardens

FIG. 7. "Waste" Working Assiduously and Subtilely.

For many years Jay N. Darling ("Ding") with brush and pen has been appealing to millions of readers of the printed page to give thought to conservation but particularly coordinated conservation. We have failed to recognize the interlocking character of our resources. Too often in the past, and also in the present, the various agencies of conservation and reclamation have worked at cross purposes.

Darling is now (1936) Acting President of the General Wildlife Federation. Formerly he was Chief of the United States Biological Survey.

of this idea aim to educate all those who are engaged in the development of the resources on or beneath the surface of the earth, to realize that it is intolerable that we, who occupy this land for a few years, should ruthlessly destroy those elements in the landscape or in the earth that are of permanent value to mankind. It is intolerable for us to destroy the beauty in the landscape. All citizens should avoid wasteful use and in every way humanly possible should prevent the unnecessary destruction of these gifts which nature has provided.

Our Responsibility. As you read the following chapters in this volume strive to recognize the significance of the problems presented and to become acquainted with the principles of conservation as applied to the particular resource or group of natural resources under consideration. The college men and women of today will hold many of the positions with large responsibilities tomorrow. We should recognize that the problems of conservation are vital to each and every citizen of the nation. Local, state, and national projects in the field of conservation present opportunities for many to be of great service. The development and administration of these projects will demand the full time of a large staff of experts. The program of conservation must have the cordial support and cooperation of all citizens whether they are developing natural resources which they own privately or developing resources on public lands. The spirit of conservation demands that we recognize limitations to our personal rights in the utilization of the gifts made by nature, and appreciate that future generations will want to make a living and provide for their families in this same habitat.

PART II

CHAPTER II

THE PUBLIC DOMAIN AND ITS DISPOSAL

By Stephen S. Visher
Indiana University

A GENERAL SURVEY

Acquisition of Areas. By the term public domain is meant the land in possession of the federal government. In the following discussion all land formerly belonging to the people as a whole is considered.

Shortly after the adoption of the constitution, the thirteen original states ceded to the federal government all or nearly all of their claims to land beyond their present borders. Thus the first of the public domain consisted of most of the land between the original states and the Mississippi River, except Kentucky, Vermont, and part of Tennessee. Other vast areas were acquired by the Louisiana Purchase, conquest from Mexico, the Oregon Compromise, and the purchase of Alaska. Smaller areas were purchased from Spain, Texas, and Mexico.

Figure 1 summarizes broadly the chief additions to the public domain. It reveals that, of the total land acquired, that ceded by the original states comprised nearly one-sixth, the Louisiana Purchase and Alaska each about one-fourth, the land acquired directly from Mexico about one-fifth, and the Oregon Compromise contained one-tenth. The land purchased from Texas (to the north of that state's present boundary) made up 4 per cent, and the purchase of Florida added about 2 per cent to the total public domain.

These lands were purchased very cheaply. Excluding the private holdings, the Louisiana Purchase cost 6.5 cents an acre; Florida, 20 cents; the tract purchased from Texas, 21 cents; the Gadsden Purchase from Mexico, 68 cents; and Alaska about 2 cents an acre.

Disposal of Areas. Their Types and General Distribution. Slightly more than a billion acres have become private or state prop-

1,700,000,000 Acres of Land

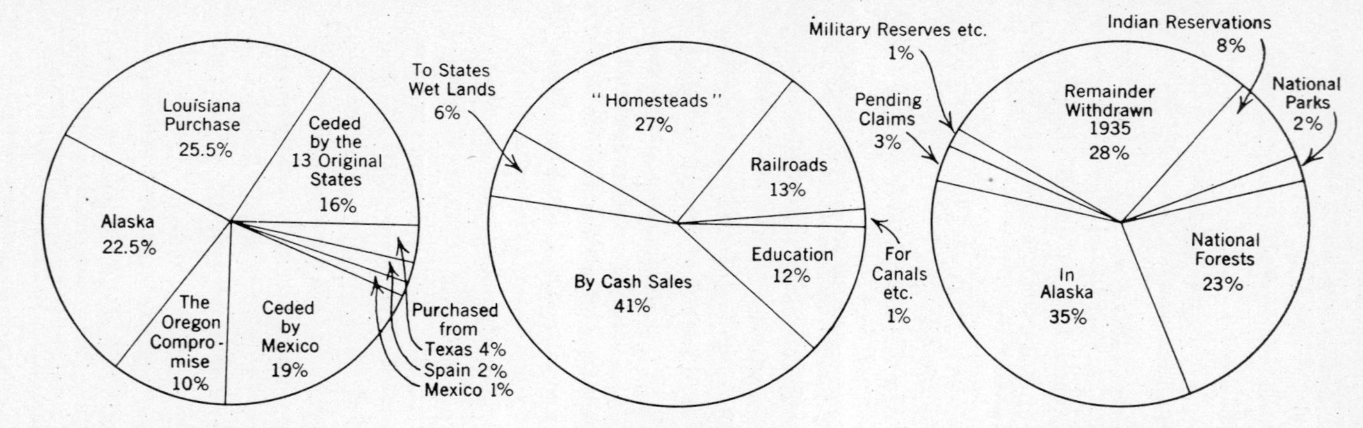

Fig. 1. Sources of the Public Domain.

Ceded by states (1781-1802) 267,731,000 acres (A) (402,700 sq. mi.); purchased from France (Louisiana Purchase) (1803) 432,988,000 A. (832,800 sq. mi.) for $27,268,000; purchased from Spain (the Floridas) (1819) 32,332,000 A. (50,500 sq. mi.) for $6,490,000; ceded by Mexico (1848) 324,993,000 A. (507,800 sq. mi.) indemnity $15,000,000 (4.6¢ an A.); Gadsden Purchase from Mexico (1853) 14,509,000 A. (22,700 sq. mi.) for $10,000,000; purchased from Texas (1850) 70,956,000 A. (110,868 sq. mi.) for $15,000,000; Oregon Compromise (1846) 166,084,000 A. (259,506 sq. mi.); purchased from Russia (Alaska) (1867) 378,166,000 A. (586,000 sq. mi.) for $7,200,000. The various additions to the national dominion included private holdings which did not become part of the public domain. They totaled 34,605,000 acres (54,070 sq. mi.) (Louisiana, 6,379,000; Florida, 2,779,000; Mexican cession, 13,675,000; Gadsden Purchase, 59,146; Texas, 6,526,100; Oregon, 2,938,000.)

1,020,000,000 Acres

Fig. 2. Disposal of the Domain.

Included in the 418,000,000 reported as disposed of "by cash sales and miscellaneous disposals" are 65,000,000 acres granted to veterans' "military bounty lands," and various other items not itemized. The price for that sold for cash was lowered from $2.00 per acre in 1820 to $1.25, and then, in 1854 (graduation law), to an average of 32 cents for 26,000,000 acres. Under the pre-emption law (1841) some 75,000,000 acres were sold at $1.25, and under the commutation clause of the homestead law of 1862 some 50,000,000 acres. Under the mineral land and coal acts some 2,000,000 and under the timber and stone act (1878) some 15,000,000 acres were sold. Under the homestead laws about 277,000,000 acres were alienated, of which about 234,000,000 acres were ordinary homesteads. The grants to railroads were 94,000,000 acres direct, and 38,000,000 acres via the states. Educational grants to the states totaled about 120,000,000 acres, about 100,000,000 for common schools, and most of the remainder for agricultural colleges or state universities. The swamp and overflowed land totaled 65,000,000 acres; internal improvements and miscellaneous totaled about 22,000,000.

680,000,000 Acres

Fig. 3. Reservations.

The national forests contain about 139,000,000 acres; the national parks and monuments about 9,000,000; the Indian reservations about 58,000,000; military and other reservations about 1,000,000; pending claims involve about 20,000,000; and unappropriated but reserved, 197,000,000 acres in the 48 states.

erty. This is about three-fifths of the approximately 1,667,000,000 acres (almost 3,300,000 square miles) which at one time or another were owned by the federal government. About half of the remaining two-fifths is in Alaska and has very little value.

The chief methods of disposal of the land are summarized graphically in Fig. 2, page 22, which reveals that about 41 per cent of the alienated land was sold; about 27 per cent was disposed of under the homestead laws; about one-eighth was granted to the states in aid of education; and another eighth was granted in aid of the railroads, most of which was given directly to railway corporations.[1] Grants to the states in aid of canals, river improvements, and roads took about 1 per cent, and the swamp and overflowed lands given to certain states comprised more than 6 per cent of the total.

The land sold, except under the "Timber and Stone Act," was located largely east of the Mississippi River or in Iowa, Missouri, and Arkansas. The land sold under the "Timber and Stone Act" (1878) was, however, largely in the fine timber tracts of the Pacific states, and northern Idaho and Minnesota.

As the first homestead law was not passed until 1862, most of the more accessible land had already been disposed of by sale or grant. The non-desert land alienated under the various "homestead laws" was therefore mostly in the second and third tiers of states west of the Mississippi river. In other words, it was in the Dakotas and Montana and the states south to Oklahoma and New Mexico. Considerable areas were also obtained by the public under homestead laws in Minnesota, Arkansas, California, and Idaho, and small amounts in northern Michigan, Wisconsin, Alabama, Mississippi, Florida, and Oregon. Almost no land was homesteaded in Ohio, Indiana, Illinois, or Iowa, and none in the states south of the Ohio River except Mississippi, Alabama, and Florida. There was no homesteading in Texas and only a little in Louisiana. Under the several "Desert Acts," which were modified homestead laws, nearly 2,000,000 acres were surrendered in Montana, nearly half as many in Wyoming, and about a third to a fourth as many in Colorado, California, and Utah, with small amounts in the other western states.

The land granted to the states in aid of education was distributed

[1] In making these grants the federal government forced the railroads to agree to transport government freight at reduced rates. These lower rates are still being exacted from the railroads. Often freight is dispatched along very circuitous routes in order that it may move over land-grant railroads. (EDITORS.)

throughout the former public domain, with, however, larger acreages in some of the poorer states. The amount, ignoring Alaska, totaled about 120,000,000 acres, nearly 200,000 square miles, an area nearly four times as large as New England. During the earlier decades of the nineteenth century only one section to the township was set aside for schools. After 1848, however, two sections to the township were given. In 1850 four sections (2, 13, 16, and 36) were reserved for the schools of New Mexico and Utah. In 1864 the same provisions were made in Arizona. Moreover, liberal grants for institutions of higher learning were made after 1852. For example, "agricultural college scrip" (certificates entitling the holder to specified acreages of public land) totaled 8,000,000 acres, a tract about one-fourth as large as Pennsylvania. In addition about 5,000,000 acres have been given to state universities. The educational grants to Florida have been greater than those to any other state. They have totaled 12,000,000 acres, or more than one-third of the state. The next in order, with 9,000,000 to 5,000,000 acres, are: New Mexico, Arizona, Utah, California, Montana, Minnesota, Michigan, and Wisconsin. A dozen other states in the Middle West and West received about 4,000,000 acres each. But Alabama, Arkansas, and Iowa received only from 1,000,000 to 2,000,000 acres. All the remaining states received smaller grants, mostly in the form of scrip, in support of their agricultural colleges, etc. The eastern states and Texas, which did not have federal land within their borders, necessarily applied this scrip elsewhere, chiefly in timbered areas in northern Michigan, Wisconsin, Minnesota, and California.

The land granted to the states for canals was mostly in Indiana, Ohio, and Michigan; grants for river improvement were largely in Iowa, Alabama, and Wisconsin; Oregon received 2,500,000 acres for roads, and Indiana and Ohio received small grants. The total grants to the states for canals, roads, and river improvement were about 10,000,000 acres, an area almost half as large as Indiana. In addition almost 65,000,000 acres of land classed as "swamp and overflowed land" were ceded to fourteen states. Florida received most, about 11,000,000 acres or nearly one-third of the state. Arkansas and Louisiana each received about 8,000,000 acres (roughly one-fourth of these states), and Michigan, Minnesota, Wisconsin, Missouri, and Mississippi each got from 6,000,000 to 4,000,000 acres. One to two million acres apiece were granted to Illinois, Iowa, Indiana, and California, and small acreages to Oregon and Alabama. (Large portions of these 65,000,000 acres were heavily timbered.) A considerable share of the proceeds from the sale of this swamp land was added by the states to their endowment of public schools.

The grants in aid of railroads, totaling 38,000,000 acres (60,000 square miles or an area almost as large as New England), were also made chiefly to the states bordering the Mississippi River. However, a few other states, Michigan, Kansas, Alabama, and Florida, each received between 2,000,000 and 5,000,000 acres. Minnesota received most: 8,000,000 acres. Of states bordering the Mississippi River, Kentucky and Tennessee received no grants in aid of railroads, and Louisiana and Mississippi relatively little.

The grants to the railroad corporations, totaling 94,000,000 acres (an area almost as large as the east north central states), were made in the Rocky Mountain and Pacific states and in North Dakota, Nebraska, and Kansas. Two-fifths went to the Northern Pacific Railway, one-fourth to the Union Pacific, about one-seventh to the Southern Pacific, and nearly as much to the Santa Fe. Because of the large grants to the Northern Pacific Railway, the states through which this line extends, Montana, North Dakota, and Washington, contained the largest acreages of railroad grants, from 9,000,000 to 6,000,000 acres each. Nebraska, Kansas, and California each had about 5,000,000 acres.

Remaining Public Land. Types and Distribution. The land remaining in the public domain is of three main types: first, land reserved for specific purposes and presumably to be held permanently for such uses. The chief of these is the national forests; smaller areas comprise the national parks and national monuments. A second type is the Indian reservations. Judging from past experience, these Indian reservations will not be permanent. A third type is the lands withdrawn pending classification and further consideration as to what should be done with them. This type includes all land recently classed as "unappropriated public land open to settlement." This last comprised about one-eighth of the total former public domain of the United States "proper" (excluding Alaska). It was withdrawn from entry by executive order in 1934 and 1935.

Figure 3, page 22, shows approximately the division of the remaining public domain as to these types. It reveals that national forests comprise about 23 per cent and national parks 2 per cent; that Indian reservations cover about 8 per cent; that the recently withdrawn public open land includes about 28 per cent, and the unreserved part of Alaska makes up about 35 per cent of the remaining public domain.

All three of these great types of public land are located almost exclusively in the Rocky Mountain and Pacific states, and in Alaska. Small areas of public land remain, however, in the western parts of the Great Plains states, in northern Minnesota, and Michigan.

A fourth, at present minor, type of public land, but a type likely to increase notably in area, is submarginal tracts formerly privately owned which have been purchased by the federal government to "withdraw them from agriculture" and for reforestation, controlled grazing, soil conservation, wild animal refuges, etc. In addition to these purchases, some tracts of tax-delinquent lands which have reverted to the states have been ceded to the federal government. Likewise some private purchases have been donated for use as national monuments or national forests.

Types of Land Involved. The public domain has included almost all the various types of land in America. Choice agricultural land was represented, for example, by much of the Corn Belt; forest land included most of the fine forests of the Midwest, as well as the superb Pacific forests; mineral lands included all the metals of the Far West; the iron and copper of the Lake Superior region; and also the coal and oil fields of the interior and the West and Alaska; grazing lands have been very widely represented ever since the acquisition of the Louisiana Purchase, which included much of the Great Plains. The better agricultural, forest, and mineral lands passed out of federal ownership soonest, and in recent decades most of the unreserved public domain has been grazing land, less valuable forest land, and waste land.

CHANGES IN THE POPULAR ATTITUDE TOWARD PUBLIC LANDS

At a time when the seriousness of the problems facing the American people is being widely though vaguely realized, it is desirable to consider what should be the program with respect to the remaining public domain. A preliminary step may properly be a survey of the chief historic changes in opinion as to various types of land. First the popular attitude is considered, and then the attitude of officials.

The attitude toward the public domain has varied as a result of five chief influences: (1) the growth of population; (2) the spread of the people made possible partly by improvements in transportation; (3) the conspicuous consequences of the exploitation of the land, especially deforestation, depletion of minerals and game animals, and recently, the striking effects of soil erosion; (4) the growing realization that natural resources are limited in amount and are being used up rapidly. (5) A fifth influence is the growing sense of responsibility concerning the welfare of the populace. Formerly little was done to ease the burden of the poor, partly because people who "could not make a go of it" in one place could readily move elsewhere and start afresh. Now, however, such movements are seldom successful, as the people of any area fill nearly all the local opportunities to earn a livelihood. Consequently vast sums are expended for relief in one form or another. The seriousness of the situation is leading many thoughtful people to consider the desirability of radical departures in our land policies.

Programs concerning the American public domain have also varied widely with changes in the popular interest in agriculture, forests, minerals, outdoor recreation, and with concern for the distant future. Wild land was long considered to have very little value. For example, Franklin was criticized by many prominent citizens for extending the national boundary as far west as the Mississippi River when he negotiated the treaty at the close of the Revolutionary War. Jefferson's purchase of the Louisiana Territory likewise was widely condemned, and Seward's purchase of Alaska was often called "sheer folly."

Likewise trees were long inadequately appreciated. Indeed, few Americans, before the coming of the railroads and settlement of the prairies, considered trees much more than encumbrances to be laboriously removed and burned. The man who cleared the most land was the popular hero, and he who did not completely clear his land was called lazy. The statement, made by those less blind than their fellows, that there would soon be a timber shortage, was widely laughed at. President Harrison, as stated in Chapter I, was the first president who felt strongly enough the necessity of forest conservation to carve forest reserves out of the public domain (1892). Not until Theodore Roosevelt's terms (1901-1909), however, were very large tracts reserved. He withdrew nearly 150,000,000 acres, in contrast with a total of about 45,000,000 acres withdrawn by all his predecessors. He included in national forests substantially all the forest lands then remaining in public ownership. Franklin D. Roosevelt (1933) was the first president effectively to encourage extensive reforestation, by means of the Civilian Conservation Corps.

Minerals, too, except gold and silver, meant little to most Americans until after 1850. Exploitation entirely without regard to the future needs was the rule. Even today persons who suggest that it is not wise to exploit immediately all mineral deposits are looked upon as queer by many people. As a result, except for the reservations by

Theodore Roosevelt, little mineral wealth of present value has been retained by the public.

Agriculture was the predominant source of livelihood of Americans until relatively recently. As late as 1880 two-thirds of the people lived on farms. Consequently the public land was generally evaluated in terms of its agricultural utility. The population spread westward year by year, creating tens of thousands of new farms, and pushing back the frontier. Nevertheless several great westward surges were prominent. The first of these followed the Revolutionary War, when the better land of Kentucky and Tennessee (only partly public domain) was occupied. From 1810 to 1850, during the steamboat and canal period, the large families of the first frontier generations, supplemented by many migrants from Pennsylvania to the Carolinas, crossed the Ohio and Mississippi rivers in large numbers. A third great surge into the public domain involved many people from New England and New York. It followed the completion of the Erie Canal (1825), Great Lakes navigation, and the early railroad extension, to 1861. This wave was the first to spread over the prairies. After the Civil War there was a fourth great westward movement, facilitated by the railroads and encouraged by the free homesteads offered by the homestead law. From 1870 to 1886 hundreds of thousands of people, mostly descendants of pioneers, moved into the prairie plains and eastern Great Plains. The dry years of the late 1880's and early 1890's checked the spread; indeed, many Great Plains counties were almost depopulated. But, commencing about 1900, a series of wet years, the enactment of legal provisions for enlarged homesteads, and the development of various inventions helpful to farmers led to another great increase in the interest in new farms. This was heightened by the opening of various Indian reservations, notably in Oklahoma, and the withdrawal of extensive tracts for forest reserves or mineral examination.

Ten million acres of homesteads were "patented" in 1910. This is an area twice as large as New Jersey. Dry years, commencing in 1910, checked the spread, but the high prices for agricultural products associated with the World War again greatly increased popular interest in agriculture, but since the land capable of adequately supporting a family on a half-section was "gone," the homestead unit was increased to 640 acres in 1916, for "stock-raising" land. Almost a frenzy of filing on land followed, partly because military service reduced the residence requirements for homesteading. The collapse of farm prices after the close of the war chilled the popular enthusiasm for farming, and the droughts and low prices for farm products during 1930-1933 put an end, for this period at least, to interest in homesteading. Moreover, in November, 1934, and February, 1935, all the remaining unreserved and unappropriated land was withdrawn by executive order.

CHANGES IN THE OFFICIAL ATTITUDE TOWARD PUBLIC LANDS

The popular attitude towards the public domain, just sketched, influenced profoundly the official attitude. Nevertheless the opinions of governmental officials had sufficient independent influence so that a sketch of changes therein is desirable.

George Washington bought and sold unoccupied lands in New York, Virginia, Pennsylvania, and Kentucky to very good effect, leaving an estate of more than $5,000,000. Many later government officials likewise considered the unoccupied lands as affording opportunities for personal gain.

Alexander Hamilton and numerous other financiers of the early years thought of the public lands as potential sources of federal revenue. From their sale much-needed revenues might be obtained with which to help pay the salaries of governmental officials, and at least the interest on the debts.

Many state officials also were interested in having their states receive grants of lands for both of the foregoing reasons. Most of the vast tracts granted to states were sold promptly, often to members of the legislature or their friends, many of whom resold at large profits. The funds obtained by the states were partly used to reduce the immediate tax burdens.

Allied to the concept that the sale of public land should help support the government was the realization that such lands could be used to help supply improvements that were desirable. The first important use of public land for this purpose was in 1802 when Ohio was admitted as a state. One full section of each township was set aside toward support of public schools. Other tracts were given, during the early decades of the nineteenth century, to aid in canal and road construction. Ere long, increases in the grants for schools were made, and also grants for colleges. When many railroads were projected into sparsely settled or vacant regions, 1865-1885, vast areas were granted to assist in their construction.

A similar use of public lands was the granting of scrip for 65,000,000 acres as partial compensation for military services. These scrips, which often were sold, may be compared with the bonus payments after the World War.

The sales of public land, however, yielded only relatively small sums, only $60,000,000 during the first half century of the nation's history and approximately $160,000,000 during the second half century, and a total to 1935 of about $250,000,000. This, to be sure, is three times as much as was paid for the purchases from France, Spain, Mexico, Texas, and Russia, but it is pitifully small as compared with the value of the lands sold. Indeed, a competent authority concluded that most of the land sold by the federal government yielded only a small fraction of what it was then worth (that is, readily salable for).[1] Almost none of it, even the choicest timber lands, brought more than $2.50 an acre, and the average was only 60 cents an acre. All the land sold during one hundred and fifty years yielded less revenue to the federal government than the taxes on tobacco yielded during six months of 1935!

Likewise the grants in aid of internal improvements, although locally and immediately helpful, nevertheless yielded results that were disappointing in many ways. For example, the 350,000 acres granted to Wisconsin in aid of the state university actually yielded less than $600,000.[2] This is only about one-tenth the sum it has received annually in recent years from taxes.

The failure of sales and grants to yield hoped-for results encouraged the conviction that the public domain was, after all, chiefly valuable as affording homes for a rapidly increasing population. The indirect taxes paid by the increased population which cheap or free land made possible would yield the chief financial returns to the government. Hence progressively fewer officials contended that the land be held for sale at higher prices. Instead, more Congressmen and other officials came to feel that it was desirable to dispose of the land so cheaply as to encourage rapid settlement.

The strong individualism encouraged by the generations of pioneer and frontier life and the conspicuous emphasis placed on real estate, partly as a result of the fact that for generations it was readily possible for any ambitious person to own land, also strengthened the conviction that private ownership was better than public ownership. The fact that public land yielded no local taxes and supported almost no population increased the strong local desire to have all public land pass into private ownership.

This desire for the alienation of public land grew until it became

[1] H. H. Schwartz, Report of the National Conservation Commission, Vol. III, pp. 390-392.

[2] Van Hise, *The Conservation of Natural Resources in the United States*, p. 290.

a firm conviction of most of the influential people in America. Numerous steps were taken to facilitate the disposal of public land, and very little indeed was done to retard its disposal. An example of this last was the fact that when land was sold it was almost always disposed of at the minimum price set by law, regardless of its true value. Likewise, for homesteading, the requirements were the minimum legal ones as to residence and improvements, very little concern being shown whether or not the man receiving the title was a bona fide settler or merely the dummy of some grasping corporation or individual.

The demand for decentralization of government and for state control aided other tendencies in bringing about extensive gifts of public land to the states, for no specified purpose. The feeling was that the states could dispose of certain public lands to better advantage than could the remote federal government. The gift of 65,000,000 acres of swamp land to the states in 1850 was an example of this policy.

The several homestead laws with their increasingly generous provisions reflect this popular desire to dispose of the public domain. Although when the famous homestead law, sponsored by Lincoln, was passed in 1862, the unit was 160 acres, nevertheless settlers were soon permitted to obtain also a preemption of another 160 acres. From 1873 to 1891 in states then being rapidly settled, a "tree claim" was also possible, giving a possible total of 480 acres. The repeals, because of graft, of the preemption and tree claim acts, in 1891, were offset in a way by increases in the homestead unit itself. This was increased to 320 acres for "desert" land in 1877 and for "dry farming" land in 1910; it was still further increased to 640 acres for "the sandhill country" of Nebraska in 1901 and for all land classified as "stock-raising homesteads" in 1916.

These liberalizations of the homestead laws were in accord with the prevailing ideal that the public domain ought to be given to bona fide settlers who would make a permanent home upon the homestead. That larger acreages of poorer than of good land were required in order to yield a livelihood should have been obvious, but was largely ignored until it was seen that few of the homesteads of the poorer agricultural land continued to be the homes of people.

The policy of the disposal of the public domain almost led to the gift to the states in 1931 of all remaining public land. Fortunately, however, there were enough Congressmen whose states would have received no such gifts of land that this step was not taken.

After nearly a century during which prompt disposal was the aim, some public land was finally set aside for permanent federal ownership. The establishment of Yellowstone National Park in 1872 was a momentous event in the history of our public domain and an example to other forward-looking countries. Since then scores of national parks, monuments, and reserves have been carved from the remaining public domain.

The establishment of the national forests, commencing in 1891 but most extensive in 1901-1909, was even more important in limiting the alienation of public land.

Another phase of retaining part of the domain for the public was the reservation of various mineral and other rights. President Theodore Roosevelt in 1906-1909 withdrew from entry 80,000,000 acres of possible mineral lands pending their classification. Those found to have valuable minerals have been retained entirely, or else the mineral rights at least have been retained to be exploited only under government control on a leasing system. Possible water-power sites were similarly withdrawn in the Pacific states and Alaska, where the potential water power is very great—more than two-thirds of that for the entire country.

The alienation of public land has apparently almost run its course. During recent years (1930-1935) only about 1,000,000 acres a year have been alienated. Most of this land was homesteaded, "applied for," five or more years previously; indeed, during recent years many homesteaders have delayed "proving up" because until full title is received no taxes are levied. From 1913 to 1922 inclusive an average of about 8,000,000 acres a year was patented, and in 1910 more than 10,000,000 acres.

Likewise the sale of public land has declined in recent years to small proportions, to much less than $1,000,000 a year since 1921, in contrast to about $2,000,000 a year between 1913 and 1920, and $5,000,000 a year from 1900 to 1912, and about $8,000,000 a year during the 1880's.

The public domain, instead of being disposed of, is now being added to notably, by purchase, tax delinquency, and gift. Moreover, there is much serious official discussion of the desirability of purchase by the federal government of many millions of acres of submarginal lands, especially in the more rugged, sandy, or rocky formerly forested sections, and in the semiarid Great Plains. Indeed, an official report of December, 1935, recommended that 650,000 farms, with a total area of 101,000,000 acres, be purchased. These farm families have been unable to make a fair living from their farms. Moreover, much of their farm land is damaged by soil erosion as a result of their efforts to farm it.

The official belief is that these 650,000 farms could more advantageously be used for forests, or in the drier regions for supervised grazing. A further significant advantage expected from government ownership of submarginal lands is a reduction of the necessary payments for relief and subsidies for schools and roads in such areas. The removal of the occupants to land upon which they can be self-supporting would lighten the tax burden for the rest of the nation.

Summary. One of the most favored 2,000,000 square miles of the entire earth was spread out before the pioneers who crossed the Appalachians in 1790. The land certainly awaited settlers, and the public policy soon came to be to encourage settlement in almost every possible way. Land was sold very cheaply, and vast areas were donated to the states and to corporations. By 1860 most of the better accessible agricultural land had passed into private ownership. Then further to encourage settlement, homesteads were given free, with the result that by 1890 the frontier was officially declared gone. Nevertheless, the rapidly increasing, land-hungry people pushed on into the poorer lands until by 1920 there remained almost no public land capable of supporting an American family on even three times the homestead unit. Except in the "ephemeral" Indian reservations, settlement and exploitation were almost unimpeded as long as fair agricultural land remained. But from 1892 to 1909 vast areas were reserved for national forests, parks, and monuments. Practically all alienation was stopped in 1934, and a reversal of policy was undertaken—the purchase of submarginal lands for addition to the reserved public domain.

THE OTHER PHASES OF LAND CONSERVATION

Most of the laws passed by Congress relating to the disposal of our public domain, as brought out in this chapter, are for the most part national in their implication yet in actual practice have had to be modified to fit regional conditions, besides meeting the political and economic demands of the times. Examples are the "enlarged homestead act" to fit regional conditions in the subhumid and semiarid portions of our country, the "desert land act," governing the acquisition of lands in the section of low rainfall, and the "swamp and overflow land act" that applies to lands in humid sections.

Conservation problems associated with the utilization of our lands are almost wholly regional. In the humid part of our country land conservation largely centers about soils, the preservation of their fertility through the maintenance of the essential elements, and the control of erosion (sheet wash and gullying). These phases are discussed in Chapters III, IV, and V. The material discussed in Chapter VIII is localized also in humid regions, but the themes of Chapters VI and VII have their setting in lands of little rain. Chapter IX, the Agricultural Prospect in America, is wholly national in scope. It gives us a view into the future. Chapters VI and VIII discuss land-utilization problems concerned with rectifying, so far as possible, the shortcomings of nature; Chapters IV, V, and VIII with problems that are imperative because of the ignorance, neglect, or thoughtlessness of man. The various phases of land conservation, together with the facts presented in Appendix I, present a picture of our land resources, their utilization and conservation, past, present, and future. (EDITORS' NOTE)

CHAPTER III

THE SOILS OF THE UNITED STATES

By Louis A. Wolfanger

Columbia University

INTRODUCTION

The soil of a nation is its most valuable material heritage. It nurtures the ever-flowing stream of vegetation from which men and their animals derive their sustenance. The preponderance of the world's organic raw materials as well as its food supplies arise from its soils through the practice of agriculture. Small groups of peoples may here and there exist for a time on the free gifts of nature, but the great civilizations of the centuries have rested fundamentally upon uncountable millions of fields planted and tended by man.

The civilization of our nation is also one that is primarily predicated upon its soil resources and great agricultural industries. Our country, taken as a whole, possesses a combination of soils and genial climates that is unduplicated in either scale or character by those of any other nation. This is a happy privilege. It offers us the opportunity to enjoy the highest standard of living, to achieve cultural progress of the first order, and to extend an assistance to others less fortunate. But great privileges are accompanied by grave responsibilities. Soils are subject to certain changes when cultivated or pastured. Change in itself is not a critical matter, since everything changes to a certain degree when put to use. The critical aspects arise when changes in soils that are subject to human manipulation are left to take a degenerative course, or are improperly directed, and when known means of maintaining the soils near their virgin level or raising them to higher levels of productivity are not employed.

These critical aspects obtain rather generally in the United States. At the end of several centuries of agriculture and pastoralism our soils are in a lower state of fertility than our scientific and practical knowledge should tolerate. Especially serious is the fact that some soil areas have so seriously deteriorated that their early reclamation will be extremely difficult and costly, if not nearly impossible. This is particularly true of the gross physical destruction of the soil body occasioned by erosion. More subtle but almost equally serious is the state of chemical, physical, and biologic degradation into which we have allowed our soils to drift. The causes are many. We have not fully appreciated either the limitations or capabilities of our soils. They were looked upon much as a mine, as simply possessing a "store" of plant foods: when these had been extracted there was little we could do except abandon the land until it somehow "recuperated." Another major cause has been the popular attitude towards ownership. Ownership has rarely been regarded as permanent but merely as a temporary convenience during which the soil could be despoiled of all it was worth. Moreover, since the keynote of American agriculture has been dominantly commercial rather than primarily self-maintenance, systems of cropping were shaped to yield the maximum cash crops or marketable livestock regardless of the toll on the soil. Whatever the causes, the general results are equally deplorable.

The remedy lies in education. Without some knowledge of the fundamental nature of soils, the changes which they undergo when utilized, and practical methods that can be employed to offset deleterious changes, conservation will make slight progress. Men do more than they know. And they will act constructively if personal advantages are in prospect.

THE FORMATION OF SOILS

Soils are highly complex entities. They are complex in composition, in morphology, and in reaction. The materials of which they are composed include not only the readily observed mineral matter which makes up the bulk of most soils, but also organic matter—both living and dead, and animal as well as vegetative—air, and water. Each kind of material named exists in varied form ranging from comparatively simple to highly intricate compounds. Moreover, each constituent occupies a specific and relative place in the soil body, so that soils are recognized as possessing morphological or anatomical organization comparable to that of other natural phenomena.

Accumulation of Soil Material. The mineral material of soils is derived from the rocks of the earth's crust, largely as a result of the action of climate, by the process of weathering. The rocks fracture physically in the face of daily and seasonal temperature changes and are acted upon chemically by water, oxygen, and other dissolved gases. New mineral compounds are produced. Rainfall penetrating the disintegrating mass tends to take up the soluble constituents that are formed, and leaves behind the insolubles and undecomposed mineral fragments. The residuum slowly acquires the characteristics that are identified as earthy as differentiated from rock. This earth-like material may either accumulate at the place where it is formed, or be first transported and deposited by water, wind, or glacial activity and then accumulate. In either event it is popularly regarded as "soil" but it is not yet a true soil from the point of view of soil science, since further major changes are still in prospect. Many earth-like materials accumulate but proceed no further in the direction of soil evolution.

The evolution of a true soil ensues when changes occur in the accumulated material in accordance with some six forces or conditions of the place where the material comes to rest. These are: (1) the climate, (2) the natural vegetation, (3) the zoological life living in and on the soil, (4) the land surface the soil occupies, (5) the period of time that has elapsed since the material accumulated, and (6) the nature of the accumulated material.

Climate. The climate of the region in which the earth-like materials accumulate is in general the broadest major factor bearing upon the character of the soils to which these materials will ultimately give rise. The climate supplies the all-important moisture conditions and fixes the temperate range within which the subsequent chemical, physical, and biological changes take place. The importance of water lies in its hydrolytic action and in the fact that it is the universal solvent which carries the oxygen, the carbon dioxide, the organic complexes, and other materials which attack the minerals and bring about further changes in the earthy mass. The climate also conditions the organic life.

Natural Vegetation and Soil Fauna. The natural vegetation and the soil fauna which establish themselves in or on the earth-like material effect the more immediate and vital fundamental changes. Living, the vegetation brings about reactions with the mineral matter in absorbing water and solubles, and exuding carbon dioxide and waste. At death the vegetation is attacked by soil microbes which, using it as a source of energy, change it to varied soluble and relatively insoluble organic materials. The insoluble materials form the more or less permanent organic constituents of the soil. The soluble materials, taken up by percolating waters, either serve as nutrients for the living plants or attack the mineral matter and modify the changes it would undergo under the attack of organic-free waters. Since the solubles yielded by different types of vegetation are different—organic matter derived from trees being unlike that of grasses, shrubs, etc.—their reaction upon the mineral components brings about the evolution of soils that are correspondingly varied. At the same time the organic products which the several classes of soil organisms—fungi, bacteria, worms, etc.—evolve from different types of vegetation are very diverse. There are also important differences in the soil reaction of the various vegetative associations while they are living. Some absorb large amounts of calcium, others, sodium. Again, plants like grasses, which propagate most of their roots in the upper part of the soil, absorb much more water than deep-rooters like trees. This confines chemical activity and leaching to comparatively shallower depths in grassland associations. In short, the organic life of a soil becomes its final arbiter, molding its specific character within the broad limits set by climate.

Land Form and Time: The Soil Cycle. Since soils occur in every state of change from the time they accumulate as mere earth-like materials until the changes wrought by their climatic and organic environment have been largely impressed upon them, they are viewed as possessing a cycle of development, or a life cycle, analogous to that of other natural objects and phenomena. Infancy, youth, maturity, and similar stages are recognized.

The infant soil is one whose materials have but recently accumulated. Few if any of the changes to be brought about by their new climatic and organic environment have been effected, especially if the materials have been transported any distance. Such soils are characteristic of floodplains, actively forming deltas, and similar depositional areas.

Mature soils are those in which the work of the climate and organic life has been largely completed. Some further changes may occur as they advance to old age, but the subsequent rate of change is now comparatively slow. The soil has reached a degree of stability and is characterized by features it has *acquired* by change rather than features it has inherited from its parent material.

As mature soils are the products of cumulative and completed change, they develop only in places where they are undisturbed by periodic erosion or further deposition, i.e., chiefly on level plain and plateau uplands, and only locally on level uplands or lowlands in hill and mountain country. Any disturbance sets back development since the newly deposited or exposed material must then be brought into equilibrium with the environment. The development of the soil cycle and the state of development of any soil, therefore, is governed by (1) the time that has elapsed since the parent material accumulated, and (2) the land surface the soil occupies. The time refers not to any precise number of years but to the period required to bring about the essential changes, be they rapid or slow.[1]

Young soils are those that have advanced beyond mere infancy but have not as yet acquired, beyond incipient or imperfect stages, the characteristics of the mature soils with which they are associated.[2] They occur mainly in hill and mountain terraine and on slopelands in plains country, where, subject to some degree of natural erosion, their development towards maturity is constantly arrested. Topography is thus an important factor in soil evolution. Since the mature soil, like the mature animal or plant, is the natural norm, the discussions that follow will refer only to the mature soil unless otherwise noted.

Parent Material. The last factor, the accumulated earth-like or parent material, though indispensable, is normally of secondary importance in determining the fundamental character of a soil. It is the material that has been *acted upon* and *changed.* It is chiefly important in young soils, and soils of low-rainfall (desert) or low-temperature (high latitude and altitude) regions where chemical and biological activity are limited and physical changes dominate. Otherwise it plays its most discernible rôle in its general bearing upon texture, coarse or sandy soils being derived from arenaceous materials, and fine or clayey soils from argillaceous.[3]

SIGNIFICANT SOIL PROPERTIES

The Soil Profile. Taking a mature soil as a whole, the most clearly defined and among the more important characteristics it acquires is differentiation into layers or horizons. These layers or horizons, taken collectively, are termed the soil's profile. The differentiation is effected through the action of a number of physical, chemical, and biological forces.

The water which penetrates the soil is the chief physical and chemical factor. It carries soluble constituents and finer soil particles from

[1] Since the time required is of a geological nature, and not that measurable by the short human generation, a soil at any given stage is more or less permanent as far as man is concerned. In other words, most soils that were young or mature in, say, Caesar's days are believed to be still largely in that stage of development today.

[2] For example, the mature soils may show a high degree of leaching and have sticky, clayey subsoils whereas the young soils may show only partial leaching and more friable, loamier subsoils.

[3] It should be remembered, however, that locally the texture may be so significant that it (and therefore the parent material) exerts a dominant influence on the fertility of the soil. (EDITORS.)

surface to subsoil. Where the precipitation is heavy, the extended transfer of fine particles ultimately converts the subsoil into a relatively denser and more compact horizon, while the surface horizon becomes relatively more porous and coarser-textured. The movement of constituents also differentiates these layers chemically. Some of the constituents are transferred to the upper subsoil, some to the lower, and some into the ground water. In regions of low precipitation such transfers are limited and confined for the most part to the upper subsoil, so that soil and subsoil are less sharply differentiated. Owing to the confusion which arises in the varied popular uses of the terms soil and subsoil, soil scientists designate the upper horizons from which material is removed the A horizon, the underlying horizon to which material is transferred the B horizon, and the more or less unchanged substratum or parent material underneath, the C horizon. The genetic relationships between these horizons is one of the important distinctions between true soils and ordinary geologic sediments that are popularly regarded as soil.

These horizons are further differentiated by the action of the natural vegetation and soil fauna. Since the greater part of the roots of most plants occupy the A horizon, it is usually the richest in organic matter, has the greatest soil population, is darkest in color, has the greatest supply of soluble nutrients (plant foods), and possesses the most favorable structure. The soil population is attracted by the plant residues available for its nutrition, and in digesting them it converts them into humus and other substances that are in general highly beneficial to subsequent plant growth. The humus formed stains the mineral mass dark in color and gives the horizon its superior structure. The nitrogen and other solubles released enrich the horizon's nutrient supplies.

The contrastive features acquired by the A and B horizons mean the development of very different growth conditions. Yet each has its special functions in supporting plant life. Despite the transfer or loss of some of its soluble constituents, the A horizon comprises the chief growth medium. It is more permeable to roots, water, and air; its nutrients are in forms most advantageous to plant use, and it is the seat of the biologic life that is so vital to the plant's economy. It is easy to see, therefore, why erosion which carries the A horizon away—although it may also penetrate the B and even the C horizon—is so destructive of fertility. The B horizon may be viewed as generally supplementary. Most plants extend at least part, and some a large part, of their secondary roots into the B horizon for water and nutrients. The value of the B horizon depends upon its permeability, its capacity to hold water, and its thickness. A good B horizon is a plant's mainstay when drought beleaguers.

The Colloidal Complex. If soils are examined with regard to their individual physical constituents, they reveal a wide variety of sizes—stones, pebbles, sand, silt, and clay.[1] The proportions of sand, silt, and clay determine a soil's texture. Soils made up chiefly of coarse particles are sandy (sandy loams, etc.); of fine particles, clayey (clay loams, etc.); of intermediate-sized particles (silt loams, etc.). Of the several sized grains that make up a soil, only the clay is significantly reactive, however, i.e., possesses the capacity to take part in the intricate chemical activities that go on in the soil. The coarser particles are chiefly the as yet unweathered but fragmented minerals. They comprise a kind of inert framework of the soil mass.

The clay derives its reactive faculties from its colloidal constituents. These colloids are the chemically complex, chemically active, jelly-like, semi-solid particles formed in the process of weathering. Commingled with them, more or less intimately, are colloids of organic character derived from the organic constituents of the soil, the whole being aptly termed the colloidal complex. Being the reactive integrant, this clay-humus complex is the very heart and soul of a soil. Its faculties, coupled with the relative proportion of the inert mineral mass, make or unmake the soil, as it were.

Owing to its reactive faculties, the colloidal complex has an important bearing upon a soil's nutritive constituents or so-called plant foods. Soluble salts formed on decomposition of the mineral and organic matter are the source of the plant's nutrients. Lacking oral and digestive organs, plants are not in a position to bite off and chew up fragments for their nutrition. All nutritive material is useless unless it is in a soluble state and capable of being taken in through roots. But in a soluble state it is subject to leaching, except for the colloidal complex which has the capacity to remove some of these salts from solution and hold them back for plant use through the process of absorption and base-exchange reaction. However, this capacity varies widely, depending on the age and composition of the colloidal complex and its environment. Colloids that are subject to severe weathering are gradually changed in composition and slowly lose these properties.

The colloidal complex is also the chief determinant of a soil's water-holding capacity. It is a virtual sponge with the ability to retain (imbibe) enormous amounts of water. The inert, coarse soil particles are

[1] Clay particles are those of less than 0.002 millimeter in diameter; silt, 0.02-0.002; sand, 2.0-0.02.

unable to retain more than a surface film. This is the reason why many sandy soils which have only a small proportion of colloids are usually droughty. Not all colloids are able to retain water in quantity, however. This depends, too, upon their age and composition.

The colloidal complex is also a major factor in defining a soil's structural capacity. A soil is said to have structure when its individual finer particles form aggregates—crumbs, granules, plates, clods, etc. The type of structural aggregate formed depends upon the nature and proportion of the mineral and organic colloids. Some mineral colloids have a high degree of plasticity when wet. This gives soil material its sticky character and causes it to form hard, clod-like aggregates on drying out. Organic colloids are only slightly plastic and coagulative. When properly proportioned to the mineral colloids they reduce stickiness and lead to the formation of soft, granular and friable aggregates. Soil material so conditioned is said to have good tilth.

The ability to form structural aggregations is one of the most important economic properties of a fine-textured soil—in sandy soils the large sand grains are roughly equivalent to the structural aggregate—since a number of functions depend upon this morphological feature. The fertility of a soil is especially closely related to its structural characteristics. If the aggregates formed are relatively small (granular or crumb structure) they facilitate root, water, and air movement because the interstices between the aggregates provide numerous avenues for their penetration and at the same time permit intimate contact between root and soil grain. Freedom of water movement is essential to good internal drainage, and most crop plants require well-drained soils. Freedom of air movement enables oxygen to penetrate the soil mass and destroy the toxic wastes which the plant generates.

The colloidal complex has therefore a number of basic relationships. Indeed, a fertile soil might be conveniently defined as one whose colloidal complexes are virile and able to enter into all the diversified relationships advantageous to plant life; an infertile soil as one whose colloids are inert, feeble, or negative in their reactions. Of the two types of colloids that enter into its composition, the organic is the more significant. It gives the soil uniqueness and identity, distinguishing it further from ordinary geological clay and other earthy formations. It endows the soil with properties and functional capacities that are peculiarly different. Lacking organic material and its swarm of zoological life, soils would be all but sterile for normal plant development. The organic complex also possesses the advantage of greater absorptivity of water and is capable of absorbing a much greater proportion of plant nutrients and retaining them in a state that is more advantageous to the plant. Its low plasticity and structural relations have already been pointed out. Many of its properties as well as those of the clay colloid and the whole colloidal complex are as yet unknown, and much remains to be learned regarding their precise bearing upon soil character. The facts outlined, however, indicate why the organic matter of a soil is a subject of such great interest.

With this background of soils in general, we can now proceed to examine the soils of the United States and some of the critical conservation problems they present.

THE MAJOR SOIL DIVISIONS

Viewed broadly, the soils of the United States comprise two very contrastive divisions which pedologists designate as pedocals and pedalfers. The pedalfers occupy the humid and dominantly forested regions; the pedocals have developed in the arid, grassland-desert regions of the continent. The pedocals are therefore confined to the West whereas pedalfers occur in both the humid East (their principal region) and in the humid West (Fig. 1).

The Pedocals. Developed under low moisture conditions and under a vegetation varying from grasses to xerophytic shrubs, the physical, chemical, and biological changes which the virgin pedocals have undergone are very different from those of the pedalfers. Physically the A and B horizons have about the same textural composition, since movement of fine particles and soluble constituents from upper to lower depths is limited. Chemically, the colloidal complex has a much more favorable composition: it is stable and relatively immobile, it is more retentive of plant nutrients and water, and it promotes the formation of a superior type of structural aggregate. While pedocals are leached to a certain degree, the average rainfall penetrates the soil to only shallow depths, rarely more than several feet, and there deposits such leached solubles as it has not given up en route.[1] At the same time, the deeper roots of the grassland or desert formation are constantly bringing the mineral nutrients they absorb to upper root levels, where, on death and decomposition of the roots, they are re-

[1] Some of the more soluble salts may be lost in the drainage waters associated with heavier rainfall, but most of the salts are dispersed rather uniformly throughout the soil. Among the salts deposited in the lower subsoil or just under it are calcium and magnesium carbonates, usually so abundantly that they are visible to the naked eye, forming flecks, streaks, and bands in the soil mass. Hence the name, pedocal, formed by adding the cal of calcium to the root of pedology, as soil science is formally termed.

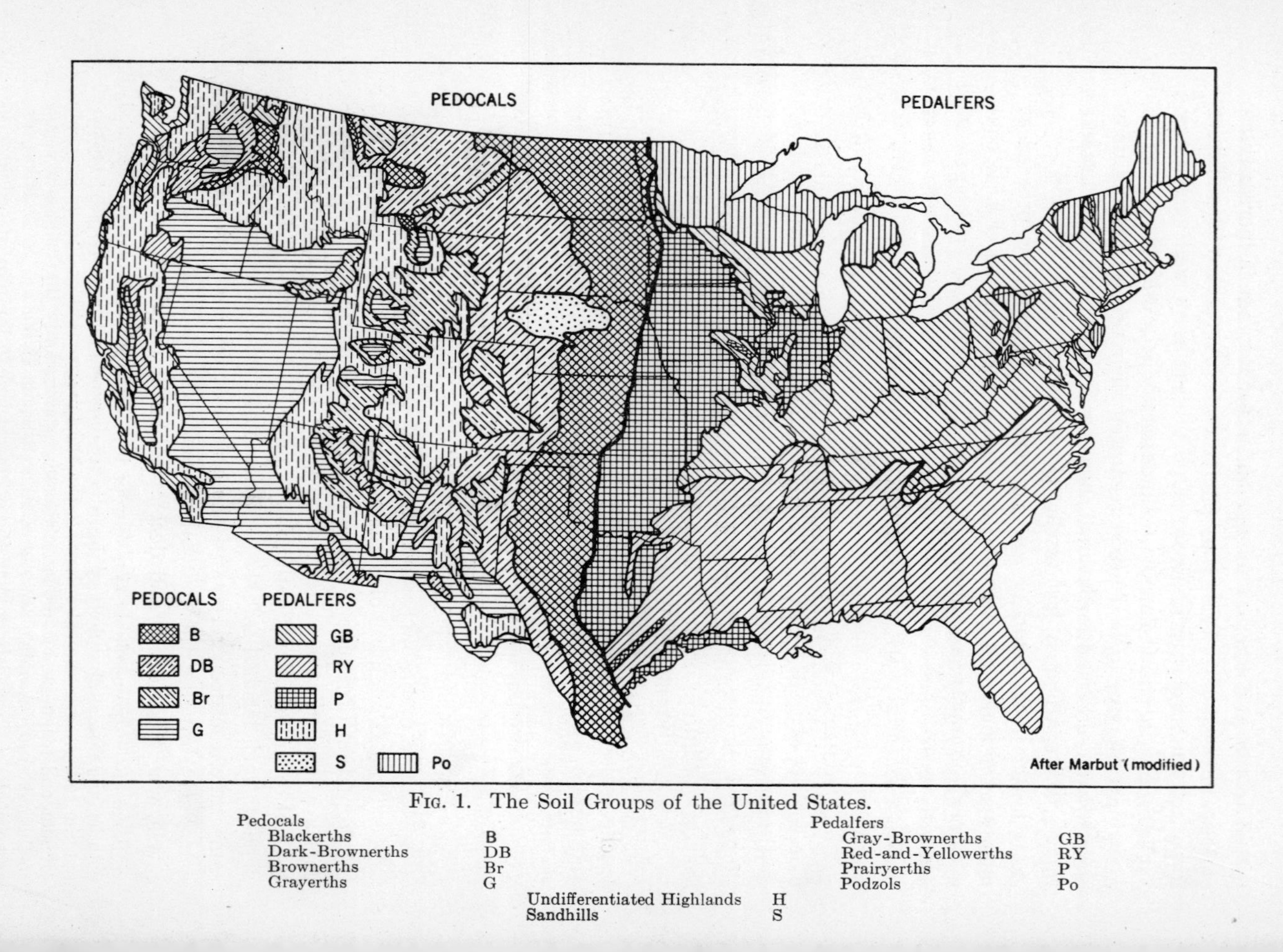

FIG. 1. The Soil Groups of the United States.

Pedocals		Pedalfers	
Blackerths	B	Gray-Brownerths	GB
Dark-Brownerths	DB	Red-and-Yellowerths	RY
Brownerths	Br	Prairyerths	P
Grayerths	G	Podzols	Po

Undifferentiated Highlands H
Sandhills S

turned to the A horizon. The soil, and especially the A horizon, the chief seat of root activity, is thus constantly rejuvenated and continues to be well supplied with mineral salts.

Coupled with this richness in mineral salts is a wealth of organic matter and organic salts. Unlike the forest formation which makes its chief organic contribution to the normal pedalfers in a *surficial* leaf fall—much of which is lost to the soil through surface washing—the grass associations annually permeate the soil *internally* with great masses of dying roots. As these decompose they literally fill the soil with organic matter and humic colloids. The more arid subregions of pedocals with sparser vegetation are, of course, proportionately lower in these materials. In brief, the pedocals are excellent soils, rich in plant nutrients and endowed with good physical qualities.

The Pedalfer. The virgin pedalfer is the antithesis of the pedocal. The heavier rainfall under which it develops—roughly 25 to 30 inches and more annually—penetrates the soil to great depths, carrying a large part of the soluble constituents beyond the reach of even the longer roots. The forest and its understory, moreover, have roots that not only are longer-lived but also take in comparatively less nutrient matter than the vegetation of the pedocal region, so they retrieve less leached salts from year to year. While the annual leaf fall yields salts and humic constituents on decay, only a part of these constituents re-enter the soil, mainly through the activity of percolating water, or worms and similar burrowers. In the course of time the soil becomes increasingly poor in nutrients and acid in reaction, and the colloidal complex is so transformed that it displays relatively inferior properties. It becomes less retentive of nutrients and water, it produces a soil of poorer structural characteristics, and the colloids of the A horizon become so unstable and deflocculated that they are in part shifted to the B horizon. As the transfer progresses, the A horizon becomes relatively loose and coarse textured while the B horizon becomes more dense and compact and less permeable to roots, air, and water.[1]

THE BROAD ECONOMICS OF PEDALFERS AND PEDOCALS

The extensive and wide-spread development of two soil divisions as contrastive as the pedalfers and the pedocals in the United States is exceedingly significant. To begin with, it means that we have two

[1] Pedalfer is derived by adding the al of aluminum and the fer of ferrum to ped. In the process of evolution a pedalfer loses its carbonates by leaching and experiences in their place a relative increase in the proportion of aluminum or iron or both.

soils of very different utility. Each soil has not only broad capabilities but also broad limitations not possessed by the other. In the second place, each soil has its distinctive conservation problems. What is generally sauce for the goose, therefore, is not sauce for the gander, although such has been the general tenor of popular thought and action. It is imperative that we keep these fundamental differences clearly in mind both in evaluating current land-use practices and in formulating policies for future action.

Utilization of the Pedalfers. Since colonization and settlement of the United States began from the eastern coast, it was instituted on soils of pedalferic character. This means that the husbandman who so laboriously hewed his farms out of the forest began his operations on a *relatively* poor soil. This was true whether he settled in New England, Virginia, or Georgia. At first he obtained fair and sometimes rather large yields. The normal virgin pedalfer usually has a modest "reserve" of plant nutrients, a friable nut-like or cloddy structure, and the great asset of a rainfall essential to a diversified agriculture. Unfortunately, however, the small reserve soon proved inadequate, the structure broke down, and yields began to decline year after year until they reached a low level at which they tended to remain indefinitely. When this happened the common practice was to abandon farm or field and clear a new one.

In passing judgment upon this practice we have been prone to be somewhat caustic in our criticism. The colonial husbandman, as well as his kinsmen who have continued the practice to the present day, have been roundly condemned as "soil miners" and even as "soil robbers" of various degrees of guilt. Although outright exploitation merits the strictest censure, and there is much to be deplored in the way our soil resources have been expended, fair judgment should not overlook the fact that the soils were relatively poor to begin with and that they had been made poor by nature herself, through the destructive action of a rainy climate, long before the Virginian planter ever set foot in the New World, and probably long before Rome, or Greece, or even Egypt flourished. In "exhausting" his soils, therefore, the husbandman was largely reducing them to a slightly lower position on the scale of poverty only, and at worst he was "robbing" a lean purse and not an exchequer.

It should also be observed that he did not irremediably debase his soils, except where his practices led to physical destruction by erosion. Such a verdict would be appropriate if soils were merely a kind of inert reservoir in which plant nutrients accumulated mysteriously and at a very slow rate analogous to most mineral deposits. Soils, however, are dynamic entities. They are constantly evolving and generating new nutrients and other constituents that determine fertility.[1] In virgin soils, moreover, these constituents appear to be commonly generated at a rate slightly more rapid than that at which the natural plant cover is able to utilize them, or leaching waters remove them, so they tend to accumulate in small amounts as a kind of "store." When the husbandman cultivates the land, therefore, and yields drop from year to year, he is in a way mainly reducing the "surplus" until an equilibrium is struck between his crops and the new constituents generated. Thereafter he merely garners the annual fertility crop, so to speak, as long as he continues to use the land.

These relationships are very important. They present an entirely different set of circumstances from those that would obtain if the soil were simply an inert plant food repository subject to complete exhaustion and ruination. On the other hand, they are not a blanket license for soil exploitation nor a spotless whitewash for past agricultural practices. But they do suggest important principles that must be taken into account in setting up future programs of soil management and reclamation.

Utilization of the Pedocals. The paradox of the pedalfer is a relatively poor soil but a good climate; of the pedocal, a good soil but a climate too dry as a whole for normal agriculture. For centuries, therefore, the pedocals of the world with their grassland and desert associations have been the domain of the pastoralist. The cultivator confined himself to oases, or at best to the subhumid fringes where from time to time he produced crops of grain. The grassland provided poor shelter for a sedentary occupant, no wood for fuel or house, and little crop variety, since the soils and climate are well adapted to little else but cereals.

The latter part of the nineteenth and the early twentieth century inaugurated a revolutionary change in these age-old relations of pedocals and pastoralism, however. While stockmen were also the first to use the pedocals of the United States, the agricultural frontier advancing westward through the pedalfers, pushed them aside, and penetrated deeply into the pedocal region. A number of factors contributed to this movement. (1) The invention of the railroad provided cheap

[1] The chief source of these constituents is the undecomposed and incompletely decomposed mineral and organic materials of the soil mass. Even though a soil may have reached maturity its materials are still subject to alteration. Soils also continue to develop downward penetrating the fresh and incompletely weathered C horizon.

land transportation to a continental interior whose rivers offer little if any opportunity for navigation. Transportation is indispensable where crop diversity is limited and all other necessities must be shipped in an exchange for the bulk crop or two that is shipped out. (2) The development of agricultural machinery provided the means of utilizing large acreages profitably. On account of the low rainfall, yields are low and much more land must be cultivated if living standards are to be maintained. (3) Since the advent of the husbandman the region has had a long rainier period that was broken only by comparatively minor droughts and that did not end until near the end of the first quarter of the twentieth century.[1] Not that the rainfall was all that could be desired, but, conjoined with the rich soils and their great water-holding capacity, it went far to compensate for the climatic limitations the region imposes. Thousands of acres were converted from their natural grass cover into grain fields.

Unlike the colonial settler, therefore, the western pioneer fashioned his cropland out of good soils. The soils, moreover, gave every promise of remaining highly fertile indefinitely. Except for such variations which the ever-fluctuating rainfall imposed, yields showed little or no decline after years of cultivation, and this without the use of either fertilizers or systematic crop rotation.

But magicians' hats beget no rabbits in reality. During late years discouraged husbandmen have been evacuating these once-productive soils as their colonial antecedents abandoned the much less fertile pedalfers. The chief reasons are two: (1) a drier phase of the rainfall cycle now holds the stage, and (2) many soils have lost their structure and are crumbling to dust. The soils' collapse is primarily due to the popular practice of growing small grains continuously on the same land, year after year, and to the gradual depletion of the organic constituents. Owing to the fact that straw decomposes slowly in an arid climate and when applied to the land "burned out"[2] the subsequent crop, the common practice for many years has been to burn the straw pile after the grain harvest, rather than return it to the land and await its conversion to organic colloids. The dry, powdery, organic-depleted soil has therefore been at the mercy of strong winds, and great dust storms have swept through the region.

[1] Cf. I. Bowman, "Our Expanding and Contracting Desert," *Geographical Review*, Vol. XXV, pp. 43-61, January, 1935. Also H. M. Kendall, "Notes on Climatic Boundaries in the Eastern United States," *ibid.*, pp. 117-124.

[2] Undecomposed organic matter has a very limited capacity to absorb water and subsequent crops tend to dry or "burn" out.

THE MAJOR SOIL GROUPS

Divisions as broad as the pedalfers and pedocals must of necessity include soils of very heterogeneous nature and the characterizations that have just been outlined must be viewed only as general and comparative. Included within each division are soils ranging from relatively low to relatively high natural fertility. The occurrence of soils of somewhat higher fertility in the pedalferic division is particularly fortunate because the rainfall is superior for normal agricultural purposes.

Both pedocals and pedalfers can be divided into four groups or types,[1] the pedocals into blackerths, dark-brownerths, brownerths, and grayerths; the pedalfers into prairyerths, gray-brownerths, red-and-yellowerths, and podzols. The order in each series is one of decreasing magnitude in natural fertility as far as the major soil division is concerned.

The Podzols. The podzols occupy mainly the eastern northern borders of the United States, although small areas occur in the higher Appalachians, the Rocky Mountains, the Cascades, and the North Pacific Ranges. The special factors in their development have been a comparatively humid climate, low temperatures, and coniferous and/or hardwood forests.[2] Subject to intense leaching because of the high precipitation-evaporation ratio, the typical podzol has lost the greater part of its soluble constituents, and is strongly acid in reaction. The colloidal complex has only a limited capacity to retain nutrient salts. Moreover, the natural vegetation returns only a small amount of salts to the surface, since the mineral plant food requirements of conifers is very low and they draw only lightly on the soil, and since the hard needle decomposes slowly. The A horizon is especially impoverished. It is deficient in nutrients and colloids and so low in organic matter that it is conspicuously gray in color.[3] The B horizon is brown and relatively heavier textured, much of the organic matter and other

[1] Actually there are several thousand kinds of soils in the United States, but these are the elementary soil groups known as the soil series which correspond in a general way to the genus classification of the botanic world. Readers interested in the detailed variations they present should consult the Soil Survey Reports of the United States Bureau of Chemistry and Soils. These soils are of very great local importance.

[2] The typical natural vegetation of the podzols is coniferous associations, but locally podzols evolve under varied vegetative and climatic conditions.

[3] The gray powdery soil material looks like ashes. Podzol, signifying ash-like and a folk-term applied to similar gray soils in northern Russia, has been adopted by pedologists to designate soils of similar character throughout the world.

leached constituents having been transferred from the A horizon. In both chemical and physical characteristics the podzols are poor soils, the poorest, in fact, of all the major soil types.

In the process of exploiting and occupying the continent, it is obvious that the podzols have been the least attractive of the pedalfers agriculturally. They have been primarily the sphere of activity of the exploitive lumberman. Such agriculture as they have had has been mainly incidental to the lumbering or mining community. This is due to a complex of factors in addition to their low fertility: their excellent stand of timber, their location, their less attractive climate, their generally rougher surface, and their often predominantly sandy or rocky or poorly drained character. Only a small part of the soils have ever been cleared and brought under commercial cultivation, and with the departure of the lumberman, the region as a whole has sunk to a low subsistence level, and abandoned farms are common.

The Gray-Brownerths. Like the podzols, the gray-brownerths occur in both the eastern and western pedalferic zone (particularly in the north Pacific states), but the principal region lies south of the eastern podzol belt. While the average rainfall is approximately the same as that of the podzols, the natural forest cover is mainly deciduous and the average temperature and rate of evaporation are higher. The soil is accordingly much less leached and only mildly acid in reaction, and the colloidal complex possesses a notable ability to retain soluble constituents and water. The native vegetation is also much more active in returning soluble constituents to the surface in the form of a heavy leaf fall. This soft litter decomposes more quickly than does the débris of coniferous forests and tends to stain the soil brown in color as worms and other burrowers incorporate it in the soil mass. As in all pedalfers the B horizon is heavier and more compact than the A horizon, but the soil has comparatively good structure and is easily cultivated. In fact, the gray-brownerths are the most fertile and productive of the normal pedalfers, and they retain their productivity much longer than either the podzols or red-and-yellowerths.

The economic history of the gray-brownerths betokens their superior qualifications. Outside of rugged highland districts, there are few areas of either young, mature, or old soils that have not been cleared and maintained in some type of cultivation or pasture. From time to time there has been abandonment of field or farm or even community, but sooner or later the axe and plow returned because the gray-brownerths have four great virtues as farm lands. Their natural fertility and physical constitution have already been discussed. Their third virtue lies in the speed at which they tend to recover their fertility when "exhausted"—the long, warm, rainy summers favor the weathering and release of new mineral nutrients while the vegetation that establishes itself on abandonment promotes the soils' organic rejuvenation at surprising speed. The fourth virtue lies in the ease with which the soils are adapted or can be adapted to any crop that can be grown in the region as far as the climate is concerned. This is due to their comparatively low proportion of plant nutrients, their mild acidity, and their relatively good structure. Most crops will tolerate mild acidity, and with a good physical constitution, the soils can be built up easily to meet the peculiar requirements of almost any crop.

No wonder the gray-brownerths were quickly, extensively and successfully occupied, then frequently abandoned, and later re-utilized. This flexibility is also the key to the present-day checkered landscape they present. As economic conditions have warranted it has been easy to mold them to orchard or grainfield, to pasture or tobacco plot, to dairy farm or truck patch or vineyard, the whole a great agricultural complex. All told, the soils comprise the most valuable type the United States possesses.[1] They form the agricultural backbone of the East and much of the cropland of the humid West. Unfortunately their productiveness has led to their utilization in topographic situations where they have been subject to serious erosion, and large areas of young soils have been critically injured in the loss of their productive A horizons.

The Red-and-Yellowerths. This group embraces two closely allied grayish soils, one of which has reddish and the other yellowish B horizons. They form the typical soils of the South, although rederths are widely scattered throughout the western pedalferic zone in small areas.

In general, both soils are of essentially similar fundamental character. The special factors in their development have been the warm and humid subtropic climate combined with a forest vegetation. The prevailingly high temperatures coupled with the humid conditions have promoted their extensive weathering and leaching,[2] so that the

[1] For a fuller account of their economic utility see L. A. Wolfanger, "Economic Geography of the Gray-Brownerths of the Eastern United States," *Geographical Review,* Vol. XXI, pp. 276-296, April, 1931.

[2] The red-and-yellowerths are a kind of transitional soil type. The type of weathering to which they have been subject is in part similar to that under which the gray-brownerths and podzols have developed (termed podzolization) and in

soils are low in soluble nutrients and the colloidal complex has only a limited capacity to retain water and soluble plant foods. Moreover, since the forest vegetation returns only a small amount of soluble materials to the surface and the leaves decompose more rapidly under the warm moist climate, a large part of these nutrients is eventually lost. As a consequence the soils are intermediate in natural fertility between the gray-brownerths and podzols. The yellowerths are the poorer soils, owing to their dominantly sandy character and to the fact that they have generally evolved under high ground-water conditions and under coniferous rather than deciduous associations as the rederths have. The great redeeming feature of both these soils is their physical constitution; both have a low or comparatively low plasticity and an open, friable character.[1] This makes them easy to till and responsive to fertilizers.

The intermediate nature of the soils is reflected particularly in the South in (1) the limited way in which they have been utilized, (2) the extensive systems of agriculture that have been employed, and (3) the wide-spread occurrence of abandoned land. Albeit early occupied and the first major soil type to attain great commercial importance with its tobacco and cotton crops, forest and cut-over woodland rather than cultivated fields still characterize the region. Cropland diversifies more than dominates the general landscape: the low fertility of the soils coupled with their humid subtropical climate holds few attractions for the farmer. The larger areas one may find under cultivation in the region are principally on superior local or younger soils. Intensive horticulture characterizes the western rederths.

The limitations of the southern soil group were a fundamental factor in promoting the two extensive systems of operation that have characterized their agriculture: first, the slave-worked plantation, and later, the cropper-operated farm unit. Both systems are poor-land-skimming as well as man-exploiting operations. The low fertility is also the root of the wide-spread land abandonment evil. The soils were comparatively easy to cultivate physically either by hand or with simple machinery, but the "reserve" of nutrients was inadequate for

---

part like that of tropical soils (termed laterization). The net result is a rather poor soil. For a brief explanation of these processes see Charles E. Kellogg, "Development and Significance of the Great Soil Groups of the United States," United States Department of Agriculture, Miscellaneous Publication 229, April, 1936.

[1] In the sandy soils this is due to their sandy texture; in the non-sandy type to the lateritic character of the clay, which is only slightly sticky.

more than a good crop or two, after which a new clearing soon followed, then another, and another, and yet others.

While the climate with its long growing season is unequaled in the variety of crops it will nurture, for the most part it is only those which require the climate for optimum growth conditions and which can shoulder the burden of fertilization that have reached any degree of importance. For these reasons, the principal crops have been largely those of commercial tenor, the sale of which can offset either the fertilizer tribute the soils exact or the expense of clearing new land every few years. The world demand for cotton has made it the leading regional crop. Less important are tobacco, subtropical fruits, and off-season (winter) vegetables. The chief non-commercial crop is corn, but it is grown mainly for local consumption, is penalized by low yields, and is chiefly grown outside of a price economy. In short, the region is one that has been marked by soil exploitation and by agricultural specialization; and woodland or forest formations still occupy a large part of the region, as much as one-half and more of the area of some states.

The Prairyerths. The prairyerths comprise a unique group of pedalferic soils. The climate under which they evolved is essentially identical with that of the gray-brownerths. Though thus susceptive to an appreciable amount of leaching, the soils are relatively only very moderately leached, since nature has given them the highly constructive grass associations,[1] instead of forests, and grasses are so much more effective in returning leached materials to the surface. The return of calcium has been especially important, since calcium tends to stabilize the colloidal complex and checks its movement to the B horizon. The B horizon is therefore but slightly if at all heavier textured than the A horizon, both A and B horizons have an excellent granular structure, and the soil has a high water-holding and food-holding capacity. The thick grass roots also make the soil rich in organic matter and dark brown in color. The prairyerth is accordingly the richest pedalfer, but it is not a "normal" soil in the sense that it has not been evolved under the forest formation.

As settlement pushed actively westward during the nineteenth century, the first settlers scorned the prairyerths under the delusion that

[1] The natural vegetation of this region would appear to be deciduous forest but unusual conditions have favored the tall grass associations. For a recent summation of some of the causes see Guy-Harold Smith, "The Prairie Peninsula," *Geographical Review*, Vol. XXVI, No. 2, pp. 323-324, April, 1936.

land incapable of growing trees was poor for crops. They preferred the local islands of forested soils in the prairie or the strips of gray-brownerths that fringe the region on its northern and southern borders.

When the husbandman finally risked the prairies, he discovered a sevenfold paradise. He escaped the labor of clearing forest. He found the moisture and sunshine ideal for his crops. He was able to plant in naturally rich soils. The soils were admirably adapted to his major crops (cereals and grasses), having nurtured their wild kin for centuries. The land was level. It plowed easily, the granular structure forming an ideal tilth. The soils did not lose their productivity after a bumper crop or two—the peerless grass had accumulated and thriftily preserved a great "store" of nutrients.

This was the promised land, and its length and breadth have been eagerly occupied. No general land abandonment here, nor landscape dominated by uncultivated native grasses! The northern part forms the heart of the great American corn belt, with its endless fields of grain and hay and pasture and livestock farms; men can produce many meat animals on rich lands. The southern part forms the rich cotton lands of the black prairies of eastern Texas and Oklahoma that contrast so strikingly with the leached cotton fields of the red-and-yellowerths.

The Blackerths. The blackerths, or chernozems as they are termed by pedologists,[1] form the first broad north-south pedocalic type lying westward of the prairyerths. The soils are the American equivalent of the renowned Russian black earth belt.[2] The subhumid climate under which the soils have developed has leached them of only their highly soluble constituents; the less soluble carbonates have been deposited in the lower subsoil, as is characteristic of all pedocals. The tall grassland associations which occupy the soils have thus been better able to return calcium and other leached solubles to the surface than in the more humid prairyerths where the movement of penetrating waters has been predominantly downward to greater depths, usually to the ground water. The colloidal complex is therefore relatively more stabilized; both A and B horizons retain the same texture

[1] Chernozem, like podzol, has been adopted from Russia, and signifies black earth.

[2] The soils are not wholly identical, since the American, unlike the Russian region, has a north-south orientation and the southern part of the belt has evolved under subtropical temperatures, and the northern part under cold continental conditions. Cf. C. F. Marbut, "Soils of the Great Plains," *Annals Assn. Amer. Geogrs.*, Vol. XIII, No. 2, 1923. A small area of blackerths occurs on the Columbia Plateau.

and are highly granular in structure; the soil is richer in plant nutrients and has a higher capacity to retain nutrients and water; and the soil is a very dark brown or black in color owing to its great content of organic matter. Unfortunately the rainfall is not high.

The blackerths comprise the greater part of the pedocals in which the agriculturist has been displacing the traditional pastoralist. To the uncritical settlers who saw no differences in the gradually changing grass associations they appeared to be essentially identical with the prairyerths, so they tried instituting the same crops and agricultural system they had practiced in the humid prairies. It soon became apparent, however, that the soils were better adapted to a more extensive system, combined with livestock produced on a semi-range, semi-feeding basis. The stock use the uncropped lands and help spread the income risk. Except for the subtropical subregion, on which cotton has been extended, the cropped land forms a gigantic grain belt whose make-up varies with the latitude—sorghum in the south; winter wheat and corn in the center; and spring wheat with minor barley, rye, and flax acreages in the north. Failure to maintain the organic supply of the soils, however, has brought the region much local grief through excessive wind erosion in the current low-rainfall period.

The Dark-Brownerths. The precipitation under which the dark-brownerth type has developed is a semiarid type, and the vegetation is made up chiefly of short-grass associations. The sparser vegetation means a smaller proportion of organic matter and nitrogen, and a lighter-colored—chestnut or dark brown—soil. The semiarid climate means a thinner soil, inconsequential leaching, and a carbonate horizon lying only a foot or two below the surface. The dark-brownerths are secondary chemically and physically to the blackerths but not in a marked degree. Their most critical limitation is the low rainfall, which is rather near the limit for agriculture.

The agricultural development that has taken place has been chiefly a marginal prolongation of the neighboring blackerth crops on an even more extensive or speculative basis. Power machinery is employed and the farm unit operated is large, sometimes even double that of the blackerths. The region marks the frontier of non-irrigation agriculture, but it is a vacillating frontier. Premium prices of the World War period, coupled with several years of higher rainfall, lured the crop-grower deeply into the region. With a narrower margin of rainfall than his blackerth brother has, he is now in dire distress or in actual retreat before the dust storm. The dark-brownerths are primarily pastoral in character and at best are fit for the plow during long and abnormally wet cycles only.

The Brownerths and Grayerths. The brownerths may be identified with the arid short-grass plains and the grayerths with the desert climate and its flora. With decreasing rainfall the soils gradually become thinner, have shallower carbonate horizons, are virtually unleached, but are increasingly lighter in color owing to the sparsity of plant life and organic matter. Both brownerths and grayerths are potentially highly fertile as far as the soils alone are concerned, but their low rainfall precludes agricultural utilization without irrigation. The time-honored pedocalic stockman is still their undisputed lord, and he has every reason to assume the continuance of his security. The brownerths naturally furnish him the better pasturage.

The Pacific Pedalfers and Pedocals. The economic relations of the innumerable and comparatively small areas of pedalferic and pedocalic types scattered throughout the Pacific coast and mountain states follow the same broad lines as the larger eastern and more central regions. The chief general exception is in the populous lowlands of the Pacific coast states where crop emphasis is principally upon specialized and high-value commercial crops such as fruits and vegetables.

SOME NATIONAL CONSERVATION PROBLEMS

The variations displayed by each of the major soil types indicate what contrastive conditions the American pioneer had to face and interpret in his sweep across the continent during the course of some three centuries. He encountered nearly every major soil type the world possesses except those of purely tropical character, and most of them were soils with which he had had no previous experience. While the effects of his "conquest" vary widely from soil to soil and therefore make the problem of conservation highly complex in the last analysis, there are certain misuses that are wide spread and applicable in some degree to our soils as a whole.

Loss of Organic Matter and Plant Nutrients. When the plant cover of an area is removed for cultivation, the important rejuvenative benefits which a soil derives from the activities of natural vegetation are seriously impaired if not entirely lost. Natural vegetation carries on a constant struggle against the destructive action of climate in an endeavor to maintain the soil productive for its occupance. In the blackerth or the prairyerth region, for example, the native grassland is a very complex formation made up of innumerable long- and short-rooted plants, and early and late flowering species, all of which are so meticulously dovetailed into the growing season and in the soil mass[1] that neither time nor space is lost in returning leached nutrients to the surface and in the production of the organic matter that is so vital to fertility. Now compare the effects of either corn, the leading prairyerth crop, or wheat, the chief blackerth grain. Since both are members of the grass family, each has some of the rejuvenative potentialities of the grassland formation. However, corn is a clean cultivated crop, so that it occupies only a small part of the soil body. In addition, the grain with its precious mineral salts which under natural conditions would largely be returned to the soil is annually removed for human or livestock nutrition, and the stalks go to feedlot or silo, whence they may or may not return, depending upon the farm practice. All or much of the mineral and organic matter the crop contains may therefore be lost, with little more than the roots and stubble left for the soil's enhancement.

Wheat is a more closely seeded crop and its roots contribute a greater proportion of organic matter, but like corn, a wheat crop has neither the root nor the time range of the natural plant complex. It also surrenders its grain to the dictum of commerce while the straw usually either rots in the barnyard or is sacrificed to the expediency of burning.

In the gray-brownerth region, the orchard is a rough equivalent of the forest formation but its general action upon the soil is much less constructive. The orchard trees are more widely spaced, the fruits and their mineral salts are sold, and the orchard floor is often clean cultivated so that it lacks the understory and its root range that is so essential in rejuvenating the natural soil. In the red-and-yellowerth region, the cotton or tobacco shrub is very different from the original deciduous or coniferous forest. The potato of the podzols is hardly an analogue of the northern forest formation.

Almost irrespective of soil or plant, and with the partial exception of legumes and certain grasses, the general agriculture of both pedalfer and pedocal has been destructive or depreciative of the natural supply of nutrients and organic matter. The extent of depletion has necessarily varied with individual practice and soil type. Here and there are individuals and communities that have carried on systems of farming in which crop rotation, legumes and other approved means of

[1] Cf. J. E. Weaver and T. J. Fitzpatrick, "The Prairie," *Ecological Monographs*, Vol. 4, pp. 109-295, 1934. See also Chapter VII, "The Problem of Our Grasslands," in this volume.

maintaining the soil fertility have been the very cornerstones of all their operations. But the fortune hunter and the ignorant have been in the majority, and in the pedalferic types, where the original content was small, both organic matter and nutrients were quickly depleted—most rapidly in the podzols and least in the gray-brownerths. While the degree of depletion has naturally been much less in the organic-rich grassland types, the rate of depletion has been rapid, especially so in the blackerth and dark-brownerth region where the straw-pile burner or perpetual cereal grower was active.

Decrease of Organic Colloids. When the organic matter of a soil suffers depletion the generation of humic colloids is necessarily repressed and the repercussions that follow are multiple in view of the varied relationships of the colloidal complex. The soil's water-holding capacity and drought resistance decline. Unless a soil is able to absorb and store surplus water it is unable to come to the aid of a crop in drought years as well as during short dry spells of normal years. While drought resistance is an absolute necessity in the blackerths or dark-brownerths because of their low-rainfall régime, it is almost equally mandatory and certainly more important for the pedalfers. These humid soils produce the greater part of our agricultural output, and their crops have not been bred for water conservation.

Reduction of humic colloids also leads to loss or debility of structure, and on its heels follow difficulties in cultivation. As the structural aggregate weakens and disperses, it forms a plastic intractable mass when wet, and hard tough clods on drying out. Such soils not only are less hospitable for plant growth but also require additional power and heavier machinery to cultivate them, and they can be worked only within narrow moisture limits, viz., when the moisture content is just low enough to reduce stickiness but not too low to form hard clods. The impairment of a soil's structural capacity is a matter of critical import because of its fundamental physical relationships and our limited knowledge regarding all the factors that bear upon its maintenance.

Susceptibility to Erosion. Loss of structure is an invariable prelude to wind and water erosion. Several references have already been made to the susceptibility of dispersed soil material to wind erosion. It is correspondingly susceptive to water erosion. Reduced or impoverished in organic constituents with their great capacity to hold the individual granules together, the soil mass becomes liquescent and begins to flow on even the gentlest slope.[1]

[1] A more exhaustive treatment of soil erosion will be found in Chapter IV.

CONSERVATION FUNDAMENTALS

While the broad course of events occasioned by cultivation has been in the general direction of soil degradation in the United States, it happily does not present a situation that is without important limiting factors which are subject to human manipulation.

The most important is obviously the interrelation of soil and vegetation. Here is the fundamental keynote and theme of the battle cry of soil conservation. It is through the instrumentality of vegetation that a soil derives the peculiar characteristics that set it off from all other earth-like entities and endow it with its unique productive qualities. In the removal of its vegetation a soil loses its chief ministrant and sculptor. It loses its source of organic matter. It loses the binding effects of the vegetation's root system and the absorptive advantages of the leaf fall. Marbut aptly called the natural vegetation of a soil its health insurance.

Although it is impossible to maintain the natural plant cover, and at the same time use a soil, there are practical means of approaching many of its beneficial effects. These are (1) the rotation of properly selected crops, (2) the use of manure, and (3) the application of compost. However, since none of these measures is adequate to replace the soluble mineral nutrients lost in the use or sale of crops, certain mineral fertilizers must also be added.

Crop Selection and Rotation. Crop selection, though probably older than history, is still in its infancy. We know really comparatively little about the significant relationships that exist between a given species and soil type, in the light of our modern understanding of soils. The plant ecologist and pedologist have just begun to explore this field. However, we have certain empirical knowledge that may be put to invaluable use in the meanwhile.

The objective in rotation should be to secure such a combination and succession of crops that their general effect will at least approximate that of the natural vegetation. A given crop may degrade a soil to some degree as regard certain characteristics in satisfying its own growth requirements, yet at the same time its production is also expected to prove constructive in other ways, directly or indirectly. Cereals, for example, use large amounts of phosphates, but their fibrous roots contribute organic matter. Legumes are capable of fixing nitrogen but absorb much lime. Different crops have different root habits and form different types of organic matter. Some penetrate deeply;

others are shallow feeders. The net effect of the several crops included in a rotation program is expected to be compensatory, the sum total of malific and benefic effects at least canceling one another, and prospectively begetting a soil that is even more productive than its virgin parent.

The most constructive crops known that can be included in a system of rotation are the legumes and the hay and pasture grasses. Their great collective value lies in the large amount of organic matter they are able to contribute and in the nutrient salts they reclaim. The profusion of finely divided quick-decaying roots they produce approximates the natural plant complex or even improves upon it in the case of the podzol, gray-brownerth or red-and-yellowerth. The value of these crops is greatly enhanced if they are used as green-manure crops, i.e., if the entire crop—root, stem, and foliage—is plowed under while still green. This often contributes more to a soil, particularly a normal pedalfer, than it receives from its natural cover. Plowing under the crop while green accelerates its decomposition and conversion to humus as well as the rate at which the mineral salts it has taken up are released.

The legumes make the more valuable green-manure crops. They are more succulent and decompose more rapidly. They are deeper-rooted and bring up soluble salts from greater depth. Their ability to penetrate compact soil material makes them especially valuable in reclaiming or maintaining clay soils in a productive state.

Manure. The use of manure to increase or support the organic and nutrient content of soils is well known. Compared with the natural vegetative cover or the green manure crop, it has certain absolute limitations since the animal destroys part of the original organic matter in its digestive processes and retains some of the salts for its own nutrition. Nevertheless, if manure is duly protected from losses by seepage, leaching or volatilization, and is properly applied, it is a priceless rejuvenator, particularly if the mineral salts that have been removed are restored by the use of chemical fertilizers. It should be noted that manure properly includes the liquid as well as the solid feces, since the urine contains a large part of the soluble salts of animal excrements.

Compost. The heterogeneous odds and ends that have little value as cash crops or feed are another source of organic matter and soluble salts. These include vegetable tops and culls, leaves, straw, stalks, and other residues that are often burned as trash or otherwise dissipated. Yet they are invaluable for making compost, and offer a very low-cost means of building or bolstering up the humus and nutrient constituents. Kept moist and commingled with lime, manure, fertilizer chemicals, or mud—there are several techniques—the organic material breaks down and forms a manure substitute. Compost is not in general use in the United States, but it is widely employed in Europe where there is inadequate livestock to produce manure; and it is one of the cornerstones of Chinese and Japanese agriculture. Combining compost with a prudent use of all animal and human excreta, and with careful systems of crop rotation, the Chinese and Japanese have sustained their centuries-old agriculture amazingly without the use of mineral fertilizers other than canal mud.

Mineral Fertilizers. Plants as a whole seem to utilize or take in a score or more of elements in the process of growth. Just what the optimum conditions are as regards kind, form, and proportion of the various elements required for a particular crop are not yet known. Despite the wide-spread impact of leaching, however, even the rather highly leached soils usually fortunately retain or seem able to generate nearly adequate supplies of most of the elements necessary to produce fair economic yields of the great majority of crop plants. Aside from organic matter, the chief exceptions which must be made up in comparatively large quantities are potassium, phosphorus, nitrogen, and calcium. Several elements, such as iron and manganese and some of the rare elements, are needed for certain soils and crops in small or very minute proportions, and often also merely to build up disease resistance.

The United States is fortunate in commanding a large part of the world's usable potash and phosphate but lacks appreciable natural nitrate resources. However, since the technique of nitrogen synthesis from the atmosphere has been so highly perfected and the chief raw material required is cheap power (coal and/or water power) the deficiency is negligible. In fact, plants are already installed in Virginia, West Virginia and elsewhere that are capable of manufacturing a large part of the national requirements, and the by-product nitrogen from coke ovens and gas producers more than equals the amount necessary to make up the remainder.

The phosphate reserves occur mainly in two general regions, the Southeast (about 10 per cent) and the Rocky Mountains (about 90 per cent).[1] In view of the superior commercial location, production is

[1] Florida, South Carolina, Tennessee, and Arkansas; and Montana, Idaho, Utah, and Wyoming, respectively.

centered in the Southeast. The total reserves of the United States approximate two-thirds of the world's known high-grade deposits.

The chief workable potash reserves occur in western Texas and eastern New Mexico, but production is just in its infancy as the exploration of the field has been undertaken only in recent years. Other important sources are some of the potassium-bearing minerals like leucite which exist in enormous quantity and appear on the very verge of being made commercially feasible also. Although exploration is by no means complete, there is ample assurance that the United States may enjoy complete independence if costs of production can be lowered.

The fourth major element, calcium, is derived from limestone, which happily is cheap, wide-spread, and exists in virtually inexhaustible quantities. The magnitude is significant since the lime content of practically every pedalferic soil is low in its natural state, and applications of tons-per-acre rather than pounds-per-acre (as is usually required with the other elements) are generally necessary. Calcium is a nutritive element, but it plays its chief rôle in its broad chemical and physical effects upon the soil as a whole. It reduces acidity. It is an important constituent of the colloidal complex. It improves the soil's structure. It stimulates bacterial action. In short, it is a fundamental element in fertility.

Conservation of Mineral Fertilizers. The necessity of replenishing the difference between the nutrient mineral constituents that are lost annually in cropping (especially potassium and phosphorus) and those naturally generated by the soil itself calls for adequate measures to conserve our resources while the reserves are still impressive and to eliminate all losses attending their utilization. The matter is intensified by the interest of the modern husbandman in stepping up the productivity of his soils to even higher than virgin levels through the use of additional quantities of chemical fertilizers. The life of the deposits can be lengthened by several approaches, (1) ending mining wastes, (2) reducing manurial losses, (3) recovering sewage, and (4) utilizing better soil and crop relationships. Sanitary engineering has now advanced to the point where fertilizer constituents from urban sewage are easily and economically reclaimed. A further study of our soils and crops should reveal soils that generate or that can be induced to generate constituents at rates more in harmony with the exactions of specific crops or groups of crops, and conversely, crops whose root systems are more effective in retrieving the leached nutrients that are carried into the B or even C horizons.

HUMAN INSTITUTIONS

While the problem of soil conservation is primarily a scientific one in soil and plant coordination, supplemented by mineral fertilizers, the degree to which any ideal program may be brought to fruition is a question of human institutions. The broad value of animal manure, green manure crops, and compost for the organic rejuvenation, and of chemical fertilizers for the mineral rejuvenation of our soils, is very generally recognized and is almost proverbial. But, like good proverbs, it suffers more from frequent quotation than use, and mere intellectual assent is barren. There is imperative need for some broad program that has impressive and very tangible economic appeals to stir men to action.

The first essential of such a program, the writer would suggest, is a primary classification of all our lands in accordance with their inherent and fundamental characteristics. This includes not only their features as soils, but also their topographic, climatic, and vegetative relationships. Small but noteworthy beginnings of such studies are already in evidence on the part of some public agencies.

The second essential is to determine public land requirements in so far as they can be visualized from both a national and a local point of view. These requirements include urban and recreational land, and land needed for forests and water storage, for stream and flood control, and for similar public activities and functions. Appropriate assignments for these purposes should be made from the land types delimited in the primary classification. Where any such lands have been alienated, proper steps should be taken to return them to public ownership.

The third essential is, broadly, to divide the remaining land into lands of "sub-marginal" character and those that appear reasonably remunerative. Since both these terms are relative, obviously neither division can be fixed and rigid, and from time to time adjustments will have to be made back or forth as scientific progress occurs or economic and political conditions change. However, whatever the character of this sub-marginal land may at any time be, it should be assigned to public ownership and management. When land is sub-marginal, men are tempted to exploit rather than conserve it.

The fourth essential is to classify the remunerative lands with regard to their prospective uses and limitations, and to grade each type on the basis of the relative costs of maintaining its productivity. These classes must also be flexible and subject to interchanges as additional research and experience accumulate. What human tragedies and wastage could have been averted had we had this information in advance of settlement, or even a decade or two ago!

The fifth essential is a system of taxation that is based not upon the rule-of-thumb judgment of the tax assessor, but upon these scientific land classes, and that penalizes the lax land exploiter who fails to conserve his soils properly as well as rewards the public-spirited conservationist who has often been more or less penalized for his constructive efforts.

Finally we need something like an annual national soil-maintenance week combined with sound programs that will catch the popular imagination and lead to voluntary cooperation and action on the part of both individuals and communities.

We are living in a pedologic paradise. We have a greater diversity of soils than any other nation. Our soils are still hardly more than virgin, and we have access to almost boundless fertilizer resources. Being dynamic entities, they have the power to supply us, for immeasurable centuries, with every prospective need that can be filled within our climatic limitations, if we only act as intelligent stewards while they are in our individual possession.

CHAPTER IV

SOIL EROSION AND ITS PREVENTION

By H. H. Bennett

Soil Conservation Service, U.S.D.A.

THE PROBLEM

Growing Realization of Dangers of Soil Erosion. It seems almost yesterday that the average American thought of erosion—if he thought of it at all—as an age-long process which sometime in the dim past carved out the Grand Canyon and the Painted Desert. For this average American, the term had no meaning applicable to his every-day existence; he defined it vaguely as an inexorable force which had sculptured the face of the earth eons ago and then ceased to function. In one sense his impression was not far from correct. Erosion did carve out the Grand Canyon and the Painted Desert, and the other great clefts and chasms which scar the surface of the globe; but it was a normal geological process proceeding so leisurely through countless ages that man has no accurate measure for its progress and little concern for its effect. Had it continued as slowly—had the rates of erosion remained at geologic norms over field and pasture—our average American of today could continue to look upon it with unconcern. For geologic erosion is a harmless process and undoubtedly has been beneficial over much of the earth's surface, probably preventing, under varying conditions, the development of undesirable areas of flat land with claypan subsoil, water-soaked plains, and severely leached soil.

Within the last few years, however, we have learned that erosion, far from being a harmless or completely beneficial process in all its manifestations, is a living, constant menace to our own security and the security of posterity. We have learned that the process does not remain at geologic norms when human factors intervene in the natural order of dynamics pertaining to the earth's surface. We know definitely that man's misguided use of the land has accelerated this ancient earth-process until it has overwhelmed enormous areas of once fertile land and impoverished even greater areas. In light of this knowledge, erosion becomes a matter of concern to everyone, since it constitutes a threat to the principal factor in our national security—our indispensable agricultural lands.

Accelerated erosion is the result of conflict between man and nature—of man's necessary interference with natural processes of land stabilization in order to provide himself with the necessities of existence. Under a blanket of vegetation, nature protects the soil from the erosive forces of wind and rain, and her protection is almost complete. Soil losses under natural conditions of vegetative cover are negligible—so small, in fact, that normal processes of soil-building are generally adequate to compensate for them.

Faced with the problems of existence, man strips away the protecting cover of vegetation, and thus rudely interferes with nature's balance. Soil is exposed to wind and rain, and rates of erosion are increased enormously. Cultivation still further exposes the soil to the cutting force of wind and flowing water, again accelerating the rates of wastage. In the one instance—under natural vegetative conditions—therefore, erosion is normal or geologic; in the other—under cultural practice—the process is speeded to abnormally destructive rates.

Certain dramatic events—terrific dust storms in the Midwest—together with the initiation of governmental effort looking to erosion control have served to focus public attention upon the damage caused by accelerated soil erosion during the time the process was hopelessly clouded by ignorance and indifference. Until recently, estimates of this damage were based at best on the observations of scientific investigators and upon very general reconnaissance data. Precise measurements and a nation-wide reconnaissance survey, made possible by the development of governmental interest in the problem, have shown these early estimates to be far short of the mark.

Why Americans Were Slow to Realize the Significance of Soil Erosion. The story of soil erosion in America is new only because America is new. Centuries before this continent was known, mighty civilizations had perished or dispersed primarily because of erosion, which owes its origin, paradoxically, to the very needs of civilization. The city of Antioch was once a great and flourishing center of world commerce. Today its ruins afford interest only to archeologists and students of ancient history; the scarred and barren hills about it bear testimony to the part erosion played in its destruction. Other civilizations also have waned and expired, but their lands were utilized for many centuries before they had to be abandoned. The evidence indicates that we have been more prodigal of our soil resources than any of these dead nations of the past. Much of the ruined land in the United States knew the plow for scarcely a generation.

With the entrance of enthusiastic colonists into the virgin paradise of America there began a transformation of the land surface at a rate probably never equaled in the earth's history. Reservoirs of population in Europe supplied in a comparatively short time millions of vigorous people to clear away the forests and to break out the prairies in their

Courtesy SCS, United States Department of Agriculture

FIG. 1. The End Result of Unrestrained Erosion: Destroyed Land and Pauperized Population, Southern Piedmont Region.

westward march of agricultural occupation. Frontiers were pushed farther and farther to the west at a pace which eliminated planning or discriminate use of the virgin land. The colonists, and after them the pioneers, were busy "subduing the wilderness," slaughtering the buffalo for their hides, clearing wooded slopes, and plowing up the matted sod of the prairies. In a land so vast there seemed no necessity for conservation in any form or degree; and in this persistent illusion of inexhaustible land resources lies the origin of the philosophy which bred land extravagance, exploitation, and destruction during more than a century and a half of national development (Fig. 1).

Today, America has banished her last frontier. The tide of empire has run its course. We have come to the limits of the good land we for so long thought limitless. We know now that the United States has none too much of good land, and we are beginning to understand also that conservation of this is of paramount national importance. We know, too, that we cannot return to pre-settlement conditions. The nation has its very roots in agriculture, and if it is to persist, its agriculture must go on. We cannot grow our corn and cotton in the woods, or produce our wheat on unbroken prairie. But if we are to continue to grow these crops, we must be prepared to compromise with nature.

TYPES OF EROSION—CONSEQUENCES OF EXPLOITATION

Sheet Erosion. Aside from the evils arising out of our traditional conception that the land resources of the United States are limitless and inexhaustible, probably the main cause for lack of interest in soil conservation has been our prevailing ignorance of erosional processes, particularly with respect to sheet erosion—the principal agency of soil impairment. Sheet erosion characteristically proceeds so slowly that farmers themselves generally have not understood it and, accordingly, have given little attention to its effects until outcroppings of infertile subsoil or bedrock appear over their sloping fields (Fig. 2). The process involves the removal of thin sheets of soil over the entire extent of unprotected areas with every rain heavy enough to cause water to flow across the slopes. Large areas are affected more or less evenly, so that the effects are difficult to distinguish except by careful comparison of the soil layers (horizons) through the profiles of virgin and cultivated areas which originally were the same.

It is easy enough to see and understand the deadly malignancy of gully erosion, although it has not been generally understood that this type of land devastation usually takes place in areas which previously have suffered from the effects of sheet washing. It is difficult to understand, however, why our specialists have devoted so little attention to the evil effects of the type of soil depletion that we call sheet erosion. Everyone has seen it going on in the muddied waters flowing out of fields and coursing down streamways, following heavy rains and sudden melting of deep snows; but few have caught the full signifiance of these silt-laden waters in relation to soil decline. Most of us have observed clear water discharged from timbered and grass-covered areas, and it would seem that this should have brought our specialists to a realization of the obvious facts that (*a*) the material suspended in these silt-gorged runoff and floodwaters is derived principally from the exposed surface of fields and pastures, and that (*b*) the continuing removal of sheet after sheet of the most productive part of the land—the topsoil—eventually will whittle away this indispensable layer.

Without going into detail, a few highly pertinent facts relating to the evil consequences of sheet and gully erosion should be emphasized here:

Courtesy SCS, United States Department of Agriculture

FIG. 2. Erosion on Summer-fallowed Land, Palouse Region, Idaho. Light colored areas sheet eroded.

1. Accelerated erosion by water never improves any part of the upland; the soil is always damaged by the process. (If erosion proceeded in such a manner as to plane off smoothly the upper layers of poor soil, down to better material, such, for example, as calcareous clay subsoil, it could then be said that the process is at least temporarily beneficial to such an area. But erosion does not proceed in any such manner, except over insignificant patches.)

2. Every rain and every melting snow removes soil from all exposed areas of soil having a slope in excess of about 0.5 per cent.

3. Every puff of wind removes soil from all areas of bare, highly desiccated loose soil, whether flat or sloping.

4. Approximately three-fourths of the land area of continental United States has a slope in excess of 2 per cent.

5. No land anywhere in the United States having a slope in excess of about 25 per cent can be cultivated safely without protection against erosion. Generally, all land steeper than about 15 per cent is doomed to eventual severe impoverishment or destruction if cultivated without protection. Most land that steep should be maintained in forest, grass, or some other protective cover of vegetation.

Wind Erosion of the Great Plains. On the eleventh day of May, 1934, the sun was blotted out over a vast area of northeastern United States by a huge dust storm that originated in the drought-stricken wheat and sorghum fields west of the Mississippi. This "dry blizzard" of sun-obscuring yellow dust which swept millions of tons of rich soil from the sun-parched lands of the Great Plains marked a stage in our system of land use that should have aroused every thinking citizen. It was a thing that never before had happened in America—not since the coming of white man. It was a historic event of far more significance with respect to the continuing welfare of the country than many of the incidents written across the pages of our histories.

This onward-sweeping dust cloud was not the mere result of an unprecedented set of seasonal conditions. For untold centuries droughts have characterized the Great Plains region. The very characteristics of the soil have been fixed by this climatic factor (the accumulation of lime, "caliche," in the mid-latitude pedocalic soils, for example). The wind which drove that stupendous bulk of soil material half way across the continent and onward over the Atlantic could not in itself have accomplished the gigantic task. The real cause was man-induced soil erosion resulting from the cultivation of those dry-land areas, plus, of course, a high degree of ground desiccation and the blowing of soil-lifting winds.

Formerly, a natural cover of grass stabilized the soils of the High Plains region against wind movement, and millions of buffalo grazed the region for undeterminable ages, with only small local damage. When this grass cover was broken, first by farmers venturing beyond the prairies and later by large-scale wheat producers with their tractors and combines, the loosened soil was laid bare to the driving force of the wind. Its natural firmness was further diminished by continuing cultivation, accompanied by decay and dissipation of the grass roots and soil-accumulated vegetable matter, and the breaking down of the natural structure of the soil—its favorable granularity and fragmental character. Thus, man with his plows and crops developed a noncohesive, powdery soil condition favoring ready lifting of the lighter, finer particles into the high pathways of air currents, leaving the coarser grains to drift at lower levels to cover productive land with relatively unproductive wind-assorted, residuary material (Fig. 3).

This is the simple physics of the process of land stripping by wind, as it is also, essentially, of the still more powerful soil-transporting force of rainwater.

Courtesy SCS, United States Department of Agriculture

Fig. 3. Wind Erosion in the Texas Panhandle.

Soil is removed to plow depth during 1934. Loose sand assorted from moving soil is stranded against nearby vegetation.

Erosion in Stewart County, Georgia. An Example of Gullying. Land impoverishment by rainwash presents physical and economic problems even more serious than those of wind erosion. What has happened in Stewart County, Georgia, is an excellent illustration of the destructiveness of water erosion. Approximately 70,000 acres—one-fourth of the area of this small county—had been essentially destroyed by gullying twenty-two years ago. Originally much of this devastated area consisted of the best types of farm land in the great Coastal Plain section of that state (such as the Orangeburg and Greenville sandy loams).[1] There is no practicable artificial means by which these devastated lands can be rehabilitated, although they could

[1] *Soil Survey of Stewart County, Georgia, Field Operations,* Bureau of Soils, United States Department of Agriculture, 1913.

have been protected in the beginning; and the wastage is marching steadily ahead through the remaining areas of good land in the county.

Some of the gullies have cut to depths of more than 100 feet, possibly to 200 feet. One of these—Providence Cave—started with the drip from the roof of a barn about fifty years ago, and has engulfed a schoolhouse, two farm buildings, and a graveyard with fifty graves.

The 70,000 acres of land destroyed by erosion in this one county represents but a minute fraction of the gigantic toll taken by erosion due to land misuse. It is merely an example of the appalling cost of

Courtesy SCS, United States Department of Agriculture

FIG. 4. Badly Overgrazed Range in Power County, Idaho.

unplanned, haphazard, reckless use of the nation's most indispensable resource—the kind of use that falsely presupposed limitless and inexhaustible supplies of productive agricultural land.

Soil Erosion in America. Soil wastage by water erosion is by no means restricted to the Southern States. It has extended from the Atlantic states to the shores of California (as in the Ventura region), from the Canadian line to the Gulf, and into the very heart of the great western grazing region (Fig. 4). On some of the important soils of southwestern Wisconsin and parts of Iowa, Missouri, Kansas, and other Central States, the rate of soil removal by rainwater flowing across unprotected slopes has been even faster than in the old sections of the East and South, although not so large an area has been ruined.

Surveys indicate that more than three-fourths of the area of the country is subject to erosion in some degree where cultivated, overgrazed, or ravaged by fire.

Available measurements indicate that at least 3,000,000,000 tons of solid material are washed out of the fields and pastures of America every year. About 400,000,000 tons of solid and dissolved matter are discharged into the Gulf of Mexico annually by the Mississippi River

Courtesy SCS, United States Department of Agriculture

FIG. 5. Corn Crop Ruined by Deposition of Erosional Débris, Southeastern Minnesota.

alone. These materials come largely from the farms of the Mississippi Basin; as alluvial deposits, they form land richer than the floodplains of the Nile. But the sediment entering the oceans represents merely a fraction of the soil washed out of fields and pastures. The greater part is piled up or temporarily lodged along lower slopes, often damaging the soil beneath (Fig. 5), or is deposited over rich, alluvial stream bottoms, or in channelways, harbors, reservoirs, irrigation ditches, and drainage canals. Once the soil leaves a field, it is as irretrievably lost as if consumed with fire, so far as that particular field is concerned.

It cannot be hauled back economically, even though temporarily stranded only a short distance down the slope.

Loss of Essential Elements by Erosion. This vast quantity of wasted soil contains 92,172,300 tons of the five principal elements of plant food (phosphorus, potassium, nitrogen, calcium, and magnesium), as computed from the average of analyses of 389 samples of surface soils collected by the Bureau of Chemistry and Soils throughout the country (1.55 per cent potash; 0.15 per cent phosphoric acid; 0.10 per cent nitrogen; 1.56 per cent lime; 0.84 per cent magnesia).[1] Of this total, 43,361,000 tons consist of phosphorus, potassium, and nitrogen, the principal ingredients of commercial fertilizer. According to estimates,[2] approximately 668,000 tons of phosphorus, potassium, and nitrogen were used in the United States during the fiscal year ending June 30, 1934. The same authority estimates the value of commercial fertilizers sold in the United States during the calendar year 1934 at $158,500,000.

In other words, erosion removes from our fields and pastures every year plant food, available and potential, amounting to something like sixty times the available plant food returned to the soil in various forms of commercial fertilizers, assuming 1934 to be a fairly representative year with respect to fertilizer usage. In this connection it should be remembered, however, that erosion removes not only the plant food but actually the entire body of the soil—plant nutrients, humus, beneficial microscopic organisms, everything. Plant food can be restored to soil worn lean by cropping or leaching, but when the soil itself is washed into the streams and oceans, ages will be required for nature to rebuild its counterpart over the denuded areas.

Thousands of farmers, operating on slopes stripped of the more productive surface layer, have but the slimmest opportunity to make a satisfactory living, regardless of price levels. They have been lowered to the level of cultivating land on which productivity has been reduced from two to ten times or more by erosion.

Wide-spread Effects of Erosion. Aside from the destruction and impoverishment of farm land, erosion carries with it consequences of vast importance to the permanence of investments of billions of dollars in navigation, power, municipal water supply, and irrigation de-

[1] H. H. Bennett and W. R. Chapline, *Soil Erosion a National Menace,* Circular 33, United States Department of Agriculture, 1928.

[2] A. L. Mehring and H. R. Smalley, *A Survey of Plant Food Consumption in the United States for the Year Ending June 30, 1934,* National Fertilizer Association, Washington, D. C., 1935.

velopments. Products of surface wash and gully excavation are carried by storm waters to be deposited in stream channels and reservoirs. Yawning gullies concentrate rainfall to pass on to streams with greatest possible speed the downpours that gather on watersheds, to gorge the channelways of tributaries and trunk streams with destroying floods. Especially significant is the rapid rate at which silting is going on in reservoirs located on streams within critically eroding areas of the country, both in the East and the West.

Some Known Losses and Their Significance. Actual losses to the nation, as now determined by exact measurements and extensive surveys, are staggering. Approximately 50,000,000 acres of once productive land has been essentially ruined for further practical crop use, and another 50,000,000 acres is in almost as bad condition. Had it been protected, or could it be restored, this aggregate of 100,000,000 acres of impoverished land, divided into farms of 80 acres each, would support 1,250,000 rural families instead of weeds and scrub.

Something over 100,000,000 additional acres, largely still in cultivation, has lost all or the greater part of its productive topsoil; on yet other millions of acres erosion is getting actively under way. Good farm land is virtually destroyed at the rate of more than 300,000 acres every year, with a still larger area undergoing severe impoverishment.

How fundamentally these staggering losses, if permitted to continue, will affect the basic agricultural prosperity of the nation is clear enough, and little reflection is necessary to appreciate the fact that hazards to our national agricultural prosperity inevitably constitute hazards also to the prosperity of every individual, no matter how far removed from actual contact with the land. We have never had, nor can we have, an enduring civilization entirely apart from agriculture.

Conservative estimates indicate that the annual monetary cost of erosion in the United States amounts to at least $400,000,000 in terms of lost productivity alone. This loss already totals probably not less than $10,000,000,000, and unless erosion is effectively curbed the probable future costs will be equally gigantic. The annual $400,000,000 direct loss would, within fifty years, accumulate to not less than $20,000,000,000; and, since unrestrained erosion progresses at an increasing rate (the subsoil usually being more erodible than the topsoil), the cost may extend to $30,000,000,000. To this would have to be added huge losses due to: (1) clogging of great reservoirs and shoaling of stream channels with the sedimentary products of erosion; (2) the abandonment of irrigated areas dependent on reservoirs; (3) the virtual abandonment of large agricultural sections; (4) the economic devastation of large western areas dependent on grazing; and (5) the transfer of large farm populations to relief rolls or other pursuits.

Probably the most accurate picture of the extent of erosion is to be found in results of a nation-wide reconnaissance survey of erosion conditions, made during the summer of 1934 by the Soil Conservation Service of the United States Department of Agriculture. This survey showed that within an area of approximately 832,000,000 acres, exclusive of the western mountains and intermountain basins, eroded land in one form or another is present either in frequent occurrence or as a prevailing characteristic. Not all this enormous area has been seriously affected; numerous areas have not been eroded at all, although falling within the broad areal classification of eroding land. For instance, nearly 49,000,000 acres were found over which, generally, there are scattering gullies but comparatively few large tracts seriously damaged by sheet erosion.

Nevertheless, serious erosion was found to be much more widespread than expected. The survey revealed that the greater part of an area of 44,000,000 acres outside of the arid western region has been essentially destroyed by wind or water erosion, so far as general use for crop production is concerned. Most of this consists of formerly cultivated good soil. Practically all the topsoil has been lost from the greater part of an area of nearly 87,000,000 additional acres. Much of this, however, is not entirely unsuited for further tillage, but the greater part has been markedly reduced in productivity, with numerous patches and some large bodies essentially destroyed.

In addition to the above severely eroded areas, the survey has revealed an aggregate of approximately 468,000,000 acres over which from one-fourth to three-fourths of the topsoil has been lost from more than 25 per cent of the land. The cultivated portion of this moderately eroded area is rapidly losing its topsoil, but much of it is still productive. The major problem involved in conservation of agricultural land relates to the areas included in this broad classification.

A large area has been seriously affected by wind erosion, principally in the Great Plains, from Texas to North Dakota. The survey shows: (1) a combined area of something over 4,000,000 acres of which more than one-fourth of the land has been essentially ruined for further cultivation, and (2) an aggregate of 56,000,000 acres with more than 25 per cent of the farm land seriously affected.

Over an area of approximately 168,000,000 acres included in the total eroding area of 832,000,000 acres (as broadly classed), erosion is rapidly getting under way in numerous localities. This is an important part of the remaining area of the nation's most valuable agricultural land and must be preserved at all costs.

Areas within which more than 25 per cent of the land has been effected as indicated:

	Acres
1. Practically all topsoil lost; severely gullied and generally unsuited for further tillage. Includes much abandoned land	48,959,596
2. Practically all topsoil lost. That part still under cultivation generally of low agricultural value. Includes much abandoned land and much submarginal land inefficiently farmed	86,782,934
3. From one-fourth to three-fourths topsoil lost. That part in cultivation advancing toward condition of Class 2, though still suitable for tillage with adequate conservation measures. Approximately 50,000,000 acres—mainly patchy areas—very severely damaged	467,875,940
4. Moderate to serious wind erosion on cultivated area	56,489,503
5. Greater part essentially ruined for further tillage by wind erosion	4,219,799

A Look Into the Future. Looking to the future, it appears, on the basis of past experience, that within the next hundred years at least 100,000,000 acres of the remaining valuable agricultural areas (or farm land) will become severely impoverished through erosion if not adequately protected. This progressive impoverishment, if permitted to continue unchecked, eventually will reduce the fertile area of farm land to not more than about 150,000,000 acres, as compared with the present area of about 450,000,000 acres. Such an area might easily prove insufficient for the maintenance of a satisfactory national standard of living.

Necessity for Control. Accelerated soil erosion and its control present the nation with a physical land crisis of enormous importance to the continuing welfare of agriculture in particular and the entire social structure in general. Moreover, beyond this most acute crisis of the whole land problem, there exists the physical fact that there can be no permanent cure of floods or prevention of stream and reservoir silting until runoff is better controlled, all the way from the crests of ridges, down across the watersheds where floods originate and silt loads are picked up, on to the very channelways of streams, which, like other conduits, have limitations upon their carrying capacity.

Control of erosion is the first and most essential step in the direction of correct land utilization on something like 75 per cent of the present and potential cultivated area of the nation. Whatever our inclinations may be, whatever opinions, conclusions, or complexities our roundtable, institute, and academic discussions may lead us to, the job of curbing erosion must be performed if the nation is to avoid early arrival at an inconceivably bad land situation. The Union of South Africa has reached this same conclusion and is now engaged in an attack against erosion in that country, employing a plan of procedure somewhat like that developed by the Soil Conservation Service for this country. The Italian government is carrying out an enormous land reclamation and conservation program—the Bonifica Integrale—the ultimate cost of which has been estimated at $500,000,000. Japan for many years has been spending many times the value of numerous critically eroding areas in order to protect indispensable valley lands from the erosional débris issuing from such sore spots. There is no reason to assume that the United States can better afford to neglect this gigantic problem of waning soil productivity than any other country.

Regardless of our great successes in breeding more productive strains of crops and the introduction of new and better varieties from the ends of the world; in spite of improved cultivation with more and better machinery, increased use of soil-building rotations, of fertilizer, and of soil-improving legumes; and in spite of all the education and information provided through our schools, colleges, societies, clubs, institutes, surveys, the press, thousands of books, and millions of bulletins, our nation-wide crop yields have not increased; rather they have decreased for some of our major crops. For example, the annual acreage yield of corn for the 10-year period from 1871 to 1880 was 27.04 bushels an acre; whereas, for the 10-year period from 1921 to 1930, the corresponding acreage production was 26.13 bushels, or a reduction of approximately a bushel an acre. That the maximum and minimum yields for single years during the former period were higher, respectively, than the maximum and minimum yields of the latter period indicate that the comparisons are significant.

When it is considered that corn growing has not been pushed out on the marginal and submarginal lands of semiarid regions upon any extensive scale, and that the crop has not suffered from any far-reaching, devastating insect or disease scourges, it is impossible to reach any other than the definite conclusion that erosion has partly thwarted our stupendous technical, educational, and practical efforts to increase the yield of this crop on a national basis. The acreage yield of corn has undergone large declines over numerous severely eroded areas. Cotton has declined in acreage yield much more than corn, and, of course, the decline in yield of both crops would have been still greater, perhaps disastrous, but for the educational, experimental, and breeding work, and better cultural practices referred to above.

EROSION CONTROL TECHNIQUES

Variables Involved. It would be difficult to conceive a physical process involving more modifying factors than soil erosion. The interdependent processes of absorption, runoff, and erosion are profoundly affected not only by slope, climate, soil, and cover of vegetation and vegetal litter, but also by the condition of the surface soil resulting from various methods of utilization, and, subsequently, by the condition and character of the different sublayers successively exposed by progressive planation. These and numerous other factors, separately and interdependently, introduce into the dynamics of this three-phase process an almost inconceivable number of highly pertinent variables.

Numerous other factors having to do with the economic and social aspects of the problem are involved in erosion-control planning for a given area. Especially important are such matters as size of farm, farm indebtedness, type of tenancy, location, traditional cultural practices, educational facilities, community spirit, and individual capacity for efficient management.

Soil type alone introduces a great variety of conditions that appreciably or profoundly affect rates of absorption (infiltration) and, therefore, of runoff and soil denudation. Texture of the surface material and inherent soil structure and consistence markedly affect rates of absorption, as do also the same characteristics as cxpressed in the widely divergent sublayers through the soil profile down to and including the horizon of parent material. Obviously, rainwater percolates into and through porous sand and gravelly soil more rapidly than through dense clay. Again, the capacities of sand or of sandy loam, fine sandy loam, gravelly loam, and other pervious materials for absorbing rainfall vary markedly with differences in depth to sublayers of relatively impervious material, such as plastic clay and dense hardpan. The fact that there are several thousand distinct soil types in the United States, occupying a great variety of slopes and subjected to a multiplicity of uses and intensities of rainfall, affords some conception of the wide range of pertinent variants, such as cannot be ignored either in research or in the development and use of practicable methods for controlling erosion. In addition to the difficulties involved with this long list of the more evident variables, the specialist interested in developing control measures is challenged by still other categories of variants, such as the less obvious effects of soil crusting, pore clogging, and those physical behaviors having to do with fundamental peculiarities of soil structure and soil suspension in water flowing at varying velocity.

None too much is known about the mechanical relation of such activities as gravitational creep, sliding, fragmentation, granulation, and dispersion to processes and rates of runoff and erosion. The causative processes involved with the formation of V-shaped gullies, as distinguished from U-shaped gullies or gullies that spread faster laterally than longitudinally, have not been adequately investigated. Differential erosion on exposed sections of soil profiles characterized by markedly different horizons is a phenomenon that lies rather completely outside the knowledge of most specialists. Very little is known about the dynamics of rill washing. The baffling contrasts revealed in measurements of runoff and erosion from plots occupying the same kind of soil, the same degree of slope, and subjected to the same cultural treatments, would seem convincing evidence that the mechanics of loading and unloading on the part of thin and thick sheets of water flowing across slopes of different cross-sectional dimensions is little understood.

Briefly stated, soil erosion presents a new and very broad field for investigational work. Fundamental studies have been neglected long enough; more specific knowledge applicable to concrete conditions is acutely needed now. Even so, we have acquired enough information at the various erosion experiment stations and through erosion surveys and soil surveys to appreciate the fact that we have made a real beginning with the study of soil-erosion processes, as well as with the development of measures of control.

Some Pertinent Investigations and Results at Bethany, Missouri. Investigations carried on at the Bethany, Missouri, erosion station on one of the most extensive soils in the rolling sections of the corn belt—glacial till soil of the Shelby series—show (Table 1) that on 8 per cent slopes, devoted continuously to corn, the annual soil loss from a representative cross-section (73 feet from upper to lower side) has been at the rate of approximately 60 tons an acre, along with a water loss amounting to 27 per cent of the total precipitation. As against this, the corresponding losses from an equal area of exactly the same kind of soil, having the same declivity and affected by the same rains, have been very much less where the plots were covered with thick-growing crops. Under alfalfa there has been a loss of only little more than 0.2 ton of soil an acre annually, along with a runoff but slightly exceeding 3 per cent of the precipitation; under timothy the corresponding losses have been about 0.3 ton of soil and about 8 per cent of the precipitation. In other words, alfalfa has been nearly 300 times and grass nearly 200 times more effective than corn as soil-conserving crops. The respective efficiencies of the two crops in relation to rainfall retention, as compared with corn, have been approximately 9 and 3 times as great. For the same period, the same type of land kept bare of all vegetation has lost an annual average of 112 tons of soil an acre, or 500 times as much as from fields devoted to alfalfa. Strange to say, however, the water loss from this area of bare fallow has been somewhat less than that from the corresponding corn plot.

TABLE 1

AVERAGE ANNUAL SOIL AND WATER LOSSES,

1931–1933, Inclusive

EROSION EXPERIMENT STATION, BETHANY, MISSOURI

Shelby silt loam, 8 per cent slope.
Mean precipitation, 33.54 inches.

Plot	Size of Plot	Treatment	Soil Loss, Tons per Acre	Water Loss, Per Cent Precipitation
1	6 x 145.7 ft.	Continuous corn	74.09	24.59
2	6 x 72.85 ft.	Continuous corn	60.80	27.41
Rotation 3	6 x 72.85 ft.	Corn, wheat, clover	18.34	13.37
Rotation 4	6 x 72.85 ft.	Wheat, clover, corn	10.36	10.68
Rotation 5	6 x 72.85 ft.	Clover, corn, wheat	7.19	11.57
Rotation 6	6 x 72.85 ft.	Clover (fertilized), corn, wheat	3.74	8.64
	Average of rotation (Plots 3, 4, 5, 6)		9.91	11.06
7	6 x 72.85 ft.	Continuous alfalfa	0.21	3.41
8	6 x 72.85 ft.	Continuous grass	0.32	7.74
9	6 x 72.85 ft.	Fallow (soil-spaded)	112.06	26.02
10	6 x 72.85 ft.	Fallow (subsoil-spaded)	73.47	24.65

From fields under a four-year rotation of corn, wheat, and clover, the acreage loss of soil has proceeded at the rate of about 10 tons annually, and the water loss has amounted to 11 per cent of the precipitation, showing that a good crop rotation is a very effective method for minimizing erosion.

These results represent averages of the three-year period from 1931 to 1933, inclusive, during which time the mean annual precipitation has been 31 inches. Over this period 208 rains have fallen at the Bethany station, 70 of which (or 34 per cent) caused runoff. Of the 42.5 inches of rainfall in 1931, 31 rains caused runoff from corn ground, these totaling 29.7 inches. Although only 16 of the 62 rains that fell in

1932 produced runoff, 19 of the 62 amounted to more than 1 inch each. Many light summer showers were completely dissipated by almost immediate evaporation from the sun-heated soil. Under certain conditions some of the heavier rains, even where falling at fairly intense rates, have been completely absorbed, whereas under other conditions lighter rains of about equal intensity have produced runoff.

In 1931, 30 per cent of all the rain that fell on the continuous corn plot (Plot 2) at the Bethany station was lost as runoff. That year 39 rains, totaling 12.8 inches, or 30 per cent of the total precipitation, produced no runoff from this plot. More than half of this 30 per cent fraction of the rainfall fell in the form of light showers that immediately evaporated. Thus, the immediate loss of rainfall for this period amounted to something above 45 per cent of the total precipitation. Since part of the remainder was lost as percolation and part as evaporation other than transpiration, the corn crop had for its use probably considerably less than half of the rainfall—perhaps something under 40 per cent.

In contrast, only 2 per cent of the rainfall of 1931 was lost from the alfalfa field (Plot 7). Thus, this densely growing crop had for its use, on the same degree of slope and type of soil, and with the same rainfall, probably in the neighborhood of 68 per cent of the total precipitation. Accordingly, quantitative references to *effective precipitation* must be specific if they are to carry any approximation of full significance.

These results, as already noted, are based on a three-year period. This, probably, is not long enough for the establishment of adequately accurate averages. Nevertheless, the results doubtless are nearly enough accurate to be highly significant. It might be mentioned in this connection that the soil depth of the Shelby silt loam on 8 per cent slopes, in the locality where these data were obtained, is approximately 7 inches, and that the rate of soil stripping under continuous corn production, as revealed in these measurements, would require, theoretically, less than 20 years to remove the surface layer down to a distinctly different sublayer, having a different rate of erosion. Actually, a somewhat longer period usually would be required for the removal of this much soil, because some of the subsurface material would be brought up and mixed with the topsoil by plowing, thus postponing for some time arrival at the stage of complete denudation of the surface soil.

That a three-year period of measurements is inadequate for final conclusions with respect to rates of erosion and runoff is indicated by the soil and water losses from a single intensive rain of 3.7 inches that fell on the Bethany station plots April 3, 1934 (3.03 inches of which fell at an average rate of 2.36 inches an hour). From the continuous corn plot the loss of soil as the result of this one rain was nearly as great as the entire loss caused by all the rains producing runoff during 1933—that is, 46 tons lost during the one rain, as against 50 tons lost during all the 1933 rains causing runoff. From this particular rain 69 per cent of the water was immediately lost as runoff, whereas only

Courtesy SCS, United States Department of Agriculture

Fig. 6. Erosion of Steep Cultivated Slope, California Bean District.
No erosion in vegetated area above.

31 per cent of the total rainfall of 1933 was lost from the same corn plot.

Tables 1, 2, and 3 show the details of soil and water losses from Shelby silt loam occupying 8 per cent slopes at Bethany, Missouri, as annual averages for (1) a three-year period, (2) a one-year period, and (3) a single exceptionally heavy downpour. Table 4 shows the corresponding losses from a 3.68 per cent slope of Shelby loam at Columbia, Missouri, as annual averages covering a fourteen-year period.

Investigation of Effect of Slope on Erosion and Runoff. It has been assumed generally that slope is the most powerful factor affecting erosion and runoff. The available data do not bear out this point of

TABLE 2

SOIL AND WATER LOSSES, 1933,
EROSION EXPERIMENT STATION, BETHANY, MISSOURI

Shelby silt loam, 8 per cent slope.
Precipitation, 31.06 inches.

Plot	Size of Plot	Treatment	Soil Loss, Tons per Acre	Water Loss, Per Cent Precipitation
1	6 x 145.7 ft.	Continuous corn	65.30	27.70
2	6 x 72.85 ft.	Continuous corn	49.74	31.00
Rotation 3	6 x 72.85 ft.	Clover	0.19	6.40
Rotation 4	6 x 72.85 ft.	Corn	27.81	22.40
Rotation 5	6 x 72.85 ft.	Wheat	0.40	8.90
Rotation 6	6 x 72.85 ft.	Wheat (fertilized)	0.53	8.60
7	6 x 72.85 ft.	Continuous alfalfa	0.26	7.10
8	6 x 72.85 ft.	Continuous bluegrass	0.18	8.50
9	6 x 72.85 ft.	Fallow (soil-spaded)	144.84	34.80
10	6 x 72.85 ft.	Fallow (subsoil-spaded)	106.76	34.80

TABLE 3

RESULT OF ONE RAIN OF 3.71 INCHES,

April 3, 1934,

EROSION EXPERIMENT STATION, BETHANY, MISSOURI

Shelby silt loam, 8 per cent slope.
3.30 inches fell at rate of 2.36 inches per hour.

Plot	Size of Plot	Treatment	Soil Loss, Tons per Acre	Water Loss, Per Cent Precipitation
1	6 x 145.7 ft.	Corn ground, bare, not plowed	53.62	66.6
2	6 x 72.85 ft.	Corn ground, bare, not plowed	45.58	68.6
Rotation 3	6 x 72.85 ft.	Clover stubble (corn to follow)	0.23	29.6
Rotation 4	6 x 72.85 ft.	Wheat (leaves 2 to 3 inches long)	11.31	72.2
Rotation 5	6 x 72.85 ft.	Clover (seeded spring 1933, unfertilized)	1.58	43.0
Rotation 6	6 x 72.85 ft.	Clover (seeded spring 1933, fertilized)	0.465	39.0
	Average of rotation (Plots 3, 4, 5, 6)		3.40	45.75
7	6 x 72.85 ft.	Alfalfa (just beginning to grow)	0.30	40.5
8	6 x 72.85 ft.	Bluegrass (just beginning to grow)	0.085	39.2
9	6 x 72.85 ft.	Fallow (soil—fall plowed)	28.49	52.7
10	6 x 72.85 ft.	Fallow (subsoil—fall plowed)	29.61	74.5

view but indicate, instead, that the kind and density of the vegetative cover are the most pertinent factors involved with erosion rates (Fig. 6). After vegetation, the character of the soil appears to have the most potent influence, at least in many instances. Under corresponding conditions with respect to cover, use of the land, and rainfall intensity, degree of slope, of course, exerts the most powerful influence, where the soils are of the same kind.

Table 5, presenting comparative soil and water losses from 8 and 3.7 per cent slopes on practically the same type of soil, shows that where the slope is somewhat more than twice as steep the soil loss from clean-

TABLE 4

AVERAGE ANNUAL SOIL AND WATER LOSSES,
1918–1931, Inclusive

AGRICULTURAL EXPERIMENT STATION, COLUMBIA, MISSOURI

Shelby loam, 3.68 per cent slope.
Mean precipitation, 40.37 inches.

Plot	Size of Plot	Treatment	Soil Loss, Tons per Acre	Water Loss, Per Cent Precipitation
1	6 x 90.75 ft.	Fallow, plowed 4 in.	41.6	31.0
2	6 x 90.75 ft.	Fallow, plowed 8 in.	41.0	31.3
3	6 x 90.75 ft.	Continuous wheat	10.1	24.0
4	6 x 90.75 ft.	Continuous corn	19.7	30.3
5	6 x 90.75 ft.	Rotation (corn, wheat, clover)	2.7	14.4
6	6 x 90.75 ft.	Continuous bluegrass	0.3	12.5

TABLE 5

LOSS OF SOIL AND WATER FROM SHELBY SOIL OCCUPYING DIFFERENT SLOPES

Location	Soil	Slope, Per Cent	Soil Loss, Tons per Acre		Water Loss, Per Cent Precipitation	
			Corn	Grass	Corn	Grass
Bethany, Missouri (4-year average)	Shelby silt loam (nearly a loam)	8.0	61	0.3	27	8
Columbia, Missouri (14-year average)	Shelby loam	3.7	20	0.3	30	13

tilled land has averaged approximately three times as great, while losses under grass were the same from both declivities. (The rainfall was somewhat lighter on the steeper slope—34 inches, as against 40 inches.)

Table 6 shows comparative soil and water losses from (1) Kirvin fine sandy loam, the most extensive and most erosive soil of the 33,000,000 acres comprised in the Texas-Arkansas-Louisiana Sandy Lands region; and (2) Nacogdoches fine sandy loam, an associated but markedly different soil (a lateritic soil).

TABLE 6

Loss of Soil and Water from Kirvin and Nacogdoches Soils, East Texas

Location	Soil	Slope, Per Cent	Soil Loss, Tons per Acre		Water Loss, Per Cent Precipitation	
			Cotton	Grass	Cotton	Grass
Erosion station near Tyler, Texas	Kirvin fine sandy loam	8.75	19	0.2	20	1.5
Erosion station near Tyler, Texas	Kirvin fine sandy loam	16.50	35	0.0	13	0.7
Erosion station near Tyler, Texas	Nacogdoches fine sandy loam	10.00	6	0.02	15	1.4

Here it is seen that doubling the slope in the case of Kirvin fine sandy loam devoted to cotton caused almost twice the soil loss, although there was no increased loss where grass was grown. In the instance of Nacogdoches fine sandy loam, the soil losses from a slope steeper than that of the nearby Kirvin fine sandy loam (10 per cent as against 8¾ per cent) were only one-third as much under cotton and one-tenth as much under grass, even though the rainfall on the Nacogdoches plots was 2 1/3 inches greater than that on the Kirvin plots, and equally intense.

Measurement of Relation of Slope and Erosion at Spur, Texas. A very interesting relationship of slope to erosion is afforded by measurements made on Abilene clay loam at Spur, Texas. Here, the average soil loss from level land over a period of eight years has been at the rate of 3 tons an acre annually where cotton was grown continuously. The corresponding losses from slopes of 1 and 2 per cent have been at the respective rates of 6 and 8 tons an acre.

Considering further the effect of slope, losses of both soil and water from the extensive Cecil sandy clay loam of the North Carolina Piedmont have been remarkably low—only 14 tons of soil an acre under cotton grown on 10 per cent slopes, with 9 per cent of the rainfall lost as runoff. Comparing these results with those obtained on a 2 per cent slope of Abilene clay loam at Spur, Texas, it is seen that although the slope of the North Carolina clay loam soil was five times as steep and the rainfall more than twice as heavy (43 inches, as against 21), and even more torrential, the erosion from cotton on the Piedmont soil was only a few tons greater (14 tons, as against 8), while the runoff was actually less (9 per cent, as against 14). This undoubtedly was due to the fact that the North Carolina clay loam is very different physically from the west Texas clay loam. It is of lateritic character. The material of lateritic soils (severely leached, with relatively high contents of iron or alumina or both) does not go into suspension as rapidly as the material of less oxidized, less leached soils of the same texture, such as the Abilene clay loam. This property alone is a source of considerable resistance to erosion on the part of the more weathered lateritic soils. It may be of interest to add here that some of the clay laterites of the tropics are almost proof against erosion.[1] The red basaltic soils of western Oregon are somewhat of this nature also, suffering but slightly from washing even on very steep cultivated slopes.

Comparison of Protective Efficiency of Grass and Forest. Table 7 shows the effects of forest cover and grass on erosion and runoff, as measured on Kirvin fine sandy loam in east Texas and on Vernon fine sandy loam in central Oklahoma. In both instances, the ground cover of litter was decidedly light as compared with the average forest-floor litter of the country.

These results show that forest, as well as good stands of grass, give practically complete protection from erosion on these very extensive and important soil types. The water losses also have been exceedingly small, especially where the ground cover of forest litter was not burned. The difference between the effectiveness of grass and forest is seen to be very slight for the regions studied. Over a period of four years the average runoff from the burned forest area in Oklahoma has exceeded by three times the loss from the adjoining unburned area of

[1] H. H. Bennett, "Some Comparisons of the Properties of Humid-Tropical and Humid-Temperate American Soils," *Soil Science,* Vol. 21, No. 5, May, 1926, pp. 349-374; and, H. H. Bennett and R. V. Allison, *The Soils of Cuba,* Tropical Plant Research Foundation (Boyce-Thompson Institute, Yonkers, N. Y.), 1928.

TABLE 7

EFFECT OF FOREST ON EROSION AND RUNOFF, AS COMPARED WITH GRASS, TYLER, TEXAS AND GUTHRIE, OKLAHOMA

Soil, Fine Sandy Loam	Mean Precipitation, Inches	Slope, Per Cent	Cover	Soil Loss, Tons per Acre	Water Loss, Per Cent Precipitation
Kirvin........	44.4	12.5	Forest	0.01	0.8
Kirvin........	44.4	12.5	Forest litter burned	0.19	2.6
Kirvin........	42.3	8.75	Bermuda grass	0.21	1.5
Kirvin........	48.8	16.5	Bermuda grass	0.00	0.7
Vernon.......	33.5	5.2	Forest	0.017	0.13
Vernon.......	33.5	5.2	Forest litter burned	0.22	5.06
Vernon.......	32.9	7.7	Bermuda grass	0.04	1.5

TABLE 8

SOIL AND WATER LOSSES FROM SOIL AND SUBSOIL OF IMPORTANT TYPES ORIGINALLY THE SAME

Location	Soil	Slope, Per Cent	Cover	Mean Precipitation, Inches	Soil Loss, Tons per Acre		Water Loss, Per Cent Precipitation	
					Surface Soil	Subsoil	Surface Soil	Subsoil
Tyler, Texas	Kirvin fine sandy loam	8.75	Cotton	42	19	71	20	23
Tyler, Texas	Nacogdoches fine sandy loam	10.0	Cotton	44	6	36	15	19
Guthrie, Oklahoma	Vernon fine sandy loam	7.7	Cotton	33	28	32	14	28
Clarinda, Iowa	Marshall silt loam	9.6	Corn	48	45	81	13	15
Hays, Kansas	Colby silty clay loam	5.0	Wheat	22	2	11	10	19
La Crosse, Wisconsin	Clinton silt loam	16.0	Corn	29	60	89	19	30
Statesville, North Carolina .	Cecil sandy clay loam	10.0	Cotton	43	14	17	9	8
Temple, Texas	Houston black clay	4.0	Corn, Oats, Cotton	27	2	11	4	8

precisely the same kind of soil, having the same forest cover. The corresponding soil loss from the burned area has been nineteen times as great.

Effect of Removal of Surface Soil on Erosion and Runoff. Generally, erosion increases after removal of the surface soil by sheet washing, and it is at this stage of progressive erosion that gullying, the beginning of the final stage of land destruction, usually sets in. Table 8 shows comparative rates of erosion and runoff from topsoil and subsoil of a number of extensive soil types, representing collectively many millions of acres of farm land. From each of these types the losses of both soil and water have been greater where, under precisely the same conditions of slope, treatment, and precipitation, the subsoil was exposed to the rains. In one instance the loss of material from subsoil exceeded that from the corresponding surface soil (both areas having been originally the same) by six times. The average loss of soil material and of water from subsoil exceeded the corresponding losses from surface soil by 98 and 44 per cent, respectively.

TABLE 9

COMPARISON OF SOIL AND WATER LOSSES UNDER CROP ROTATIONS ON EIGHT IMPORTANT SOILS

Location	Soil	Slope, Per Cent	Rotation	Mean Precipitation, Inches	Soil Loss, Tons per Acre	Water Loss, Per Cent Precipitation
Bethany, Missouri	Shelby silt loam	8.0	Corn, wheat, clover	34	10	11
Columbia, Missouri	Shelby loam	3.7	Corn, wheat, clover	40	10	24
Hays, Kansas	Colby silt loam	5.0	Wheat, Kafir, fallow	22	10	16
Guthrie, Oklahoma	Vernon fine sandy loam	7.7	Wheat, sweet-clover, cotton	33	6	12
Temple, Texas	Houston black clay	4.0	Cotton, corn, oats	27	6	5
Tyler, Texas	Kirvin fine sandy loam	8.75	Cotton, corn, lespedeza	42	16	18
La Crosse, Wisconsin	Clinton silt clay loam	16.0	Barley, corn, clover	29	21	13
Statesville, North Carolina	Cecil sandy clay loam	10.0	Corn, wheat, lespedeza, cotton	43	7	10

Effect of Crop Rotations on Soil and Water Conservation. Table 9 shows the effect of crop rotations on erosion and runoff for a number of important soils. In every case the rotation materially reduced the losses of soil, as compared with the losses from the same kind of land, occupying the same declivity, and receiving the same rainfall, where a clean-tilled crop was grown; and in all but one instance the runoff from areas under continuous clean tillage was greater. The saving of soil ranged up to six times greater than where a one-crop system of clean culture was practiced, with a corresponding conservation of rainfall amounting to nearly three times as much. The average saving over single-crop culture for the eight types studied amounted to 164 per cent of soil and 37 per cent of water.

Effect of Length of Slope on Soil and Water Losses. Table 10 contains sufficient data with respect to effect of length of slope on rates of runoff and erosion to indicate that this is a deeply complex problem. With some soils, as the Houston black clay of central Texas, both ero-

TABLE 10

EFFECT OF LENGTH OF SLOPE ON EROSION AND RUNOFF

Location	Soil	Slope, Per Cent	Pre-cipi-tation Inches	Treat-ment	Slope Length, Feet	Soil Loss, Tons Per Acre	Water Loss, Per Cent Precipi-tation
		7.7	33.5		36.3	23	15
Guthrie,	Vernon fine	7.7	33.5	Cotton	72.6	28	14
Oklahoma	sandy loam	7.7	33.5		145.2	40	14
		4.0	27.0		36.3	15	13
Temple,	Houston	4.0	27.0	Corn	72.6	12	12
Texas	black clay	4.0	27.0		145.2	11	10
		8.75	42.0		36.3	13	17
Tyler,	Kirvin fine	8.75	42.0	Cotton	72.6	19	20
Texas	sandy loam	8.75	42.0		145.2	36	19
		16.0	29.0		36.3	12	19
La Crosse,	Clinton silty	16.0	29.0	Corn	72.6	60	19
Wisconsin	clay loam	16.0	29.0		145.2	68	15
Bethany,	Shelby silt	8.0	34.0		72.6	61	27
Missouri	loam	8.0	34.0	Corn	145.2	74	25
		9.4	32.0		36.3	47	12
Clarinda,	Marshall	9.4	32.0	Corn	72.6	45	13
Iowa	silt loam	9.4	32.0		145.2	48	12
		5.0	22.0		36.3	2.2	10
Hays,	Colby silty	5.0	22.0	Wheat	72.6	2.1	10
Kansas	clay loam	5.0	22.0		145.2	2.5	9

sion and runoff have been greater on uniform slope cross-sections of short length; with others, as the Vernon fine sandy loam of central Oklahoma, the corresponding losses have been greater on the longer slopes.

Effect of Season on Soil and Water Losses. Generally erosion is most rapid in spring and summer, especially in the humid East. In the Pacific Northwest, specifically in the Palouse wheat belt of southeastern Washington and adjacent Idaho and Oregon, much serious erosion is caused by melting snow, from December to March, in fields of winter wheat seeded on summer-fallowed ground. August and September generally are the months of most excessive soil washing over much of the arid and semiarid grazing areas of the Southwest. In general the period of heaviest erosion is that season represented by a combination of unstable ground condition and intensive rainfall. This obviously is dependent on climate and type of land utilization. In most humid sections heaviest erosion takes place in the spring on freshly plowed land, provided the heaviest rains fall at that time. In the same locality the season of most disastrous washing for the following year may be delayed until summer or late summer, if the most intense rains chance to be delayed that long.

NATIONAL CONTROL ACTIVITIES

Origin of the Service. The Soil Conservation Service is an outgrowth of the Soil Erosion Service, a new agency established in the Department of the Interior during October, 1933, under authority of the National Industrial Recovery Act. On March 25, 1935, by order of the administrator of the Federal Emergency Administration of Public Works, the Soil Erosion Service was transferred from the Department of the Interior to the Department of Agriculture. On April 27, 1935, the president formally approved an act of Congress (Public No. 46, 74th Congress) directing the secretary of agriculture to establish an agency in the Department of Agriculture to be known as the Soil Conservation Service.

The Work of the SCS. The objective of the Service is to propagate the use of soil-conservation practices in agriculture. To this end its program comprehends distinct but interrelated fields of activity involving (*a*) demonstration of practical and effective measures of soil conservation by actual work on the land (Fig. 7) in cooperation with land-owners, (*b*) consistent development and improvement of control measures through research and field tests, and (*c*) continuing educational activity with respect to the evils of erosion and the necessity for overcoming these evils.

Demonstration Areas. The nucleus of the program is a series of watershed demonstration areas within which the Service, in cooperation with farmers, applies to the land a carefully devised, adaptable plan of soil and moisture conservation. This plan involves the adaptation of engineering, vegetative, and cultural methods of erosion control and prevention according to the peculiar problems presented within the

SCS, United States Department of Agriculture

FIG. 7. Gully Controlled with Vegetation and Inexpensive Dams.

watershed. The individual size of these watersheds, of which 141 are now (1936) under way in forty-one states, ranges from about 25,000 to 16,000,000 acres. A large number of CCC camps are assisting in the program, operating for the most part on separate areas, covering about 15,000 to 30,000 acres each.

The demonstration areas are selected on the basis of (*a*) the representative nature of erosion problems within the project boundaries, in so far as those problems typify conditions over a large surrounding region; (*b*) availability of the area for inspection by a large number of farmers; (*c*) suitability of the land to the application of a unified erosion-control program; and (*d*) willingness of farmers in the area to cooperate with the erosion specialists in performing the necessary work.

Formulation of detailed working plans follows the selection of the area and the appointment of a project staff. All members of the technical staff cooperate in devising these plans to assure the coordinate use of various erosion-control measures, both mechanical and vegetative, in accordance with the peculiar needs and adaptability of every parcel of land to be treated. Actual specifications for the work are based on field studies to determine the physical and chemical characteristics of the soils, degree of slope, extent of erosion, adaptability of crops, prevailing agricultural practices in the areas, and other factors influencing erosion. With the aid of this information the farmer and erosion specialists go over the farmstead, study it in detail on the ground, plan a course of procedure by assigning each acre to a particular use, in accordance with the needs, adaptability, and appropriate place in a carefully planned, integrated land-use program for that one farm.

Farmer cooperation is assured through a five-year agreement between the Service and the individual farm owner or operator, under which the latter agrees to furnish as much as possible of necessary labor and materials in return for scientific direction in the required land treatment. The farmer agrees also to carry out for a minimum period of five years the practices recommended by the specialists; the Soil Conservation Service in turn agrees to furnish materials, heavy equipment, and labor which the individual farmer is unable to supply.

Work of CCC Camps. In addition to its demonstration projects, the Soil Conservation Service directs the erosion control activity of approximately five hundred CCC camps assigned (early in 1936) to such work. In some instances the camps are operated in connection with demonstration areas. The larger number, however, work as independent units under the technical supervision and direction of the Service, and in cooperation with soil-conservation associations of farmers.

Land Rehabilitation. Three of the demonstration projects, by far the largest included under the national program, are more of the order of land-rehabilitation and utilization projects, and are located for the most part on land owned or controlled by the United States. These involve 17,000,000 acres on the Navajo Indian Reservation in Arizona and New Mexico, 8,200,000 acres within the watershed of the Gila River in the same states, and 11,500,000 acres within the watershed of the Rio Grande in New Mexico.

Experimental Stations of the SCS. Research activities of the Soil Conservation Service center in thirteen erosion-control experiment stations located in major agricultural regions of the country. Studies looking to the development of new control methods and improvement of old methods, and investigation into factors affecting the rates and intensities of erosion, are carried on at these stations. Projected plans call for the development of climatic, physiographic, and comparative watershed studies.

An important related field of investigation involves reconnaissance and detailed surveys to determine the extent of sedimentation in reservoirs, stream channels, and irrigation systems, due to excessive erosion in contributing watersheds.

Studies of Silting of Irrigation Dams. The Navajo project comprises lands which contribute vast quantities of silt to Boulder Reservoir, and involves the preparation and application of comprehensive erosion-control, land-use, and range-control measures. It also involves reorientation of the entire agricultural economic system of the 45,000 Navajo Indians. The Gila project involves seriously eroding lands from which destructive quantities of silt are pouring into Coolidge Reservoir. The Rio Grande project covers the most densely populated region of New Mexico, where serious erosion threatens to force abandonment of large agricultural areas. The Elephant Butte Reservoir, subject to rapid silting, is also involved with the problems of this project on the watershed of the upper Rio Grande.

Sedimentation surveys are under way not only in the southwestern but also in the central and the southeastern sections of the country. Of 56 reservoirs, studied in the Piedmont section of the Atlantic seaboard, 13 of major capacity were found to have silted to the brim within an average period of 29.4 years. It has become apparent that the irrigation civilization of the West is endangered by this rapid filling of storage reservoirs, which menaces the investment of hundreds of millions of dollars and the social security of millions of people. A complete topographical survey of the area to be inundated at Boulder Dam is included within the scope of these sedimentation studies. In cooperation with the Reclamation Service of the Department of the Interior and the Coast and Geodetic Survey of the Department of Commerce, the Soil Conservation Service has begun a survey of the reservoir basin so that topographic changes caused by deposits of erosional débris can be measured by future comparative surveys. This is regarded as an important preliminary step in connection with planning for protection of Boulder Reservoir from destructive sedimentation.

Nurseries of the SCS. In order to develop special types of erosion-control plants for use by the demonstration and CCC projects, and to carry on necessary tests with native and foreign plants, the Service operates a number of nurseries in various parts of the country. At the present time (1936) approximately 60 nurseries are in operation in 41 states. About 500,000,000 seedlings will be produced annually. About 2,000,000 pounds of tree seed have been collected.

Something over a million pounds of seed of twenty-odd species of native grasses were collected during 1935 for use on erosion projects of the low-rainfall areas, where commercially available grasses cannot be grown successfully. It is hoped to create sufficient interest in these activities to induce farmers to take up seed collection as a source of income, and so establish a new industry in the Great Plains and other parts of the West where grass seed collection has received little attention in the past. Thousands of acres will be returned to trees and grasses by means of this work, and lands now being abandoned will be made to produce some return. Emphasis is being placed on producing plants having economic value, as well as value for conserving soil.

Physiographic Study of Erosional Processes. Still another activity involves a physiographical study of erosional processes to determine the normal rate at which erosion would proceed over a landscape undisturbed by cultivation, by grazing of domestic animals, or by structures, highways, and other cultural features. There is a definite need for a thorough understanding of normal processes of erosion in the formulation of a long-time program of land management and in order to ascertain the effectiveness of erosion-control measures. These studies are already under way in the Plateau region of the Southwest, to determine the extent to which arroyo cutting or trenching of alluvial valley-fill can be prevented through the use of measures of erosion control.

PLAN OF PROCEDURE IN EROSION CONTROL

The method of attack employed in this national program for erosion control and prevention is essentially a coordinated plan of correct land use, involving the application not only of direct methods for minimizing the effects of erosion by retarding runoff, but also of indirect methods, such as the retirement from cultivation of steep, highly erosive areas from which accelerated runoff descends with destructive effect upon lower cultivated areas (Fig. 8). Such critically erosive lands are being planted with thick, water-saving, soil-holding crops, such as trees, grass, alfalfa, lespedeza, sorghum, and clover.

The national soil conservation program represents the first attempt in the history of the country to carry out large-scale, comprehensive erosion and flood-control operations applying to complete watersheds, from the very crest of ridges down across the slopes to the banks of streams. The projects are neither engineering, nor forestry, nor cropping projects, but a combination of all these, operated conjointly with such reorganization of farm procedure as the character of the land

Courtesy SCS, United States Department of Agriculture

FIG. 8. Land Destruction by Erosion in Spite of Terracing.
This Piedmont Hillside should never have been cultivated because of its steepness.

indicates as being necessary. The procedure is based on the best information in the possession of scientific agriculturists: agronomist, forester, range specialist, soil specialist, erosion specialist, agricultural engineer, economist, extension specialist, game specialist, and geographer, and involves the application of accumulated knowledge pertaining to the great multiplicity of variables affecting the three-phase process of absorption, runoff, and erosion, employed not as single, uncoordinated implements of attack, but collectively, according to the needs and adaptability of the land.

Part of the cultivated land is being protected with the relatively new system of strip-cropping, under which clean-tilled crops, as cotton, corn, and tobacco, are being grown between parallel bands of grass, lespedeza, sorghum, small grain, and other dense, non-tilled crops planted along the contours (Fig. 9). These latter crops catch rainwater flowing down the slopes, spread it out, and cause the suspended soil to be deposited and much of the water to be absorbed by the ground, thus protecting the crops growing on the plowed strips below. The strips are so arranged that their position can be changed from time to time to fit into adaptable soil-improving crop rotations. On some slopes, strips of permanent protective cover will be planted to trees, shrubs, and vines.

Courtesy SCS, United States Department of Agriculture

FIG. 9. Strip Cropping on the Contour.

Non-tilled crops slow down runoff to protect tilled crops below. Southwestern Wisconsin.

The American type of terrace—embankments adjusted to the contour for arresting the flow of erosive water and passing it off slowly to the sides of fields in order to minimize its destructive erosive effects—is being employed where applicable (Fig. 10), and in some regions certain types of land, especially summer-fallowed ground and the smoother areas of low rainfall localities, are being scarified with a machine which scoops out about 10,000 basin-like holes to the acre, each of which retains or causes the absorption of about five gallons of rainwater. Contour cultivation, contour furrowing of pastures (Fig. 11), listing (ridging) (Fig. 12) of land affected by wind erosion, and interrupted furrowing (or "basin" furrowing) are among other mechanical methods giving good results where applied to adaptable lands. In the wheat areas of the Great Plains and the Pacific Northwest, fair

Courtesy SCS, United States Department of Agriculture

FIG. 10. Grassed Waterway to Carry Runoff from Terraces to Foot of Hill without Gully Development, Southwestern Wisconsin.

Courtesy SCS, United States Department of Agriculture

FIG. 11. Pasture Protection by Contour Furrowing, North-central Kansas.

to good control of erosion is being obtained by plowing down the stubble (rather than burning it) in such a way that part of the straw protrudes above the ground, affording considerable surface protection, especially against wind.

LOOKING AHEAD

Looking ahead, the course the nation must pursue if this is to be a permanently productive agricultural country is clearly marked out. With the facts before us and numerous demonstrations of effective

Courtesy SCS, United States Department of Agriculture

Fig. 12. Listing (Ridging) on the Contour not only Reduces Wind Erosion but Conserves Rainfall, Great Plains—Western Kansas.

practical procedure on the open land where everyone can see the work and understand it, to choose to do nothing, to continue with our wholesale practices of waste, would be the equivalent of consciously encouraging tragic land disaster to the nation. We can no longer afford to flinch at the cost or waste precious time with quibbling over nonessentials. The longer we defer carrying out actual control, the more difficult and costly will be the inescapable task ahead. A goal should be set for completing the major part of the job of prevention and control, and every effort should be made to attain that end ahead of time if possible. The recommendation of the Land Planning Committee of the National Resources Board in this connection is as follows: "A national policy of erosion control should contemplate initiation of erosion-control measures on all land now seriously suffering from erosion within about ten years in order to secure reasonable control of erosion within about twenty years, and to establish preventive measures on practically all of the better lands of the country subject to this hazard within a generation."[1]

It is scarcely necessary to add the obvious fact that success with any national program for erosion control will call for persistent co-operation among federal and state agencies, farmers, business men, and educators.

[1] Part II, Section III, *Report of the National Resources Board,* Washington, D. C., December 1, 1924, pp. 173-174.

CHAPTER V

TREE CROPS

By J. Russell Smith
Columbia University

THEIR RELATION TO SOIL CONSERVATION

In primitive societies the woman was usually the farmer. According to our best guess it was this ancient woman who domesticated wheat, barley, rye, corn, cotton, and nearly all the staple field and garden crops of European and American agriculture.

Today the agriculturists must develop new crops—crops that grow on trees. Tree crops are needed as helps in solving one of the most menacing problems confronting the American future, the problem of the gully—soil erosion.

Every American schoolboy and girl should work on the following problem as soon as he or she has reached decimals: take the figures from Dr. H. H. Bennett's record of soil destruction given in the preceding chapter of this book, and estimate how long the United States will last, if soil erosion continues at the present rate. The answer would shock even the fifth-grade child. He could then appreciate the gravity of a destructive force which has already caused counties in Georgia to lose half their farm population, which surveys by the Tennessee Valley Authority show to have ruined in a century 60 per cent of the land that has been cleared above the Norris reservoir.

How does it happen that modern agriculture is so devastating? The gully is the new phenomenon. Primitive agriculture did not result in much soil erosion. The American Indian and primitive agriculturists in other parts of the world had no plow; they scratched the ground a bit, planted a small patch, and before the soil began to wash away they abandoned the patch for another, and let the healing growth of weeds and grass, briars, bushes, and trees hold the earth until clearing time came again.

The northwest Europeans do not have the gully problem. Any observing traveler can demonstrate this to his own satisfaction in Ireland, Wales, England, Scotland, Norway and Sweden, and between Copenhagen and the Alpine pastures and to the Channel coast of France. In the entire journey one would not see a single raw, cutting gully. Other signs of erosion would be almost completely absent. The only exception might be a few old ones but completely healed with grass. The Mediterranean countries are not so blessed.

NEW FACTORS IN AMERICA

Why does northwest Europe escape erosion when erosion is rapidly transforming large parts of the United States into an agricultural desert? Because we have been unintelligent in transplanting European agriculture to the United States. We have resembled the pet beaver, who, with an instinct to build a dam, built one in the office where he was confined. Following traditional methods, the beaver built his dam, but he builded regardless of environment. Trees or office furniture were all the same to him, so he chewed up chairs and tables, and stuffed the crevices with the pages torn from the books he found on the shelf. The dam in the office did not provide water because the beaver had built regardless of the environment.

Those who brought agriculture from Europe resembled the pet beaver in the office by not observing the proper relationship between their new environment and five things that were new to them—corn, cotton, tobacco, thunderstorms, and the absence of turf.

Cotton, Corn, and Tobacco. One reason why northwestern Europe is so free from soil wash is that neither corn, cotton, nor tobacco is grown. The major crops are wheat, oats, barley, rye, clover. These plants stand close together with scores or hundreds of plants to the square yard. Their tops cover the ground fully; their myriad roots quickly penetrate the earth and hold the soil against the force of running water. Marked differences exist where corn, cotton, and tobacco are grown, as in the United States.

The plants of these three crops stand far apart, with space enough between rows to allow the cultivator to pass; sometimes it passes both ways. Many times during the period of plant growth the cultivator tears up the top earth, loosening it ready to be carried away and destroying any surface roots that might hold it.

The Thunderstorm. Northwest Europe has few thunderstorms. The rainfall is light. The amount of rain that falls an hour is slight. The runoff is weak. But in this country, from the Rocky Mountains eastward, the standard type of summer rain is the thunderstorm, with water pouring upon the earth at the rate of one, two, three, four, five, or even six inches an hour. Six inches an hour nets 680 tons of water to the acre (an hour). Here are the figures from a recent measured erosion experiment at the Soil Erosion Experiment Station, Temple, Texas.

> The rainfall of April 2, ranging at different places from 1.09 to 1.72 inches, produced some striking results. The rate of intensity was approximately 4 inches per hour. Land planted to corn, with rows up and down a 4 per cent slope, eroded at rates ranging from 5 tons to nearly 10 tons per acre in terms of dry soil. The actual sludge or mud washed from the same areas during this single rain, ranged from 9.65 to 14.89 tons per acre. The runoff ranged from 43 to 50 per cent of the total rainfall of 1.72 inches. . . .
>
> Land having a crop of oats on a 4 per cent slope, incurred soil losses ranging from only 0.01 ton to 0.2 ton per acre of dry soil. The runoff from this oat field ranged from as low as 0.4 per cent to 3.34 per cent of the total rainfall of 1.72 inches.
>
> Land having a cover of Bermuda grass on a 4 per cent slope sustained a soil loss of only 0.02 ton per acre, dry weight, while the runoff was 1.33 per cent.[1]

The writer has seen one thunderstorm in northern Virginia which caused a little stream whose length was less than half a mile, draining about 100 acres, to become 100 feet wide. As it overflowed a cornfield meadow, it removed the soil in a wide stretch to the depth that the earth had been plowed. As the swollen stream crossed the farm it ripped out seven fences, including 60 feet of stone fence. And on hillside cornfields of residual soil, derived from the underlying trap rocks, the water probably removed in a few hours as much soil as could be produced by five or possibly ten thousand years of weathering.

The clean-tilled crop and the thunderstorm are the major factors in the present progressive ruin of American croplands. But Dr. Bennett has shown you in the preceding chapter that there are also other agents of destruction.

Absence of Turf. So far as the writer knows, no one has called attention to the influence of the turf-forming grasses which prefer cool climates, such as that of northwestern Europe and New England and the north Pacific coast region of the United States. Good turf is scarce in the American cotton belt—another reason why erosion is so bad in that land of summer thundershower, heavy winter rain, and no protection by freezing.

[1] "One Hard Rain Did This," by E. B. Deeter, in *Soil Conservation*, August, 1935.

WE NEED TO DEVELOP CROPS THAT GROW WITHOUT TILLAGE

Many crop-yielding trees exist in many parts of the world. It is strange that we have made so little use of them in systematic agriculture. The following paragraphs present examples of little-used crop-yielding trees.

Keawe. On the various Hawaiian Islands there are thousands of acres of copse, thicket, or forest—whatever one may call it—of the keawe tree, probably a mesquite (*Prosopis julifera*). This leguminous tree yields beans valuable for forage. Experts at the Hawaiian agricultural station state that:

> It has taken possession of large tracts of otherwise unoccupied land, prospers where the soil is too dry for any other crop, and produces a verdure and shade where otherwise there would be an almost barren waste, and yields a pod of high feeding value. . . . Thus far there has been no cultivation of algaroba. The thousands of acres of trees stand, for the most part, in rocky soil where cultivation would be practically impossible. . . . It has been found that the [bean] yield per acre varies from 2 to 10 tons. This yield varies but little from year to year and occurs in two crops per year, the figures given covering the sum of both crops.

This yield is astonishing, and even more astonishing is the value of the beans. When the beans and pods are ground together to make meal, 100 pounds of it equals in feeding value 80 pounds of good barley meal. Some very astonishing facts have been secured from a ranch manager in charge of 21,000 acres of waste and pasture land attached to a sugar estate on the island of Maui. The manager was in charge of 200 dairy cows, 800 cattle, 700 horses and mules, and 250 pigs, and had a corps of accountants keeping an elaborate system of agricultural accounts.

When questioned as to the productivity of the keawe, he replied as follows: "You can take cattle, lean ones, that weigh 500 pounds; and if you put six of them on an acre of good keawe, they will average better than 2 pounds a day on raw beans which they pick up for themselves. You can take the season from the middle of July, and the six cattle will gain 1,200 pounds and sometimes will go to 1,600 pounds of beef per acre on land with rainfall of 20 inches a year." Every year from 1,000 to 1,400 tons of these beans were ground into meal for feeding to livestock exactly as the American dairy farmer uses cottonseed meal, bran, or other mill feeds.

When one considers than an acre of good Kentucky bluegrass pasture or the rich pasture of old England will produce 150 pounds of mutton per year, while an Illinois farm in corn and alfalfa will make about 450 pounds of beef and pork per year, the keawa bean tree, with 1,200 to 1,600 pounds of animal gain per acre per year, looms up as one of the king crops of the world.

The Carob. Perhaps you have wasted some sympathy on John the Baptist because he ate locusts, or on the prodigal son because he ate husks. As a matter of fact, both fed upon the sugary materials which the carob tree packs into the large, thick pod in which its small, hard beans are embedded. For 2,000 years at least the carob bean, still called "locusts," has been a standard article of food in many Mediterranean countries. Carob beans may be bought almost any day in the year from pushcarts on the lower east side of Manhattan Island.

The writer has seen carob trees growing on a great variety of rocky and other hillsides, in Spain, Portugal, Algeria, Tunis, and other Mediterranean countries, and has found the beans selling at the same price as Indian corn, and yielding the same or greater amounts an acre. The trees live for generations and perform their marvelous production of food in climates too dry for corn. In Tunis carob trees thrive in places where the rainfall is only 10 inches a year.

American Cousins of Keawe and Carob. Since the keawe is tropical and the carob requires the orange climate, neither tree can become a major crop in the greater part of the United States. Fortunately these plants have hardy American cousins. Several species of bean-yielding mesquite thrive in the area from central Texas to Utah and southern California. The mesquite fed the oxen that pulled the caravans of the Forty-niners, as they had fed deer and Indians for unknown periods of time before, and numerous herds of the white man since.

The honey locust tree (*Gleditsia triacanthos*) yields a bean which in all important economic aspects is the duplicate of the carob and the keawe. (Fig. 1.) Some years ago, wishing to find out the qualities and locations of the best specimens of this large frost-resistant tree, the writer offered prizes through the *Journal of Heredity*. He was amazed to get a bean 16 inches long and nearly 2 inches wide. Seventeen of the dried pods weighed a pound. The sugar analysis was 29 per cent, which is much higher than in sugar cane or the sugar beet. Twenty-five per cent of this sugar will crystallize like our common sugar. The remainder is an insoluble variety of sugar from which molasses can be made. These figures indicate a potential sugar crop

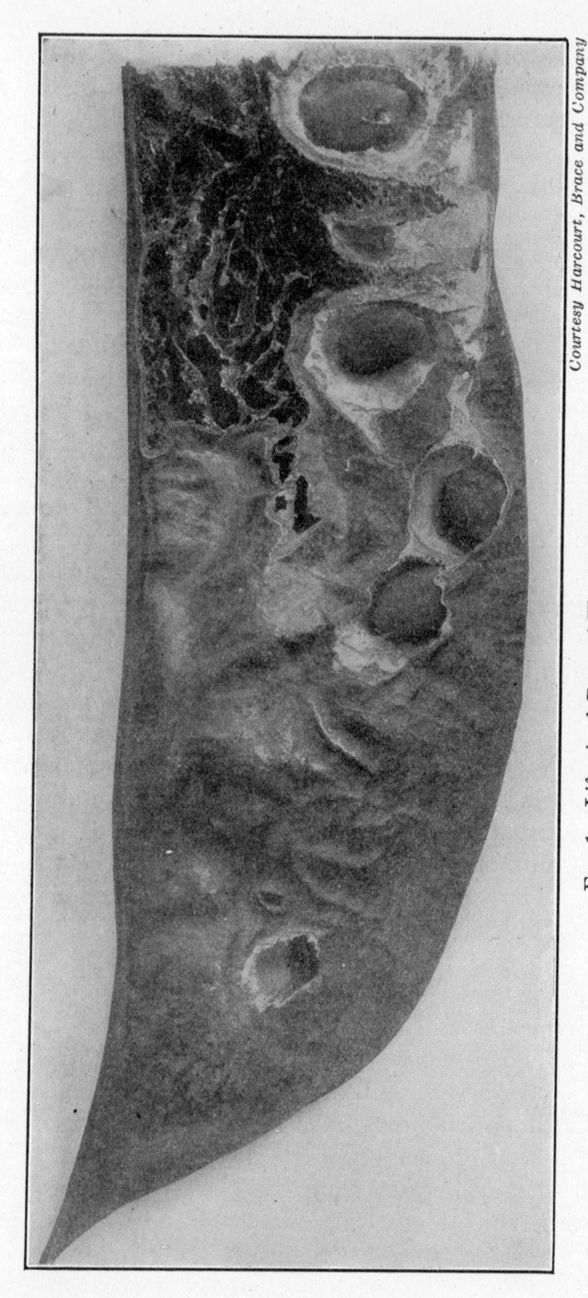

Courtesy Harcourt, Brace and Company

FIG. 1. Life-sized Part of Honey Locust Bean.

This won the prize given by the American Genetics Association, 1927. The black part at the upper right is the mass of sugar exposed by cutting away a part of the hull of the bean.

which, like the beet, could have a residue rich in cow feed, enough molasses to make it sweet, palatable, flesh-forming, fat-forming. The protein of the beans provides tissue-building material.

But this prize bean has been eclipsed by beans found by Mr. John W. Hershey, tree crops expert for the Tennessee Valley Authority, Knoxville, Tennessee. He discovered some in 1934 that carried more than 32 per cent of sugar.

The number of pounds to the acre that the honey locust may be expected to yield is at present unknown. We know, however, that this is a fine timber tree, and produces heavy crops of beans. Some trees yield annual crops of beans. The more sugary ones are eaten greedily

Courtesy Harcourt, Brace and Company

FIG. 2. Panorama in the Zone of Grafted Chestnut Trees, on a Mountain Side in Corsica.

The stone houses are in the villages whose inhabitants are supported by these orchards.

by farm livestock. The tree grows wild from Florida to southern Canada, from New England to the Great Plains, where it ranks high as a drought resister. The honey locust has been successfully introduced into the western third of the United States—a most promising crop tree, merely awaiting intelligent experiment.

The Chestnut. The chestnut tree is proving to be an excellent support for the man of the mountains. One can ride mile after mile through chestnut orchards on steep mountainsides in Corsica (Figs. 2 and 3). The slopes greatly resemble hundreds of mountainsides of Appalachia. One passes through village after village of substantial stone houses. In addition to his house in the village, the average villager has the following property: a small vegetable garden, usually terraced to keep the earth from being washed away or from creeping downhill—many gardens are situated below the spring and can therefore be irrigated—

a few acres of grafted chestnut trees (Figs. 4 and 5), a few milk goats, possibly a cow, perhaps a horse or mule, and a pig or two.

The chestnut is to him the sole crop aside from the garden, as is corn to many an Appalachian mountaineer. The chestnuts, when gathered, are dried in kilns over a slow fire. Dried chestnuts, may be kept as corn is kept. The horse and pig grind the dried nuts for food. Gentle beating knocks off the shells, and the meats are often ground to be used for making bread. With goats' cheese, garden stuff, and a little pork, this makes the food of the villager. The goats browse the grass

Courtesy Harcourt, Brace and Company

FIG. 3. Characteristic Road in the Chestnut Section of the Corsican Mountains. Note the steepness of the slope and the fact that every tree is a grafted chestnut.

and herbage that grow beneath the chestnut trees. The pigs are fattened on the chestnuts that people have not been able to find under the leaves at harvest time. Now comes the important part of the story. This culture has gone on for generations, but the soil is intact, although the slopes are as steep as the roof of a house. When a big old tree, perhaps past the century mark, begins to decline in productivity, the farmer cuts it down and takes it to the tannin extract works. A younger tree, which he has planted a decade or two before, is already well established, ready to reach into the vacant space and grow in the sunshine.

"How long has this been going on?" the notary of the village was asked.

"Oh," said he, "a hundred years—five hundred years—always."

The last claim was a little sweeping, for chestnuts were introduced into Corsica with the Roman army in the second century. However, the permanence of this mountain agriculture puts us to shame when compared with our destructive methods in Appalachia.

The Cork Oak. The cork forests of Spain and Portugal are almost as suggestive as the widely distributed chestnut orchards of the northern Mediterranean region. The cork tree yields a stripping of bark every nine or ten years. Like the chestnut, the cork oak and its attendant grass and bushes hold the soil against erosion, while sheep, goats, and other animals forage beneath the trees. The acorn crop produces millions of dollars' worth of pork annually, and the wood of the old tree is at last multifariously useful in a land where wood is scarce.

Courtesy Harcourt, Brace and Company

FIGS. 4 & 5. Hybridized Trees in Corsica.

The little tree in front of the man's hat on the ground is of the same age and the same hybrid parentage as the larger tree of which a branch is drawn in front of the man—evidence of the extreme variations produced by hybridizing.

TREE CROPS FOR THE DRY LAND

A most interesting landscape is that of the Matmata tribe of Berbers in central Tunisia. They live in a highly dissected limestone plateau of low elevation but very rough topography resembling some parts of the Appalachian region. The rainfall there fluctuates from 4 to 10 inches a year, averaging about 7.5.

These people have built loose stone dams across the gulches. The rapid runoff from the desert shower rainfall quickly fills the space back of the loose stone dams with earth. Every time the gully runs with water this earth mass is saturated, and thus feeds a few olive trees or date trees that are planted in this man-collected bit of naturally irrigated alluvium. These olive trees are robust, vigorous-looking, thick-foliaged, and altogether compare well with those in Spain, Portugal, Algeria, Palestine, Syria, Anatolia, Italy, France, Arizona, and California.

These gulch-fed and gulch-watered crop trees are the mainstay of this tribe of Berbers. Their utilization by irrigation of the water that falls during a shower is closely akin to the way the Indians of Arizona and New Mexico use water to feed their peach trees, and their corn and pumpkin patches. If someone would bring together all the examples of this kind of agriculture in the world, it would be both surprising and instructive.

Courtesy Harcourt, Brace and Company

FIG. 6. Terracing Checks Soil Wastage.

Terraces made on the exact horizontal to hold rain and prevent loss of both water and soil. The rows of apple trees beside each terrace trench have now become a very productive apple orchard although planted on a badly eroded hillside.

By extending this process of the conservation and utilization of a scant rainfall very large areas of arid land might have their gullies (arroyos) converted into long lines of verdant, crop-yielding trees, preferably of the forage-bean-yielding types, as this crop would fit so perfectly into the pastoral use to which these arid lands in all continents are and must be put.

A NEW HILLSIDE CULTIVATION TECHNIQUE

The writer has been suggesting the wide possibilities that lie in the development of a plowless agriculture for dry land, for steep land, and for rough land. But there is a widespread belief that trees will grow better if the ground around them is cultivated. Because of this fact many an American orchard has been cultivated until the soil was well-nigh ruined. But recently a discovery has been made as a result of tests of a great number of methods of managing soils in orchards.

The Agricultural Experiment Station at State College, Pennsylvania, has carried on the tests over a period of twenty-five years. The plot which was kept cleanly cultivated almost washed away, although the

Courtesy Harcourt, Brace and Company

FIG. 7. A Sample of Food Nuts.

At bottom two American hazels, two European filberts of the parent trees which were hybridized. All the rest are the fruit of this cross. Some of the nuts are larger than either parent—proof that hybridization produces qualities not present in either parent.

slope was very slight. In about sixteen years the exhaustion of vegetable matter caused the soil almost to collapse. The earth became so hard that when plowed it came up in chunks the size of a man's head or even larger, and almost as hard as sun-dried bricks.

The orchard culture almost universally recommended as ideal had been: plow in the spring, keep the soil cultivated until some time late in the summer, then sow a cover crop to grow during the late summer and autumn, to protect the ground through the winter, to be again plowed up in the spring. The surprise was that this method did not do as well as was expected, apparently because the cultivation beneath the hot sun burnt out the vegetable matter.

Plots left in sod that was repeatedly mowed and allowed to rot showed that the vegetable matter had great difficulty in getting back into the earth; instead it decayed on top and passed much virtue off into the air.

The best results, to the surprise of every one, were obtained by a thorough ripping up of the soil with harrows, spring tooth or disk, some time between November and the beginning of spring growth. The ground was *not plowed,* but the sod was thoroughly ripped up and much of it turned over so that it could decay and quickly become part of the soil. Clover was sown, mowed once or twice during the summer, and the accumulation again harrowed in the next year. This annual destruction of the sod permitted the spring fertilizers to reach the tree roots rather than to be eaten up by the grass. The grass, grassroots, and chunks of sod prevented erosion, even on slopes that were steep. The vegetable matter thus worked into the soil held moisture and carried the orchards through droughts (Fig. 6).

In what climate belts is this process applicable? Experiment alone will tell, but presumably it is appropriate where corn will grow, perhaps even anywhere that orchards are cultivated. Certainly it is producing great results on some very steep Appalachian hillside apple and peach orchards where it has been adopted as standard practice.

This method carries with it the possibility of the extension of a *cultivated* tree crop agriculture on millions of acres of steep land which would be ruined by the older orchard tillage system, which was almost universally considered to be necessary five years ago. The new method is really a very great discovery, for it opens the way to the intensive use of millions of acres of hill lands without destroying them.

APPLYING THE SCIENTIFIC METHOD

It is time we began to supersede the agriculture that depends upon the chance findings of the primitive woman with the agriculture that depends upon the systematic and scientific efforts of educated workers, both male and female.

There is every reason to believe that the trees of the world can give us the basis for many new crops—almost a new agriculture—if we will apply the scientific method as follows:

1. Search the world's forests, groves, and fence rows for the best wild trees that nature has produced by chance.

2. Take these chance trees, and by systematic application of the laws of genetics breed far better ones. Now that we have in our possession the science of breeding, through Mendel's law, rediscovered in 1901, we are in a position to do this.

3. Conduct experiments in farm management to make good farm plans around the chance trees that are already growing, and from the better ones that can be produced by plant breeding.

The Example of the Oak. The oak tree may be cited as an example of the potential raw material with which man may deal in these three important activities. The acorns which the oak tree showers down in the autumn are nuggets of carbohydrate that differ from corn in food value by having more fat and less protein. They are good food for many kinds of animals, including man. Acorns have fattened the bear, the deer, the wild hog, and other forest denizens through millenniums and probably through geologic epochs. They are this year fattening millions of man's domestic swine, as they have done for centuries.

Most acorns have a somewhat bitter taste owing to the tannin they contain. Here and there in the United States, as well as in Spain, Portugal, and probably other countries, the acorns of a chance tree are free of tannin; then the acorn is sweet and pleasantly edible. A few of these trees here and there have been propagated by grafting, as are other orchard trees, and the acorns are grown and used as a crop. In some Mediterranean countries acorns are roasted and eaten just as chestnuts are.

Primitive man discovered that the bitter tannin is soluble in water, so he crushed the acorns, soaked them for a time to make them sweet, and then made bread. This bread may have been used ten times as long as man has used wheat. It is even possible that the human race has eaten more tons of acorn bread than of wheat bread. John Muir, the California naturalist, assured us that it is the best of bread, as demonstrated by his use of it as his chief nourishment on mountain-climbing expeditions. The acorn carries enough fat to be both bread and butter.

There is a record of a California valley oak that yielded a measured ton of acorns. The ilex, or evergreen oak, native to Mediterranean climates, is a heavy yielder of acorns. One tree the writer saw in southern Portugal had an average crop of 20 bushels of acorns despite the fact that it had a spread of only 51 feet.

There is no measured evidence on an acre basis to prove it, but pending disproof the writer will believe—very stoutly believe—that, if planted to the best existing oak trees, many tens of thousands of square miles of Appalachian ridge and hill land would yield more pounds of food for man and pig by way of acorns, per decade for the next thousand years, than the same area will yield of corn in the one decade during which the mountaineer is now ruining it. This would result if it were planted to a stand of the best wild acorn trees that could now be found in that region, and plant breeding is yet to be heard from, with its presumably (almost certainly) more productive trees, and better quality of acorns.

PLANT BREEDING

This new power that has so recently become available to man permits us to take two plants of the same or allied species, hybridize them, and get new combinations of the qualities of both parents, and new qualities that previously existed in neither parent. For example, one J. F. Jones of Pennsylvania, far less publicized than Luther Burbank, hybridized a European filbert and an American hazelnut, and using one-quarter acre of ground got offspring bearing nuts larger than those of either parent, and some smaller than those of either parent, some so puny that they looked like sub-Arctic dwarfs.

THE WORK AND THE RESULTS

Although any owner of a small plot of ground can do some of this work, it especially needs the aid of continuous institutional support. If exploration and crop creation could receive appropriations equal to the cost required to build, maintain, and operate one battleship we could, if we wished, soon transform millions of acres of hillsides from gullied ruin, poor pasture, or poor forest into first-class crop land, yielding grass and also honey locust beans for stock food and sugar; persimmons and mulberries for stock food; acorns and chestnuts for stock food, commercial starch, and bread, made in factories as are peanut butter, lard, crackers, jam, and other canned foods. There might be scores of other crops, but if these five should make good they could be the basis of a vast hillside agriculture. There could be a satisfactory *permanent* agriculture if we should add to them permanent pasture and a small area of non-eroding hillside terraces, valley bottoms, and hilltop flats for corn, alfalfa, and gardens. America need not wash away.

CHAPTER VI

UTILIZATION AND CONSERVATION OF OUR ARID AND SEMIARID LANDS

By Ralph H. Brown

University of Minnesota

INTRODUCTION

Early Conceptions of the West. By 1850, its "manifest destiny" having been fulfilled by expansion to the Pacific Ocean, the United States found itself in possession of vast western territories and quickly formed states about which little was actually known. Cartographers of the period, seeking to fill this gap in geographic knowledge, had replaced the innocuous term "unexplored" with the phrase "the Great American Desert," thus giving apparent authenticity to vague concepts which had already become popular. It was not until 1879 that Powell's classic *Report on the Lands of the Arid Region of the United States* was published, more clearly defining the limits of the arid region and presenting for the first time a thoughtfully considered and coherent program for its proper utilization.

The Powell report, from certain standpoints, appeared opportunely. A considerable part of the arid region still remained within the public domain and as such was susceptible of a land policy shaped to meet the special requirements of that region. Moreover, the undesirable consequences of the lack of an arid-land policy had already appeared to such an extent that those in authority might well have taken counsel. Nevertheless, the challenge was not accepted and no definite policy was followed, save that based on the presumption that it was desirable to have the West settled as rapidly as possible.

Early Proposals Not Followed. Classification of the arid lands preceding their transference to private hands was strongly urged. Only within recent years, however, has such classification been attempted. Many saw the necessity of radical changes in the legal conveyance of these lands in order to provide farms and holdings suitable not only in size but also *in shape* for their presumed utilization; instead, the range-township-section survey method was applied wholesale throughout the arid lands. Others foresaw the undesirable consequences of the extension of the homestead law into the arid lands; modifications of the existing law, they said, would prove inadequate. Nevertheless, Congress continued to dally with compromises with the original law. Before the passage of the Taylor Grazing Control Act of 1934 a writer was eminently correct in stating that "no [public] land law has ever been made by the federal government that is satisfactorily adapted to the arid region."

Arid-land Problems Brought to the Fore in the 1930's. Arid-land-utilization problems, long in the making and concurrently recognized by a few authorities, were dramatically forced upon the public attention by the prolonged if not unprecedented period of below-normal rainfall occurring in the 1930's. In many ways—by wide-spread "dust-storms," by publicity given "the drought," by accounts of "stranded populations" in need of "resettlement in more suitable environments"—public attention was at that time drawn to the arid lands much as it was in the 1860's when the "Great American Desert" was still a reality. It was borne in upon the public mind that our arid-land resources had been greatly impoverished and that vast areas of dry land had been unwisely plowed. This destructive exploitation seemed all the more unbelievable because the arid region had been, comparatively speaking, so recently a part of the public domain. Was not nearly all the remaining public domain still within the arid lands? Apparent chaos was worse confounded by the spectacle of the continued reclamation of arid lands on a new and grandiose scale, through the construction of immense dams, while, in other parts of the country, agricultural land was being retired from crop production by a hastily created federal bureau known as the Agricultural Adjustment Administration.

EXTENT OF ARID AND SEMIARID UNITED STATES

The arid-land problems of the United States have been rendered all the more acute and complex by the vastness of the area considered to be arid and semiarid and a certain confusion as to the extent of each.

There has been and is considerable diversity of opinion as to the definition of the terms "arid" and "semiarid" and consequently of the areal extent of these climates in the United States. Obviously both are deficient in rainfall. In relation to what, then, or in respect to what purpose, is this rainfall deficient? In their earlier usages in this country, as Webb has pointed out, these were relative terms applied by a people entering regions of less rainfall than that to which they had been accustomed in the humid East; for example, Spanish explorers had less to say about aridity than the Anglo-Americans. Later authorities have tended to define the arid and semiarid regions in terms of their suitability to normal agricultural practices. That is to say, the arid and semiarid lands comprise that part of the West in which the rainfall is insufficient, over any considerable period of time, for the successful production of crops by ordinary farming methods. In the absence of known methods of predetermining the amounts of effective rainfall below which ordinary agriculture becomes unsuccessful, human experimentation on a gigantic scale has been undertaken in this country. Such experimentation has resulted in some conspicuous successes, it is true; but more commonly it has ended in stark tragedy. Many writers, in deference to the wishes of the inhabitants of the regions about which they were writing, have used, in place of the apparently libelous words "arid" and "semiarid," the more cautious but possibly misleading word "sub-humid." The word "sub-humid" has been increasingly used in a more technical sense and should not be confused with "semiarid." The sub-humid belt, otherwise known as the "black earth belt," is the transition area from semiarid to humid and is not considered in this discussion of the arid lands.

The map which is reproduced on page 118, much simplified from the original, has much to commend it for the present discussion. In the first place the extent of the dry climates has been fixed upon it by taking account not only of the annual rainfall but also of its effectiveness as influenced by evaporation. Separation of the United States into a humid East and an arid West at the 20-inch rainfall line, though a common procedure, is not satisfactory. Very important also is a precise separation of the arid area from the semiarid, because problems of land utilization and conservation differ in the two and are generally more critical in the semiarid portion.

For a second reason this map is eminently suitable because its boundaries, though fixed in a scientific manner, coincide closely with the general opinion of authorities on arid-land problems. Had Powell drawn a map definitely outlining the lands of the arid region about which he so wisely wrote, it would have differed but slightly from this. Powell estimated four-tenths of the United States to be arid and semiarid; sixty years later, Thornthwaite's stricter analysis has largely confirmed the earlier opinion (Fig. 1).

The dry climates, continuous as a semiarid belt from north to south along the western Great Plains, encircle the southern end of the Rocky Mountain system, indeed overspreading its lower ranges and outliers, and to the west grade into the desert. The desert appears as two large

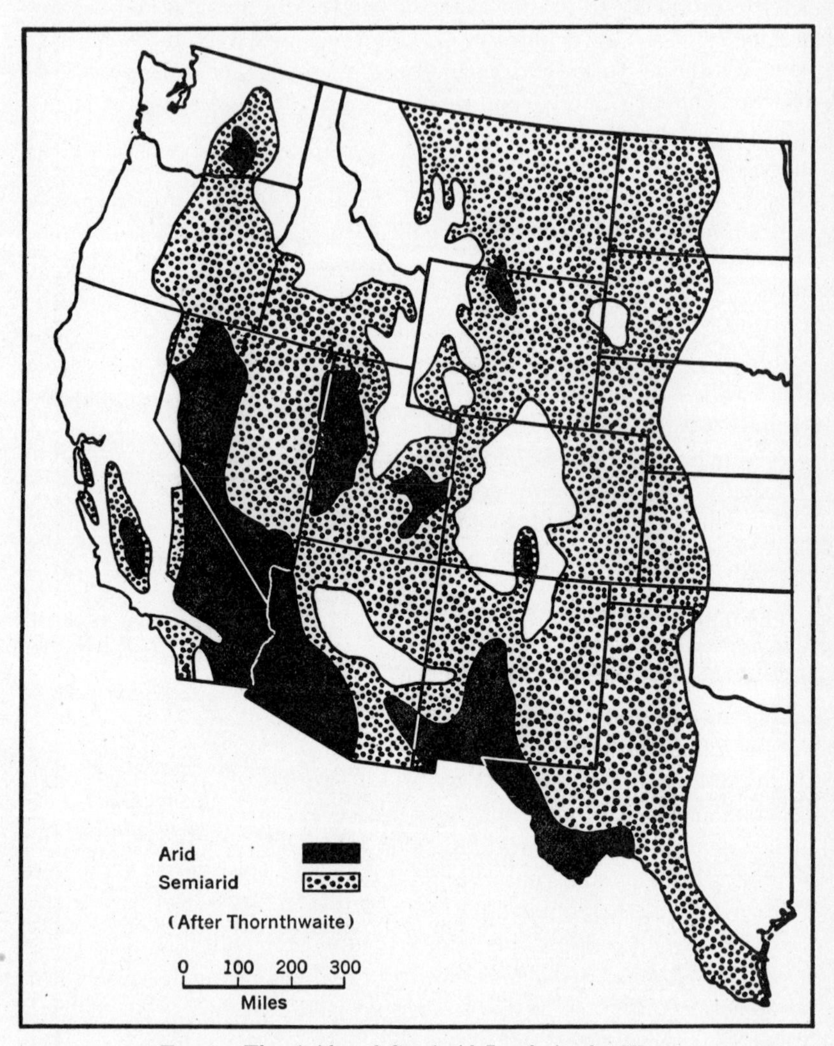

FIG. 1. The Arid and Semiarid Lands in the West.

nuclei, one in southern New Mexico and western Texas, the other in the Great Basin and Range province of Arizona, California, and Nevada. Two fingers of humid climate thrust southward: one along the Pacific coast and the other coinciding with the northern Rockies, thus interrupting the continuous stretch of aridity. The greater part of the West is, therefore, semiarid rather than arid. This fact increases rather than lessens the arid-land-conservation problem since semiaridity is likely to invite the agricultural use of much essentially non-agricultural land.

UTILIZATION OF RANGE-LAND RESOURCES

Natural Vegetation the Greatest Resource. The principal natural resource of this vast dry region, especially during the early stages of its settlement, was its treeless natural grassland vegetation. The land, as such, has but slight value. Grasses of various species, heights, and densities are the typical vegetation type of our semiarid and arid lands. In general, this resource was, and is, most abundant in the semiarid regions where various types of grasses—grama, wheat-, needle-, wire-, and buffalo-grass and blue-stem—originally clothed the lowlands and benches of the western Great Plains and northern interior plateaus. In the more arid regions "bunch-grass," "greasewood," and mesquite are more common. Although shorter than the prairie grasses of the Middle West, the plains grasslands offered great opportunities for livestock grazing. The grasses, curing on the stem, are available for feed at all seasons and may be cut for hay. Moreover, the grasses have remarkable recuperative qualities under reasonable utilization, since their growth is by joints rather than by stem ends, the lowermost joints being beyond the reach of grazing cattle. (Fig. 2.)

Water a Vital Resource. Water is essential, however, if these grazing resources are to be made available to man's use: water for livestock subsistence and sometimes also for supplemental irrigation in forage production. This placed a premium upon the possession of "water-holes" (perennial streams, springs, wells) in a region where water is naturally scarce. With the water went the control of the adjacent range land which in the 1860's was largely unfenced public land, and there thus developed and spread with great rapidity an indigenous industry remarkably well adjusted to the environment as it then was—the range livestock industry. The tripartite nature of this typically American institution is quaintly characterized by Osgood in these terms: Western cattlemen furnished the experience, the East furnished the capital, and the federal government provided the grass. With the last named contribution we are now principally concerned.

Impoverishment of the Range. Cattlemen of an earlier day who had, by extra-legal methods, acquired "rights" to public range land, could reasonably be expected to exercise care in its utilization. By the farsighted, over-grazing was recognized as a sure road to eventual failure. Thus, wise cattlemen sought to prevent range deterioration by various practices: shifting "bunches" of cattle from one range to another, possessing range headquarters in various parts of the country, limiting the number of head per range, and utilizing high-altitude pastures, if ranch location made this feasible, for summer grazing. By the last practice, the lower-altitude range land could be preserved for winter feeding.

FIG. 2. Typical Semiarid Range Land in Northwestern Montana.

This range, in the upper Missouri Valley, is now used principally for winter grazing. Areas with this surface in the western plains are commonly referred to as "benches."

This state of affairs was destined to be short-lived because of the encroachment of others upon the ranges. Despite strong defensive measures such as stock associations and boycotts against newcomers to protect "accustomed ranges" of those first on the scene, "nesters" (later settlers upon the habitual range of an earlier stock-grower) and hated sheepmen established themselves. The result was that even in the 1890's over-grazing had become a serious problem. The native grasses, though naturally recuperative under conservative use, were partially destroyed by unregulated grazing by sheep as well as by cattle. Range deterioration was presumably most severe after years of deficient rainfall which not only limited the height of the grasses, but induced the harassed stock-growers to overload the range in the succeeding season.

There is no certain knowledge of the magnitude of the losses resulting from over-grazing in the semiarid grasslands. Authorities believe that nearly all the range has suffered more or less severely in this way. Since 46 per cent of the United States is range land nearly all of which is within the arid and semiarid regions, the losses are obviously on a tremendous scale. The present range capacity of the remaining 168,-000,000 acres in the public domain is known with greater exactitude. It is authoritatively stated that the range land remaining in the domain has lost from 40 to 50 per cent of its original capacity. The Science Advisory Board lists the losses from over-grazing as follows: (1) reduction in amount of vegetation and extermination of certain species, (2) replacement by plants of low edible value, and (3) soil wash and wind erosion induced by the dry climate. From the last arise such losses as derangement of stream flow and increased silting of reservoirs.

Dry Farming. Over-grazing, however, was only one of the processes involved in the impoverishment or destruction of the original great resource of the arid lands. A very great reduction in original resources has resulted from the plowing of semiarid land for farming purposes.

A suitable preface to the consideration of dry-land farming is provided by excerpts from the 1934 report of the National Resources Board, as follows:

> Throughout the period of westward expansion the public policy was one of getting the land settled and improved as rapidly as possible. Certain features of this policy, as exemplified by the homestead laws, established a size of farm and a type of farming pattern poorly adapted to many areas, especially in the drier, more inaccessible or otherwise poorer lands of the semiarid west. Under the assumption that the process of carving out farms could continue successfully in the semiarid regions if the 160-acre homestead were increased, the Enlarged Homestead Act of 1911 and the Stock-Raising Homestead Act of 1916 [discussed in Chapter II] were passed, permitting entry of 320- and 640-acre homesteads respectively.

The modified homestead laws, the nature of which has been outlined in Chapter II, gave encouragement to homesteading in the semiarid lands. Many other factors, also, played important parts in inducing agrarian settlement in the dry lands. Homesteaders themselves were often not conscious that their chosen lands lay in a semiarid climate. The rainfall differences between the sub-humid and the semiarid belts become most apparent over a five- or ten-year (or longer) period: the rainfall régime in the two belts is often exactly similar. The extremes of aridity and humidity are easily discernible, even to the inexpert, but in passing from one extreme to the other the observer is often insensible to the gradations in the transition. No signposts appear to warn the newcomer that long-period climatic records unmistakably demonstrate semiaridity in the western Dakotas, Kansas, and Nebraska whose eastern portions are sub-humid or humid. Successive years of above-normal rainfall, though representing a shorter period than the below-normal rainfall years, nevertheless serve to dispel fears of aridity. Besides, many asked, does not rainfall follow the plow? And was not the climate changing for the better? Many homesteaders believed that the larger acreages allowed them under the enlarged homestead acts would in fact offset handicaps of environment, if such there were.

Moreover, much enthusiasm had developed over the possibilities inherent in the practice of "dry farming" and it seemed to many in the 1880's and later that the unirrigable dry lands would in this manner at last be "conquered."

Dry farming, a practice of long standing in the Old World and anciently employed for subsistence farming by Indians in the Southwest, seemed to offer possibilities also for commercial agriculture in the Great Plains. The apparent success of crop production in the sub-humid belt was mistakenly assumed to presage an equal success if practiced in regions still less humid. This idea was apparently justified at different times by the rapid westward advance of the farming frontier, an advance, however, which was not always permanent and which coincided with periods of above-normal rainfall. These years of abundant crops gave encouragement to unwise settlement by people in various walks of life, the majority of whom were ill prepared to engage in a most exacting type of farming, and induced others, more competent, to depart from strict dry-farming practices. (These practices involve (*a*) selection of drought-resisting crops (*b*) preparation of fields in order to increase the proportion of rainfall entering the soil, and (*c*) measures to reduce the amount of water lost by evaporation.) Much so-called dry farming in the western Great Plains became, in fact, the farming of dry lands with humid-land crops and methods.

The successive advances and retreats of agrarian settlement in the western plains form an oft-repeated story. Let the following account suffice, for, though it was written in 1899 and concerned only the High Plains, it is descriptive of conditions toward the end of any of the constantly repeated "drought periods" and of many large sections of the arid and semiarid West.

> The experiment was tried on a scale and with a recklessness that promised heavy disaster in case of failure. Failure, in fact, followed, and disaster, with almost complete depopulation, has resulted. Especially was this the case with the High Plains which presented the maximum inducements of fertile soil and unbroken smoothness of surface. (W. D. Johnson.)

Successful ventures in dry-land farming form exceptions to general rules. Such success, where substantiated with data, may be attributed to rigid observance of dry-farming principles or exceptionally favorable natural conditions or both. In some localities, as in portions of the San Joaquin Valley of California, dry-land farming is favored by a fortunate rainfall distribution. In some parts of the Great Plains, the soils favor the retention of moisture, as, for example, the Pierre clay loam in the Belle Fourche area of western South Dakota. Where tracts are occasionally inundated, or where fields receive drainage from a large surrounding country or seepage from adjacent irrigation projects, farming without irrigation may be successful.

Losses Resulting from Plowing Native Sod. There is no adequate measure of the magnitude of the losses resulting from this spread of farming into areas unsuitable to it. Large areas have suffered from the complete destruction of the natural grass cover and the attendant wind erosion of the unprotected soil, a subject treated in the preceding chapter. Figure 3 gives a suggestion of the wide-spread changes resulting from plowing of land. The shaded areas represent lands "within which arable farming should ultimately be encouraged to withdraw, mainly because experience has demonstrated the land to be too poor to provide adequate family living and support public institutions and services."

Grazing-land Conservation Measures. Conservationists have pointed out that this country has never maintained services for grassland preservation comparable with measures relating to forest protection. Until quite recently the significance of the grasslands as a natural resource has been recognized by only a few.

In 1879, Powell made recommendations which he framed into congressional bills having a broad view to the proper use and preservation of "pasturage lands," as he termed them. These bills provided for classification of the arid region into irrigable, timber, and pasturage lands. As to the last he recommended that no holding be less than 2,560 acres, that each holding should include some irrigable land for raising stock fodder and subsistence products, that the boundaries of the holdings be determined by topographic features and water supply, that residences should be grouped, and that pasturage farms should not be fenced but held in common. What Powell proposed was essentially a continuation of the spontaneous type of land utilization then

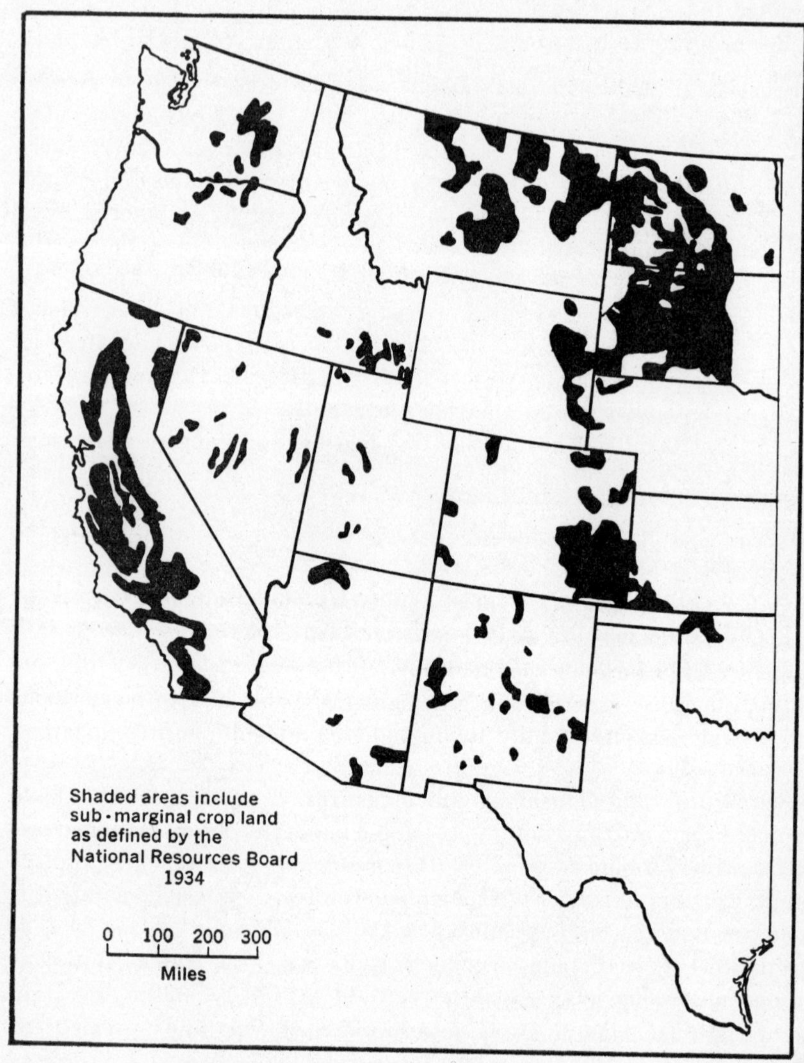

FIG. 3. Sub-marginal Croplands in the West.

prevailing—a legalization, as it were, of an existing condition. In weighing the merits of the proposal it should be borne in mind that this type of land utilization had evolved from the experience of those who had learned both the limitations and opportunities of that part of the country. Though essentially a colony plan of settlement, the colonists presumably would have been derived mainly from the people already resident in the arid region.

Powell's proposals broke too sharply with past traditions and thus were regarded unfavorably. The plans were not acceptable to the lawmakers because, it was said: (*a*) the area of four sections was obviously too large for a private holding, (*b*) the legal conveyance of land by metes and bounds would surely lead to confusion, (*c*) the use of pastures in common savored of communism. It mattered little that Powell had anticipated these objections with able arguments; Congress considered the enlarged homestead adequate and refused to entertain the idea of any change in the method of parceling the land. As a result, stockmen were compelled to gain by subterfuge that which they were not allowed legally, and in various ways many of them acquired control over such areas of range land as were suitable to their needs.

Other conservationists have proposed, from time to time, public land lease systems patterned after the Texas leasing method, and many have favored the permit system which has been so successfully used in the national forests. (See Part II: Our Forests.)

Recent Measures to Preserve Public Domain Range Land. The Taylor Grazing Control Act, passed in 1934, represents a frontal attack upon the problem of range-land conservation. Commentators, in approving the act, uniformly express regret that its provisions were not extended to include all remaining public lands. In its present form, the act authorizes withdrawal from entry of 80,000,000 acres of unreserved and unappropriated public domain. This will allow official control over a vast area of public range, impoverished, to be sure, but still capable of rehabilitation. The act delegates, to the bureau of grazing control, broad powers of range regulation, including the use, regulation, preservation, and rehabilitation of the portions of the public domain affected by the act. Grazing districts are to be organized and a system of leasing instituted after the manner of the national forest permit system. Provisions are made for the sale and exchange of isolated tracts in order that ranges may be consolidated. The act, so far as it affects the specific areas involved, will put an end to unwise homesteading under existing laws. It will also be of direct service to stock farms already in existence in the vicinities of the Taylor Act reservations.

Protection of Privately Owned Range Land. In other parts of the country somewhat similar results have been obtained, though on a smaller scale, by "community pastures" such as those west of Great Falls, Montana. On such pastures care is taken to prevent over-grazing. "Public pastures" are also to be found in various parts of the West, as in the plateau west of the Roswell artesian basin in New Mexico. Community and other pastures are articulated with lower-lying irrigated land which is used to produce hay and fodder for the winter

FIG. 4. An Early Day Ranch House in the "Powder River Country" of Wyoming, Headquarters for the Cross H Ranch.

It has survived the many changes in ranching which have occurred since 1880.

feeding of livestock, and grains for finishing sheep and cattle for market (Figure 4).

IRRIGATION

Great Importance of Water. The arid and semiarid West has largely been rendered habitable and its latent resources made available to man by the use of water for livestock subsistence and irrigation. Water, a vital resource in any environment, assumes more than ordinary significance in the less-than-humid regions. In the arid and semiarid West, the conservancy of water becomes of paramount importance.

Water assumes first place among the natural resources in the arid lands of the Southwest and of the Great Basin. In the sub-humid and semiarid regions of southern California water has, especially in recent times, been increasingly used for the production of exotic plants and fruits marketed in all parts of the country. In the semiarid Great Plains and intermontane country, on the other hand, irrigation water has been used primarily in the support of livestock production, which remains the dominant industry of these lands. This use has called for the wide-spread irrigation of native grass pastures, of hays both native and exotic (such as alfalfa, sudan- and brome-grass), of other roughage and stock-feed cereals often cut for hay, and of corn, sorghums, and other fodder canes. True, crops of more directly marketable character have made their appearance under American semiarid irrigation —sugar beets in the north and cotton in the south—but they only serve to draw attention to the main fabric of the irrigated cropland into which they are recent and perhaps not permanent importations. Irrigation in semiarid United States is not of a spectacular type and has thus suffered belittlement by those who believe that only cash crops or crops of unusual character are worthy of artificial watering. Irrigation as practiced in our semiarid lands is of a serviceable type and is appropriate to this general region.

Contrasts in the Necessity of Irrigation in the Arid and Semiarid West. Authorities who were eye-witnesses of the early stages of western settlement constantly emphasized the necessity of irrigation in the semiarid as well as in the arid regions. Settlers in the deserts, where rainfall is consistently negligible, understand that irrigation is essential. On the other hand, it is possible that homesteaders in the semiarid lands are less easily convinced of this necessity or, provided they are cognizant of the desirability of irrigation, lack either the water which makes it possible or the knowledge to use it which makes it successful. Even if water be available in the semiarid regions, seasonal rainfall is occasionally adequate to "make a crop" without resort to a practice which is both costly and time-consuming. Moreover, the majority of farmers in the western Great Plains brought with them into the semiarid belt methods of farming and types of crops adapted not only to more humid climates but also to the farm units made available to them under the enlarged homestead acts. A worthy ideal certainly was W. D. Johnson's program for the High Plains, in connection with which region he wrote in 1899: "Provision must be made for at least supplemental irrigation and the necessity for resort to such artificial aid will be imperative most of the time and advantageous always." It is regrettable that in the actual course of settlement a rule so wise as this one has not been followed.

American experience has shown once again that irrigation is less a science than an art, an art which becomes institutionalized but slowly —more slowly in the semiarid than in the arid West. True enough, irrigation has been practiced for centuries in the Old World, but contributions from these sources to American problems have been few indeed. Pueblo Indians and even their cliff-dwelling ancestors in the Southwest depended upon irrigation, but the hard-won experience thus gained was not to become a heritage of the westward-advancing American people. Spanish-type irrigation has been important as a background for present-day Mediterranean agriculture in southern California, but this has contributed little if anything to irrigation practice, say, in Nebraska. It is always necessary to realize that the settlement of our arid and semiarid West has been essentially an Anglo-American occupance. This means that such irrigation practices as were to be worked out in our semiarid and much of our arid lands were to be typically American, a phase of pioneering which is still largely in progress.

Various types of "enterprises" have been responsible for the development of American irrigation. The three which have contributed most to the development of this practice have been singled out for special study. These are (1) colony or communal enterprises, (2) cooperative and commercialistic enterprises, and (3) federal reclamation schemes.

Colony or Communal Irrigation. The first phase of large-scale American irrigation was that associated with colonies—groups organized by a central authority migrating as a body and settling in a site selected with a view to its irrigability. Usually the site was selected in advance of migration, but in any event the necessity of irrigation was recognized from the outset. Since the cooperation of many was required to dig ditches of sufficient length and capacity to irrigate any considerable acreage, it is perhaps not too much to say that the colony plan was enforced by the necessity of this practice.

The Mormon irrigation colony, selecting in 1849 the piedmont alluvial fan of the Wasatch Range near Great Salt Lake, was organized around ecclesiastical authority. Later, the Colorado piedmont was selected by numerous colonies, some of which were definitely communistic, others inspired by "land companies," still others with the central idea of social betterment. The German Colonization Company, a communistic venture, settled in the Wet Mountain valley in southern Colorado in 1869. In 1871, the Chicago-Colorado Colony, a "land company" scheme, moved in on a predetermined site on the St. Vrain River where the city of Longmont is now located. Most famous of all was the Greeley Union Colony, organized by Horace Greeley, one of whose phrases growing out of this movement—"Go West, young man!" —has become an American tradition. The confluence of the Cache la Poudre and the South Platte, because of its ample water supply, large level areas, good soil, and other advantages, was selected as the site of the Greeley Colony.

Elements in the Success of Colony Irrigation. Long since abandoned as such, the areas developed by the colonies remain today among the more successful and best-developed projects in the West. Elements to be considered in this connection are as follows:

1. The areas settled by colonies were deliberately selected for that purpose. Of the numerous possibilities presented at the time, the choicer localities were selected. Generally speaking, sites were chosen which offered the least physical resistance to irrigation. Most desirable were relatively small but perennial streams whose waters could be diverted by small dams into easily constructed ditches and canals. Other factors also entered into the selection, such as markets provided by mining camps and the presence or possibilities of roads and railroads.

2. Communal organization, when wisely managed, was undoubtedly an advantage. Irrigation requires the cooperation of many individuals having a community of interests. The colonists soon had the advantages offered by a quickly formed community—schools, stores, churches, etc.—features slow to develop under the usual form of pioneering in new lands. Captain Dutton in 1879 said of the Mormon Colony: "This communal arrangement has been attended with great success so far as the development of water resources is concerned and the system of management has ordinarily been so conducted that the general welfare has been immensely benefited."

3. These older irrigated areas have outlived the period of experimentation which is characteristic of newly settled areas. They have, so to speak, "come of age." By trial and error numerous early mistakes were corrected and irrigation became an essential part of the economy of the region. Among the more important practices developed by the earliest irrigation communities were those dealing with the control of water.

Customs of Water Use Upheld by Legal Procedures. The diversion of water from stream channels to irrigate land at some distance necessitated the abandonment of the "riparian doctrine" of the common law which is adhered to in the humid East. This doctrine rules in essence that riparian (river-bank) landowners along a non-navigable stream have certain rights to that stream: the stream must not be diminished in volume or polluted in quality. Since irrigation requires the withdrawal of water from the river channel and since most of this water will not be directly returned thereto, such a doctrine could not apply. In place of this regulation there developed in the arid West the practice of appropriating and diverting water from river channels, a custom which was in due time approved by various state legislatures and upheld in numerous court decisions.

In actual fact this custom first made its appearance in placering for gold in California, in which state modifications of the riparian doctrine govern the law of waters. This is known as the "California doctrine." Wiel says of the California practice that "riparian rights are firmly established in California side by side with the law of appropriation, the former for public land and the latter for private land." In the Rocky Mountain states the "Colorado doctrine" is applied. In this doctrine, riparian rights are entirely swept away in favor of "prior appropriation." The Colorado doctrine decrees that the first user of water for beneficial purposes has the prior rights over later users. That is to say, prior appropriation bestows rights in streams according to the relative time of beginning use—"first come, first served." This has been called a "pioneer doctrine, one to fit the development of sparsely populated and rough regions of any kind."

Prior appropriation gives to the appropriator a "water right" which is entirely distinct from the "rights to the ditch, canal, or other structure in which the water is conveyed." Rights to the ditch give authority for the conduction of water by *A* across the land of another, *B;* but this does not convey ownership of the land upon *A* nor does it confer rights to the use of the water upon *B*. A "right to the ditch" is legally defined as an easement upon the land.

Over-enthusiasms Regarding Irrigation. The early success of irrigation experienced by the colonies was the basis for numerous enthusiastic statements with regard to the future possibilities of this practice. In the 1880's and thereafter, much fallacious and misleading literature appeared on the subject of irrigation. Unfortunately, many of these false ideas have persisted in widely read articles and textbooks down to the present.

In an attempt to combat the traditional idea that the Great American Desert was a worthless waste, land and railroad companies with plots to sell deemed it necessary to exaggerate the productivity of irrigated land. This was accomplished by advertising in popular magazines or in literature financed by railroads and distributed by land companies. One such magazine, issued by the National Land Company for the Kansas Pacific and Denver Pacific railroads, bearing the stirring title *Star of Empire*, circulated not only in this country but even in western Europe. Its pages contained stories of the extraordinary productivity of irrigated land in Colorado. The stories were made more realistic by pictures of "typical" products: huge pumpkins, enormously tall cornstalks, and wonderful potatoes. Companies with land to sell emphasized the rich soil, "unimpoverished," as it impliedly was elsewhere, "by abundant rainfall," also the continuous sunshine, the freedom from anxieties about rainfall, the absence of weeds, the pleasure of watering one's own land. One gathered that the life of the irrigation farmer was a round of pleasure and that success was guaranteed. Similarly roseate ideas about irrigation were broadcast by books, an example being Smythe's *The Conquest of Arid America* (1907) in which different chapters are entitled "The Blessing of Aridity," "The Miracle of Irrigation," and "The Better Half of the United States." Though somewhat more restrained in tone, chambers of commerce in numerous western cities continue to emphasize the great advantages of irrigation, and the majority of geography textbooks contain at least a paragraph extolling the extraordinary value of irrigated land.

What is the truth of the matter?

Early enthusiasms about irrigation have been greatly tempered by experience, especially so far as the usual staple crops are concerned. Farming is not an exact science; consequently comparisons of production to the acre may fail to reveal inherent capacities of land to produce. It is extremely doubtful, however, that data would warrant the assumption, usually tacitly made, that irrigated land in this country as a whole is more productive than good humid land. Probably no irrigated area in the West surpasses in productivity a similar area in the Lancaster lowland of Pennsylvania, assuming equal growing seasons in each. Too often comparisons are made between some particular irrigated area producing a specialty crop, and some humid-land area of staple crop production. The annual average production to the acre of irrigated wheat on the Greenfields Division of the Sun River project in Montana is consistently below fifteen bushels. Such data as these throw a reasonable doubt upon the validity of the generalization that irrigated land is *ipso facto* more productive than other farm land. Costs of production are ordinarily higher under irrigation than under natural rainfall. Many irrigated areas produce above-average yields at first simply because the soil is virgin; later on, averages decline. Certainty of production is generally greater, on the whole, than when dependence is placed upon natural rainfall, but most irrigation farmers are by no means freed from anxieties about rainfall. Projects free from weeds early in their experience may easily become over-burdened with them (sunflowers, for example) in time because running water is one of nature's best methods of distributing weed seeds.

The value of our irrigated lands to the nation should not be measured in terms of productivity but in terms of their stabilizing effect on developed communities and industries in a vast part of the country where, without irrigation, both would be out of the question.

Cooperative and Commercialistic Enterprises. Since the 1880's, irrigation in the West has been extended principally by means of associations and cooperative schemes using capital furnished by their members. Usually, irrigation of this sort followed rather than preceded settlement and has thus become a significant element in the fabric of agricultural life in the areas developed in this way. Funds were raised by selling stock, the amount of which entitled its owner to a certain quantity of water, usually from one to two acre-feet to the acre. Engineering companies contracted to lay out the main ditch and lateral system and to construct such diversion dams as were necessary. The water users improvised their own ditch systems on their farms.

Localities offering slight obstacles to irrigation development have generally been watered in this way. The vast majority occur on either slope of the Rocky Mountains and in the Great Valley of California. Innumerable small but dependable streams, issuing from the higher mountain slopes, naturally invited the diversion of their waters for irrigation.

Occasionally artesian supplies have been developed, wherever such supplies are economically recoverable. This has been done almost entirely by individual effort, in contrast to the joint-stock companies of surface drainage irrigation. In strong artesian basins each farm has its own well or perhaps several wells flowing naturally or aided by pumps. Even in the larger artesian basins this well water is supplemented by water diverted from surface drainage. This is true of the San Luis Valley of Colorado, whose artesian water is used mainly for domestic and livestock water supply, the bulk of the land being irrigated from the Rio Grande. In the Roswell artesian basin, west of the Pecos River in southern New Mexico, about 85 per cent of the cropland is irrigated from flowing and pumped artesian sources, and the remainder from numerous Pecos tributaries. At Riverside, California, the land is irrigated by utilization of both surface and underground supplies. The opportunities for watering land from underground sources are very limited and are likely to become more so with the exhaustion of artesian supplies.

An excellent example of the cooperative and commercialistic enterprise is furnished by the Big Horn Mountain piedmont in Wyoming.

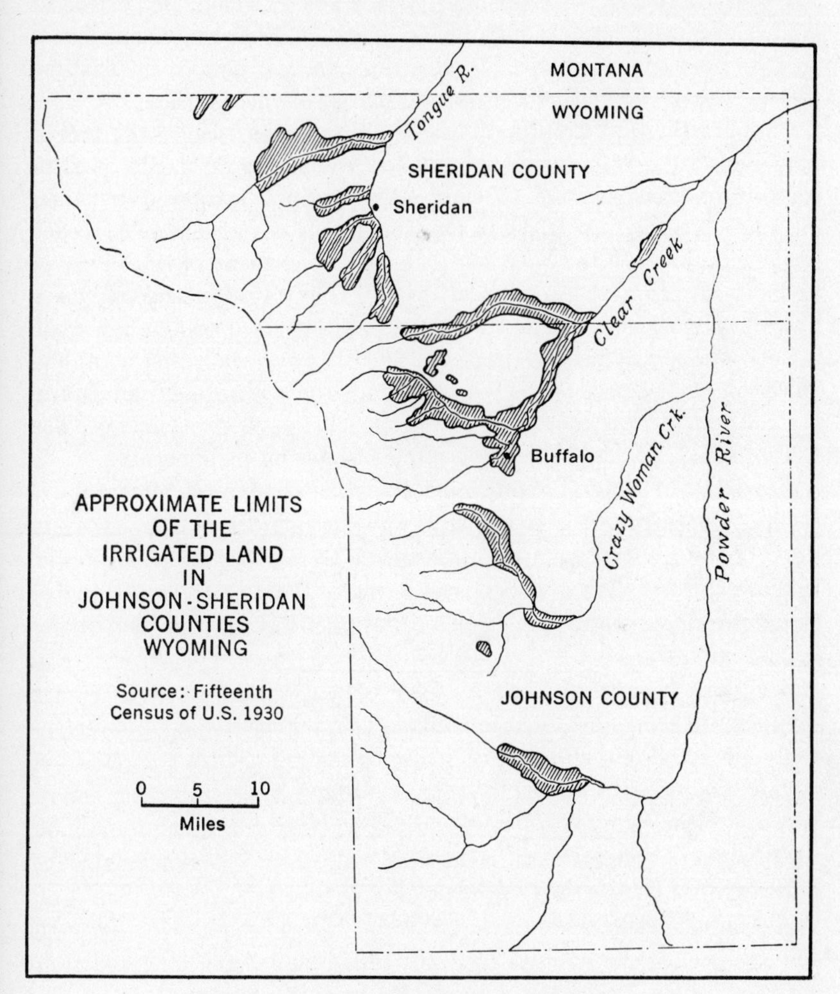

Fig. 5. Typical Irrigated Areas in Wyoming.

The map, Fig. 5, shows the linear arrangement of the irrigated area along the base of the mountains. The irrigated areas become larger and extend farther from the mountains in proportion as the mountains increase in altitude toward the north and thus have longer, more dependable streams. All this irrigated land, a minute fraction of the total area of the "Powder River country," was developed after 1880. The amount of irrigated land is determined by the limited water resources: much more land could be irrigated with greater mountain precipitation. This statement is as applicable to the entire West as to this part of it. Figure 6 shows an enlargement of the irrigated area along Clear Creek

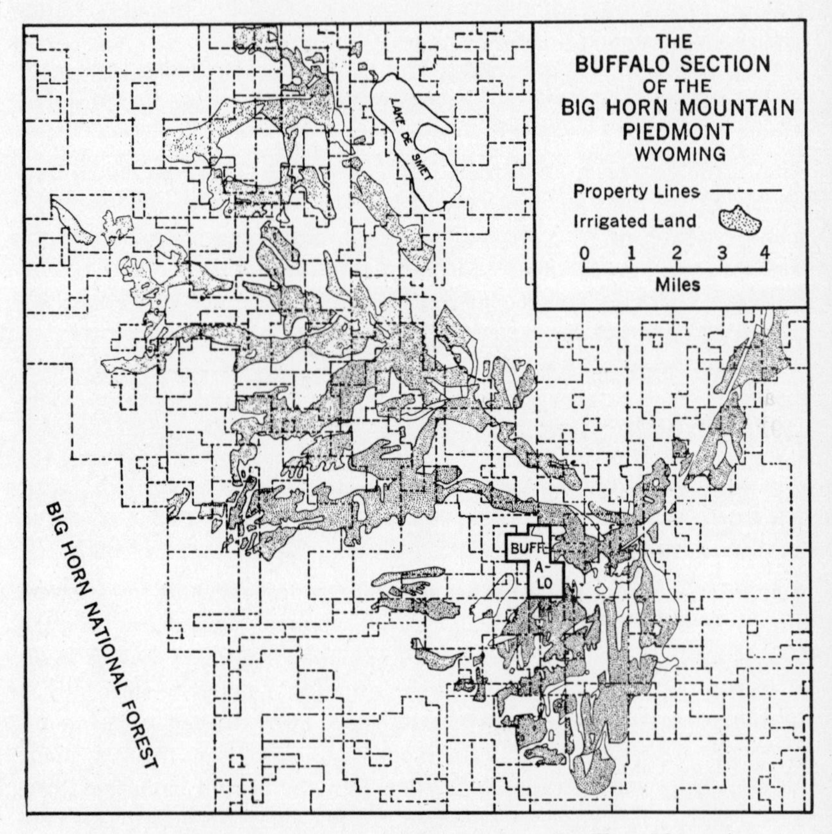

Fig. 6. Irrigated Lands in the Piedmont of the Big Horn Mountains.

near Buffalo. This map indicates the patchy character of the irrigated area, owing to the relatively high relief along the mountain front, much land lying above stream diversion points. The map also shows that nearly every farm or "ranch" has some irrigated land upon which to depend for livestock feed and forage, occasional cereals, and subsistence crops. On the other hand, no farm is entirely irrigated, each possessing areas of grazing land useful for winter feeding. Here, as in other mountain piedmonts adjacent to national forests, summer grazing in high altitudes is practiced. This irrigated area is typical of our semiarid West.

Federal Reclamation Schemes. The Federal Reclamation Act of 1902 sounded a new note in American irrigation. The Bureau of Reclamation, entrusted with working out its provisions, was faced with the task of forwarding what has recently been termed "the only public settlement activity prior to the World War."

It is proper to regard federal reclamation as an inevitable consequence of the general policy of the United States consistently maintained to "get the land directly into the hands of small owners who shall also be cultivators of the soil." The residue of the public domain remaining at the time was largely arid and semiarid, and its settlement was meeting with increasing physical resistance. Certain authorities had recognized the necessity of irrigation for proper agricultural settlement, though few considered federal or state aid and some had, indeed, advised against it.

The act was, in the beginning, a home- and community-building measure, not a conservation policy. Preliminary plans began in 1888-1891, when surveys were conducted for selection of reservoir sites. According to a recent authority, "the Chittenden report of 1897 was the first official advocacy of governmental participation in irrigation projects." This report recommended the construction of reservoirs, properly (it said) to be done by the federal government because (1) irrigation is an interstate matter, (2) other natural resources such as forests were directly related to water storage, (3) the federal government was the largest landowner in the West, and (4) public sentiment was in favor of such action. Between 1897 and the framing of the Newlands bills in 1901, the idea of federal aid in irrigation had extended to the point where reservoirs were considered inadequate—provision must be made for delivering water to the land. Thus grew the idea of irrigation projects. The Newlands bill became law in 1902 when President Theodore Roosevelt took occasion to state his view that, since it was the duty of the government to dispose of land to settlers, it was also incumbent upon the government to place water upon it for irrigation.

Early Objections to Federal Reclamation. A measure so unusual as the Reclamation Act was bound to elicit much open criticism, especially from spokesmen in the humid East. Six arguments were leveled against this form of federal aid. It was said of the act that it (1) was unconstitutional and (2) savored of paternalism. Moreover, the act was condemned because (3) it did not promote the general welfare, particularly since (4) over-production of foodstuffs would result. Many voiced the opinion that (5) this was an unwarranted form of competition with individual effort in other parts of the country and that (6) the expenditures would be enormous, out of proportion to any benefits derived. Arguments for federal reclamation took the following lines: (1) The act was constitutional because it promoted general welfare. (2) The projects would relieve dangers of overpopulation. (3) The projects would serve as pioneering outposts around which settlement could gather. (4) The act contemplated the conservation of natural resources, a necessity to which the nation was at that time becoming awakened. (5) The crops grown on the projects would be consumed locally and therefore not sold in competition on eastern markets. (6) Federal reclamation was no more paternalistic than was river and harbor improvement, and it was equally general in its benefits to the nation. (7) The projects were to be self-liquidating through repayment by the settlers. Some of the arguments on both sides were obviously specious.

Later Criticisms of Federal Reclamation. Criticisms of federal reclamation did not cease with the enactment of the Newlands bill; indeed, the subject has remained one of highly controversial character. Some of this controversy would be eliminated if the parties to the debate considered, in broad perspective, the *general arid-land policy* of the United States, concerning which there is, indeed, much to criticize. It should be kept in mind that federal reclamation has been only one phase of that policy, an aspect of such tangible character as to lend itself to much adverse criticism.

Accomplishments, Merits and Shortcomings of Federal Reclamation. From the material standpoint, the Reclamation Bureau has created thirty-one projects of which three have been abandoned. Fifteen projects, in whole or in part, have been turned over for operation by irrigation districts or water-users' associations, though the government retains title to and management of the works in all cases. The area involved amounts to 2,025,500-odd acres comprising 40,000 farms and supporting 150,000 people directly and perhaps 500,000 indirectly. This has been accomplished at a cost, in 1934, of approximately $227,-437,000, a figure exclusive of Boulder Dam which was undertaken separately and mainly for purposes other than for irrigation. The per-acre costs have been high, as shown by the above figures, higher by 175 per cent than was originally estimated and greater too than revenues from the sale of public lands which were supposed to have furnished the working capital. Contributing to the high costs have been the engineering difficulties met with and the inclusion of considerable areas of privately owned land within some of the projects. This was a departure from the original intent of the act which was to render irrigable previously unoccupied portions of the public domain. A considerable portion of the costs has not been repaid by the settlers even though no interest was charged and the period allowed for repayment has been extended. Moreover, some of the original costs have been "written off." Most of the projects include areas provided with irrigation facilities but not yet occupied by farmers. Mainly, the projects have been developed in areas presenting such physical and legal difficulties as would have discouraged private development. The necessary engineering works have been of such elaborate nature that, in the public mind, federal irrigation has assumed greater importance than it really merits. According to the last census, the Reclamation Bureau had developed but 7.6 per cent of the total irrigated land in the country.

Various are the interpretations which have been placed upon these accomplishments of the Reclamation Bureau. Critics in condemning federal reclamation are wont to say: (1) Many, perhaps the greater number, of the projects have not been successful. This, it is said, is indicated by the failure of landholders to make repayments of original costs. (2) It follows, therefore, that federal reclamation has been a form of subsidizing of agriculture which is unfair to farmers elsewhere. Such subsidizing is all the more to be deplored since it has masqueraded under the name of a home- and community-building enterprise. (3) There is no need for further extending the area of farmed land; indeed, no such need existed even at the time the act became law. It is said that pressure brought to bear on Congress to pass the act was misinterpreted as a popular demand for farms and homes. The possibilities of speculation in land provided the real reason for the clamor referred to. (4) This form of paternalistic federal aid has undermined self-reliance and reduced high ideals of citizenship.

On the other side, these answers are frequently heard: (1) The success of a project or of all projects together cannot be judged solely upon the dollar basis. (2) Irrigation renders farming and stock-raising more successful and stable. Since the country deemed it desirable, wisely or unwisely, to have the arid and semiarid lands occupied in this manner, it is logical that the settlers should be supplied with the opportunities of irrigation. Failure to take advantage of these opportunities should not be regarded as a failure of the project. (3) Many present-day difficulties within the projects are granted, but it is claimed that some of them, at least, result either from country-wide agricultural maladjustments or from the residuary effects of earlier troubles which, in the light of experience, have been or are being corrected.

In this connection the National Resources Board lists these difficulties: (*a*) poor selection of settlers, (*b*) maladjustments in number and size of farms and types of farming, (*c*) tax delinquency and frequency of transfer, and (*d*) tenancy. It is said that the projects suffer from the undesirable forms of tenure common to those sections settled under earlier land laws. In an attempt to correct these difficulties, the reclamation service has lately stressed soil and land classification, elimination of land speculation, and more rigid selection of settlers as to financial equipment and experience. (4) It is too early to render a competent decision upon the success or failure of reclamation. Irrigation practice develops slowly even under favorable circumstances. Projects in the semiarid region have met with the greatest difficulty; the readjustment of farming systems under irrigation is a slow and difficult one.

Irrigation Resources. In 1929, in the seventeen western states which lie wholly or in part in the arid and semiarid region, slightly less than 19,000,000 acres of land were under irrigation. This area is approximately equivalent to the combined areas of New Hampshire, Vermont, and Massachusetts. The figure includes only that land which was artificially watered or which received seepage from canals, reservoirs, or from other irrigated land in that year. Not included are small acreages of bottom lands subject to early-season or other opportune floods which sufficiently moisten the soil for crop production, a practice aptly called "floodwater farming," and characteristic of the more favorable sites along the Rio Grande in New Mexico and in southwestern Colorado. Neither does the above figure include the area for which irrigation works were available but not farmed, nor the total area in irrigation enterprises.

With 6,000,000 additional acres of land, capable of irrigation with present facilities, left unirrigated during the last census year, it may be inferred that the present irrigation works are used to about three-fourths of the available capacity. In other words, the complete utilization of irrigation facilities already available would allow for a considerable increase in the area actually irrigated. This fact should be considered very carefully by those who advocate the creation of entirely new projects, especially in view of the strong presumption that the irrigable portions of existing projects could be placed under irrigation with greater economy than a completely new and untried project.

Distribution of Irrigated and Irrigable Lands. The distribution and areal extent of irrigated areas and the most recent opinion as to the

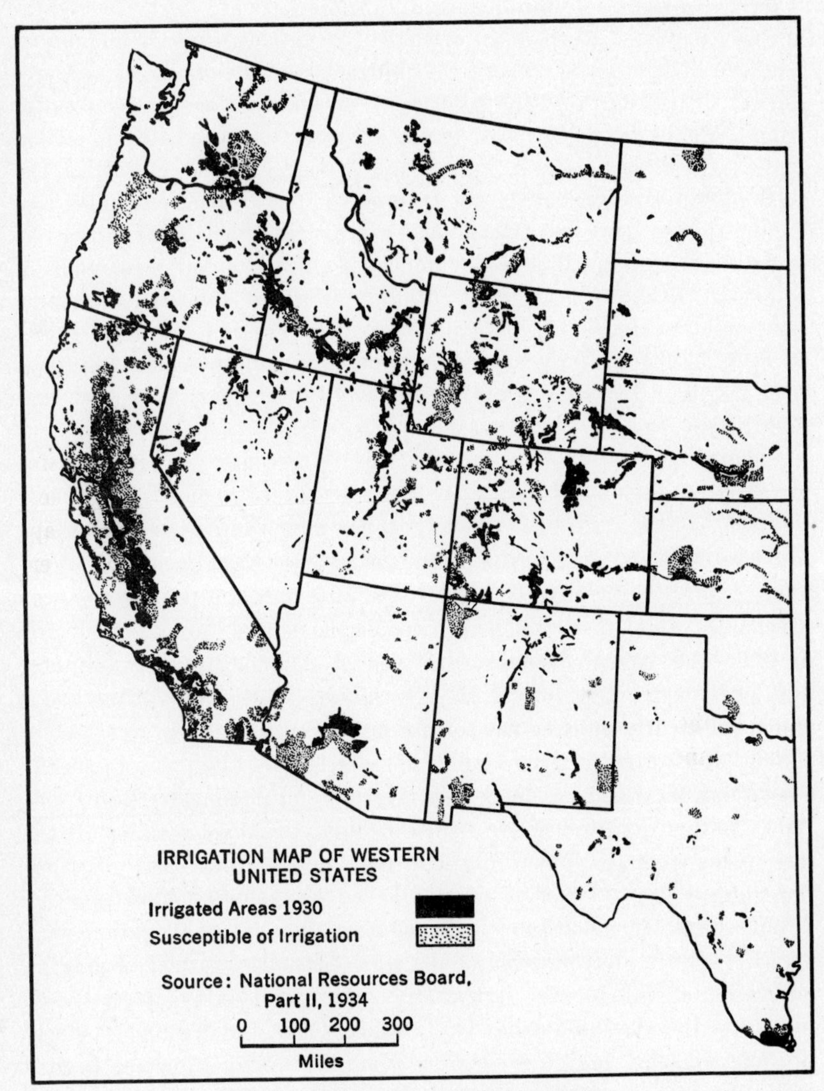

FIG. 7. Irrigated and Irrigable Lands.

possible future limits of irrigated land are indicated in Fig. 7. The more important features shown by the map are as follows: (1) The majority of the irrigated areas are of small extent. The largest continuous areas under irrigation occur in the Great Valley of California and in the northern Colorado piedmont. (2) As shown by the linear arrangement and position of irrigated areas, the water used is derived largely from rivers in high altitudes. Underground sources are used only to a slight extent. (3) The largest proportion of irrigated land occurs in the semiarid rather than in the arid regions. (4) Regions susceptible of future irrigation lie in the same general localities as areas already irrigated.

Arable Land Exceeds the Irrigable. Considering the arid and semiarid West as a whole, the principal factor which limits irrigation is the water supply. Arable lands are far greater in extent than irrigable lands. If all the natural precipitation were stored and used for irrigation—manifestly impossible—the area would not far exceed that shown as "susceptible of irrigation." As a general rule, within most irrigation projects of all kinds, there is insufficient water to irrigate all lands which have facilities for irrigation, or, to use a familiar expression, not all lands "under the ditch" are irrigated. This causes privation among water users during critical periods of the growing season, especially when mountain precipitation has been, for several years, below normal. In considering relatively small areas, where the water supply is ample, the limits of irrigation are fixed by such features as local relief, soil conditions, and climate.

The Irrigation Capacity of Streams. The water supply is the principal factor determining the present and future extent of irrigable land. In the absence of storage reservoirs, the capacity of a stream to irrigate land is limited by its flow during the growing season, the so-called critical period. Theoretically, the minimum flow during the critical period should be the basis for determining the amount of land which should be irrigated. The practical capacity of a stream is thus determined by its flow when that is least at the time when needs are greatest. In actual practice, however, the average flow at that time, sometimes even the maximum flow, has been the basis used. This has resulted in over-expansion of irrigated areas and individual privation and ill-feeling during seasons or years of deficient precipitation in the drainage basin. With the construction of reservoirs for storing surplus or floodwaters during the non-irrigating period, these rules are necessarily modified. The federal reclamation bureau, through its ability to make long-period studies of stream flow prior to project selection, has been generally proficient in adjusting available water supply to available land area.

Conservation of Irrigation Resources. Complete conservation of irrigation water—that is, the full utilization of such water wisely and with the absolute minimum of loss and no waste—has rarely been uppermost as an objective among irrigators of land. In all probability, the full conservation of water in this use is an unattainable ideal, but an ideal, nevertheless, which is worthy of a close approach. That the people as a whole are concerned in some measure with the conservation of water is reflected in the declaration by thirteen western state legislatures that unappropriated water is the "property of the public," by four others that water is the "property of the state," and by still another (California) that such water is the "property of the people of the state." Again, court decisions have generally upheld the principle that water must be used for a "beneficial purpose," at the same time, and with some contradiction, preserving individual rights to the use of water. Since water is scarce and since there are competitive uses for the same water supply, it is desirable that irrigation water be used for the highest purposes, with little loss and no waste.

The Highest Use of Water Not Always Possible. The highest use of irrigation water would be in watering the best—let it be called Grade A—land, in the proper amounts to raise such annual and perennial crops as are suitable to the environment and general economy of the region. Uses not quite so high, but still desirable, are the watering of lower-quality, but not inferior, land, for pastures as well as for tilled crops and orchards. The irrigation of inferior lands and for less productive purposes becomes increasingly undesirable until it is definitely wasteful. The irrigation of inferior land for lowly purposes may be rightly condemned since it is generally possible to use the same water elsewhere with more beneficial results.

At first thought it would seem possible always to utilize the available water for its highest, or at least for a high, purpose. Arable land greatly exceeds the irrigable, and this makes for an apparently wide choice in the selection of such lands as are to be irrigated. Moreover, there is no legal barrier to the conveyance of water far from its origin to irrigate Grade A land at any distance from the source of supply.

Granting all these favorable conditions, nevertheless many practical considerations have prevented, and many always prevent, a wise and wasteless use of irrigation water. Water is used with varying effectiveness. Different irrigated regions, even different sections of the same project and individual farms within the same section, may represent all the possible steps from the highest uses to the lowest, and from use of water with essential loss to its misuse with great waste. These practical considerations relate to such diverse matters as the physical limitations in the control of water, interstate conflicts over water rights, the misuse of the appropriation doctrine, and the degree of skill, experience, and public-spiritedness of the water user (Fig. 8).

The range of effective choice in the selection of lands to be irrigated is narrowed by the practical impossibility of conveying water long distances. The water of a stream or of a well penetrating an underground supply must, in most instances, be used in the general vicinity of the

FIG. 8. Typical of American Irrigated Areas is the Valley of the Rio Hondo, Capitan Mountains, New Mexico.

The better lands below the canal lines are used for orchard and field crops; higher lands for grazing. The limited water supply is used carefully.

stream or well. It follows, therefore, that Grade A land means the superior land in that general vicinity and not at some remote site, say a hundred or more miles away. The radius over which water can be conveyed is lengthened by advances in engineering technique and by the expenditure of funds. Perhaps, at the outset, irrigation is limited to bottom lands fed by short ditches; later, long canals heading farther upstream increase the effective irrigable area and permit the selection of better land; still later, efficient diversion and storage dams greatly amplify the possibilities. There is a financial limitation, however, to the construction of long canals and elaborate diversion facilities. Moreover, the longer the canal the greater must be the head of water to cause flow and the greater the possibilities of loss through evaporation and seepage. Losses from these sources are especially likely if, as is usually true in America, the canals are unlined, open trenches.

In the majority of irrigated regions, water is conveyed considerable distances and is transferred from creek to creek and from one canal to another, in order to adjust the supply of water to the supply of suitable land. In this respect, the prior appropriation doctrine has been of untold benefit since it permits the selection of superior lands at any distance from the water supply. In Colorado and New Mexico, water is pumped across or led by tunnel through the continental divide in order to use the surplus water of one slope to supplement the deficient supplies of the other. A spectacular example of water diversion accomplished by costly engineering is provided by the Uncompahgre project in western Colorado. Most of the water used in this large federal project is derived from the Gunnison River through a seven-mile-long tunnel driven through the Mesa Inclinado which separates the two rivers. The ample waters of the Gunnison could not be used in its narrow canyon, and the small Uncompahgre River was inadequate to irrigate its wide lowland.

The practical irrigable area is further limited by the gravity-flow irrigation method largely employed in the West. Since the better lands lie at greater or less altitudes above stream levels, and since pumping water to higher levels is costly and rarely possible, the usual practice is to divert the water at a point upstream where its elevation exceeds that of the place where delivery of the water is desired. Commonly, the gradient of the canal system exceeds that of the natural slope, thus eliminating the higher elevations from the irrigable area. Often these higher lands are physically as desirable for farming as the lower and are usually superior to the bottom lands. The practical upper limit of irrigation is thus more or less permanently fixed by the highest canals and ditches, which may or may not correspond with the altitude of the superior lands.

The available water supply is generally apportioned among the water users upon a rough areal basis—so many acres of land, so much water for irrigation. The amount needed varies broadly with the rate of evaporation, more water to the acre being needed in the southwest than in Montana. This factor has been roughly considered in determining the duty of water, but rarely such important items as (1) soil and subsoil characteristics, (2) natural slope, and (3) varying needs of different crops. The result is that some areas are allowed too much water and others receive too little, but space does not permit a further consideration of these factors. American irrigation would be greatly benefited if the amount of water furnished by rainfall during the growing season were disregarded. Though an annual growing season rainfall in amounts up to five inches may be "normal" to the region, this amount is by no means assured. Therefore, the extent of the area to be irrigated should be regulated entirely by the controlled supply.

Conflicts over the Use of Water. Conflicts over the use of water have occasionally prevented the best utilization of the available supply. Such conflicts arise between various parties, but only interstate conflicts will be considered. Long rivers which rise in one state and flow into another or others—such as the Arkansas, the Colorado, and the Rio Grande—have frequently been the source of interstate disputes. Kansas, operating under the riparian doctrine, and adjacent Colorado, following the prior appropriation rule, have come into conflict over the Arkansas River which rises in Colorado. Each state has disputed some of the claims of the other, leaving water rights in an insecure position. A most serious dispute has arisen over the use of the water of the Colorado River, whose basin involves seven states and part of Mexico. A former president has called this river the most important natural resource of the Southwest. Various compacts have been agreed upon only to be disrupted at a later time by a member state rescinding an earlier decision. One of the major difficulties is that the water of the river rises mainly in Colorado but California seems likely to be most benefited.

Water Losses Incidental to Irrigation. In the artificial watering of land a certain loss of water is unavoidable. Completely to conserve water would place an unwarranted value upon this resource in comparison with other resources and with man himself. Were the conservancy of water the only desirable end, then the water should be used high along the stream's course, conveyed in enclosed aqueducts to adjacent fields, spread over them with the utmost care, and re-used on lower-lying lands. Such restrictions, however, would be neither desirable nor possible. The land adjacent to streams in their upper courses is likely to be unsuitable to farming, the cost of elaborate canals is generally out of the question, and painstaking care in irrigation is scarcely to be expected. In point of fact, water must be carried over considerable distances to desirable land, and it must be conducted by such means as are within the reasonable limits of achievement. In so doing, some water is necessarily lost by evaporation and some by seepage. The latter, however, may not be a total loss since there is the possibility of a return flow.

At the same time, there is no doubt that losses in the handling of water generally exceed the amount which is unavoidable. Canal systems, well made in the beginning, deteriorate in time and need constant repair, which often is not accorded them. Active erosion gouges out portions of ditches, concrete weirs and checks are dislodged at "drops" in canals, flumes and pipe lines develop leaks, sedimentation in the lower end of the lateral system diminishes capacity, and thrifty weeds choke ditches and line their embankments. Deterioration occurs so gradually that it may escape observation until the task of repair seems out of proportion to the benefits to be derived thereby. Water users along a ditch suffer unequally. Those toward the end of the system and with later water rights are mainly affected. Their combined protests may not be sufficient to result in bringing about the necessary repairs in the ditch above them.

Water is wasted in other ways, sometimes with deliberation. The irrigation of uneven surfaces is likely to result in waste of water. The leveling of land preparatory to its irrigation is an uncommon procedure; as the majority of irrigators will tell you, "The land is just as God made it." The scraping of large fields with fresnos is a laborious and costly task, and farmers fear that in so doing inferior soil and stones will be brought to the surface. Misuse of water rights may easily lead to water waste. In order to preserve a right originally acquired, irrigators sometimes water land unnecessarily, or, in order to preempt a right in anticipation of some future need, water may be used in advance of any real need for it and on inferior soil. These wastes prevent the use of the same water elsewhere for beneficial purposes and are likewise harmful to the land.

Long-continued irrigation disturbs the normal balance of soil constituents to such an extent that the soil may become non-productive. Soil with poor under-drainage easily becomes water-logged. Consequently few irrigated areas are lacking in extensive "seeped land" and swamps which occur in poorly drained areas. The increased water upsets the normal equilibrium between the soluble and insoluble constituents of the soil. If water is used excessively in poorly drained areas, various kinds of alkali accumulate in the topsoil from which evaporation is rapid. If the alkali is sufficient in quantity and kind this may be ruinous to the soil. Commonly, water-logged and alkalied soils occur together and both are symptomatic of excessive use or accumulation of water and the lack of natural or artificial under-drainage. Irrigation experience has amply demonstrated the desirability of providing drainage along with irrigation facilities. Nevertheless, it is difficult, if not impossible, to anticipate the particular sites where drains may later prove necessary; and in any event to provide them is a costly undertaking. To provide them at the outset would increase the cost of the land, which is, even without artificial drains, already expensive and often over-capitalized. Thus, most drainage systems are developed after the need for them has become apparent and are usually correctives of an existing condition rather than preventives of a condition likely to occur.

ARID AND SEMIARID LAND CONSERVATION IDEALS

The arid and semiarid lands belong to that great group of resources which are best conserved if wisely used without waste. Because these resources have been misused in the past, replacement of original resources, where that is possible, is now necessary. Rehabilitation of misused grasslands by replanting over-grazed and unwisely plowed areas is a real necessity. The pasturage possibilities of the grasslands should be viewed, as they were in the nineteenth century, as their highest form of use. Irrigated land should be articulated more closely with grazing land—each is fundamental to the other—but there is no indication that any appreciable increase in the irrigated area is desirable. Improvements of present irrigated regions and possibly moderate expansion within the irrigable portions of present projects of all kinds are ends more to be desired than the development of new projects. Clamorings for new projects in unsettled areas should be strongly resisted. Better and more complete use of water for higher purposes should be encouraged; but even if such encouragement be lacking, gradual improvements in irrigation practices may be reasonably expected as the art of irrigation becomes more familiar to those who have undertaken to master it.

CHAPTER VII

THE PROBLEM OF OUR GRASSLANDS

BY V. E. SHELFORD AND H. C. HANSON[1]

University of Illinois — *North Dakota Agricultural College*

THE IMPORTANCE OF GRASSLANDS

Grassland is one of the largest of all vegetational formations. Shantz[2] estimates the land area of the earth's surface as follows:

Desert	13,000,000 square miles
Forest	17,000,000 square miles
Grassland	22,000,000 square miles
Total	52,000,000 square miles

Furthermore, Shantz and Zon[3] have estimated that 38 per cent of the total area of the United States is grassland. Approximately half of the world's total land area can never be cultivated. It is important to learn as much as practicable concerning its uses for other purposes. The desirability of vastly expanded continuous scientific work in what is with little doubt one of the most important land areas of the world, both theoretically and practically, needs no elucidation.

Grassland is characterized by the dominance of perennial grasses. Numerous broad-leaved herbs, or forbs, may be present, but the grasses because of their ability to grow densely, often producing as many as 500 to more than 2,000 stalks to the square meter, are in control of the factors necessary to life, as light and soil moisture. The root systems of grasses are finely branched and permeate the soil from the surface to as deep as 8 and 10 feet in lowland species. These roots ramify the soil so thoroughly that but few other kinds of plants can compete with them for moisture. It has been demonstrated that it is practically impossible for a tree seedling to live in a dense sod. Owing

[1] The authors are indebted to the other members of the National Research Council's Committee on the Ecology of Grasslands of North America, viz., C. T. Vorhies, W. P. Taylor, B. C. Tharp, A. O. Weese, J. E. Weaver, B. Shimek, and K. M. King, for notes and suggestions.

[2] *Encyclopædia Britannica,* 1930, pp. 858-960.

[3] Atlas of American Agriculture, 1924, p. 3.

to the numerous fine roots, and, in some grasslands, rootstocks and rhizomes, saplings thrive for a while, then die and decay. Grassland soils usually contain more organic matter than forest soils. In Illinois it was determined that forest soils had only 25 to 50 per cent as much organic matter as grassland soils.

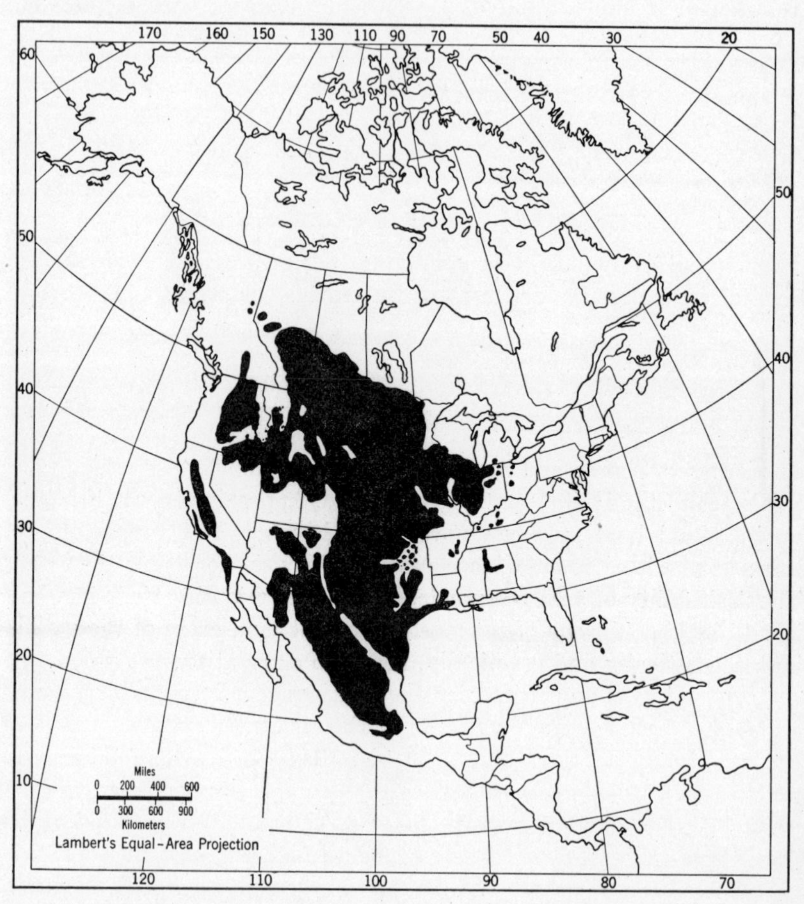

Fig. 1. Generalized Map of the Grassland of North America, shown in black.

Usually only one to two or three species of grasses dominate a particular grassland area. In the vicinity of Lincoln, Nebraska, the prairie was shown to have 237 regular species, of which 38 were grasses, 18 were sedges, and the rest broad-leaved flowering plants. Although grasses and sedges constituted only one-fourth of the total species, they made up nine-tenths of the vegetation growing on the land. Only

4 of these 38 grasses were classified as dominants. Investigations on a mixed prairie near Fort Collins, Colorado, showed that western wheat grass was the dominant in a total of 109 species. Grasses are able to dominate in regions where grasslands occur because they can grow successfully under limited moisture conditions but where the rainfall is sufficient in amount and frequency to provide for their growth and

FIG. 2. A Tall-Grass Prairie near Hawley, Minnesota.

This tall-grass prairie about 9 miles from Hawley, Minnesota, shows very little disturbance. The chief dominants are big bluestem, prairie dropseed, and Indian grass.

reproduction. Irregular drought periods, fatal to trees, are withstood by grasses.

Grasslands Classified. There are seven main kinds of grasslands. The *true prairie,* now mostly plowed up, extends from Manitoba into central Oklahoma and includes most of the prairie region east of an irregular line along the ninety-seventh and ninety-eighth meridians. Shimek estimated that originally Iowa was seven-eighths prairie. The leading dominants, occurring as sod or bunch-formers, are needle grass, dropseed, bluestem, panic grass, and wild rye. The *coastal prairie* occupies a strip of land in Texas and Louisiana near the Gulf of Mexico. The chief dominants are a bluestem and a needle grass. The *short-*

grass plains and *mixed prairie* types occupy the area between the true prairie and the eastern limits of the Rocky Mountains. The chief dominants in the former are the short-grasses, especially grama grasses and buffalo grass. In the mixed prairie medium tall grasses, as western wheat grass and western needle grass, are associated with the short grasses. The *desert plains* grassland extends from southwestern Texas westward into southern New Mexico, Arizona, and northern Mexico.

FIG. 3. Mixed Short and Tall-Grass in Western North Dakota.

The dominants are western needle grass (conspicuous white stalks), blue grama, and western wheat grass. A small herd of antelope still frequents this area.

The chief dominants are several species of grama grass, three-awn grass, and mesquite grass. According to F. E. Clements, the *Pacific prairie* formerly occupied extensive areas in valleys and foothills in California and Lower California. The former bunch-grass dominants —needle grasses, June grass, wild ryes—have been largely replaced, owing to over-grazing and fire, by annual weeds such as wild oats, ripgut, foxtail chess, and wild barleys. The grasses of the *Palouse prairie* are in large part responsible for the productiveness of the wheat lands known as the Palouse. At one time this grassland occupied an extensive area in eastern Washington and Oregon, northern Utah, and

Southern Idaho. The major dominants are bunch grasses—bluebunch wheat grass, sheep fescue, and giant wild rye.

WHAT HAS HAPPENED TO OUR GRASSLANDS?

> It was not until the white pioneer crossed the Wabash River in his westward advance that he beheld the prairies in all their splendor, and all their monotonous magnitude. These prairies presented varying aspects. The early settler avoided them at first in part for the reason that he thought them not fertile because treeless, and in part because they did not furnish the much needed building materials, fuel and water; but as his experience increased, there were added to these reasons the menace of the prairie fires and terror of winter storms. But the real rich beauty of the prairie was developed only after mid-summer when myriads of flowers of most varied hues were everywhere massed into one great painting, limited only by the frame of the horizon, uniform in splendid beauty, but endlessly varied in delicate detail. In the fall this in turn was followed by the rusty-red or brown expanse of drying grasses which portended the coming of the terror and the splendor of that scourge of the early prairie settlers, the prairie fires, whose fascinating fury can be appreciated only by those who in earlier years had the privilege of looking upon them in hopeless helplessness. (B. Shimek.)
>
> This grass, big bluestem, forms a close sod and under good growing condition may reach the height of 10-12 feet. The early settlers say that they were unable to locate cattle on the prairie except by climbing some elevation and watching for the waving of the tall grass as the cattle walked through it. (H. C. Sampson.)

Little effort was made to use the midwestern prairie in its original condition. There was a wild scramble to turn it over, much of it "wrong-side up." In the plains and foothills there were other wild scrambles to graze every blade of grass, not even leaving enough for winter grazing or, more important, for seeding. The grasslands were destroyed or wantonly damaged by burning, over-grazing, mowing too close or too late, plowing and cultivating, planting to "timber claims," irrigating or flooding, and lowering the water table by artificial drainage. No thought was given to investigating how these native grasslands could serve as they were. No—the ideas, if any existed, were "free soil" and "free grass," and "get it while the getting is good." There were no attempts to utilize native grasses as forage plants under partial cultivation or reasonably restricted grazing. To be "good" it would appear that a plant or animal must be brought from Europe or Asia, so as to favor spectacular description and gather favor and votes for the importers. The native grasses did, however, survive the recent droughts better than imported grasses, and attention has been directed toward testing them as forage plants.

ANIMAL LIFE OF THE GRASSLANDS

The grasslands originally supported an excellent group of animals. The immense herds of bison meant free meat and free hides, later free bones. Bison fitted the climate and grassland so well that its population exceeded the present human population on the same area. That it was destroyed instead of domesticated or at least maintained as a game animal is an outstanding monument to human prejudice. The antelope was also an important game animal. Associated with the spectacular ungulates were the wolf, coyote, and numerous well-known rodents such as the prairie dog. The management of the animals of the grasslands was in general less intelligent than that of the grass itself.

The western Europeans who colonized the grasslands had spent thousands of years in the western European deciduous forest and perhaps 150 years in the deciduous forests of North America. There was no scientific information to guide them in the utilization of the grasslands, and the prejudices which they had developed toward certain animals in the deciduous forest were a total misfit in the grassland area.

The Rodent Problem. The rodents of the grassland, particularly ground squirrels, prairie dogs, kangaroo rats, and jackrabbits, have long constituted a problem in grazing areas as competitors with livestock. Their increases on the plains, following settlement, are well described by Merriam in the Year Book of the United States Department of Agriculture for 1901. "On many parts of the plains prairie dogs were more abundant in 1900 than formerly and their colonies had overspread extensive areas previously unoccupied. This is due to the aid of the settlers (1) by decreasing the animal's natural enemies, and (2) to a minor extent by increasing the food supply. The settler waged warfare against the coyotes, badgers, hawks, owls, snakes, and other predatory animals which previously held the prairie dogs in check. The prairie dogs had multiplied until they had become a pernicious enemy to agriculture."

For example, Merriam mentions that one South Dakota settler stated that about 1885 his children noticed two or three burrows about a mile from his house, and in 1900 they had spread over and occupied a full quarter section (160 acres), having surrounded his house and taken possession of all the land near it. Merriam also cites many examples of losses. A cattle ranch had its carrying capacity cut from 1,000 cattle to 500 by an increase of prairie dogs which extended to cover 300 square miles. In the same area there was a decrease in population and the abandonment of a post office.

The damage done by prairie dogs consists in the loss of grass eaten and buried under the mounds and injury of stock from stumbling in the holes. Running horses sometimes trip and break their legs, and in a few cases riders are alleged to have been injured and even killed. These horses and rider difficulties have been commonly stressed only regarding the badger.

Grass leaves and stems form the normal food of the prairie dog. In addition to this, grass roots, other plants, seeds, and sometimes insects, are eaten.

The work of the hog-nosed snake, blue racer, ferret, and five or more species of weasels and especially the badger and coyote and kit-fox, all of which take toll of rodents, makes it appear entirely probable that a system of rodent control by flesh-eaters could be worked out so as to save the expense of poisoning and shooting them at frequent intervals. A considerable number of rodents are useful. It is an established fact that under certain conditions rodents may be more helpful than injurious because of their largely beneficial influence on the soil, their serving as a food supply for valuable fur-bearers, and their insectivorous habits.

Evidence is accumulating that certain rodents increase in numbers under over-grazing. Similar relationships have been determined for certain species of grasshoppers, which are able to injure range vegetation only under conditions of over-grazing. Little detailed work, however, has been done in the determination of such relationships, and a great deal of information of value in the control of the animal components of the grassland communities may be gained by research.

An Experiment in Rodent Control. The Santa Rita Experimental Range of the United States Forest Service is an area on which a long-time set-up of fenced plots and enclosures, an expensive and very complete climatic station, and a new 20-year transect have been provided by four cooperating research agencies for the express purpose of scientific experiment on range management, including rodent studies.

To give relief employment, the destruction of the rodents was suggested. Vorhies states that the original proposal was for "complete eradication" of rodents, but this was modified when its practical impossibility was pointed out. It finally involved destruction of jackrabbits, Merriam and banner-tailed kangaroo rats, round-tailed ground squirrels, and the incidental destruction of no one knows what or how many other forms of animal life.

The Santa Rita Range is carrying about 1,200 cattle, 40 acres to the animal; it should have less if it is in fact to be restored, and it might carry somewhat more if it were fully restored. Vorhies felt safe in asserting that results of the rodent and rabbit reduction will be slight and so evanescent as not to be definitely measurable. He proceeds to estimate cost and savings as follows:

> "Nearly $8 per head of livestock on the range was spent on the control work. The cost was *19* cents per acre, which seems cheap enough until we learn that the cattlemen are paying scarcely *4* cents per acre per year for it. Comparing the cost on the basis of livestock values, we get an interesting result. The estimated cost of killing 12,280 jackrabbits was $2,885.92, or about 32 cents per jackrabbit. According to Taylor and Vorhies it takes 74 antelope jackrabbits or 128 California jacks to consume as much valuable forage as one cow. Therefore to remove the antelope jackrabbit equivalent of one cow cost $23.68; and to remove the California jack equivalent of one cow cost $47.36; the livestock was worth possibly $20 to $25 per head. Was it good economy, aside from any other question? Would any cattleman spend that much on his range to get rid of rodents?
>
> It was argued in support of the project that it would be a grand-scale "experiment," but the cattle on this range are owned by private parties, for whom a profit must be maintained and proper controls are not possible. A major rodent control operation over an entire range with no check areas or areas on which the major factors may be varied, cannot be a *scientific* experiment.
>
> What of the effects on wildlife? Aside from the direct effects on the rodents results are for the most part not clearly discernible as yet. The sole scientific result on the animal side is the check on numbers of jackrabbits. Cottontails were not included in the original project, but the control leader found *some* grass in cottontail stomachs and proceeded to kill off several hundred, though the cottontail is already a game animal. There seems to be a great dearth of hawks on the reserve. Whether this is due to the campaign we cannot say. Coyotes seem to be about as plentiful as before. We can form no opinion as to the present status of the fur-bearers. Quail have not notably benefited. One worker familiar with the Reserve says, "There is no wildlife there since the campaign," and that is my own impression.
>
> The value of such campaigns is questionable when there is no accompanying reduction of livestock pressure. "Rodent control" on an unprecedented scale is an open sesame for allotments of emergency

funds. Projects are in operation on most of the Indian reservations in Arizona. A Forest Service investigator recently gave me his impressions of the rodent control work on the great erosion project of the Navajo Reservation, which were pretty much in line with my own reaction. While apparently setting out to exterminate the prairie dog, no one seems to remember that the Navajo likes the animal for food.

Grasshopper Control. In grassland regions, most insect pests such as grasshoppers are native species, and measures for their efficient control must be based upon exact knowledge of interrelationships and behavior; also, control by cultural methods instead of by chemical means promises possibilities of large savings and more effective results. To foretell grasshopper conditions, large areas of undisturbed grassland, on which the abundance and condition of the eggs can be determined, are essential.

OVER-GRAZING OF THE GRASSLANDS

A picture of the evils of our grazing is well presented in the recently published Second Report of the Science Advisory Board:

> Overgrazing has affected in all probability most of the grasslands; we have no quantitative information on this point. The results of overgrazing are principally (1) that overstocking of pastures reduces the total amount of growing vegetation and tends to exterminate certain species, (2) that plants of low edible value, or none, will replace in part the original vegetation and (3) that, by diminution of surface cover, soil wash and wind erosion are introduced and, under the semi-arid climates of our great grazing lands, speedily assume serious proportions. It is a peculiar quality of overgrazing that, degeneration once having set in, it is very unlikely that it is stopped thereafter. In any fully stocked range an adverse season results in damage to the vegetation, which could be compensated subsequently only by a sufficiently sharp reduction in stock to give the pasture the chance to recover. As the result the carrying capacity of a large part of our range lands has declined seriously and is continuing to do so, and some of them have become nuisance areas to lands below them because the rains run off more rapidly from the sparsely covered slopes and the increased run-off carries more sediment onto the lowlands.
>
> The outstanding case of the third type, the regions of unbalance as to the national economy, is the Great Plains. In view of its upsetting influence on the economic situation of the country it is probably the most critical region in the United States. Any national land program will have to come to grips with this situation. It is a region of large surplus of staple crops, of highest climatic variability affecting production and of large potential increase of crop acreage,

with minimum density of agricultural population and low value of permanent improvements. A comprehensive study of conditions and potentialities on the Great Plains is one of the most badly wanted items for national economy. A Great Plains commission could strike at the heart of the agricultural surplus problem more directly. The increase in field area in that section in the past quarter century has been far in excess of the estimated 40,000,000 acres of present surplus crop land in the United States. The area annually harvested in the Great Plains is distinctly in excess of this amount, and the amount of land in reserve, that has been planted in boom years and may come into production again, is huge. Our wheat and barley surplus, and in large measure that of cotton, are accounted for by the Great Plains. The plowing up of the Great Plains and the release of crop land from feed production for food production throughout the country are the two primary elements that have produced and maintained agricultural unbalance in the United States. In many parts of the Great Plains the crop hazards from climatic variability are such that the establishment of socially and economically healthy communities is doubtful. Improvements in many sections are meager, population is sparse and, at present, large amounts of land are held by mortgages that are tax delinquent and tax reverted. In no part of the country could an extensive program of land retirement be initiated with equal effects on crop surplus, with as little disturbance of population and at such low cost. The proper, permanent, and balanced use of the Great Plains in the national economy is one of the most pressing problems before the nation. Its successful resolution will be a major achievement for American science and administration.

WHAT HAS, CAN, AND MUST BE DONE TO CONSERVE OUR GRASSLANDS?

The healing of the numerous gashes, listed above, which have cut deep into one of the chief national resources, grasslands, must be based upon facts, methods, and principles that research has proved to be sound. Research is an absolute prerequisite to the formulation of adequate remedial measures. Agencies of state and nation that are planning land use must have a large fund of grassland research data upon which to draw if the plans are to be scientifically sound. It has been realized for several years by a few ecologists that our grasslands, one of the major resources of the United States, have received woefully inadequate fundamental research. The great cereal-growing and grazing areas of central North America were originally grassland. The grassland flora and fauna have intimate relations with land use, particularly with soil development, erosion control, water conservation, and wildlife. The best agricultural soil has been developed under grassland conditions, supporting a large animal community characterized by many of the best-known large mammals and birds and many rodents and small carnivores, as well as reptiles and invertebrates. Its original life has largely been destroyed without adequate study, from the standpoint of either pure or applied science. Results valuable to the general sciences of paleontology, geology, geography, botany, and zoology, and especially to modern ecology, could have and still can be obtained. Representatives of all the species of animals are still available for research purposes.

The Division of Range Research of the United States Forest Service in connection with the Southwestern Forest and Range Experiment Station has conducted research in the desert grassland in the vicinity of Las Cruces and south of Tucson, Arizona. The Northern Rocky Mountain Forest and Range Experiment Station started work in 1931 at Miles City, Montana, in the mixed tall and short grass climax. The recently established Rocky Mountain Forest and Range Experiment Station at Fort Collins, Colorado, will probably conduct work in the mixed tall and short grass climax. Most of the investigational work by the Forest Service in the climatic grasslands is devoted to management and restoration of the range for grazing purposes. Other research work by these stations on grasslands is conducted in shrub or tree climaxes. Fundamental research at these stations is somewhat limited because of the urgency of the needs and demands of livestock producers. The Soil Conservation Service has collected seeds of numerous species of grass, many of which have been planted in their nurseries. Additional plantings are being made in 1936 to test the value of these grasses especially for erosion control under different conditions. Methods have been devised for seed collecting and cleaning. The distribution and habits of grasses have been studied to some extent. In places the Soil Conservation Service is emphasizing the need for seeding much of our plowed land to grass. In this work as well as in that of the Forest Service many additional basic research data are needed in order to plan efficiently for scientific land use.

In order further to stimulate, organize, coordinate, and develop basic grassland research the Committee on the Ecology of Grasslands in North America was formed as one of the technical committees of the National Research Council. The committee has had two field meetings, one in 1933 in the grasslands of western Texas, the second in 1935 in the grasslands of western North Dakota. Several indoor sessions have been held in connection with the annual December meetings of the American Association for the Advancement of Science. Extracts from the report of the 1935 field meeting will show the principles and procedures that are being recommended:

> The thorough study of native grassland is basic to the solution of many problems of complicated nature whose clarification can be reached only by long, continued research. Succession has never been studied on controlled areas, and the role of animals has never been determined and their use in natural control of rodents has never been studied. Because of the importance of a knowledge of community dynamics in ecology, grazing, forestry, agriculture, and erosion, etc., pure scientific studies are of vital importance not only to ecology, but as checks in the applied fields. The importance of such problems is now exemplified by various phases of the national emergency. The solution of national problems, such as dust control, soil erosion by wind and water, floods, deforestation, range depletion, wildlife dissemination or extermination, water conservation, must be in essence ecological if it is to be adequate. In grassland areas this must be based upon research on native grassland, undisturbed. Fundamental to national welfare in these matters is the elimination of cropping over considerable areas of submarginal prairie or plains land, which should be in grass. In the elimination or drastic restriction of grazing on considerable areas of desert land, in order that the maximum vegetation cover should be encouraged, the National Administration is acting with great wisdom in planning to effect these ends.
>
> It was proposed that eight study centers, so spaced as to represent the various types of grasslands in North America, undertake cooperative correlated study. These centers would have their headquarters at the following institutions: University of Arizona, University of Texas, University of Oklahoma, University of Nebraska, State University of Iowa, University of Illinois, North Dakota Agricultural College, and the University of Saskatchewan. At each of these institutions there are one or more investigators of the problems under consideration. Some of the investigators are very well known for work already published. No provision thus far seems feasible for a center in the bunch-grass areas of the northwest. Each study center is represented on the National Research Council committee. Also at each center there is a local committee set up by the Ecological Society of America. The Committee's aims are to improve the quality of the research in progress and provide land and other resources which will give continuity to the investigations by the interchange of ideas, the standardization of methods, and the correlation of the work at the different centers.

SUMMARY

1. Native grasslands, one of the major resources of the United States, have been destroyed in large part. There are no public reservations of

any size where the tall grasses are preserved. The animal life has been reduced far below the conditions of the eastern deciduous forests. Most of the eastern and midwestern universities own a small area of forest, but almost none of the institutions in the grasslands have any land for the study of grasses. The acquiring of these is a most urgent problem.

2. National economy now requires its restoration in many places where it was destroyed and also requires planned use of the areas yet remaining. Restoration and scientific planning must be based upon a firm foundation of fundamental research. This foundation is utterly inadequate to support the large superstructure of a changing land economy placed upon it. The National Research Council Committee on the Ecology of Grasslands in North America began in 1933 to help in coordinating, organizing, and developing basic grassland research. Foundational work has been started, but much remains to be done. The first step is provision for land adequate for instruction near the universities of the grassland area.

3. An area somewhat larger than Yellowstone Park should be set aside (see Fig. 4, Chapter XIX, on Wildlife) and plain animals should be reintroduced and managed on a hands-off basis.

4. The restoration of perennial grass cover on plowed and overgrazed areas is a process requiring 40 to 100 years—no one really knows how long. Seed plants are often wanting, but native plants are always safer and usually as good as or better than the spectacularly introduced species. Research on the native species and methods of hastening succession is imperative.

5. Biological control of rodents on the range seems entirely possible of development and should be made the subject of serious experimentation.

6. Continuous ecological study is essential to an understanding of climate and weather in relation to grassland utilization and forecasting of unfavorable periods.

CHAPTER VIII

RECLAMATION OF WET AND OVERFLOW LANDS

By George J. Miller

State Teachers College, Mankato, Minnesota

Our arable lands may be extended by irrigation of arid areas or by drainage of wet lands. These wet lands constitute the country's greatest reserve of agricultural land that is economically available when the pressure of population makes it desirable to draw upon it. In general, the term includes any land that normally has so much water in the soil that the land cannot be used for agricultural purposes. Such areas vary from swamp conditions to land that is too wet for use other than pasture, too wet during some years, or too wet during part of a growing season. Any planned economy designed for the general welfare of the nation should include some practicable system of reclaiming wet lands, as large areas of these lands are potentially highly productive and capable of sustaining a large population.

DISTRIBUTION OF WET LANDS

Location and Types. Wet lands are found in every state, but by far the greater portion is in the eastern half of the country, associated with its spacious plains area that is now highly productive and sustains a large population. In general, wet lands fall into four classes on the basis of origin and location. The coastal swamp and wet prairie lands are found chiefly along the Atlantic and Gulf coast from Chesapeake Bay to southern Texas; the most extensive alluvial bottom lands are in the lower Mississippi basin south of the mouth of the Ohio River; the glacial swamp and wet lands are included chiefly within the Great Lakes states; and in the western half of the United States are located those seepage lands commonly associated with irrigation enterprises, and also some river overflow and coastal lands. The potential value of these wet lands for agricultural purposes is highly varied, as the soils range from high to low fertility. As a rule the areas having good soil, that could be drained at relatively low cost, have been reclaimed first and are in use. Numerous factors have contributed to the delay of reclamation and utilization of the remainder of the wet lands, such as low fertility, cost of clearing cut-over lands or timbered land, high cost of protection from river or tidal overflow, need for large-scale and costly ditch construction, and decrease in the value of agricultural land and agricultural products.

Drainable Land. Figure 1 shows the location of wet lands that are considered physically available for drainage. It is estimated that the drainable area in the United States is 91,000,000 acres. However, when deductions are made for areas of deep peat and coastal marsh lands unsuitable for crops, it is probable that not more than 75,000,000 acres can be reclaimed at a cost that would justify drainage. If we assume the smaller figure as the practical one, it represents an area as large as the combined area of New York, New Jersey, Pennsylvania, Massachusetts, Connecticut, and Rhode Island; an area nearly as large as Italy, or the British Isles, or nine times that of the Netherlands, which now supports a population of more than 7,500,000 people. Some of these lands are now utilized for pasture or for crops in favorable years, but about three-fourths are swamps that are not now used for agricultural purposes. Approximately 68 per cent of the area requires clearing of trees, stumps, or brush. Most of the soil would be highly productive when drained, but in some of the areas the soils are of low fertility or the soil texture is not favorable for crop production. About two-thirds of the land requiring drainage before use is located in the South and one-half the remainder is in Michigan, Wisconsin, and Minnesota. Much of the wet land in these states is peat bog without tree growth. In the South, practically all the wet lands need both draining and clearing except the tidal marshes, Gulf coastal prairies, and the Florida Everglades and prairies.

It is estimated that one-third of the drainable wet land may be drained at an average cost of $30 an acre. However, the total cost to the individual owner will be increased in proportion to the cost of clearing the land, of farm ditches, buildings, roads, and other necessary improvements. Drained lands have certain marked advantages in that there is very little waste land, the loss by erosion is at a minimum, and such lands are relatively little affected by drought. It may be desirable from the standpoint of both individual and public welfare to transfer many farmers from some of the poor, hilly, upland farms to the productive drained land. Many of these poor upland farms offer no possibility of providing adequately for those who endeavor to cultivate them. Such abandoned farms could then be used for purposes to which they are best adapted. However, no drainage or transfers

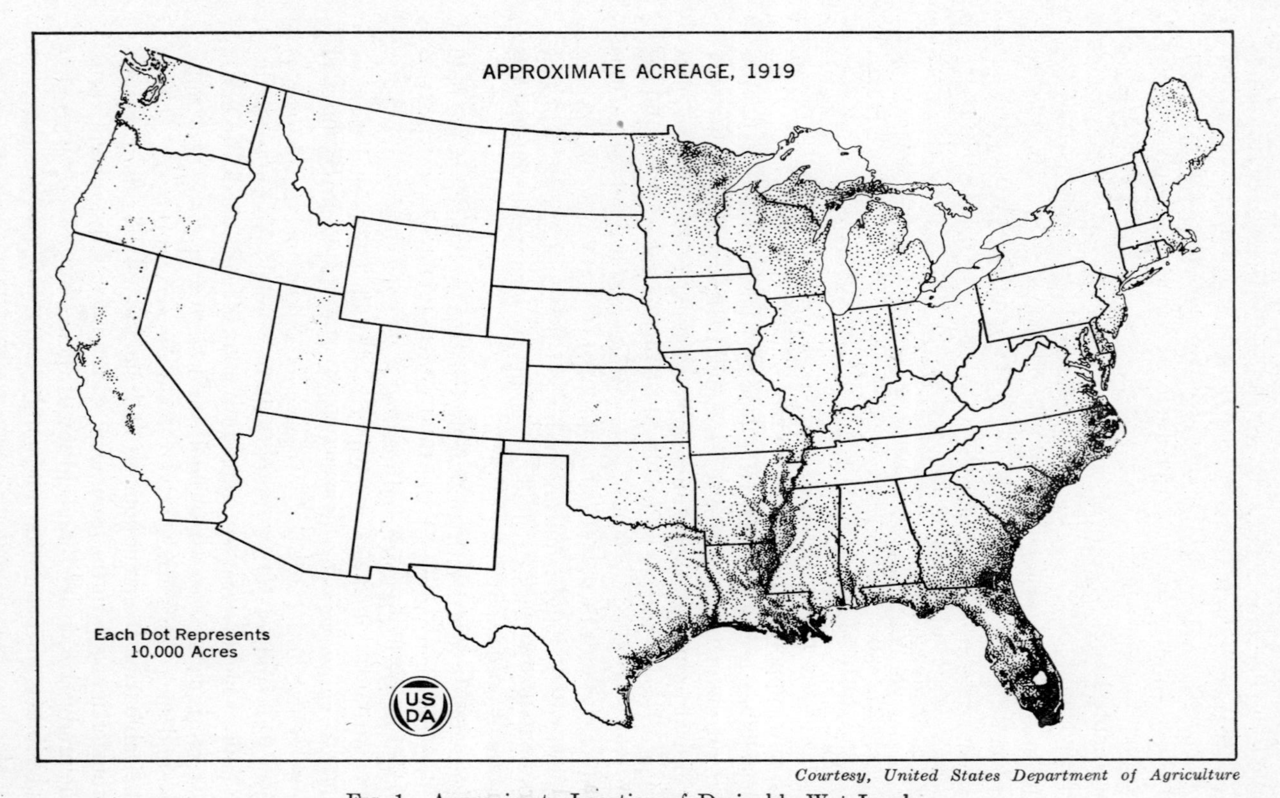

Courtesy, United States Department of Agriculture

FIG. 1. Approximate Location of Drainable Wet Lands.

The physically drainable area is about 91,000,000 acres, but only approximately 75,000,000 acres can be drained at a cost that would justify the undertaking. It is estimated that three-fourths of the total area is swamp or timber land not now used for agriculture.

should be undertaken without adequate evidence that the probable return from the reclaimed land, and the improved living conditions, justify the cost. Action should be taken only after scientific investigation and careful planning based on a broad view of the problem and of the general welfare. If this is done, many of the unfortunate mistakes of the past will be avoided. We should also be sure that the value of the wet land as wildlife refuges and for recreational purposes is not actually greater, from a long-time viewpoint, than the value of that land for agricultural purposes. Evidence at hand indicates that by 1960 at least 10,000,000 acres now too wet for crops will be drained. It is also estimated that approximately 17,000,000 acres of marsh land, having little or no agricultural use, should be set aside as migratory bird refuges.

THE PURPOSE OF DRAINAGE

The chief purpose of most drainage enterprises, thus far undertaken, has been to remove a surplus of water from lands in order that they might be used for agricultural purposes. In general, the purposes are to drain land already in farms and swamp land that is unfit for use without removal of the surplus water, to prevent damage from seepage and alkali in irrigated areas, to prevent overflow on agricultural land, and to reduce the losses from floods, particularly along rivers or tidal marshes. All other purposes of drainage have thus far been largely secondary.

In the north central states the chief purpose has been the drainage of wet lands in cultivation so as to increase crop production. However, these states, especially Wisconsin, Missouri, and Minnesota, have extensive enterprises for the reclamation of swamp land, and others for the prevention of overflow along numerous streams, as in Illinois and Kansas.

Most of the lands being reclaimed from swamp conditions are located along the Atlantic and gulf coastal plains from Virginia to Texas, in the delta of the Mississippi, in Wisconsin, and in northern Minnesota.

The removal of seepage and alkali from irrigation is the principal purpose of drainage in the mountain states and of some enterprises in the Pacific states. However, reclamation of wet and swamp lands has made progress in California and Oregon, and Washington has considerable areas the primary purpose of which is the improvement of land in farms.

Enterprises designed to provide protection against overflow are located chiefly in the river bottoms of the central states, the Piedmont section of the south Atlantic states, the Great Valley of California, and the coastal sections of Washington and Oregon. Much of this land was in cultivation before drainage, but crop losses resulted from occasional overflow.

PROGRESS IN RECLAMATION

State Ownership and Regulation. Under laws passed by Congress in 1849 and 1850, the federal government conveyed the swamp lands to the states in which that land was located. Most of this land has since passed to private ownership. At first most of the drainage was done by individuals on their own farm land, largely by the construction of small ditches or by the use of tile. However, it soon became evident that satisfactory results could be obtained in many cases only by cooperative development of large units, as the main drainage ditches must pass through adjoining property, and the cost of large and long ditches was too great to be borne by an individual owner. This led many states to develop an extensive system of drainage laws so that cooperation among a large number of owners was possible and the cost could be distributed in proportion to the benefits derived. All such laws also take into consideration public welfare, such as increasing the taxable property, public health, and improvement of

TABLE 1

LAND AND CAPITAL, BY PURPOSE OF DRAINAGE, 1930

Purpose of Drainage	Land		Capital Invested to Jan. 1, 1930	
	Acres	Per Cent	Dollars	Per Cent
All enterprises	84,408,093	100.0	680,732,880	100.0
Reclamation of swamp land not previously in farms	22,858,597	27.1	211,575,252	31.1
Improvement of land already in farms	53,026,596	62.8	364,299,640	53.5
Removal of seepage and alkali from irrigation	3,395,144	4.0	39,283,693	5.8
Protection against overflow	5,127,756	6.1	65,574,295	9.6

public highways. The 1930 census reports thirty-five states having laws providing for an organized system of drainage, six states that permit separate organization of drainage units, and seven states that do not provide for independent drainage organization. The significance of the problem and public interest in drainage in the thirty-five states reporting drainage enterprises is indicated by the fact that the various laws in these states comprise more than 7,000 pages. That public interest continues in the problem is evident from recent legislative activity: during the legislative sessions of 1925-1926, 79 additions were made to the drainage laws in thirty-two states; in 1927-1928, 121 drainage enactments were made in thirty-five states; and 95 statutes were added to the drainage laws in 1929. Although the state laws have many things in common, they differ to meet specific needs of the state and the type of drainage, e.g., drainage of land in farms, drainage that concerns flood control as well as reclamation of agricultural land, drainage of swamp lands, and protection from seepage and alkali in some irrigation areas. In general, they also provide that the cost shall not exceed the benefits to be derived from the land reclaimed, and that a method of assessment be established that will meet financial obligations. Under these laws, thirty-five states now have 84,408,000 acres in organized drainage enterprises representing an investment of $680,-732,000 and an annual maintenance and operating cost in 1929 of $7,-605,000. This huge development is distributed through 67,927 organized drainage enterprises. (Table 1.)

Drainage data for the thirteen states reporting no organized enterprises are probably only approximate.[1] It is likely that such drainage is confined chiefly to land in farms and has been provided by individual owners. In 1930, approximately 1,380,000 acres of farm land were provided with drainage in these states. (See Figs. 2 and 3.) Some of these states have large areas of drainable land.

Method of Organization. As previously stated, the drainage laws of the various states are designed to meet the specific needs existing in the states, and hence the method of organizing of drainage enterprises varies accordingly. In sixteen states the legislatures have conferred the authority upon county, district, or circuit courts; in fifteen states the authority to organize drainage districts is vested in the governing body of the county in which the larger portion of the proposed enterprise is located; in two states the clerk of the superior court is vested

[1] The states not reporting organized drainage enterprises are Alabama, Connecticut, Delaware, Maine, Maryland, Massachusetts, New Hampshire, New Jersey, New York, Pennsylvania, Rhode Island, Virginia, and West Virginia.

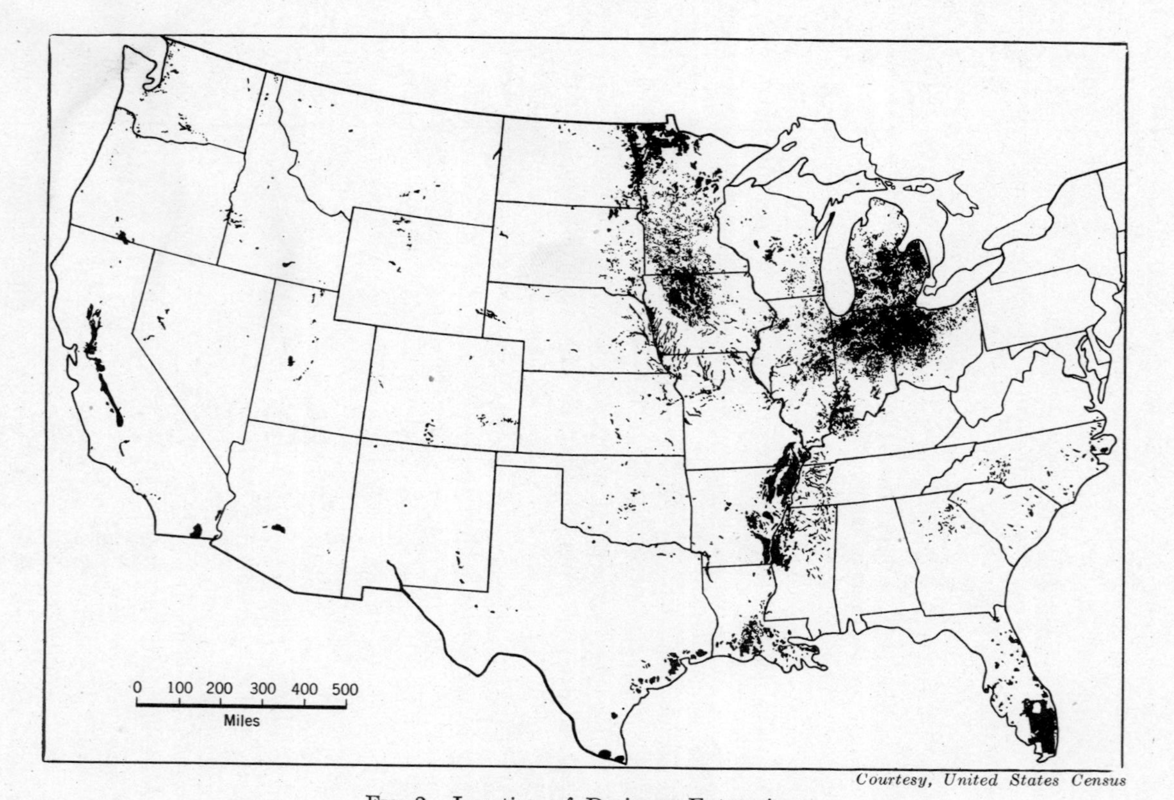

Courtesy, United States Census

FIG. 2. Location of Drainage Enterprises.

Two-thirds of the land in drainage enterprises, in the thirty-five drainage states, is north of the Missouri and Ohio rivers.

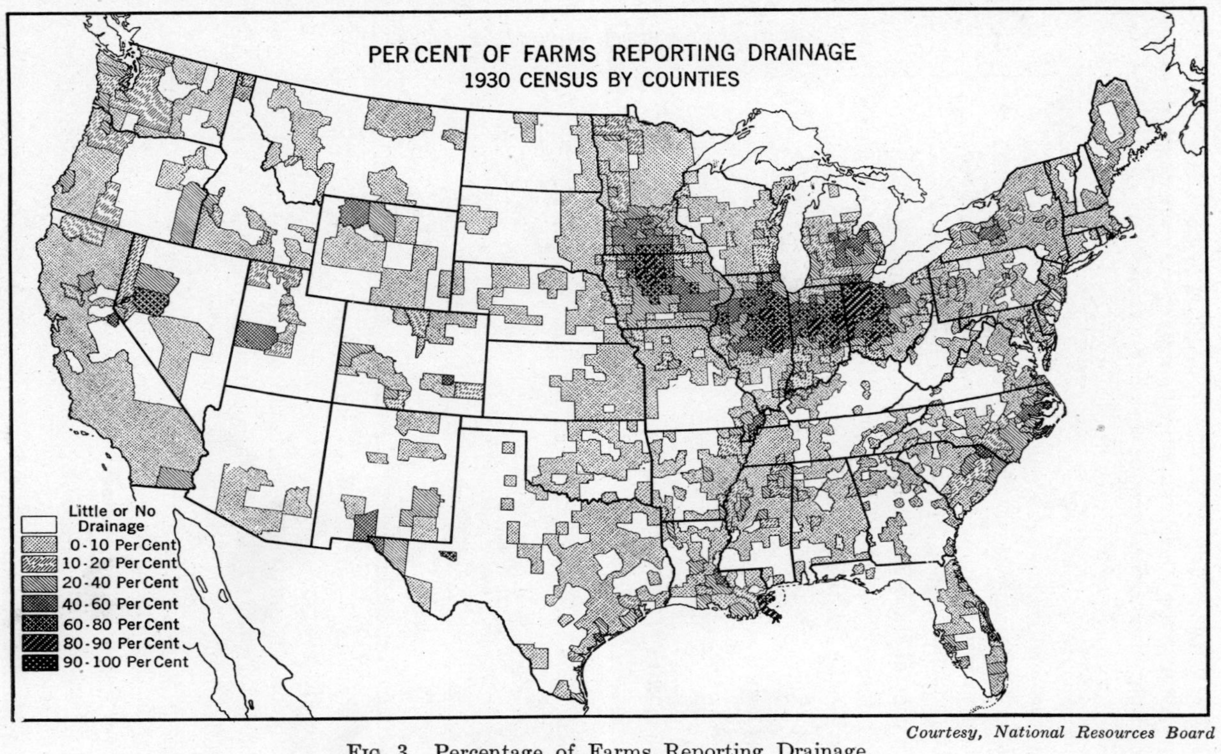

Courtesy, National Resources Board

FIG. 3. Percentage of Farms Reporting Drainage.

with the authority, and boards of drainage commissioners have jurisdiction in the two remaining states out of the thirty-five having organized drainage laws. In 1930 approximately 95 per cent of all enterprises were either organized drainage districts having their own independent officers, or state, county, or township enterprises under control of public officials.

Of the 84,408,000 acres in organized drainage enterprises in the thirty-five drainage states, 56 per cent was developed by the county method of organization. These enterprises represented 42 per cent of the capital investment. This type of organization is dominant in the north central states and is more common in those states where systematic drainage first began. It is probably best adapted to small enterprises having relatively simple drainage problems (See Table 2.)

TABLE 2

PERCENTAGE OF ACREAGE IN ENTERPRISES ACCORDING TO METHOD OF ORGANIZATION (35 STATES)

Groups of States	District	County	Township	Irrigation Enterprises	Commercial Development	Individually Owned	State Projects
South Atlantic.......	97.5	0.3			0.6	1.6	
West south central...	93.1	1.5	0.4	0.8	0.1	4.1	
East south central...	85.2	14.0				0.7	*
Pacific..............	51.8	3.8		41.8	0.1	1.9	*
Mountain...........	41.2			56.9	0.4	1.5	
East north central...	16.5	83.0	0.4		*	0.1	*
West north central...	16.4	79.7	*	1.1	*	0.1	2.6
35 drainage states....	38.6	56.3	0.2	3.1	0.1	0.9	0.7

* Less than 0.1 per cent.

The drainage district type of organization contains 38 per cent of all land in drainage enterprises and has more than half of the capital investment. This method is well adapted to large enterprises that must establish long-time credit, with complex drainage problems that may be better handled for the whole planned area, and with one set of officers who may carry on the enterprise. This is the dominant type in the major drainage enterprises of the South.

In the Pacific and mountain states, many of the drainage enterprises are associated with irrigation districts, irrigation and drainage being coextensive in area.

Individually owned drainage enterprises are wide-spread and vary from the installations on a small farm to those of several thousand acres. The larger individually owned enterprises are in the cotton belt of the South, where many cotton plantations containing more than 500 acres are privately drained. The largest acreage of individually owned drainage projects is in Louisiana.

Growth of Organized Drainage. Although drainage of wet lands on a small scale was undertaken early in our history, the era of rapid expansion occurred during the years 1905-1919. Approximately four-fifths of the total acreage of land in drainage enterprises was added to the total during that fifteen-year period. The spur of high land values and high prices for agricultural products stimulated rapid development and over-expansion, resulting in a vast acreage of unoccupied and undeveloped land. Decrease in land values and value of agricultural products has left a very small market for the unsettled drainage areas and a corresponding high cost of maintenance upon the land occupied by farms. Though many of these enterprises were ill-advised, and should not have been undertaken at the time, they do not represent a complete loss as the land that is suitable for occupancy will ultimately be settled. It is estimated that 7,987,000 acres are now available for settlement. Approximately three-fourths of the entire area was classified as improved land in 1930. Approximately 24 per cent was classed as idle, 9 per cent as unfit for crops owing to inadequate drainage, 14 per cent as woodland, and about 11 per cent as unimproved. Most of the idle land was swamp land in Wisconsin, north-

TABLE 3

GROWTH AND CONDITION OF LAND IN DRAINAGE ENTERPRISES, 1930

Date of Organization	Land		Land in Enterprises				
			Condition of Land				Land Available for Settlement
			Improved Land		Woodland	Other Unimproved Land	
All Enterprises	Acres 84,408,093	Per Cent 100	Acres 63,514,081	Per Cent 75.2	Acres 11,310,402	Acres 9,583,610	Acres 7,987,171
Before 1870...	919,117	1.1	827,666	90.1	86,247	5,204	992
1870–1879....	2,516,942	3.0	2,319,680	92.2	172,517	24,745	1,583
1880–1889....	6,052,807	7.2	5,626,614	93.0	337,306	88,887	18,738
1890–1899....	5,957,503	7.0	5,389,675	90.5	362,512	205,316	9,123
1900–1904....	7,665,823	9.1	6,533,061	85.2	665,857	466,905	192,428
1905–1909....	18,328,017	21.7	11,877,969	64.8	2,569,401	3,880,647	2,562,423
1910–1914....	16,448,377	19.5	11,850,168	72.0	2,519,243	2,078,966	1,822,444
1915–1919....	15,802,902	18.7	11,088,824	70.2	2,898,877	1,815,201	2,016,905
1920–1924....	7,428,179	8.8	5,431,945	73.1	1,304,536	691,698	1,101,174
1925–1929....	3,288,426	3.9	2,568,479	78.1	393,906	326,041	261,361

ern Minnesota, and the South. In such land, settlement advances slowly after the principal drains are constructed.

Drainage in the Great Lakes. Reclamation of wet lands has been carried on extensively in the Great Lakes states. The retreating ice of the Wisconsin stage of glaciation distributed the glacial drift very unevenly, thus forming many large and small depressed areas without natural drainage lines. In some of these undrained depressions extensive swamps developed, especially in northern Minnesota and Wisconsin; in others the glacial till, which varied from heavy, stiff clay, to sandy loam, remained too wet for agricultural use without artificial drainage.

A large portion of northwestern Minnesota was covered by glacial Lake Agassiz. In general this ancient lake bed varies from very flat to gently rolling land with shallow depressions and was originally largely forest covered. However, there are also many much deeper depressions of vast areal extent in the accumulated waters of which there developed great peat swamps or "muskegs." The reclamation of these swamps required drainage operations on a large scale, and here we find the only state drainage projects in the north central states. Drainage was stimulated by the high prices for land and agricultural products. Similar swamp conditions and ill-advised drainage efforts are found in the peat and sandy soil swamps of central Wisconsin, where some of the enterprises have been abandoned and the area returned to swamp. The deep peat soil was found to be poor for agricultural purposes because of deficiency in certain mineral plant foods essential to successful crop production. Peat soils are also susceptible to killing frost during the growing season and to fire during the dry season. Such peat fires destroy the humus covering, which usually necessitates more drainage, and increase the difficulties of the farmer. These conditions have led to tax delinquency and reversion of some of the land to the state or counties. In the flat, fertile lands of the Red River Valley drainage is needed over extensive areas of farm land. Development of drainage, however, must be associated with conservation of ground water for stream maintenance and domestic purposes. The area presents a complex and interesting problem.

About two-thirds of the land in drainage enterprises in the thirty-five drainage states is north of the Missouri and Ohio Rivers. Exclusive of large swamp areas in Wisconsin and northern Minnesota, most of the land was in farms before regularly organized drainage enterprises were established. With the exception of the state drainage

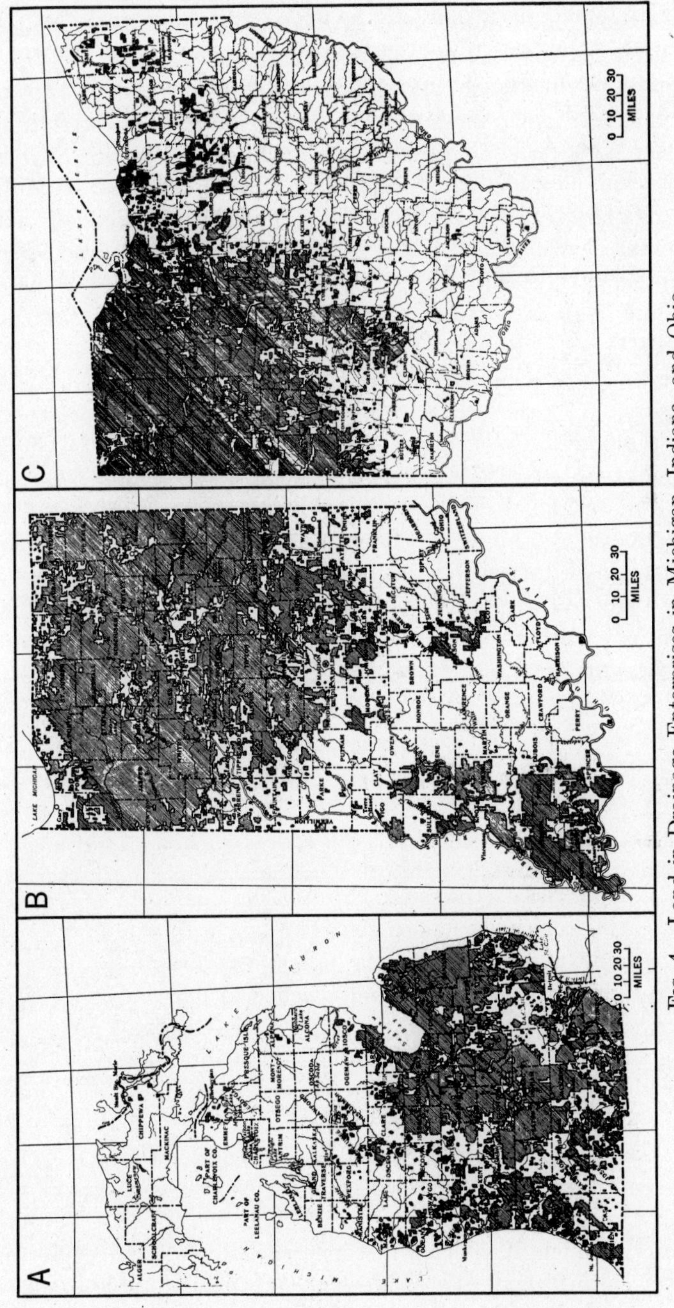

Fig. 4. Land in Drainage Enterprises in Michigan, Indiana, and Ohio.

Michigan has 25 per cent of its land area in drainage enterprises, Indiana 44 per cent, and Ohio 31 per cent. After United States Census.

projects in northern Minnesota, most of the enterprises are small compared to those in the southern states. The east north central section has approximately 95 per cent of all the drainage enterprises less than 100 acres in size, and about the same proportion of those between 100 and 200 acres. The four states of Minnesota, Indiana, Michigan, and Ohio have approximately 39,000,000 acres in drainage enterprises. A high percentage of the drained land is improved. Much of the unimproved land is included in the peat and sandy soil swamp areas of northern Minnesota and Wisconsin (Table 4). Most of the northern

TABLE 4

Distribution and Status of Drainage Enterprises

	No. of Enterprises	Acres in Enterprise	Percentage of total Acreage	Average Acreage in Enterprise	Percentage Improved	Acreage Available for Settlement
East north central..	57,462	33,485,000	39.7	1,196	89.3	249,100
West north central..	7,565	23,690,000	28.1	3,863	78.0	1,759,300
South Atlantic.....	369	6,941,000	8.2	22,682*	17.5	2,659,100
East south central..	751	4,167,000	5.0	5,840	64.4	740,100
West south central..	1,177	11,340,000	13.4	10,971	62.0	2,322,500
Mountain states....	218	1,969,000	2.3	9,051	86.5	150,100
Pacific states.......	385	2,812,000	3.3	7,533	88.4	106,100
35 drainage states..	67,927	84,408,093	100.	1,892	75,2	7,987,100

*Deduct unreclaimed area of Everglades Drainage District and the average is 14,710 acres.

half of Indiana, the northwestern third of Ohio, and the southern part of Michigan is relatively flat or gently rolling with extensive areas of ancient glacial lake beds. Here the practice of draining excess water from farm land is wide-spread. Indiana has 44 per cent of its area in drainage enterprises, Ohio 31 per cent, and Michigan 25 per cent. Drainage in this area has been installed primarily to improve the yield on land already in farms. A similar reason accounts for the drainage in north central Iowa and much of the land of central Illinois. These states have approximately 2,000,000 acres available for settlement in the present drainage enterprises, which represents an area nearly three-fourths as large as the state of Connecticut. This constitutes a large reserve much of which will come into use as the need for additional agricultural land arises. Most of the crops suitable to the latitude may be produced upon these lands.

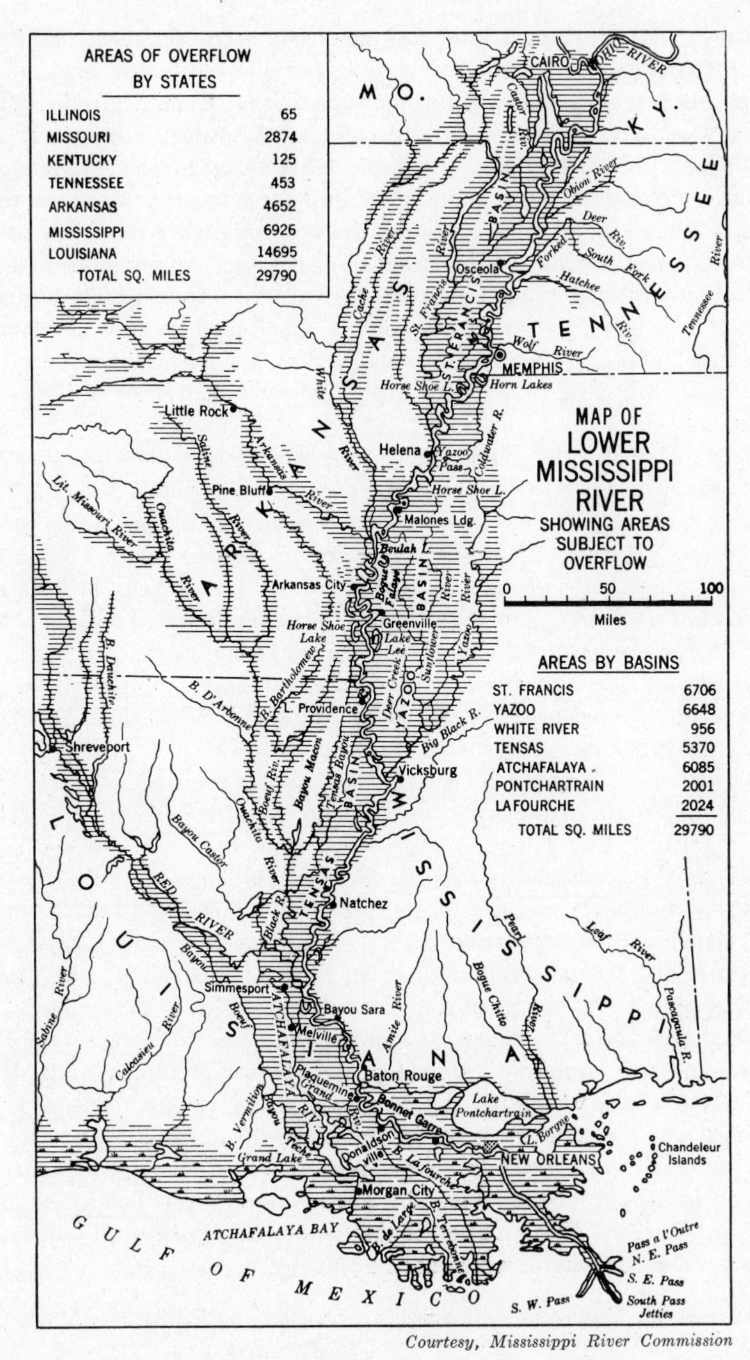

Courtesy, Mississippi River Commission

FIG. 5. The Lower Mississippi Basin Flood Control and Reclamation Area.

The primary purpose is flood control. However, prevention of floods, combined with drainage, will make permanently available a large acreage of fertile agricultural land.

Lower Mississippi Basin Region. South of the mouth of the Ohio River is a vast area of overflow alluvial river bottom and delta land. Much of this land will be highly productive when drained. Other areas should be reserved as wildlife refuges. At present 60 per cent of the population of the Basin live in the Alluvial Valley and 40 per cent on the uplands. A much larger population can be supported on the fertile lowlands and on a far higher standard of living than now prevails, if adequate flood protection and drainage are provided and a better system of land tenure established for the settler. About a third of the land now protected from flood is unoccupied because of inadequate drainage. Drainage is essential, not only for agricultural use of the land, but also to prevent water pollution and provide sewage disposal.

The reclamation of these lands is associated with development of navigation on the Mississippi River and with protection from floods. Before the construction of levees, approximately 20,000,000 acres were subject to overflow. This is about equal in area to South Carolina. About three-fourths of the area is swamp land, timber land, and lakes. Less than a fourth is now used for any form of cultivation. Work now in progress under the Flood Control Project authorized by Act of Congress in 1928 will give flood protection to approximately 13,000,000 acres. This leaves 7,000,000 acres subject to inundation at intervals varying from one year in three to one year in fifteen. Of the 7,000,000 acres, approximately 4,400,000 are situated in the low lands below the mouth of the Arkansas River on the west side of the Mississippi River, and will receive the same protection from the existing levees at the heads of the basins as heretofore. These 4,400,000 acres comprise the land embraced in the Boeuf and Atchafalaya floodways and the Red River backwater area. Other areas which are subject to overflow and which are not likely to be reclaimed include (1) the backwater areas at the mouths of the Arkansas, White, Yazoo, and St. Francis rivers; (2) the narrow strip of land lying between the highlands and the river and extending from above Memphis to Baton Rouge on the east side of the river where the amount of land reclaimed would not justify levee construction; (3) a strip of land about five miles in width extending from near Cairo to near New Madrid on the west bank of the river. This area is likely to be flooded about once in ten years.[1] Reclamation of these lands for agricultural purpose, as a primary objective, would not be justified.

[1] Data on the Mississippi Basin supplied by courtesy of Charles Senour, Senior Engineer, Mississippi River Commission.

Along the Ohio River the maximum area ever covered by flood waters is about 550,000 acres. It is unlikely that such an extensive flood, which would cover much upland, will occur more frequently than once in a century. However, the river bottom lands are flooded at least once a year. These lowlands include swamp and marsh land that might be reclaimed for cultivation if there was urgent need for more agricultural land. The reclaimable area, however, is estimated to be considerably less than 55,000 acres. It is estimated that more than 90 per cent of the overflow land is now under cultivation.[1]

GAINS AND LOSSES FROM DRAINAGE

The gains that may be expected from drainage lie chiefly in the increased value of the land, the value of the products to be obtained from that drained land, the ability of the land to provide homes and to sustain an increased population, and in matters that may be classed as public welfare such as elimination of insect-infested swamps. It is well known that swamp lands are a favorite breeding ground for the malaria-carrying mosquito. From the standpoint of health the elimination of the disease-carrying mosquito from regions of human habitation would be of inestimable value.

Present drainage enterprises in the thirty-five drainage states have cost an average of $8 an acre. The highest acre cost has been in the Pacific ($27) and mountain ($14) states; the lowest, in the east north central states ($6) and in the west south central states ($6). It is estimated that under present conditions about a third of our drainable lands may be reclaimed at a cost of about $30 an acre. If we assume such reclaimed land to have an average value of $60 an acre, the total value becomes a huge figure. Even though it seems idle to speculate in such matters, yet it is interesting to contemplate the average annual crop production that might be expected from these lands and the millions of people who might find homes upon them. It is, however, equally idle to assume that this vast acreage of wet land will be reclaimed in the near future. The present supply of agricultural land usable without further drainage is adequate for present needs. No new enterprise should be undertaken without the assurance that the benefits to be derived from drainage justify the cost. Further, losses from drainage of some of the swamp areas may be greater than any gain. Some of the areas already drained were formerly splendid wildlife refuges and breeding grounds. Their present agricultural use is insig-

[1] Data supplied by courtesy W. I. Gregory, Principal Engineer, United States Engineers Office, Louisville, Kentucky.

nificant in comparison with their value in their natural state. It should also be borne in mind that some of these areas have a high recreational value for the hunter and the nature lover, and provide excellent plant and animal habitats for scientific study.

SUMMARY

When the pressure of population upon the productive lands becomes sufficiently severe, either in the nation as a whole or locally, the drainable wet lands of the United States will come into use. There should be a genuine need for such land before extensive reclamation is authorized. At present these lands represent one of the great potential assets of the nation. The development of such lands in other countries, as in Netherlands, indicates what may be done and the crop production that may be expected. The 75,000,000 acres of drainable land is nine times the entire area of the Netherlands, including its drained and undrained area. The assumption that any wet, swamp, or marsh land is suitable for agriculture when drained has led to the undertaking of many unwise drainage projects, and consequent disappointment and loss. Some of these enterprises should be abandoned and the swamp land utilized for more appropriate purposes such as forests, wildlife refuges, or marsh hay land. The present enterprises include an acreage available for settlement nearly as large as the estimated needs for the next quarter century. Further developments should be based on clearly demonstrated need for cropland, public welfare service such as maintenance of health and prevention of floods, ample evidence that the probable returns from drainage will warrant the investment, and careful consideration of the possibility that the wet lands, especially swamp lands, may not really be worth more to man if left in their natural state.

CHAPTER IX

THE AGRICULTURAL PROSPECT[1]

By O. E. Baker

Senior Agricultural Economist, U.S.D.A.

In times of cataclysmic change like the present it requires courage —or foolhardiness—to forecast the future. But the problems that are arising are urgent, and the first step toward solving them is to determine the trends, measure the magnitude of the factors involved, and venture to estimate the consequences according to certain apparently reasonable assumptions.

The agricultural situation has many aspects, but only four will be considered in this chapter, and each of these necessarily very briefly:

1. The prospect for consumption of farm products.
2. The prospect for production of farm products.
3. The prospect for standard of living among rural people.
4. The prospect for rural education and culture.

THE PROSPECT FOR CONSUMPTION OF FARM PRODUCTS

The prospect for consumption of farm products is considered first because production is not likely to depart far from consumption demands during any long period, and because it is possible to forecast consumption in the near future with more confidence than any of the other three aspects of the subject noted above. The prospect for consumption of farm products depends on the future population of the nation, on consumption per person, and on net exports or imports. Of these three factors by far the most important in the future, as in the past, will be, doubtless, the number of people in the nation.

[1] This chapter consists in large part of excerpts from official reports and from public addresses published or mimeographed by various institutions. It is, therefore, recognized by the publishers of this book as not copyrighted, and may be quoted from freely, but it is hoped that in making quotations the source will be referred to.

See Appendix I for data on the agricultural resources of the United States.

The Population Prospect. The population of the United States can be predicted for a few decades to come with more certainty than any other factor affecting the agricultural prospect, partly because over 90 per cent of the people who will be living in the nation in 1940, and about 75 per cent of those who will be living in 1950, are living today; and the number who will die each year can be predicted quite closely by applying tables of expectation of life, such as are used by

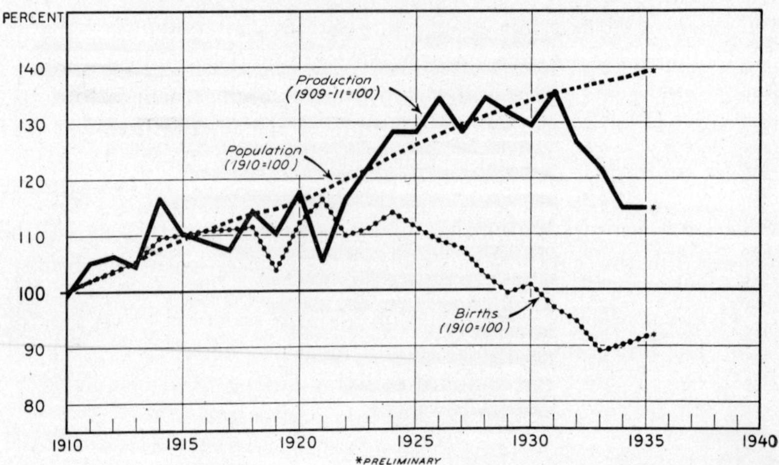

FIG. 1.

The progress of population growth was remarkably steady until recently, only the influenza epidemic of 1918, which affected both births and deaths, causing a waver in the line. But in recent years the decline in births, supplemented by the restrictions on immigration, has caused population to increase much less rapidly. Agricultural production, on the other hand, has fluctuated notably. From 1910 to 1915 it increased as rapidly as population; from 1915 to 1921 the trend of production was about horizontal; from 1921 to 1926 a probably unprecedented increase occurred; from 1926 to 1931 the trend was horizontal again, and since 1931 the trend has been rapidly downward. This recent decrease is attributable mostly to extraordinary drought, but it seems not unlikely that soil erosion and depletion of organic matter, as well as of the minerals essential to fertility of the soil, are exerting an influence on crop and pasture yields. But far more important than the recent decline in agricultural production was the 21 per cent decline in births from 1924 to 1934. The rise in births in 1934 and 1935 is associated with the increase in marriages in 1933 and 1934, after the depression decline. This rise in births, like that of marriages, is probably transitory.

insurance companies. Relative to immigration, the second factor affecting the population prospect, there is less certainty; but in view of the fact that it required 50 years to change the attitude of the American people toward immigration, and that there is no serious suggestion at present of a reversal in this attitude, nor is there likely to be so long as unemployment persists, it seems safe to dismiss this factor of immigration in considering the population prospect during the next decade or two. The third and most important factor in the population prospect is the number of births. As the future trends relative to births are less certain than those relative to deaths or immigration it is desirable to consider the matter more fully.

Since 1921 fewer children have been born each year in the United States than in the year preceding, with five exceptions—1922, 1923,

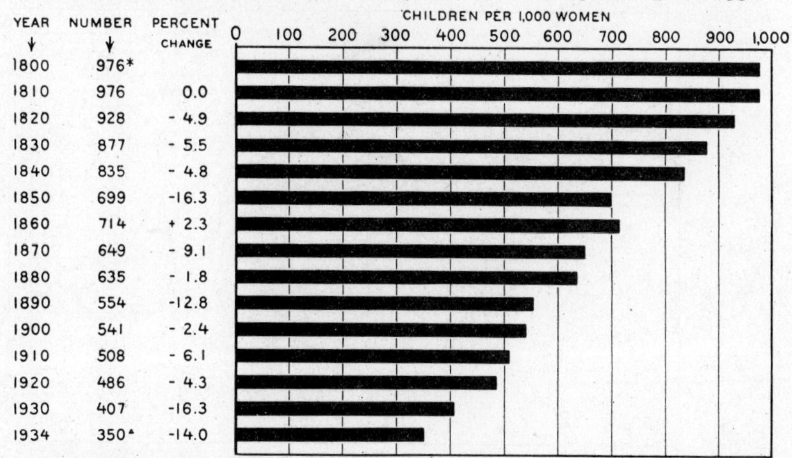

U. S. Department of Agriculture *Neg.* 27323A *Bureau of Agricultural Economics*

FIG. 2.

The birth rate, as measured by the ratio of children under 5 to women of child-bearing age, has been decreasing in the United States for more than a century. From 1920 to 1930 the decline was over twice as rapid as in previous decades, except those ending in 1850, 1870, and 1890, when it is evident there was an abnormal under-enumeration of young children. From 1930 to 1934 the decline was almost as great as in any previous decade. The significant fact shown by the graph is that the declining birth rate is a long-time trend, and that the rate of decline has become more rapid in recent years.

1930, and 1934, and, probably, 1935. In 1921, the peak year in number of births in the nation's history, nearly 3,000,000 children were born, and in 1924 almost as many, but in 1935 probably about 2,300,000. The decline in births since 1924 has been at the rate of, roughly, 60,000 a year, and this decline has persisted in prosperity as well as depression (Fig. 1). However, from 1930 to 1933 the decrease averaged 100,000 a year. This more rapid decline was associated with the decline in marriages during the early years of the depression, but in 1933 marriages increased 100,000, many of these having been postponed during the depression, and in 1934 births increased 40,000. This increase in births persisted until July, 1935, when the decline was, apparently, resumed.

The enrolment in the first six grades of the public schools is now declining. In the first grade the decrease has been about 100,000 a year for several years past. A similar decrease is extending into the upper grades. Although the number of births started to decline in 1922

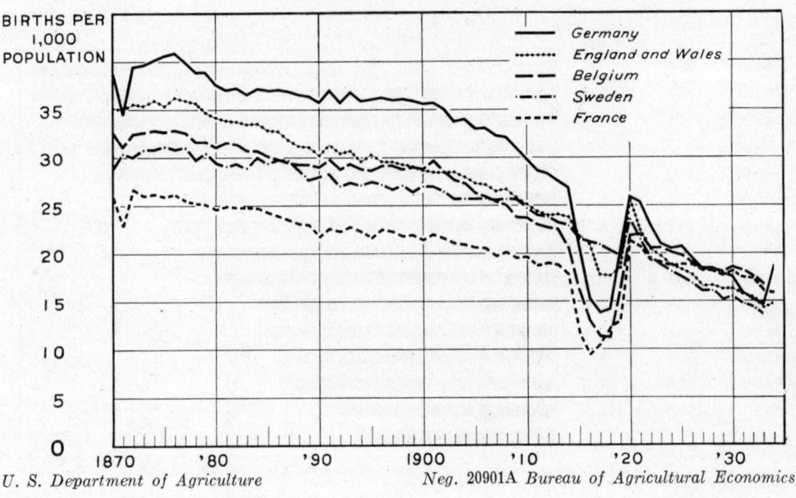

FIG. 3.

Birth rates are declining in Northwestern Europe, which has hitherto provided the principal export market for American farm products. This trend has persisted wherever industrialism and urbanization are important. In Great Britain the population will reach a maximum probably in 1940, and soon after will begin to decline. In Germany the maximum may be reached a few years later, and, unless the birth rate rises, the decline later will be rapid, since 10 adults are having only 7 children. At this rate Germany in a century will have about one-third the present population, unless there is immigration from abroad. But in 1934, the birth rate in Germany rose notably, doubtless in part as a result of increased marriages after the depression and of decreased abortions. Now it is declining again.

(but not notably until 1925), the birth rate has been declining for more than a century in the United States and for more than a half century in northwestern Europe (Figs. 2 and 3). For many decades the increasing number of females of child-bearing age, the heritage of the higher birth rate of a generation previous, and of immigration, more than counterbalanced the declining birth rate.

Several causes have been assigned to this declining birth rate, such as the disillusionment that followed the World War, in association with the high cost of living in the cities, the widening desire for higher education for the children with associated considerations of prudence, the cravings for luxury, amusements, and social position, which only a rigid restriction on the size of the family can provide in many cases, and, more recently, uncertainty as to one's job or income. Other influences sometimes mentioned include the changes in religious authority and the spread of information as to methods of birth control. But back of it all lie a philosophy of life, and individual judgments as to what is worth while. And back of the philosophy of life lies the constant pressure of an economic system. As with the restrictions on immigration, there are no signs of a reversal of the attitude of the American people toward the size of the family, and the most reasonable assumption seems to be that the birth rate will continue to decline for at least a decade. Indeed, the trends in England and Germany, where the decline in number of births began in 1909 and still continues, suggest that the decline in the United States may continue for 15 years more and perhaps much longer.

But not enough children are now being born in the United States to maintain the present population permanently, and only a rise in the birth rate or relaxation of the restrictions on immigration, associated with opportunity for employment, can prevent a declining population as the large number of middle-aged people today—the heritage of the higher birth rate and heavier immigration of the past—grow old and die. The facts in the population situation should be faced. The outstanding fact is this, that throughout the European sphere of civilization, the birth rate is declining rapidly. Scarcely less significant is the fact that in Great Britain, France, Belgium, Germany, Austria, and the Scandinavian nations, as well as in the United States, not enough children are now being born to maintain permanently their present populations.

In Italy, Spain, eastern Europe, and Russia there is still a large excess of births over the number necessary to maintain population stationary, but in these countries also the trend of the birth rate is downward. In Japan, the declining birth rate, particularly in the cities, suggests that a stationary population of less than 80,000,000 will be reached within 30 years.[1] But in India, despite the abject poverty, population continues to increase at an amazing rate; and in China the increase is prevented only by the wars, famines, and pestilences that Malthus described.

It appears that the modern urban industrial and commercial system, with its economic and social corollaries, now tends to reduce the birth

[1] See Uyeda, Teijiro, "Future of the Japanese Population," published by the Japanese Branch, Institute of Pacific Relations, Tokyo, 1933.

rate below the level of population maintenance, or at least is associated with such a trend, as universally as the self-suffering agricultural system is associated with a birth rate that would induce a rapidly increasing population, except for the restraint exercised by the checks that Malthus described. In every state of the United States, without exception, the ratio of children under 5 years of age in 1930 to women

NUMBER OF CHILDREN UNDER 5 YEARS OF AGE PER 1,000 WOMEN 15 TO 45 YEARS OF AGE ON APRIL 1, 1930, URBAN COMPARED WITH RURAL POPULATION IN UNITED STATES

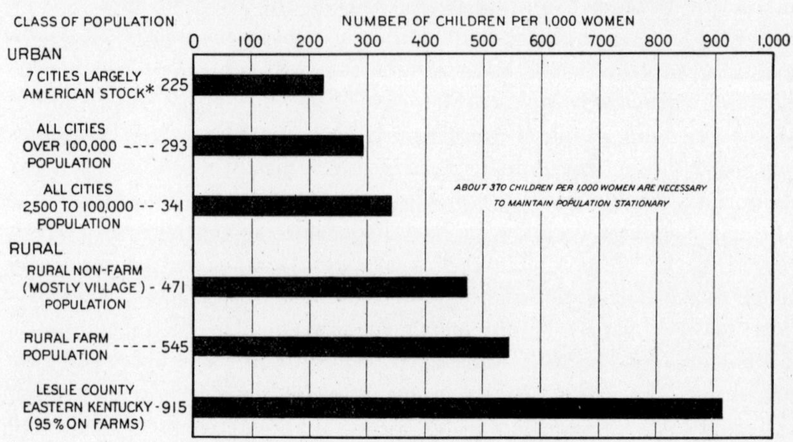

*PORTLAND (OREGON), SAN FRANCISCO, LOS ANGELES, KANSAS CITY, ST. LOUIS, NASHVILLE, AND ATLANTA

U. S. Department of Agriculture *Neg. 25167 Bureau of Agricultural Economics*

FIG. 4.

About 370 children under 5 years of age per 1,000 women 15 to 45 years of age (child-bearing age) are required to maintain our population stationary at the present expectation of life of 61 years. In 1930 the seven cities largely of American stock, represented in the top bar of the graph, lacked, therefore, about 40 per cent of having enough children to maintain their population permanently without accessions from outside, and all cities of over 100,000 population had a deficit of over 20 per cent, while the smaller cities had a deficit of nearly 8 per cent. On the other hand, the rural non-farm (mostly village and suburban) population had a surplus of over 25 per cent, and the farm population a surplus of nearly 50 per cent. In 1930 urban deficit and rural surplus about balanced. Now there are no longer enough children being born to maintain the population of the nation permanently stationary.

15 to 45 years of age was smaller in the urban population than in the rural; and this is true also of every nation of Europe that collects birth statistics, likewise of Canada, Australia, New Zealand, and Japan. Moreover, in every state in the United States, except New Jersey, the ratio of children to women was lower in the large cities, that is, those over 100,000 population, than in the smaller cities. In the large cities the number of children is now (1936) only two-thirds to three-fourths sufficient to maintain population permanently stationary without accessions from outside; in the smaller cities the deficit is 10 to 15 per cent; but in the rural non-farm (mostly village) population there is a

25 to 30 per cent surplus, and in the farm population a 40 to 50 per cent surplus (Fig. 4).

The fundamental cause of this wide difference which has developed between the urban and rural population with reference to reproduction of the race is, in the author's opinion, that agriculture is a family affair, whereas in urban industry and commerce the individual is the economic unit. In agriculture the wife is almost essential to success, and the children can help with the work, with benefit usually to their health and character, and almost pay their way from 10 years of age onward. In urban industry and commerce, on the other hand, the wife generally contributes little to the family income, unless she is employed outside the home, in which case it is difficult to raise a family. Moreover, many children are a heavy load for most urban fathers to carry in climbing the ladder of success. It costs probably three times as much to raise and educate a child in the city as it does on the farm. The social code, if such it may be called, which is characteristic of the people in the cities within the European sphere of civilization, and which grows out of the economic system, tends to promote depopulation. This social code is permeating the rural regions, and may induce in some of these regions a birth rate insufficient to maintain population stationary. This has already occurred in many departments of France.

Because this social code is based largely on the economic system, and because the ideals, habits, and customs of a people change slowly, it seems unlikely that the birth rate will rise in time to prevent a decrease in population in North America and the nations of northwestern Europe. Already England and Germany are almost at the peak of population—30 years after the decline started in number of births. Following a decade of nearly stationary numbers, the decrease in population will become increasingly rapid in these countries, unless births increase or there is heavy immigration from southern or eastern Europe or the Orient. There are now about 10 per cent fewer children under 5 years of age in the United States, and 8 per cent fewer 5 to 10 years of age, than when the census was taken in 1930; and it is possible, if not probable, that by 1940 there will be 20 per cent fewer children under 10 years of age than in 1930. This means fewer marriages a quarter century hence, and correspondingly fewer children in the second generation, if present attitudes persist. A change in ideals appears essential if modern civilization is to avoid a decline in population that may become rapid, persistent, and progressive.

However, the population of the United States will continue to increase for at least 10 years, probably 15 years, possibly 25 years,

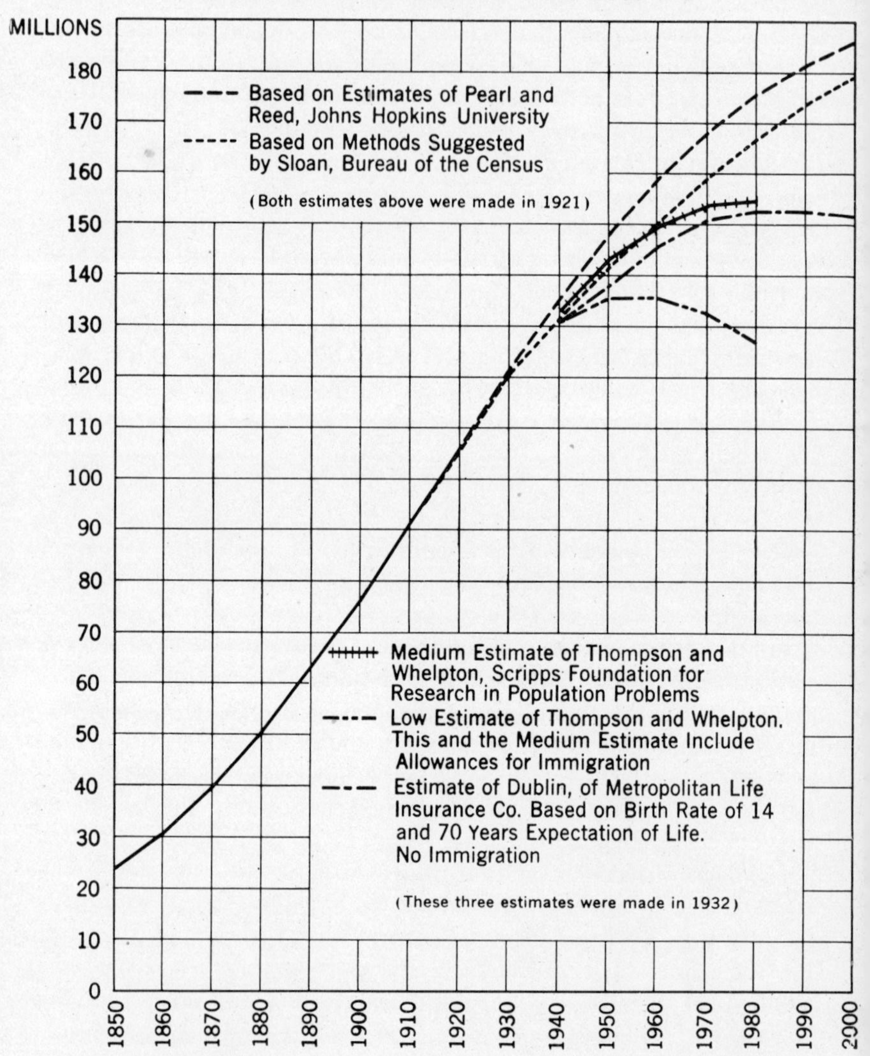

U. S. Department of Agriculture *Neg.* 10622 *Bureau of Agricultural Economics*

FIG. 5.

Thirteen years ago Professors Pearl and Reed, of the Johns Hopkins University, on the basis of population trends, estimated that the United States was slowly approaching a stationary population of nearly 200,000,000, to be reached about the year 2020. But the rapid decline in the birth rate since 1921 indicates a maximum population of 135,000,000 to 140,000,000 about 1950, unless the immigration laws are changed. Moreover, unless the birth rate rises or immigration increases, a decline in the nation's population will set in a few years later. However, the prospect is that the population of the nation will not diverge more than 10 per cent from the present number within the next 25, possibly 40, years.

principally because the large number of middle-aged people must first grow old and die. The people who are old now were born 70 or 80 years ago, when the population of the nation was much smaller, and although the birth rate was much higher than at present, births were less numerous. But population was then increasing rapidly, and almost every year more children were born than in the year before. We now have, therefore, more old people each year than the year before. The increase in persons over 65 years of age was 34 per cent between 1920 and 1930, and such an increase will continue for several decades to come.

The prospect is that soon after 1950, possibly before, population will become practically stationary, and by 1960 or 1965 it will have started to decline (Fig. 5). The people of the nation should look forward to an increase of population between now and the peak year considerably less than that which has occurred since the World War, and then a decrease which will accelerate at about the same rate as the present increase, provided, of course, that the birth rate does not rise or immigration increase greatly. By 1975, or perhaps earlier, the population of the nation may have fallen to or below the present level. For a third to a half century to come, therefore, the population of the nation seems likely to remain within 10 per cent of what it is at present. This may be compared with an increase of 16 per cent between 1920 and 1930.

But although the total population of the nation may not change greatly for a third to half a century, there will be great changes in the number of children and of old people, and there may be great changes in the number of people living in rural and in urban territory.

At 2.5 acres of crop land harvested per person, practically the figure for average domestic per capita consumption during the last decade (see later discussion), the nation will need by 1940 about 330,000,000 acres of harvested crops, and if present exports are maintained about 30,000,000 more acres to produce these exports. This total of 360,000,000 acres is practically the same as that reported by the census for 1929, but about 25,000,000 acres more than those harvested in 1935. When the peak of population is reached, probably soon after 1950, about 10,000,000 acres more than in 1940 would be needed, other factors remaining unchanged. Let us consider, therefore, the prospect for change in the next most important factor affecting the consumption of farm products, namely, diet and per capita consumption of cotton, flaxseed, tobacco, and other non-food farm products.

Consumption of Food Per Person. The need for farm land is greatly affected by the diet of a people. In the United States there are required to feed the average person at present not only about 2.5 acres of crops, but also about 6 acres of pasture, much of which, however, in the arid West is of low productivity. In Germany it requires only about an acre of cropland and 0.5 acre of pasture to feed the average person, in China only 0.5 acre of cropland and practically no pasture, and in Japan only 0.25 acre of cropland. The acre-yields of the crops are

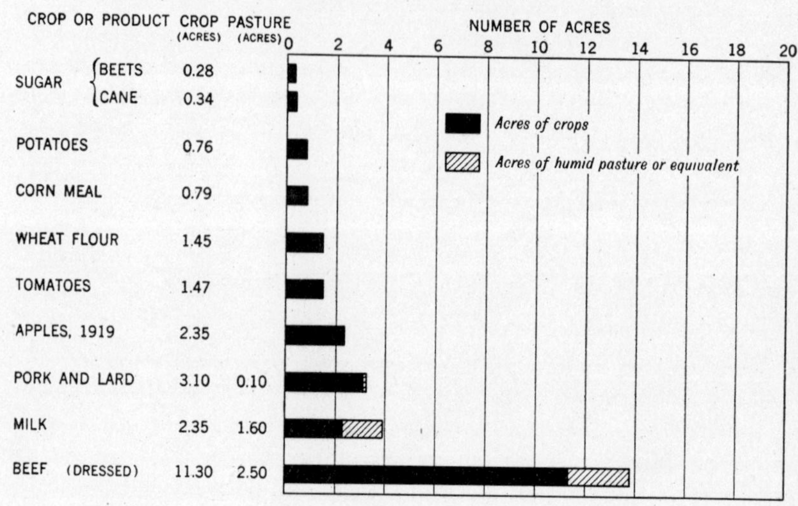

Fig. 6.

One-third of an acre in sugar crops produces about as many calories of food as 0.75 acre of potatoes or corn, or 1.5 acres of wheat or tomatoes. But, lacking protein and fat, a person could not live on sugar alone. The cereal diet would maintain health much longer. To maintain health permanently meat, milk, or other foods high in protein and fat should be added. These require 3 to 4 acres of crops and pasture to yield the same energy value in pork or milk, or about 14 acres devoted to beef production. In explanation of the title, the yearly per capita disappearance of foodstuffs in the United States is about 1,400,000 calories.

higher in Germany and Japan, possibly in China also, than in the United States; but the major cause of this difference in area required to feed a person is diet.

The difference is still more extreme if the various foodstuffs be considered. If it were possible for a man to live on sugar alone only 0.33 acre, at the average acre-yields in the United States, would be sufficient (provide enough calories) to feed a person for a year. Of corn or rice about 0.75 acre would be needed, and of wheat 1.5 acres (Fig. 6). But when the corn is converted into pork and lard, it requires nearly 600 pounds of corn to produce 100 pounds of hog, live weight; and the hog dresses out only about three-fourths edible products, but pork and associated lard have an average calory value per pound twice that of corn. Consequently over 3 acres of cropland plus a little pasturage are required to produce the equivalent food (calory) value in pork to that produced by 0.75 acre of corn. The dairy cow is even more economical than the hog in use of crop area required to produce human food, about

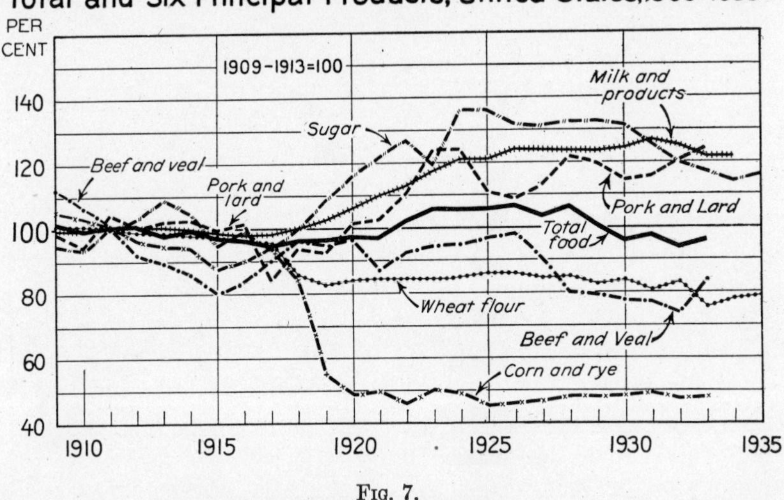

Fig. 7.

The World War restrictions, the Prohibition Amendment to the Constitution, the prosperity of the urban people during and after the War, and other influences worked significant changes in the diet of the American people. The per capita consumption of corn for human food apparently dropped one-half between 1911 and 1920, and of wheat about one-sixth mostly between 1917 and 1918; while the per capita consumption of sugar increased a third between 1918 and 1924 and of pork and lard about a fourth between 1919 and 1923. The curve for beef and veal shows a cycle 17 years in length, with a slightly downward trend, but the per capita consumption of milk and dairy products has been well maintained. Combining all the foods, it appears that normal acreage required for production of the diet was about as large per person prior to the depression as prior to the World War, but that there has been a slight downward trend since 1928. The meat and milk estimates are preliminary and subject to correction.

2.33 acres, but requires much more pasturage, (nearly 1.66 acres). To produce beef of equivalent food (calory) value, however, requires over 11 acres of crops and about 2.5 acres of pasture. It is clear that a large shift in diet from the cereals toward animal products, particularly beef, would involve a great increase in need for farm land.

Several outstanding changes in diet[1] have occurred since the beginning of this century, the most important of which from the standpoint of land use has been the decline in the use of cereal foods. The

[1] Most of this statement is taken from the *Report of the National Resources Board,* Washington, D. C., December, 1934, pp. 114-116.

total per capita consumption of all cereals apparently has decreased from about 380 pounds at the beginning of the century to 330 pounds before the World War and to 250 pounds in recent years. Most of this decrease has been in wheat flour (from 225 pounds about 1900 to 207 during 1909-1913, and 173 in recent years) and in corn meal (from about 100 pounds in 1900 to 66 pounds apparently during 1909-1913 and 26 pounds on the average for 1929-1933) (Fig. 7). Had the per capita consumption of 35 years ago persisted, over 20,000,000 more acres of cereals than at present would be needed to feed the American people, and had the pre-war per capita consumption been maintained, over 15,000,000 more acres would be required.

As a partial substitute for decreased cereal consumption the American people have increased the per capita consumption of sugar from about 60 pounds around the year 1900 to 78 pounds during 1909-1913 and about 98 pounds during the past decade. However, consumption fell to 95 pounds in 1932-1933. But since the area devoted to sugar crops in the United States is only about 1,000,000 acres (three-fourths of the sugar consumed coming from Cuba and the insular possessions), the increase in acreage required for the larger use of sugar is insignificant compared with that involved in the decline in use of cereals.

Nor is the decrease in per capita acreage required for cereal foods counterbalanced by an increase in use of meat. The per capita consumption of beef and veal at the beginning of the century, also the average during 1909-1913, was over 70 pounds, and of pork was about 60 pounds. Now these figures are practically reversed. Totaling the meats (including 5 to 7 pounds of lamb and mutton, but excluding lard and poultry), it appears that there has been a decline in per capita consumption from an average of about 140 pounds at the beginning of the century, also during the 5-year period preceding the World War, to about 134 pounds during the last 5 years. This decline, however, may be owing in large part to the lower stage in the cycle of production during the more recent period. The shift from beef toward pork has had relatively small influence on the crop acreage required to produce the meat supply but has notably reduced the pasturage needed.

A shift has occurred also from apples toward citrus fruits and grapes, but the total consumption of fruit per capita has remained more or less constant. However, the acreage required to produce the larger quantities of citrus fruit and grapes is probably not as large as would have been needed to produce enough apples to take care of the former larger consumption. The use of many kinds of vegetables has increased, but the acreage of land involved in this increase is very small and is little more than that involved in the decreased per capita consumption of potatoes.

Milk and its products, which constitute the most important food in the American diet, measured in crop acreage required for production as well as in value, apparently changed little in per capita consumption between the pre-war years and the pre-depression period. The per capita production of milk, practically all consumed in the United States, was about 777 pounds in 1909 and about 809 pounds in 1929, according to computations based on the census; but owing to the shift in date of enumeration from April 15 to April 1, it is probable that actual increase in production per capita was somewhat larger. Comparing the estimates of milk consumption for the 5-year periods centered on these two census years, it appears that the per capita increase was 4 to 6 per cent. This increase would require about 2,000,000 acres of cropland for its production. Prior to the depression there was an upward trend in urban consumption of milk per capita, but the trend was largely offset by the trend of migration of population from the country, where per capita milk consumption was high, to cities, where, in spite of the gradual increase, it was relatively low.

Butter consumption has fluctuated between 17 and 18 pounds per person for many years, except that during the World War and for a few years afterward it ranged from 14 to 16 pounds. Cheese consumption has ranged from 3 to 5 pounds and has been higher in recent years. Whole milk, cream, and ice-cream consumption per person increased in the cities during the decade of urban prosperity after the war. From 1923 to 1929 the increase was nearly 7 per cent. But from 1929 to 1933 consumption fell 5 per cent. It is to be hoped that with the return of prosperity the upward trend will be resumed. However, it must be recalled that beer now competes more or less with milk as a beverage.

Totaling the per capita crop acreage normally required to produce these and other foods (on the basis of the yield per acre during 1923-1932), it appears that there was no material change in aggregate acreage per person between the 5-year period preceding the World War and the 5-year period preceding the depression. Measured in calories of energy provided by the diet, the decline apparently was about 3 per cent from 1909-1913 to 1925-1929 and somewhat more during the depression. Most of the decline was accounted for by wheat and corn, with a little decline in milk and poultry products during the depression. Doubtless the principal explanation of the decline in cereal consumption, as compared with pre-war years, lies in the decreasing proportion of the people engaged in outdoor or manual labor. However, the important fact is the very slight change that has occurred in aggregate consumption of food per person. The farmers continue to produce in depression as well as in prosperity, and the people continue to consume.

Changes in Use of Non-food Products. The trend in per capita consumption of cotton in the United States remained remarkably steady for 30 years prior to the depression at about 25 pounds. Increasing industrial use counterbalanced the declining use for clothing. In the year 1931-1932 the per capita consumption fell to 18 pounds, but during the year 1932-1933 it rose to 23 pounds; in 1933-1934 it was 22 pounds, and in 1934-1935 only 20 pounds. The per capita consumption of tobacco increased little, if any, from the beginning of the century to the beginning of the World War, then rose during the War, decreased 20 per cent after the War, and remained more or less constant afterward until 1929. During the depression it declined, but is now rising. The per capita consumption of flaxseed increased greatly during the decade of urban prosperity and construction preceding the depression, but declined even more during the depression.

Aggregate Acreage per Capita. During the past decade (assuming the average acre-yield of each crop for the decade), it has required about 1.9 acres of crops per person to feed the people of the United States, including seed, but excluding the diminishing acreage needed to feed the horses and mules used in producing these farm products. To produce the non-food farm products consumed by the people has required 0.2 acre of crops per person. Domestic consumption of farm products per person, excluding the acreage needed to feed the horses and mules, has required, therefore, during the past decade, about 2.1 acres of crops. To this should be added about 0.4 acre per person (1933) required to produce feed for the horses and mules used in producing for domestic consumption. In other words, nearly 2.5 acres of crops are required, as previously noted, to provide farm products for the average American at present. If the number of horses and mules continues to decline, this acreage will, probably, decline; but should they increase the acreage will rise.[1]

Outlook for per Capita Consumption. Of the many factors that affect the diet of the people or the use of non-food farm products the

[1] The 1935 census returns, as interpreted by Mr. C. L. Harlan, of the United States Department of Agriculture, indicate that the number of work stock will continue to decline until late in 1937 or 1938, but that after that time there probably will be some increase.

only one that can be forecast with considerable confidence is the age of the people. Since 1930 the number of children under 5 has decreased about 10 per cent, and of children 5 to 10 years old about 8 per cent, as previously noted. Several recent studies indicate that children consume 50 to 100 per cent more milk per capita than adults. If by 1950 there are 15 per cent fewer persons under 20 years of age than in 1930, and 65 per cent more people over 65 years (the increase from 1920 to 1930 was 34 per cent, and a similar increase must continue for several decades), and assuming a per capita consumption for persons under 20 years of age 50 per cent greater than for those 20 to 65 years of age and 100 per cent greater than for those over 65 years, there may be a decrease in per capita consumption of milk during these 20 years, other factors remaining equal, of 3 to 4 per cent. It appears probable also that children eat more eggs than adults. On the other hand, the use of cereals and many other foods by children is probably considerably less than by adults. Since adults will constitute an increasing proportion of the population for at least several decades to come, it appears that the per capita consumption of cereals, sugar, meats, and the fats, and, to a less extent, of the vegetables and fruits, should continue to increase for some years after the population of the nation begins to decline. However, the income of the people and the prices of the foods may exert a much greater influence upon consumption than the changing age composition of the population.

Moreover, fewer children in the future should help many families to maintain a higher standard of living, including the use of the more expensive foods—meats, fruits, and vegetables. In particular, it is desirable that the use of milk increase. In a study of diets at four levels of income, the Bureau of Home Economics recommended the use, in both the "adequate diet at moderate cost" and the "liberal diet," of about twice the present per capita consumption of milk. There are millions of people in the cities, and millions more on farms, particularly in the South, who greatly need better food. Their health and efficiency undoubtedly could be materially improved by adequate nourishment.

Yet the fact remains that despite a declining size of family for many years in the past and advancing per capita income in the cities prior to 1930, consumption per capita of the meats, as a whole, and of the fruits did not increase, while the increase in use of milk apparently did little more than restore the loss that occurred during the World War years. During these years a much greater decline occurred in the use of the cereals, and if the proportion of the people engaged in outdoor employment continues to decrease, it is possible this trend may continue. It appears more likely, however, that the per capita consumption of the cereals has, during the past decade, reached a new level which will be fairly well maintained.

With reference to per capita consumption of farm products as a whole, as measured by per capita land requirements, the safest assumption appears to be that the remarkably stable conditions which have characterized the past quarter century will continue for a quarter century to come. The domestic consumption of farm products, should no great effort be made to alter the diet or influence the consumption of the non-food products, probably will vary primarily with the changes that may occur in the population of the nation. If the purchasing power of the mass of the workers should increase or decrease materially, however, the consumption outlook might be considerably altered.

The Prospect for Exports of Farm Products. The United States has three major agricultural regions peculiarly fitted by climate, soil, and the lay of the land for the production of a surplus of a certain farm product—cotton from the cotton belt, wheat from the wheat belt, and corn or animal products from the corn belt. The advantages of the cotton and corn belts are in several ways unique, and even the wheat belt has certain advantages over other wheat belts of the world. The farm products from these great surplus-producing regions were used to pay back the money the American people borrowed from Europe to build railroads and make other internal improvements in years past; and later, after the debts were paid, they stimulated, in part, the great credits to Europe, which Europe has found it difficult to repay. It is in these surplus regions, where commercial agriculture is dominant, that the decline in prices of farm products during the depression had such devastating effects.

The American cotton belt, China, and, possibly, Brazil, are the only large areas outside of the tropics which possess both temperature and rainfall conditions suitable for the production of cotton.[1] China imports large quantities of American cotton when prices are low. Production of cotton in Brazil is increasing but is yet small compared with that in the United States. In the river bottoms and in the western

[1] The main cotton-producing areas in Brazil lie north of the tropic of Capricorn and should be classed as tropical, but may become important in world trade. Egypt and Russian Turkestan are both dependent on irrigation for cotton production, and the irrigated area is relatively small in extent. In Argentina a little cotton is grown without irrigation, but the prospect for large production is yet uncertain.

portion of the United States cotton belt much of the soil is fertile, and in the eastern portion the normally high value per acre of the crop permits the practically universal use of fertilizers. Moreover, the cotton belt possesses a large supply of low-priced labor peculiarly adapted to the culture of this crop, and, in addition, the people of the South during a hundred years have accumulated a vast fund of experience and skill in both the production and marketing of the crop.

About half the cotton of the world is grown in the cotton belt, and, until recently, this region was holding its own in the world's markets. The exports of cotton from the United States constituted a larger proportion of the cotton exports from all cotton-producing countries during the crop year 1931-1932, also during 1932-1933, than before the depression, and as large a proportion as during the 5 years preceding the World War. Indeed, the exports in these two years were larger than in any previous years in the nation's history, except the crop years 1910, 1911, 1912, 1926, and, possibly, one or two other years. The foreign markets for cotton have not been so restricted by tariffs or quotas as they have for wheat, for the nations that import most of the American cotton do not grow the crop, with the exception of China. Nor has imperial preference been extended in the case of cotton by Great Britain, doubtless in part because the granting of such a favor to her dominions or colonies would become a handicap in competing with other cotton-manufacturing nations in the sale of goods on the world's markets. However, it must be recognized that some cotton-importing countries find it difficult to obtain funds to purchase cotton, and that nationalistic trends persist. Exports of cotton from the United States, prior to the recent disparity between prices in the United States and outside, constituted about three-fourths of the value of all agricultural exports, but in 1935 contributed only 55 to 60 per cent.

The great uncertainty in the cotton belt is the perfection of a cotton picker. If such a machine became widely used it would, no doubt, lower the cost of production, and this would be an advantage in world competition. This advantage probably could be maintained, because the principal competing countries are Egypt, India, and China, where the use of modern machinery is not profitable because of the very low price of labor, and Brazil, concerning which it seems too soon to speak. But a cotton picker would given an advantage, within the cotton belt, to areas of level land, and to those where the management of the land could be readily consolidated into larger units. The mechanization of cotton production would be likely to lead to notable regional shifts in production, and to serious social problems, as well as to raise new problems of land utilization.

The wheat regions of the Northwest and the Southwest likewise have advantages in climate or soil over most other wheat-exporting regions of the world, but they also have economic disadvantages. The natural advantages are less frequency of frost than in the prairie provinces of Canada, and probably less danger of drought than in most of southern Russia and of Australia, although the 1934 drought in both American wheat fields equaled, perhaps, any known in the history of Russia or Australia. But in much of Argentina and of the Danube Valley climatic conditions are probably as favorable as in the United States. Important disadvantages of the wheat belt of the United States are generally high wage rates and high transportation costs to tidewater.

But these natural and economic factors, which in the past tended to balance, so that all these countries continued to export their surplus of wheat, have now been eclipsed by political factors. Tariffs, quotas, or other restrictions have been placed upon imports of wheat by practically every European country, and in several countries these regulations have been supplemented by governmental aides to the wheat industry. Because of these barriers, and because of the generally higher prices for wheat in the United States than in other exporting countries in recent seasons of drought and resulting deficit, the exports of wheat have sunk to an insignificant figure.

Looking to the future, it is well to recall that the European barriers upon wheat imports have been erected to protect the farmers in these countries, and where the farmers constitute only a minority of the population, the governments are, nevertheless, profoundly concerned over the welfare of the farming class. The peasants are recognized as a bulwark of the state. They are providing far more than their share of the citizens and soldiers of the future, and should war come they must also be depended on to provide the needed food. Moreover, the population of Germany and France will cease to increase probably within a few years, unless more fecund peoples move into these countries in unprecedented numbers. In Great Britain a practically stationary population has already been reached. By 1950 the population of Great Britain will have fallen probably a half million below the maximum, and by 1960 two million or more below. Similar declines may be expected in Germany and France, and later in all the countries of northwestern Europe, except, possibly, in the Netherlands. A declining population is likely to mean a declining consumption of wheat unless there is a continued shift from rye to wheat, a development which has occurred in several European countries. Even should nationalistic policies in northwestern Europe be modified gradually, declining population, supplemented probably by advancing agricultural technique and by increased use of other foods such as fruit and dairy products, seems likely to lessen the need for imported wheat. Exports of wheat from the United States have been on very low levels during the past two years, owing to deficits in domestic supply. The prospect for recovery of the predepression levels is not bright, but better weather conditions in the Great Plains will almost certainly again induce a surplus. So long as world demand remains at its present low level, however, this surplus may find a market only at low prices. This will tend to reduce both production and exports. The problem of shifting from wheat to other uses of the land seems likely to remain acute, particularly along the arid margin of the wheat belts.

Let us now turn to the corn belt—that great food-producing region which extends from central Ohio to western Nebraska, stretching northward into Minnesota and southward across much of Missouri. Nowhere else in the world is there a contiguous area of such magnitude so fertile and so productive of cereals. Corn by nature is a very productive crop, yielding about twice as much food per acre as wheat or oats, and the physical conditions in the corn belt are peculiarly favorable for the production of corn. The summer rainfall of the humid tropics is combined with a soil whose fertility is locked up by its frozen condition during much of the winter. And not only is there the summer rainfall of the tropics, but also the high summer temperatures, so favorable to the growth of corn. The underlying rock in large areas of the eastern portion is limestone, which characteristically produces a fertile soil; in the western portion the extensive wind-blown soils, derived in large part from the more arid regions to the west, are also generally rich in lime. Moreover, the soils of most of the eastern corn belt were rejuvenated a few thousand years ago by the glaciers that extended far south in this region. These glaciers ground off portions of the underlying rock and brought this unleached material, with its generally high content of lime, phosphorus, and potash, to the surface. This fertility has been preserved over much of the corn belt by the grass vegetation, for just as forests tend to promote the leaching of the lime, potash, and nitrogen out of the soil by the rains, so do grass roots tend to raise these elements of fertility to the surface. Nowhere else than in the central corn belt is a humid climate combined with a grassland soil, except for a small area in Argentina. The United States produces from half to two-thirds of the corn crop of the world, and nearly two-thirds of the corn crop of the United States is produced in the corn belt.

The corn belt has appropriately been called the heart of American agriculture. Into it flow the stocker and feeder cattle from the West for fattening, to supplement its home-grown stock, and out of it flows more than two-thirds of the beef and pork consumed in the eastern, northern, and, to a lesser extent, southeastern sections of the country. It supplies, moreover, most of the exports of pork and lard, and, in addition, ships corn and hay in large quantities to the eastern and southern markets. Although the corn belt includes only 8 per cent of the land area of the United States, it possesses more than a fourth of the cattle, about a third of the horses, and more than half of the hogs of the nation. It has long been the great surplus-meat-producing region, and has now become a great surplus-milk-producing region as well.

Of the production of animal products in the corn belt a very rough estimate indicates that 8 to 10 per cent was sent abroad during the 5 years prior to the depression, mostly in the form of pork and lard. In 1932 and 1933 these exports averaged only a little over half as much, and in 1934 and 1935 were only about one-third as large. As with wheat, tariffs and other restrictions, especially quotas, are interfering with exports of pork and lard. The restrictions have not yet become prohibitive, except in Germany. Deep concern is felt over trends in Great Britain, which is the most important market for American hams and bacon, because of quota restrictions. Exports to Great Britain from the United States at present are restricted to about 8 per cent of the total British imports from foreign sources of supply, which in terms of American production is an insignificant amount. The future of our exports of animal products is uncertain, but the trend is not encouraging. The prospect of a declining population in the industrial nations and the defense reactions that are resulting, the development of manufacturing in many nations producing raw material, scattered throughout the world, usually behind the protection of tariff barriers, and debts and monetary difficulties, have induced a decline in international trade which may prove permanent. These developments, and others, suggest that the depression is not an episode, but the beginning of an epoch.

It should be recalled, however, that the population of the United States is still increasing. This increase was about 4 per cent from 1930 to 1935. It probably will be 3 per cent more by 1940, and perhaps as much more by 1950. If per capita consumption of pork during recent years persists, and that of lard increases somewhat, the present production will be no more than sufficient to supply domestic needs in about a decade.

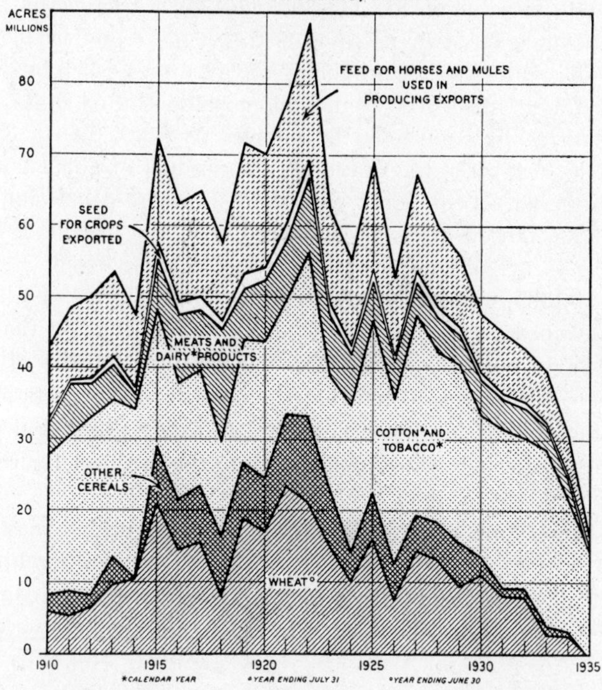

FIG. 8.

The acreage required to produce the net agricultural exports from the United States reached a peak about the beginning of the century and again during the years 1919-1922. From the high point of over 80 million acres in 1921-1922 the area declined to less than 20 million acres in 1934-1935. This was less than half that in the very low year 1909-1910. Cotton, including the estimated acreage needed to grow the feed for horses and mules used in production, required one-half to three-fourths of the total acreage during the years 1924-1932. In 1934-1935 cotton and tobacco were almost the only major farm products the exports of which exceeded the imports. This was in part owing to the drought which greatly reduced the production of wheat and other cereals, of beef and pork, and, to a less extent, of dairy products. Acreages are calculated on acre-yields of the crop the preceding year.

Meanwhile, the decrease in exports of these products is raising serious problems of land utilization in the corn belt. However, some consolation may be found in the fact that a reduction in the acreage of corn, the cultivation of which facilitates erosion, will tend to conserve the fertility of the soil. There is little doubt that in much of the corn belt the proportion of the cropland in corn is too great from the standpoint of a permanent agriculture.

Considering the net exports of farm products as a whole, it appears that 30,000,000 to 40,000,000 acres of cropland are required (1932-1934) to produce these exports, whereas during the 5 years prior to the depression about 60,000,000 acres were so used on the average, and during the decade of maximum exports, 1915-1924, about 70,000,000 acres were required (Fig. 8). This includes an allowance of 18 to 25 per cent (decreasing with passage of time) for crop feed consumed by horses and mules used in producing the exports. If such by-products as mill feed and cotton seed that remain in the United States are allowed for, these figures should be reduced by 4,000,000 to 6,000,000 acres. The lost export market involves the product of about 25,000,000 acres of cropland, as compared with the 5-year pre-depression period, and about 35,000,000 acres as compared with the decade 1915-1924. The decline in acreage required to produce the exports of 1933-1934, and of 1934-1935, was largely owing to cotton, the price of which was being maintained above the world level. In view of the fact that cotton in recent years normally constitutes nearly three-fourths of the exports measured in acreage, and that the prospect for exports of cotton is improving, it may be that a new level of exports has been reached.

Summary. Let us now summarize as to the prospect for consumption of farm products:

1. The population of the nation will increase probably 3,000,000, possibly 4,000,000, by 1940, and as much more, perhaps, by 1950. This means that, if other factors remain equal, from 7,500,000 to 10,000,000 more acres of crops will be needed by 1940, and probably 15,000,000 to 20,000,000 acres more than at present by 1950. But other factors may not remain equal. An acreage much greater than this might readily be released by a lowering of the standard of living, and in other ways. On the other hand, the use of more meat and milk in the diet would increase the need for land.

2. But the consumption of farm products per person has changed little in the aggregate for 30 years, as measured in land requirements, although notable shifts have occurred in diet, and doubtless will continue to occur. In particular, the increase in consumption of beer (as compared with prohibition years) and decrease in number of children suggest a lesser demand for milk, unless the great value of milk as a food for adults, as well as children, can be further impressed upon the people. But considering the consumption of farm products as a whole,

the best guess appears to be that there will be no notable change in the national per capita acreage requirement.

3. For exports, likewise, it now seems likely that there will be in the near future no change of great magnitude in aggregate acreage required for their production. But the decline in exports of wheat and pork products suggests the need for a contraction in wheat acreage, as compared with the pre-depression area, and for a shift temporarily at least of several million acres from corn to other crops or pasturage.

However, before reaching a definite conclusion in this matter of adjustments in acreage of wheat and corn, or that the increase of population will require a few more million acres of crops by 1940 and still more by 1950, it is necessary to consider the prospect for agricultural production per acre. Without any increase in acreage or acre-yields of the crops, agricultural production increased about 20 per cent during the decade preceding the economic depression. This great increase in production per acre was owing largely to changes in agricultural technique and shifts in the relative importance of the crops and livestock.

THE PROSPECT FOR AGRICULTURAL PRODUCTION

The population of the United States increased by about two-thirds between 1900 and 1930, agricultural production about one-half, crop acreage about one-quarter, and total labor in agriculture about one-tenth (Fig. 9). Although population increased more than agricultural production, aggregate consumption of farm products per person did not decline materially, because more of the production was consumed at home and less was exported abroad. At the beginning of the century the farm products exported required for their production nearly one-fourth of the total crop acreage,whereas during the 5 years centered on 1929, only about one-seventh was required. Between 1930 and 1935 the population of the United States increased about 5,000,000, or 4 per cent; agricultural production decreased about 10 per cent, but much of this decrease was owing to unprecedented drought in 1934, with resultant reduction in feed and livestock; crop acreage harvested declined about 8 per cent; and labor employed in agriculture, though in part not fully employed, has increased apparently 10 to 20 per cent.

The trends of a century have been reversed during the depression. Instead of a rapidly upward trend in production, a decline has occurred. Instead of an expanding crop acreage prior to 1918 and a practically stationary acreage from 1918 to 1932, a contraction has taken place. Instead of a decreasing proportion of the "gainfully employed" in the nation engaged in agriculture—from 54 per cent in 1870 to 21 per cent in 1930—an increase has occurred, apparently, to 25 per cent or more. This estimate assumes that the "unemployed" in the cities are not gainfully employed, and that the youth backed up on farms are gainfully employed. Instead of increasing production per worker in agriculture—about threefold during the century prior

AGRICULTURAL PRODUCTION, CROPS HARVESTED, FARM LABOR, AND POPULATION, 1897-1935

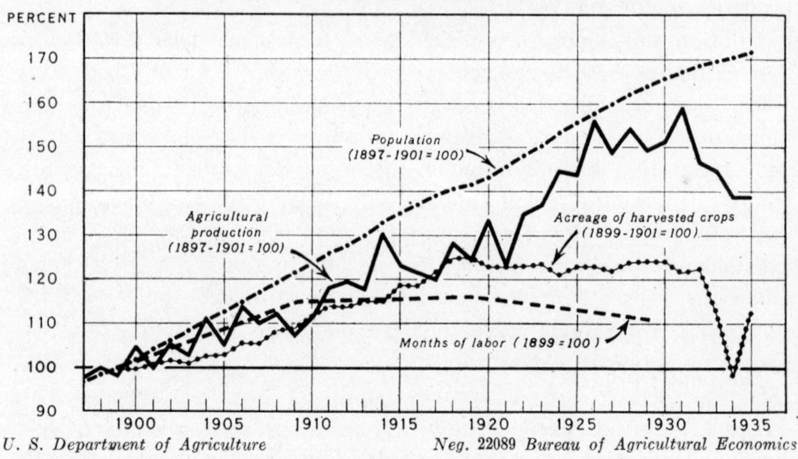

Fig. 9.

Agricultural production from 1926 to 1931 was about 50 per cent greater than at the beginning of the twentieth century, crop acreage was nearly 25 per cent greater, and quantity of labor employed in agriculture in 1929 was 10 to 12 per cent greater. Production per acre, therefore, increased about 20 per cent, and production per man about 35 per cent. Most of this increase occurred after the War. The trend of production has been rapidly downward since 1931, owing principally to exceptional drought and the agricultural adjustment program. The base period 1897-1901 was opulent in the relation of production to population, about one-fourth of the production being exported, as compared with less than one-eighth at present. Consumption per capita has been well maintained, except during the War years, when the decline in consumption was attributable mostly to foods, and during the depression years, when the decline is largely attributable to non-foods—cotton and flax particularly.

to 1930—a notable decrease has occurred. Let us consider the factors that influenced these trends before and during the depression.

Factors Affecting Agricultural Production. Despite the depletion in land resources described in Chapter IV the trend of agricultural production for the nation as a whole was rapidly upward until 1926, the losses in soil fertility having been more than balanced by advances in agricultural technique. As in coal mining, although the resources were being reduced, methods and machinery improved so rapidly that a troublesome surplus of products developed, and the less favorably situated or less efficient producers were being forced to the wall. These advances in technique that have followed the application of science to agriculture and associated industries have been myriad in number, but nearly all may be grouped with reference to the increase of production into six classes:

1. Those that have promoted the expansion of the agricultural area.
2. Those that have caused increased acre-yields of the crops, including shifts from less productive to more productive lands.
3. Those that have substituted mechanical for animal power on farms, thereby conserving feed and increasing production of animal products (other than power).
4. Those that have led to shifts from the less productive toward the more productive crops per acre.
5. Those that have led to shifts from the less productive toward the more productive classes of animals per unit of feed consumed.
6. Those that have resulted in increased efficiency in utilization of feed by each kind of farm animal.

Expansion of the Agricultural Area. The agricultural occupation of the world is a relatively recent development. The area brought under the plow during the past century has been as great, probably, as in all the centuries preceding; and between 1900 and 1930 it was two-thirds as great, apparently, as in the 70 years preceding. Prior to 1850 agriculture had developed mostly in forested regions, where streams or springs were abundant, or in desert areas reclaimed by irrigation. The vast subhumid and semiarid grassland areas were the grazing grounds of nomads. Most of the expansion of the crop area during the past 85 years has occurred on these grassland areas, notably the prairies and plains of North America, the Russian steppes, the Argentine pampas, and the semiarid lands of Australia. The utilization of such lands for crops was made possible by the invention of well-drilling appliances, which provided water for man and beast, by the railroads, which brought wood and coal to the settlers and carried their wheat and meat to market, and by the invention of grain seeding and harvesting machinery, which enabled one man to do the work of five, releasing the other four for employment in urban industries.

Recently the tractor and the combine have facilitated the further expansion of grain production along the arid margin of these grassland areas. During the decade 1920-1930 the wheat area in our Great Plains states increased about 8,000,000 acres, and in the prairie provinces of Canada by about 7,000,000. But in the United States as a whole between 1919 and 1929 there was practically no increase in the crop area, expansion on the semiarid lands of the West being balanced by con-

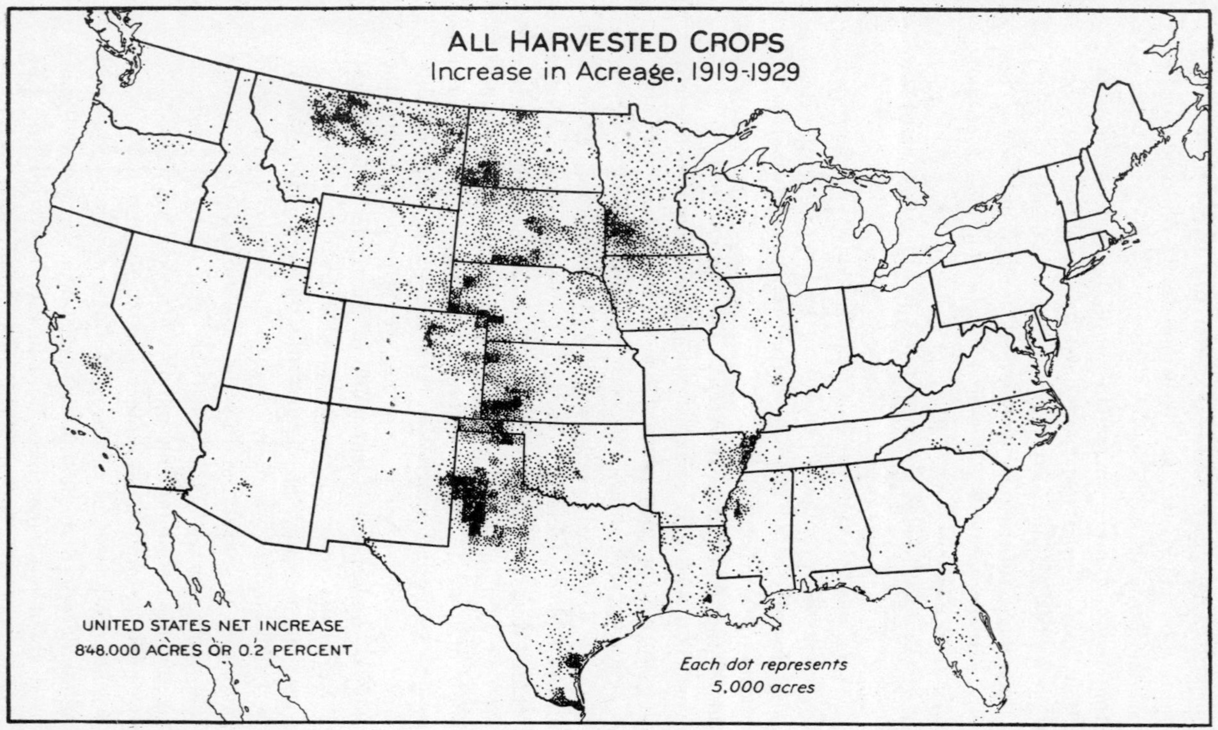

U. S. Department of Agriculture — *Neg.* 29189 *Bureau of Agricultural Economics*

FIG. 10.

The increase in acreage of crops harvested between the Census years 1919 and 1929 occurred mostly in the semiarid portion of the Great Plains Region, where the tractor, combine, and other labor-saving machinery made it possible to grow grain on the level land profitably at the prices then existing. A notable increase occurred also in southwestern Minnesota and in the Mississippi River bottoms of Mississippi and northeastern Arkansas. In both these areas much land had been drained, but most of the Minnesota gain was because of a severe drought in 1919. The increase in the 1,130 counties in the United States reporting an increase between these census years exceeded 30,000,000 acres.

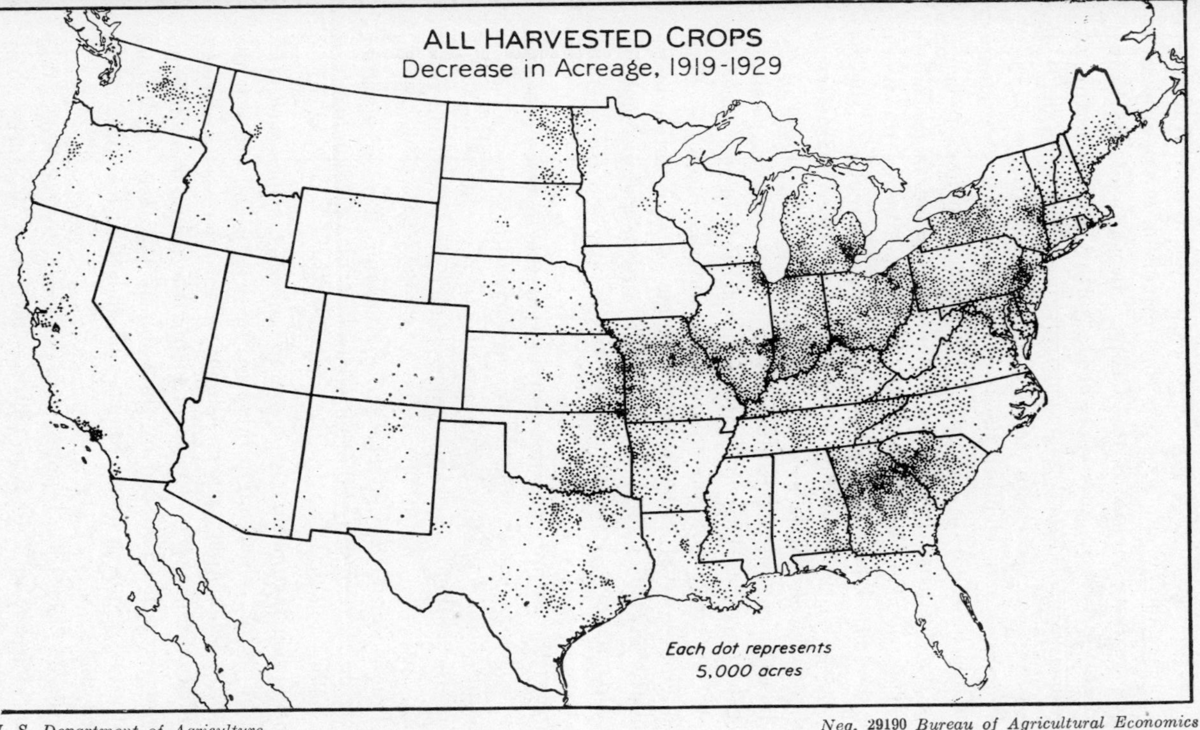

U. S. Department of Agriculture Neg. 29190 *Bureau of Agricultural Economics*

FIG. 11.

A decrease in acreage of crops occurred between 1919 and 1929 in most of the originally forested portion of the United States. The decrease in the nearly 2,000 counties reporting a decrease exceeded 30,000,000 acres. The outstanding decrease was in the Piedmont Region of Georgia and South Carolina, and in a belt extending from southern New England across New York and Pennsylvania, southern Michigan, Ohio, Indiana and southern Illinois, and most of Kentucky and Missouri, to eastern Oklahoma and north central Texas. Part of the land no longer cultivated was used for pasture, part lay idle, and part grew up to brush. The farms in these areas are generally small, and the soils poor or fair, although some are good.

traction in the humid areas of the South and East (Figs. 10 and 11). The increase in agricultural production after the World War must, therefore, be ascribed to other factors than expansion of the crop area.

Changes in Acre-yields of the Crops. In parts of the United States, notably in the Atlantic states from North Carolina northward, where commercial fertilizers are extensively used, the acre-yields of the crops have been increasing rapidly. But in most of the northern and western states acre-yields of the crops are more or less stationary, and in the South, where the cotton boll-weevil has extended its depredations to the northern edge of the cotton belt, except in the northwestern sector, acre-yields normally are lower than before the World War. For the nation as a whole there has been, apparently, a slightly downward trend in the composite acre-yield of the twelve major crops since the early years of the century. Evidently all the efforts of the federal Department of Agriculture and of the state agricultural colleges, experiment stations, and extension services, plus the powerful influence of the agricultural press, scarcely counterbalanced the effects of erosion, crop removal, leaching of the soluble salts, oxidation of the organic matter in the soil, and devastations of insects and of plant diseases. With reference to pasture, both the acreage and the carrying capacity have been declining for many years.

Looking to the future, it is not certain that the farmers, with the aid of the various agencies, will be even as successful as in the past in counteracting the effects of soil depletion upon acre-yields of the crops, considering the nation as a whole, unless higher prices of farm products permit extensive use of fertilizers on the less erosive lands, for the depletion of soil fertility by erosion is advancing at an accelerating rate. However, the safest assumption appears to be a stationary average acre-yield of the crops.

Evidently other factors than extension of crop area or increased acre-yields of the crops—which might be called the length and breadth and height of crop production—must account for the increase in agricultural production during the decade preceding the depression. Agricultural production is not bounded by three dimensions; but, like higher mathematics, it has also a fourth dimension—indeed, it has even a fifth and a sixth dimension.

The increase in agricultural production per acre after the World War was owing almost wholly to four factors which were of scarcely any importance in pre-war years.

Decline in Horses and Mules. The most important of these factors was the substitution of gasoline for horse feed. There are two final consumers, so to speak, of farm products—human beings and horses or mules. All other consumers, such as cattle, swine, sheep, and chickens, are intermediate to human consumption. At the close of the World War there were about 29,000,000 horses and mules in the United States, including over 2,000,000 in cities. These horses and mules consumed the products of 80,000,000 to 90,000,000 acres of cropland, besides much pasturage. On January 1, 1936, there were only about 16,000,000 horses and mules in the nation. This decrease of 13,000,000 horses and mules released the products of 35,000,000 to 40,000,000 acres of cropland. Moreover, the decrease in horses and mules was greatest in the richest agricultural regions, notably in the corn belt and in the southern portion of the hay and dairy region. Most of these 40,000,000 acres, more or less, are now being used for the production of meat and milk, or are lying idle. However, the number of colts raised is now increasing. The number of horse colts on farms in 1935 was 15 per cent larger than in 1930, but of mule colts 34 per cent less. When births of colts will equal deaths of horses and mules cannot be stated with certainty, but it may occur in 2 to 4 years.

It is well to recall, however, that improvements in tractors and tractor machinery will almost certainly continue to be made, whereas improvements in horses and mules as sources of power will make slow or no progress. The use of the Diesel engine in tractors gives promise of reducing the cost of operation, and the placing of pneumatic tires on tractors has apparently increased their efficiency as well as the comfort of operation. Furthermore, if the attitude of young people at present is indicative of what it will be in later life, it appears that comfort and speed will be esteemed fully as much as economy. By 1940 it may develop that several million acres more of cropland will have been released for other uses by the decline in horses and mules.

Shifts from the Less Productive to the More Productive Crops per Acre, and Vice Versa. The second most important factor in causing an increased production on a stationary crop acreage during the decade preceding the depression was the shift from the less productive toward the more productive crops per acre (measured by a 10-year average acre value), notably from corn toward cotton in much of the South, from wheat toward corn in southern Minnesota, the eastern portions of the Dakotas, and eastern Kansas, and from grain and hay toward fruits and vegetables in California and elsewhere (Fig. 12). Apparently these shifts resulted in increasing crop production by the equivalent of about 14,000,000 acres of cropland between 1919 and 1929.

During the depression the trend of cotton acreage has been downward, while that of corn in most of the cotton belt has been upward. This trend in cotton acreage was accelerated by the Agricultural Adjustment Administration control program. Likewise, in the wheat belt, the trend of acreage was downward, and probably more wheat land has reverted to pasture or lies idle than has been put into corn or other

LESS PRODUCTIVE COMPARED WITH MORE PRODUCTIVE CROPS PER ACRE AND MEAT AND MILK ANIMALS PER UNIT OF FEED CONSUMED, PERCENTAGE CHANGE IN ACREAGE OR NUMBER, 1900 TO DATE

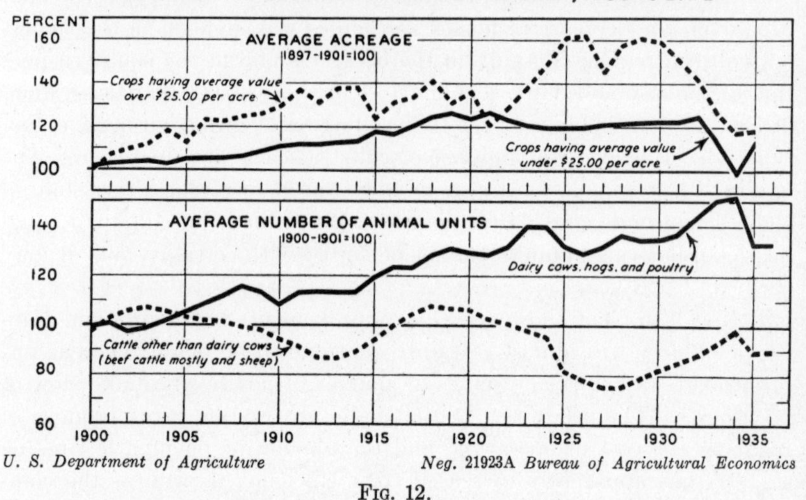

FIG. 12.

The acreage of crops having a high average value per acre (over $25 during the period 1925-1929) increased more rapidly prior to the depression than that of crops having a lower average acre-value. From 1921 to 1926 the increase in acreage of the more valuable crops was notable. Likewise, the number of dairy cows increased notably while that of beef cattle, which produce much less human food per unit of feed consumed, has remained about stationary, or declined slightly, after allowance is made for the cycle. These trends tend to increase production per acre, but during the depression, and with the development of the Agricultural Adjustment Administration Program, the trend has been toward the less intensive use of cropland.

productive crops. This trend also was accelerated by the governmental control program. In the corn belt the acreage of corn reached a maximum in 1932 and declined in 1933. The drought and the corn-and-hog program caused a further and unprecedented decline in 1934, with a recovery in 1935 to 14 per cent under the pre-depression level.

It is interesting to note that shifting the use of land from the more productive crops to the less productive pasture or cover crops was the principal means adopted by the Agricultural Adjustment Administration in restricting production. For this reason it is difficult to forecast the future with reference to the influence of this factor upon agricultural production per acre. By 1935, however, the equivalent of 14,000,-000 acres of crops, more or less, that were gained during the decade preceding the depression by shifts in relative importance of the crops was lost, and, perhaps, as much more. It is possible that this trend toward less productive crops will continue—the governmental program promoting such a trend—until the time when population begins to decline. In particular, cultivated fields that are eroding badly should be and probably many will be put into forage crops or pasture, perhaps, even into forest.

Shifts from the Less Productive to the More Productive Classes of Farm Animals per Unit of Feed Consumed. Likewise there was a shift during the period between the World War and the economic depression from the less productive classes of food-producing animals toward the more productive classes, principally from beef cattle toward dairy cattle, hogs, and poultry. (See Fig. 12.) Beef cattle require the products of about 11 acres of cropland, besides much pasture, to produce as much human food, measured in calories, as about 2.3 acres of cropland and 1.7 acres of pasture used to feed dairy cows, or 3.1 acres of cropland used to feed hogs. (See Fig. 6.) The consumption of beef and veal per person since 1928 has been only about 80 per cent of the pre-war level, while the per capita consumption of pork rose 15 to 20 per cent above the pre-war level, and of milk was above that level in most years from 1920 to 1933. This shift toward the more productive classes of farm animals per unit of food consumed during the decade 1919-1929 was equivalent, apparently, to the production of about 9,000,000 acres of cropland. The future influence of this factor of shifts in relative importance of the animal products is difficult if not impossible to forecast, for it depends not only on changes that may occur in the preferences of the people and their income, but also upon cycles of beef and pork production, the results of the recent drought, of governmental policy, and other influences.

Increased Production of Meat and Milk per Unit of Feed Consumed by Each Class of Farm Animals. Lastly there remain to be noted the improvements that have occurred in the efficiency of use of feed, particularly by dairy cows, by hogs, and by poultry. Between the 5-year period preceding the World War and the 5-year period preceding the depression there was an increase, apparently, in production of milk per cow of nearly 15 per cent. The better cows ate more, but it is doubtful if they ate 10 per cent more, on the average—perhaps only 5 per cent more. The cow-testing associations were, apparently, approaching their objectives. Likewise with hogs, during the four years 1930-1933 the estimated number of hogs on farms January 1 averaged about 5 per cent less than during the four years following the World War, and only 7 per cent larger than in the four years preceding the War, whereas the production of pork and lard was nearly 15 per cent greater than in the post-war and 44 per cent greater than in the pre-war period. Better sanitation is resulting in larger litters being raised, and feed formerly lost in the dead pigs now goes to market in live hogs. Improvements in feeding practices, particularly the use of minerals and legumes, have also resulted in economy in use of feed. It may be roughly estimated that the equivalent of 5,000,000 acres of cropland have been contributed to agricultural production since the World War by improvements in animal husbandry.

Here again it is hazardous to forecast the future, but it is perfectly safe to say that a wide margin remains for further improvement. Records of cow-testing associations, for example, indicate that the greatest production of milk per unit of feed consumed is attained in herds averaging 10,000 and 12,000 pounds of milk yearly per cow. Even at the rapid rate of increase in production per cow during the 20 years preceding the depression, it would require more than a century to attain a level of 10,000 pounds per cow.

The Four Factors Considered as a Whole. These four means of increasing agricultural production—substitution of gasoline for horse feed,[1] shifts from the less productive to the more productive crops per acre, shifts from the less productive to the more productive animals per unit of feed consumed, and, finally, increasing efficiency in use of feed by each class of farm animals, achieved principally by better feeding, breeding, and selection—increased agricultural production by the equivalent of nearly 50,000,000 acres during the decade 1919-1929. Adding the 20,000,000 acres, more or less, released for home consumption by the decline in exports, it appears that the increase of farm products thus made available for domestic consumption was equivalent to the production of about 70,000,000 acres of cropland. On the other side of the ledger there was, first, the increase in population of 17,000,000, with a consequent increase in need for cropland of about 45,000,000 acres; secondly, the improvement in diet, notably more milk and pork, that required the products of 15,000,000 to 20,000,000 more acres than would have been required by the war-time diet; and, thirdly, a slight decrease in acre-yields of the crops.

[1] That this substitution involves an expenditure for gasoline, and may not alter crop production, does not change the fact that it results in an increased quantity of products leaving the farm.

Looking to the future, it seems reasonable to expect that several million acres more will be released before 1940 by the further decline in horses and mules, and presumably the improvements in animal husbandry will continue and release a few million additional acres by that time. On the other hand, partly as a result of governmental effort, there has occurred recently a notable shift from the more productive crops toward the less productive crops or to pasture, and if control is continued and urban income rises, the trend in the conversion of forage and hay crops into beef rather than into pork may become notable. On the whole, perhaps the best guess at present is that these four factors, all of which operated to increase production for a decade or more after the World War, will counterbalance one another during the next few years. It seems likely that the major changes in production which may occur will be accomplished mostly by means of the factor that was so effective during most of the period prior to the World War, namely, the acreage in crops.

The Prospect for Changes in Crop Acreage. The two outstanding factors in the long-time outlook for crop acreage are the decline in births and the decline in soil resources. It appears probable that the decrease in soil resources, owing to losses described in Chapter IV, is not proceeding at a rate more rapid than 5 per cent a decade. The number of births in the nation has decreased more than 20 per cent during the last decade. But it requires about 30 years, or a generation of time, for a decline in births to be reflected in a declining population, assuming no net immigration; the effects of depletion of soil resources upon agricultural production are likely to become manifest more rapidly.

On the basis of the assumptions previously noted, except that of a decline in specific birth rates during the next 25 years no greater than that which has occurred during the last 5 years, the compilers of the *Report of the National Resources Board* estimated the future acreage requirements for crops as is shown in the table on page 210.[1]

It seems likely to the writer, however, that the number of births will decline more rapidly than was assumed in the estimates of population (those of Dr. Thompson, of the Scripps Foundation) on which this table was based. But up to 1950 the figures in the table can scarcely prove far wrong. These 1950 figures may prove to be near the maximum. The 367,000,000 acres needed (following the low estimates for exports) is only about 7,000,000 acres more than were harvested in

[1] *Report of the National Resources Board,* Washington, D. C., December 1, 1934, p. 126.

TABLE 1

Acreage Requirements for Domestic Consumption and Exports—United States Farm Products

(Millions of Acres)

Year	Wheat			Corn			Oats			Barley		
	Domestic Consumption	Exports	Total	Domestic Consumption	Exports	Total	Domestic Consumption	Exports	Total	Domestic Consumption	Exports	Total
1940	46.1	5.8–7.8	51.9–53.9	98.8	2–3	100.8–101.8	37.3	0.3	37.6	9.7	0.7	10.4
1945	47.4	5.8–9.7	53.2–57.1	101.6	2–3	103.6–104.6	38.3	.3	38.6	9.9	.7	10.6
1950	48.5	5.8–9.7	54.3–58.2	103.8	2–3	105.8–106.8	39.2	.3	39.5	10.1	.7	10.8
1955	49.2	5.8–9.7	55.0–58.9	105.3	2–3	107.3–108.3	39.7	.3	40.0	10.3	.7	11.0
1960	49.6	5.8–9.7	55.4–59.3	106.1	2–3	108.1–109.1	40.0	.3	40.3	10.4	.7	11.1

Year	Cotton			Tobacco			Hay	Other Crops	
	Domestic Consumption	Exports	Total	Domestic Consumption	Exports	Total	Domestic Consumption	Total	Total Crops Harvested
1940	18.0	22.0–24.6	40.0–42.6	1.1	0.8	1.9	67.9	37.7	348.2–353.8
1945	18.5	22.0–25.8	40.5–44.3	1.2	.8	2.0	69.8	40.6	358.9–367.6
1950	18.9	22.0–27.1	40.9–46.0	1.2	.8	2.0	71.3	42.1	366.7–376.7
1955	19.2	22.0–28.3	41.2–47.5	1.2	.8	2.0	72.3	42.6	371.4–382.6
1960	19.3	22.0–29.5	41.3–48.8	1.3	.8	2.1	72.9	42.6	373.8–386.2

The basic assumptions underlying these estimates are that:

1. Per capita consumption of food crops will continue at about pre-depression levels.
2. Increased efficiency in the production of livestock products from feed will be reflected to a substantial degree in greater per capita consumption, thus resulting in little net change in the per capita acreage required to produce livestock products for human food.
3. The number of horses and mules for power will be about the same in 1940 as in 1934, and after 1940 the number will increase about in proportion to total acreage.
4. Exports will be approximately as given in the export section of the text. For several crops, both a high and low estimate are given, separated by a dash.

In these instances, the total acreages are also given as high and low estimates.

Should exports fall below these estimates, or drastic changes occur in the proportion of the various livestock products consumed, or mechanization develop more or less rapidly than here assumed, corresponding changes would occur in the acreage requirements. The assumptions given above, however, appear to be the most tenable for the purpose of forming a reasonable estimate of land requirements for the next quarter of a century, it always being understood that any land program should be sufficiently flexible to allow for such significant changes as develop.

1919 and again in 1929. Should exports of farm products increase to the maximum estimates used in the table, only about 18,000,000 more acres of crops would be needed by 1950—or, perhaps, for many years thereafter. This is 5 per cent more than were harvested in 1919 and 1929.

In other words, the nation appears unlikely to need more than a slight increase in the crop area, provided that acre-yields of the crops

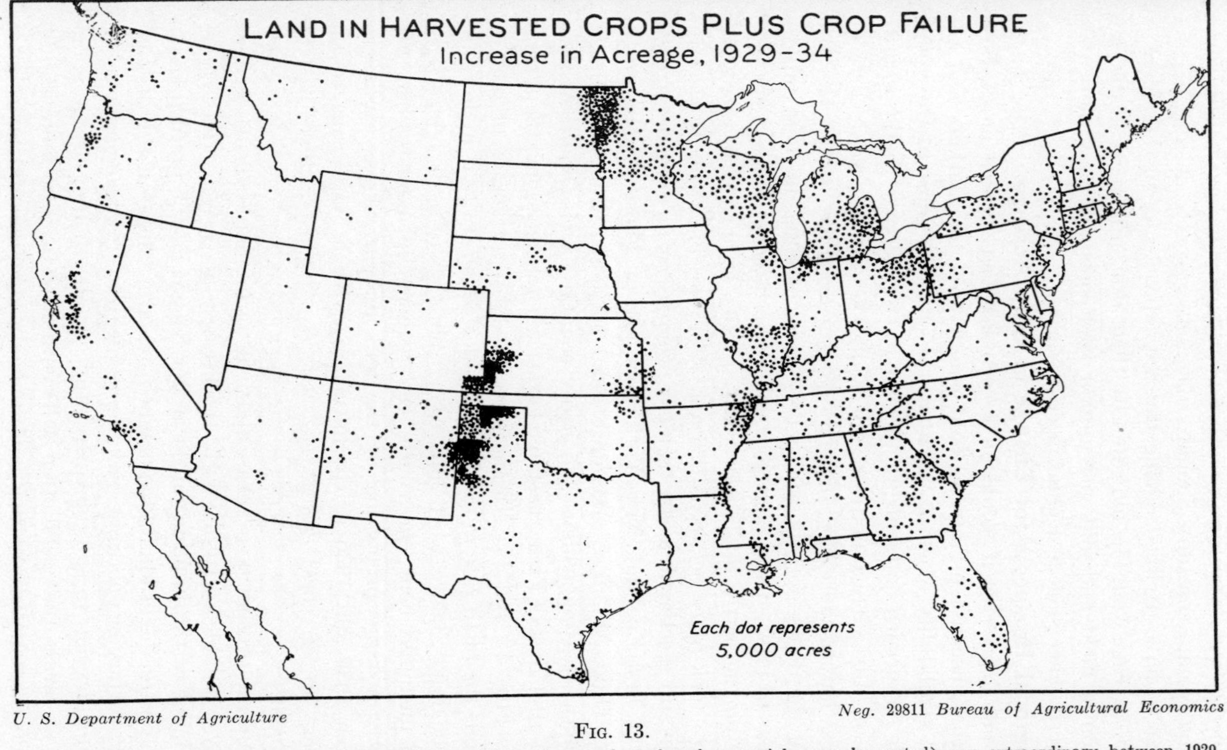

U. S. Department of Agriculture *Neg.* 29811 *Bureau of Agricultural Economics*

FIG. 13.

The change in acreage of crops harvested plus failure (crops planted and perennial crops harvested) was extraordinary between 1929 and 1934. The increase in the "dust bowl" of the Texas Panhandle, and southwestern Kansas, was in crop failure rather than crops harvested, for this was the center of the drought area. But the increase in the dairy belt from northwestern Minnesota to New England was real and, apparently, reflects an attempt by the farmers in this region to produce more of the feed they require. In southern Illinois and in the southern states the increase occurred more frequently on poor land than on good land, and, in general, in the areas of less commercial rather than more commercial agriculture.

and the efficiency of livestock in transforming feed into human food do not diminish, also that the other factors affecting agricultural production remain constant. Should crop yields per acre decline, as they appear to have declined during the last 30 years, a further increase in crop acreage would be indicated by 1950. But an increase in the production of meat and milk per unit of feed consumed may more than counterbalance such a decline in crop yields.

Regional Prospects for Change in Crop Acreage. Prior to the economic depression it would have been assumed without much question that, because of interregional competition for markets and the ready availability of employment in the cities for most of the young people not needed on farms, the decline in crop acreage would occur in areas of hilly surface or poor soils while the increase would develop in areas having more level or fertile lands. (See Figs. 10 and 11.) But during the depression the youth have been backing up more rapidly in areas of hilly surface and poor soils than on good lands. Very generally on the better lands a decrease in crop acreage (harvested plus failure) took place between 1929 and 1934 (except in the Texas Panhandle and the Pacific coast regions), whereas an increase occurred in most of New England, New York, New Jersey, Pennsylvania, northeastern Ohio, Michigan, Wisconsin, and northern Minnesota, also in the southern Appalachians and many counties in the South Atlantic and Gulf Coastal Plain, east of Texas, as well as along the Pacific coast (Figs. 13 and 14). In the areas of hilly surface or of poor to fair soils the birth rate in the farm population generally is higher than on good lands, hence when migration from the farms is retarded by urban unemployment, the youth tend to back up more readily. Apparently a large proportion of the half million increase in farms between 1930 and 1935 in the nation as a whole was owing to the backing up of rural youth as well as to the back-to-the-land movement.

If urban prosperity returns and non-farm employment becomes readily available to rural youth, the greater increase in crop acreage will almost certainly occur on the better lands, and the pre-depression trend toward the gradual abandonment of farm land in many districts of hilly surface or poor soils may be resumed. But if urban employment does not develop in sufficient magnitude to absorb the surplus population on farms, that population will continue to back up more rapidly in areas of poor than of rich land, unless a governmental program of resettlement facilitates migration. In many hilly or rolling districts where erosion is rapidly reducing the meager soil resources, particularly

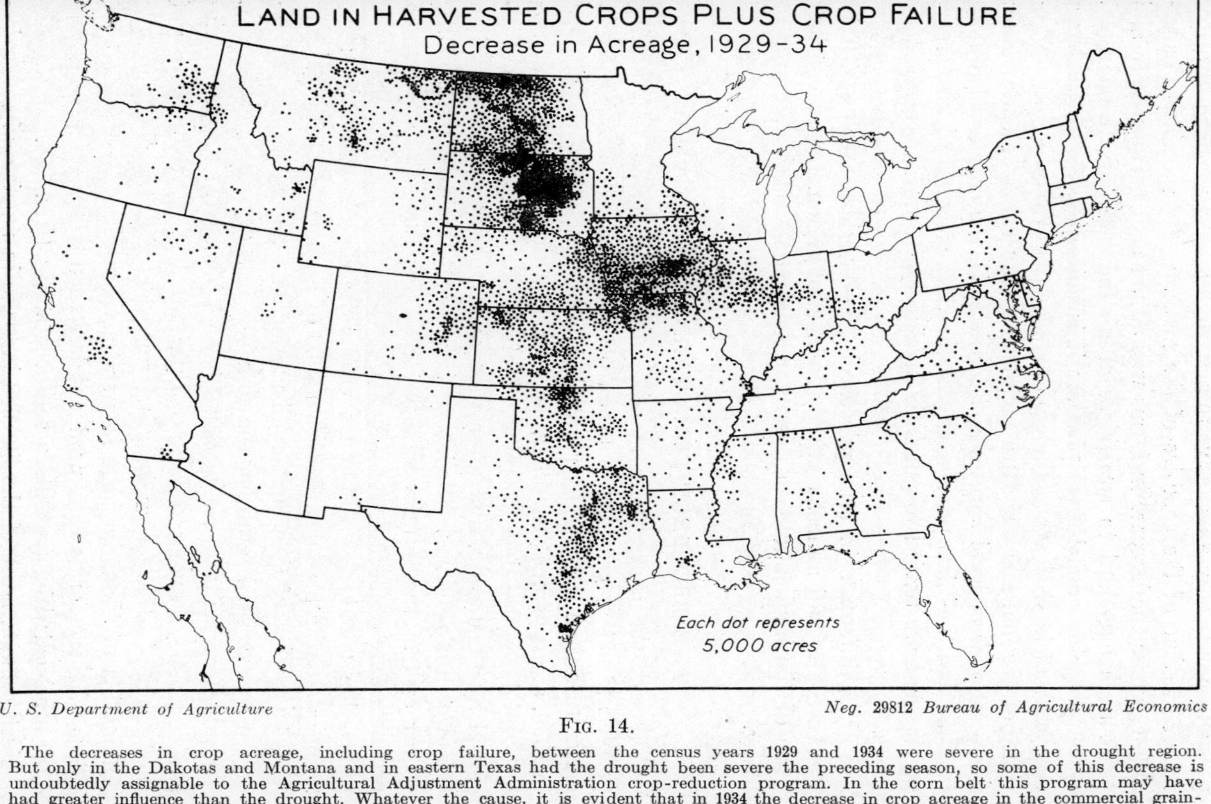

U. S. Department of Agriculture *Neg.* 29812 *Bureau of Agricultural Economics*

FIG. 14.

The decreases in crop acreage, including crop failure, between the census years 1929 and 1934 were severe in the drought region. But only in the Dakotas and Montana and in eastern Texas had the drought been severe the preceding season, so some of this decrease is undoubtedly assignable to the Agricultural Adjustment Administration crop-reduction program. In the corn belt this program may have had greater influence than the drought. Whatever the cause, it is evident that in 1934 the decrease in crop acreage in the commercial grain-producing areas was extraordinary. In the counties reporting a decrease in the United States the total decline, as compared with 1929, was 24,606,500 acres.

those where the birth rate is high, such a governmental program may prove to be the only alternative to persistently heavy expenditures for relief. In some of the counties of the southern Appalachians, for example, where the increase in farms was 50 per cent between 1930 and 1935, from one-third to two-thirds of all the families are on relief. Without such a resettlement program it is quite possible that, after a few years of land clearing, the crop acreage may decrease largely because of erosion, and the farm population may continue to increase; while in areas of level surface and fertile soils, the crop acreage may increase and the farm population decrease, for commercial farmers in particular have tended to purchase machinery in preference to hiring labor.

Such a difference in economic levels between large regions in the United States will almost certainly induce migration. Let us consider some of the implications in migration relative to rural standards of living.

THE PROSPECT FOR STANDARD OF LIVING

Although the contrasts in standard of living among the farming people are not so great as in urban occupations, they are greater in agriculture than is generally realized. Approximately half the farmers in 1929, a prosperous year in agriculture according to post-war standards, produced less than $1,000 worth of products, including those consumed by the family, and more than one-fourth produced less than $600 worth of products. It is interesting to note, incidentally, that the 49 per cent of the farmers who produced less than $1,000 worth of products were responsible for only about 11 per cent of the commercial production (products "sold or traded" to use the census phrase); the 28 per cent who produced less than $600 of products contributed only 3 to 4 per cent of the commercial production—no more than the increase from a good rain over the corn belt in a dry season (Fig. 15). To reduce agricultural production 10 to 15 per cent, as appeared desirable a few years ago to dispose of the "surplus," by the purchase of the least productive (submarginal) farms, would involve, therefore, the elimination of about half the farmers of the nation. More than two-thirds of these farms that produced less than $1,000 of products in 1929 are located in the sixteen southern states (Fig. 16).

Furthermore, most of the 500,000 increase in number of farms between 1930 and 1935, revealed by the census, took place in regions characterized by hilly or poor land and small farms, notably in the southern Appalachians and the Ozarks and around the cities, particularly the industrial cities and those with poor, low-priced land adjacent. About 250,000 new farms apparently were started in "problem areas." This is several times as many farms as it is proposed to purchase for conversion to forest or pasture under the federal land utilization and resettlement program.

Estimated Value of Products Classified into Value of Products Groups, United States, 1929

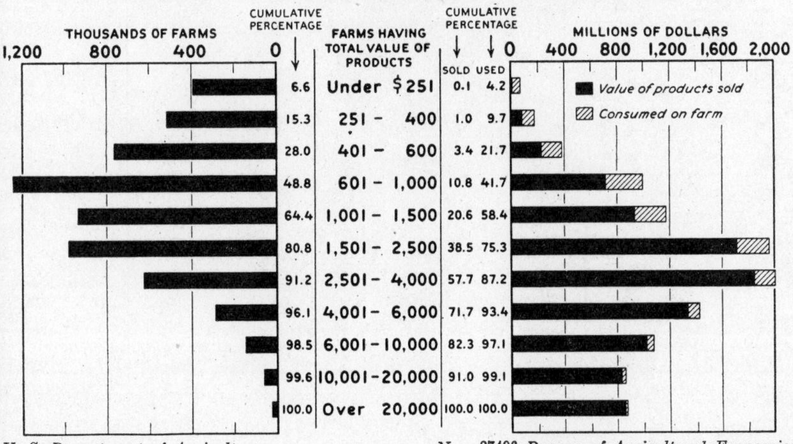

U. S. Department of Agriculture *Neg.* 27496 *Bureau of Agricultural Economics*

FIG. 15.

In the census year 1929 more than one-fourth of the farms in the nation produced less than $600 worth of products, including the products of the farm used by the family. But this fourth of the farms contributed less than 4 per cent of the farm products sold or traded. Nearly half of the farms in 1929 produced less than $1,000 worth of products, but this least productive half of the farms contributed only about 11 per cent of the commercial production of the nation. Undoubtedly the other half, the more productive farms, could, within a few years, readily produce this 11 per cent. Half the farms of the nation are not needed to provide the city and other non-farm people with food and fibers. But the less productive half of the farms are supplying more than their share of the children that migrate to the cities, and the cities may soon need people almost as much as food.

Instead of an increase in the size of farms, which had been in progress for many years, particularly in the better farming regions, an average decrease of about 10 per cent in arable acreage per farm in the nation as a whole took place between 1929 and 1934. Many of the young men, because of inability to obtain employment in the cities, backed up in rural areas, married, and started to farm. Other youth, and older people also, returned from the cities. Farms have been divided, fields have been rented, abandoned farms have been reoccupied, and forest lands have been cleared. Between 1870 and 1930 agricultural production per worker increased about 150 per cent. From 1930

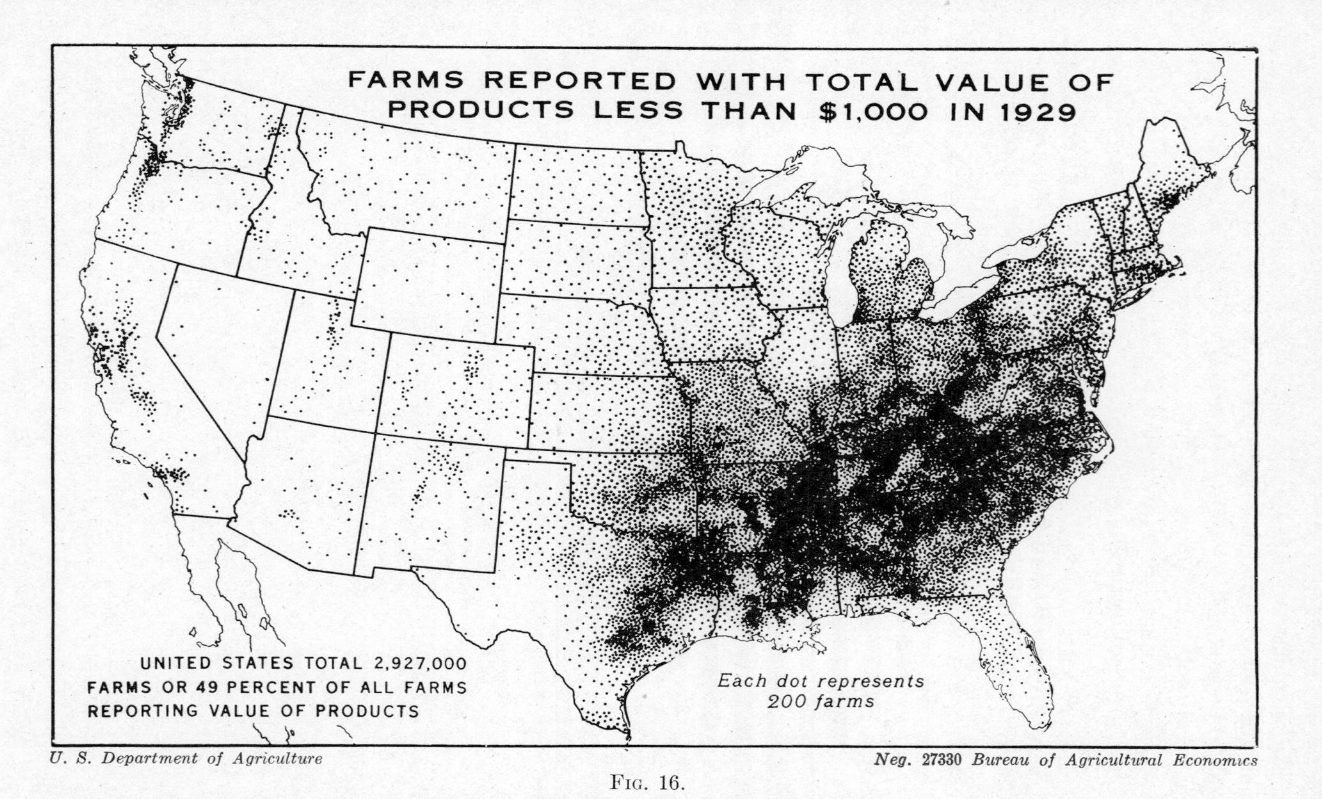

U. S. Department of Agriculture *Neg. 27330 Bureau of Agricultural Economics*

FIG. 16.

Over two-thirds of all the farms that produced less than $1,000 worth of products in 1929 were located in the 16 southern states. In the North these farms are most numerous in the northeastern states, Ohio, Michigan, Indiana, southern Illinois, and Missouri. Two-thirds of all farms in the southern states produced less than $1,000 of products. It is probable that the "peasants" of northern Europe produce more than $1,000 worth of products on the average; and it is certain that the standard of living among the farmers of northern Europe is higher than that in our South. Nearly two-thirds of the net migration from farms during the decade 1920-1929 was from the 16 southern states. (See Fig. 17.)

to 1935 the decrease was probably 20 per cent. Part of this decrease is attributable to weather conditions, part to the Agricultural Adjustment Administration program, but about half, apparently, to the increase in workers on farms. The trend of a half century has been reversed. Most of the new farms that have been established appear to be small farms. Many of these would probably be classified as part-

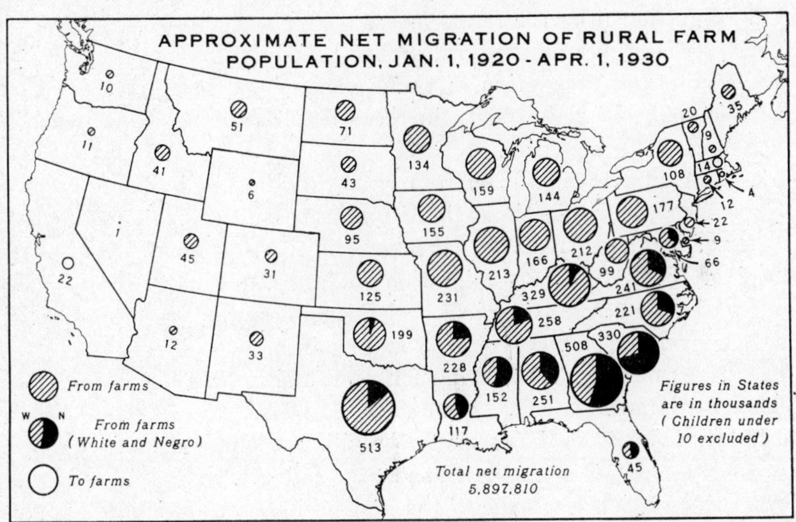

U. S. Department of Agriculture Neg. 25165 *Bureau of Agricultural Economics*

FIG. 17.

Nearly two-thirds of the net migration from the farms during the decade 1920 to 1930 was from the South. Negroes constituted one-third of this migration from southern farms. A majority of these migrants were between 15 and 30 years of age. The birth rate was high among southern rural people, and economic opportunity was less than in the North. If it costs in the South only $2,000 to rear and educate a child to the age of fifteen ($135 a year and no allowance for interest), these 3,800,000 migrants from farms in the southern states represent a contribution, roughly, of $7,500,000,000 made during the decade by the farm population of the South to other parts of the nation, mostly to the cities. Map from "Recent Social Trends," McGraw-Hill Book Company, New York, 1933.

time or self-sufficing farms. The standard of living, except for food, undoubtedly has declined materially in most farming areas.[1]

The Outlook for Rural-urban Migration. Looking to the future nothing is certain, except that the situation will be different from what it is today. The standard of living among the farming population appears likely to depend largely on the extent and direction of migra-

[1] See E. L. Kirkpatrick, Rosalind Tough, and May L. Cowles, "How Farm Families Meet the Emergency," *Wisc. Agric. Expt. Sta. Res. Bull.* 126, January, 1935, particularly appendix Table E; and Ruth Crawford Freeman, "Living Expenditures of a Group of Illinois Farm Families, 1930, 1931, 1932," *Ill. Agric. Expt. Sta. Bull.* 406, September, 1934, p. 399.

tion from the farms. Migration may take several courses, but it seems likely that the dominant trend will be in one of the following directions:

1. Resumption of the large and wide-spread net movement from the farms to the cities prior to the depression (Fig. 17). This was greater than the natural increase (excess of births over deaths) between 1920 and 1930, and farm population declined.

2. Migration from the farms in the poorer agricultural areas to the farms in the richer agricultural areas—principally from the South to the North—and occupation of farms vacated by death of the owner and not desired by the youth in these better farming areas, who, in turn, migrate to the cities.

3. Migration to and from farms more or less in balance in most regions. This has been about the situation considering the years 1930-1935 as a whole. In 1930 the net migration from farms was practically nothing. In 1931 the net migration *to* farms, according to the estimates of the Bureau of Agricultural Economics, was over 200,000 and in 1932 over 500,000. But in 1933 and again in 1934 the net migration *from* farms was over 200,000 in each year, and in 1935 it was probably somewhat larger.

4. Migration from the farms to the villages, supplemented, perhaps, by some migration from the cities to the villages.

Let us consider first some of the implications involved in a resumption of the rapid growth of the cities, as in 1920-1930 (with wide-spread decrease of the farm population), not only with reference to standards of living, but also with reference to the regional prospects for population growth and to land utilization.

Implications in Resumption of Heavy Farm-to-city Migration Relative to National Population Growth. An important consequence of a resumption of the migration from the farms to the cities would be a more rapid decline of the national birth rate than otherwise. Even should the birth rate fall no farther among either the farm or the city populations, the national birth rate would continue to decline because the proportion of the population having a low birth rate would increase and that having a high birth rate would decrease. A continued decline in the nation's birth rate will result after a few years in a declining population, unless the restrictions in immigration are relaxed, or unless there is a notable lengthening of the average span of life. Neither can be expected. It is possible that administrative restrictions on immigration might be annulled and the quotas restored. This might admit, if employment were available, a couple of hundred thousand immigrants a year, which would counterbalance the average decline in births (1924-1934) for only 3 or 4 years. It is probable that the expectation of life at birth may increase from the 61 years at present to 64 or 65 years, and it is barely possible that the increase may extend to 70 years. This would permit a proportionate decline in the birth rate (7 per cent and 17 per cent). The birth rate fell more than 2 per cent a year from 1924 to 1934.

It is assumed by many people that a decreasing population would result in a higher standard of living, presumably because of the tendency to concentrate agricultural production on the better lands, mineral production on the richer deposits, and industrial production in the more efficient factories. It is the author's opinion that these hopes will prove illusory, particularly if the decline in population is rapid. Vacant houses, empty storerooms, idle factories, abandoned farms will tend to lower rents and interest returns and thereby temporarily lower the cost of living, but the lessened return to capital is likely to depress gradually the spirit of enterprise, and may well lead to increasing dependence upon government. If the prospect of profit disappears such a result is certain. The decreasing number of children will probably diminish the incentive for saving. It is possible that progress in technique may more than counterbalance the trend toward consumption of capital, but this is by no means assured. Vacant buildings and abandoned lands are likely also to exert a depressing psychological influence. The greatly increased proportion of old people may have, likewise, a depressing effect.

More serious from the national standpoint than the immediate effects of a declining population will be the great difficulty of stopping the downward trend. The insufficient number of children in one generation to maintain population stationary will result in a smaller number of mothers, who will, unless the birth rate rises rapidly, give birth to a still smaller number of daughters. Thus a downward spiral in population is engendered. The probability is that once a decline in population sets in, caused by volitional control, it will become persistent and progressive.

Regional Prospects for Population Growth if Pre-depression Cityward Migration Is Resumed. If the cities again attract the surplus youth from the farms, it appears probable that the changes in population in the various parts of the United States will be similar during the coming decade to those during the decade 1920-1930, except in degree. Unless the restrictions on immigration are relaxed, the increase in the nation's population will be only about half as great during the decade 1930-1940 as during the decade 1920-1930. More than half of this increase during the last decade occurred north of the Potomac and Ohio rivers and east of the Mississippi, and a similar proportion, assuming pre-depression migration, seems likely to persist. California and Texas doubtless will continue to gain in population, and, possibly, Oklahoma. The Great Plains states, however, may follow the lead of Montana in experiencing a decrease in population. The continued mechanization of grain production probably will lead to larger farms, and be accompanied by a continued decrease in the farm population of these states. Moreover, with fewer farm people to be served, and with a poor prospect for any material increase in manufacturing in the Great Plains region, a stationary or decreasing urban population appears not unlikely. In the "Old South" the outlook is uncertain. Probably migration would about balance natural increase in many of these states.

This will mean heavy migration from the South, for 10 adults on southern farms are raising about 15 children. Should the birth rate remain stationary these 15 would have 22 children, and these 22 would have 33 children. In a century population would treble without migration. In the large cities of the North (or the South), on the other hand, 10 adults are having only 7 children. If the birth rate remained stationary, these 7 would have only 5 children, and these 5 only 3½. Without accession from outside, the population of the cities would decline to one-third in a century. Doubtless birth rates will continue to decline, rural as well as urban, but if the past forecasts the future the urban decline will be faster. One thousand southern farm people whose children and grandchildren remain on farms may have 10 times as many descendants a century hence as 1,000 city people.

Apparently, the people who will provide the surplus youth to the cities immediately or eventually will be principally the mountaineers of the southern Appalachians, the small farmers of the cotton belt, the hill folks along the Ohio River and its tributaries, the Mormons of Utah and Idaho, and other small or more or less self-sufficing farmers who have been partially isolated by their environment or other conditions from the influences of modern urban civilization.

If heavy migration of young people from the farms to the cities is resumed, some of these rural regions may decrease in population because of the migration, but some may increase because of the high birth rate or industrialization. Wages have been lower in these regions of surplus population than elsewhere, and if this condition persists and other costs of manufacturing and distribution are no higher, this cheap labor, if it is also efficient, as it generally appears to be, is very likely to promote the further development of industry.

Another class of territory which will tend to increase in population is that which attracts the wealthy and the old. Wealth is concentrating in the cities and probably in increasing degree in the hands of the elderly. The elderly will increase rapidly in number during the next few decades—persons over 65 increased 34 per cent between 1920 and 1930, and a similar increase will persist for at least two decades. Regions having a pleasant climate, beautiful scenery, and recreational facilities are likely to increase in population long after the decline begins in some less attractive parts of the nation.

Viewing the nation as a whole, if most of the increase of population takes place in the cities, the decrease in the farm population is likely to be almost universal, since the expansion of dry farming in the Great Plains region and development of new irrigation and drainage enterprises, which accounted for many of the local increases in farm population between 1920 and 1930, cannot be expected to provide so many new farms during the next decade. Population doubtless will decrease in many cities also. Between 1920 and 1930 there were 532 cities of more than 2,500 people in which a decrease of population was recorded, including four of between 100,000 and 250,000 population.

Cityward Migration and Land Utilization. With reference to land utilization a resumption of the cityward migration in pre-depression magnitude is likely to be associated with much the same consequences as those which characterized the decade 1920-1930. The trend toward the concentration of agricultural production on the more level, the more fertile, or the more favorably located land with reference to markets, or on land possessing peculiar advantages of climate, doubtless would continue. Agriculture would become probably even more commercialized, mechanized, possibly more specialized, and fewer people would be needed to supply the nation's need for food and fibers. Many farms in hilly regions, and many on poor soils, or on soils whose fertility has been depleted by erosion, also farms remote from good roads or other means of transportation, would be abandoned. Between 1920 and 1930 most of the increase in crop acreage occurred in the Great Plains region and on the Mississippi River bottom lands (Fig. 10). Almost everywhere in the originally forested region of the East and South a decrease in crop acreage occurred (Fig. 11). With resumed migration from the farms to the cities the decline in crop area in the East and Southeast might be expected to continue.

Migration from the Poorer to the Richer Agricultural Areas and from the Richer Areas to the Cities. The migration from the farms to the cities may become increasingly triangular in character: the movement of rural youth from the poor farming areas, particularly in the South, to the better farming areas, particularly in the North, increasing in magnitude, while the movement of youth from the better farms to the cities is resumed in pre-depression numbers. Such a trend is possible, if not probable, because:

a. The trend in the cities is toward an increasing proportion of the population engaged in distribution (trade and transportation) and the services (clerical, personal, professional, and governmental), while the number of factory workers and unskilled laborers decreases both relatively and absolutely. The great surplus was and is in unskilled labor. About two-thirds of the unemployed report their last occupation as in the unskilled and semi-skilled labor classes, whereas only about 45 per cent of all gainful workers were employed in such classes just prior to the depression.[1]

b. Owing primarily to relatively poor educational facilities in poor farming areas, particularly in the South, large numbers of the youth in such areas are fitted to perform only unskilled or semi-skilled labor when they move to the cities. They will, therefore, it seems likely, have greater difficulty than before the depression in obtaining employment in the cities. The youth in the richer farming regions, on the other hand, owing to better educational facilities, also to home environment and training possessing a larger urban influence, should have less difficulty in obtaining employment.

c. The number of old farmers has been increasing rapidly, particularly in the North, and the number of farms vacated by death will soon increase, indeed, is doubtless increasing at present. In the east north central states the number of farmers over 65 years of age increased from 107,000 in 1920 to nearly 130,000 in 1930, and in the west north central states from 77,000 to 110,000. If the children of many of these farmers, particularly the sons, have gone to the cities, it is probable that as such farmers die or retire the farms will be rented to tenants. And tenants from poorer farming areas, with lower standards of living, seem likely to obtain some of those farms, particularly the less desirable.

That such a migration from southern farming areas to the northern states was in progress before the depression is indicated by the 1930

[1] Federal Emergency Relief Administration, "On Relief," Washington, May, 1935, Chart XVII.

census returns on state of birth of the farm population. In Ohio about 10,000 persons in the farm population had been born in states to the north (New England, New York, the Lakes states, the Dakotas and westward), about 16,000 in states to the east (Pennsylvania and New Jersey), about 23,000 in states to the west (Indiana, Illinois, Iowa, Missouri, and west), but over 53,000 in states to the south (Maryland, West Virginia, Kentucky, Arkansas, Oklahoma, and states to the south). In Indiana, 8,000 had been born in states to the north, 24,000 in states to the east, 31,000 in states to the west, and nearly 40,000 in the South. In Illinois 13,000 were born to the north, 33,000 to the east, 29,000 to the west, mostly in Missouri—doubtless a large proportion of these in the Ozarks—and 34,000 in the South. In Missouri the corresponding figures are 27,000, 56,000, 27,000, and 85,000.

The net migration from farms in the southern states during the decade 1920-1929 was nearly 4,000,000. Only a small portion of this movement was to farms in the North. But with a condition of unemployment persisting in the cities, and with California no longer welcoming immigrants without capital, and with youth backing up on southern farms at the rate of 100,000 or perhaps more a year, the movement to northern farms may take on unprecedented magnitude.

To these youth migrating from southern farms even the income of a tenant on the better farms of the North may mean a higher standard of living, but as compared with the standard previously maintained by the owner, the usual result will doubtless be a reduction in the standard of living.

Migration to and from Farms about in Balance in Most Regions. The birth rate among the farm population of the United States as a whole was sufficient in 1930 to cause an increase of about 50 per cent each generation should no net migration occur. The birth rate in general is highest where the land is poorest and the income from farming is lowest, notably in the southern Appalachian area, the Ozarks, and much of the far South. In these areas, where population has been backing up rapidly during the depression, a large proportion of the population is already on relief. Unless new crops or types of farming are introduced, or great advances occur in prices of farm products or in skill in farming—none of which can be depended on to occur, indeed seem rather unlikely—a continued increase in the population of these regions, provided the present proportionate dependence on agriculture persists, cannot result other than in a further decline in the standard of living, unless expenditures for relief increase greatly. The poor people in the South constitute, in the writer's opinion, the greatest rural problem in the nation, yet they also constitute one of its greatest resources. It seems almost certain that they will be in increasing degree the progenitors of the nation's citizens of the future.

In the North, on the other hand, where the rural birth rate is lower and the farms are larger, no net migration of youth from farms might result in a rising standard of living. The cost of the contribution which the farm people have made to the productivity and prosperity of the cities, suburbs, and villages in the form of youth ready for life's work is greater than is commonly recognized. If it costs $2,000 to $2,500 (at pre-depression prices, perhaps $3,000 on northern farms) to rear and educate the average child on American farms to the age of 15, when he may be assumed to be self-supporting—and $150 a year does not seem an excessive estimate of the cost of food, clothing, medical services, education, and all the incidental expenses—then the 6,300,000 net migration from the farms during the decade 1920-1930 represented a contribution of about $14,000,000,000, or $1,400,000,000 a year. This was almost equal to the value of the wheat crop plus half that of the cotton crop during that period.[1]

Nor is this all. When the farmer and his wife grow old and die the estate is divided among the children. During the decade 1920 to 1930 about one-fifth of the farmers and their wives died, and these estates were distributed among the children. One-third to one-half of the children had moved to town, and those children who remained on the farm had to mortgage the farm in many cases in order to pay the brothers and sisters who lived in the cities their share of the estate. A rough estimate indicates that between $3,000,000,000 and $5,000,000,000 was drained from the farms to the cities and villages during the decade incident to the settlement of estates. This was an annual movement of $300,000,000 to $500,000,000, which was three to four times the annual value of the wool clip of the nation.

Although it is not intended to draw up a balance sheet of rural-

[1] It is recognized that in the South particularly had these youth remained on the farms the pressure of population on the meager natural resources would doubtless have induced a decline in the standard of living. But this does not alter the fact of the great contribution made by the farm people to the cities in this flow of youth. These youth have great value, and they were almost a free gift. The large cities (those over 100,000 population) had to feed, clothe, and educate less than half of the people who started to work in their offices, stores, and factories between 1920 and 1930—about 40 per cent came from the rural regions, 20 per cent from foreign lands, and only about 40 per cent from the cities themselves. State aid to rural schools has had ample justification. Had the cities borne the cost of all rural education during that decade their contribution would not have balanced that made by the rural people to the cities in the feeding, clothing, and other costs involved in rearing the migrating youth.

urban contributions, it is worthy of note, in passing, that there are great movements of farm wealth to the cities in addition to those incident to migration. Interest on debt paid to persons other than farm operators amounted to about $7,500,000,000 during the decade 1920-1929, and rent paid to persons other than farm operators amounted to about $10,500,000,000.[1] These payments are of a different character from the movement of wealth incident to migration, but there can be little doubt that portions of these payments were for the use of capital that had previously been transferred to the cities as a consequence of migration. The total of these interest and rent items, it will be noted, is only a little greater than that represented in migration, including the wealth that flowed to the cities in the settlement of estates. The total movement from these four sources appears to have been about $36,000,000,000 during the decade, or $3,600,000,000 a year, which was one-third of the average annual gross income of all farmers during the decade.

It seems quite likely that the cessation of this transfer of wealth to the cities would more than counterbalance the slow decrease in agricultural production per worker that probably would result in most of the North from cessation of migration to the cities. But without migration from rural areas, or from foreign countries, most cities would soon decline in population, and such a decrease in the commercial market might seriously depress the prices of farm products. However, such a decline in the commercial market appears almost inevitable eventually, because not enough children are now being born in the United States to maintain its population permanently stationary.

Migration to the Villages. The hope of preventing a declining population in the United States, without lowering the rural standard of living, appears to reside in a migration from both the cities and the farms to the villages, where conditions are more favorable to the rearing of a family than in the cities. This improvement in environment undoubtedly will need to be energized by a change in the philosophy of life on the part of many people, particularly the development of the family ideal and of a willingness by parents to sacrifice for the sake of children.

As yet, however, there is no clearly defined trend toward the decentralization of industry. The proportion of the nation's industrial workers living in the major industrial areas, in smaller industrial areas,

[1] Bureau of Agricultural Economics, *Crops and Markets*, November, 1932, p. 440, and July, 1927, p. 254.

and in villages and small towns has remained remarkably constant for a third of a century at least. The following table, prepared by Dr. Creamer, while employed by the Study of Population Redistribution, shows, however, that there has been a significant trend from the interior of large cities to their perimeters, and some trend toward the smaller industrial centers.[1]

TABLE 2

PERCENTAGE DISTRIBUTION AMONG TYPES OF LOCALITIES OF THE AGGREGATE OF WAGE JOBS IN MANUFACTURE IN THE UNITED STATES, 1899–1933*

Years	Industrial Areas			Other Cities of 100,000 Population	Peripheries of (D) Cities	Important Industrial Counties	All the Rest	Total
	Principal Cities (A)	Satellite Cities (B)	Industrial Peripheries (C)	(D)	(E)	(F)	(G)	
1933......	33.1	2.6	18.7	6.7	1.6	10.3	27.0	100
1931......	35.2	2.9	18.2	6.9	1.7	9.7	25.4	100
1929......	35.1	2.9	18.2	6.9	1.6	9.3	26.0	100
1919......	36.1	3.6	18.6	6.3	1.6	8.3	25.5	100
1899......	39.5	3.7	14.6	5.9	1.1	8.4	26.8	100

* Creamer, Daniel B., *Is Industry Decentralizing?* Univ. of Penn. Press, 1935, p. 10

During the depression the industries that relocated, involving, however, less than 1 per cent of all wage earners in industry, did tend to decentralize, as is shown in Table 3.

Should this trend continue and gain momentum, which is possible but scarcely probable, the standard of living among farmers should be

[1] Probably no device can do more than postpone the consequences of the persistent downward trend in births in the cities. Some cities are and all could be made pleasant places in which to live. Cities are the result of science, of progress in technique, and of "division of labor," and make modern standards of living possible. They provide markets for farm products and furnish the farm people with machinery, radios, household appliances, and most of the amenities of modern life. But with these good things have come also concentration of wealth, gradual proletarianization of the people, economic insecurity, crime in unprecedented magnitude, increasingly frequent disintegration of the family, and a reproduction rate now so low in the large cities that it would cause a decline of one-third in population each generation were there no accessions from outside. More serious, the decline in the birth rate is most rapid among the more intelligent and capable people. Can the good things of urban life be kept and the bad things sluffed off? Only through a profound change in the ideals of the people. This change, doubtless, will come first, if it comes at all, among the more intelligent classes—the business and professional groups.

higher than under conditions of migration to the cities, or of no net migration:

TABLE 3

SUMMARY OF NET CHANGES OF RELOCATED PLANTS IN THE UNITED STATES BY WAGE JOBS, 1928–1933

Net Gain or Loss (–) in Wage Jobs

Years	Industrial Areas			Other Cities of 100,000 Population	Peripheries of (D) Cities	Important Industrial Counties	All the Rest
	Principal Cities (A)	Satellite Cities (B)	Industrial Peripheries (C)	(D)	(E)	(F)	(G)
1932–33	– 4072	–901	2277	–893	1192	595	1802
1930–31	– 6585	1053	3559	446	112	34	1381
1928–29	–10529	–683	7332	871	412	1520	1077
1928–33	–21186	–531	13168	424	1716	2149	4260

1. The great economic advantages of the division of labor would be retained.

2. The closer market should diminish the costs of distribution of farm products, and these savings should tend to be divided between producers and consumers.

3. The near-by village people would help to bear the cost of many improvements, such as better roads and schools; this would enable farmers to have electric light, hospital facilities, and other services that were not previously economically feasible because of the sparse population of the agricultural area.

4. Farm youth, while still living at home, might find employment in the neighboring village; and in several types of farming in which work is slack at certain seasons, the farmers themselves might supplement the income from farming by temporary employment in the village industries or commercial establishments. Nearly a third of all farmers in 1929, according to the census, "worked for pay at jobs not connected with the farm they operated," and nearly an eighth worked more than 100 days in the year on such jobs.

5. Finally, in the village economy both the child and the aged can contribute to their own support, with benefit to their health and character, if the work is moderate. Gardening and the care of chickens,

sometimes of a cow also, provide almost as great opportunity for the employment of such labor as on the farm. This contribution of the child toward his or her support from perhaps 10 years of age onward, as well as the smaller cost of living in the village, particularly lower house rentals or values, should encourage larger families. These conditions seem likely also to encourage the movement of many old people to the villages from the cities.

Migration, of course, is not the only factor that will influence the rural standard of living in the future. The character and the conservation of the soil resources are also of great importance. And fully as important as the soil resources are the economic and social institutions, and the spirit, industry, and intelligence of a people. But all these factors tend to be reflected in migration.

THE PROSPECT FOR RURAL CULTURE

The prospect for rural culture, like that for standard of living, depends in large measure on the direction and extent of rural-urban migration. If migration from the farms to the cities is resumed in pre-depression magnitude, and in particular if such migration takes on increasingly the triangular character of movement of southern rural youth to northern farms and of northern rural youth to the cities, with probable increase in tenancy and absentee landlordism, the prospect is for a gradual change in northern rural conditions. Should migration from southern to northern farms become of great magnitude, rural culture in the North may tend to approach that in the South.

But should the employment situation in the cities retard the return of pre-depression conditions and result in a balance, more or less, between migration to and from farms, the prospect is for the development of a rural culture influenced greatly by the regional philosophy of life and soil resources. Owing to the lessening commercial demand for farm products as the cities decline in population, the farm people would undoubtedly try to produce many of the things they have become accustomed to buy. This trend toward self-sufficiency probably would affect rural culture profoundly. Many industries would be carried on within the home as they were a century ago; but doubtless the electric motor would generally supply the power, and technical knowledge and skill would be more complete than they were in the pre-commercial era. In such a culture some things which are now considered necessities, automobiles for example, might become luxuries; yet the happiness and the health of the people might be no less than today. It would be a simpler culture in all likelihood, semi-rustic in character, yet probably richer in sentiment and in the satisfactions of the spirit.

Undoubtedly, the family would become a more fundamental institution than it is today in our urban civilization. It may be that such an economic and social system is the alternative to socialism in some form, for an economic system and culture which does not provide for the reproduction of the race is certain to fade away. And the rapid downward trend in the birth rate in Russian cities suggests that socialism also may fail to provide sufficient incentive to family life and aspirations to prevent ultimately a persistent decline in population.[1]

Should decentralization of industry and commerce increase and rural and urban merge in what has been called a "rurban" civilization[2] the cultural consequences would also be profound. In southern New England there is much decentralization of industry and intermingling of rural and urban life. Conditions here might be considered a forecast of what would develop in many other parts of the United States. Part-time farms are numerous and most full-time farms are small and not highly productive, yet half to three-fourths of all farms have telephones, electric light, and water piped into the house, and one-third to one-half of the farm houses have bathrooms. These are higher ratios, except for telephones, than in all other states, with the single exception of California. There are also many beautiful rural houses of excellent architecture in New England—the highest state average value of farm dwellings in the entire nation is in Connecticut. These states rank near the top of all states likewise in school facilities and in school attendance, and the institutions of higher learning are renowned. Yet the rural birth rate remained practically stationary for 30 years from 1900 to at least 1930—the only portion of the United States where this is true—and the rural birth rate is almost high enough to counterbalance the small urban deficit and maintain population stationary. These things are not the result of unusually fertile soil, or of rich mineral deposits, but, instead, of a philosophy of life that stresses frugality rather than extravagance, culture rather than consumption, and the home as the ultimate measure of success.[3] Rural New England has de-

[1] However, the imminent danger in the U.S.S.R. is overpopulation. The rural birth rate is still very high, and the rural people constitute 75 per cent of the nation's population. Within 60 years at the present rate of increase Russia would have the population of China today.

[2] This word *rurban* was coined by Dr. C. J. Galpin, formerly head of the Division of Farm Population and Rural Life, in the United States Department of Agriculture. It is needed, and will, it is hoped, come into general use.

[3] See "Vermont: A Way of Life," by Walter Hard, *Survey Graphe,* July 1, 1932 (Vol. 68), p. 301.

veloped a civilization which deserves consideration by the people in other portions of the United States.

Among another people, particularly a people having a different philosophy of life, the results of the decentralization of industry might be different. If it facilitated the dissemination of urban ideals, particularly those that promote "conspicuous consumption," it might accelerate the decrease in the rural birth rate and hasten the decline in the national population.

It is hazardous to venture an opinion as to the future direction of rural-urban migration; nevertheless, it seems probable that there will be little development of decentralized industry in the coastal plain of the South, little, if any, in the Great Plains region of the West, and probably not much further development of industry in the western portion of the corn belt or the western cotton belt, or in the winter and spring wheat regions.[1] In these regions of commercial agriculture migration of the surplus youth from the farms to the cities and villages, and to farms in other regions, appears likely to continue until the birth rate falls to a level sufficient only to provide the farm population economically needed. It seems probable, furthermore, that the trend, particularly in the western cotton belt, the western corn belt, and the wheat regions, will be toward more machinery, larger farms, and a smaller farm population.

Probably also tenancy will continue to increase, and rent and interest payments will continue to be made to people living in the cities. The soil, meanwhile, will be gradually depleted of its organic matter by the tillage of the crops, notably corn, and in the South, cotton, unless a large proportion of the land is put into hay and pasture; the phosphorus and other elements of soil fertility will be slowly removed by the shipment of portions of the crops and of livestock to consuming areas, and restoration will require heavy expenditures for fertilizer or feed; erosion will tend to increase unless great efforts are made to control it—in brief, both the natural and human resources will tend to be depleted.

On the other hand, there may be further development of industry in rural portions of the Piedmont region and of the southern Appalachians, also in the corn and dairy belts as far west as the Mississippi River and, probably, on the Pacific coast. These regions may slowly,

[1] The proportion of the nation's factory wage-earners located in the west north central states has been declining since 1899 at least, and in the west south central states there has been no increase since 1919; see Creamer, *Is Industry Decentralizing?* Table 2, p. 13.

but probably only partially, approach the New England type of culture and agriculture. Hay and pasture appear likely to become more important, because of the favorable climate, the near-by urban markets for milk and dairy products, and the trend toward part-time farming, in which, owing to the high cost per acre of plowing and cultivating the land, there is a tendency to depend on pasturage for chickens, goats, or a cow. The denser population, particularly around the cities and towns, would justify extension of electric power wires, and gradually good roads would be provided to almost every farm. Farm children would be transported to village or town schools, and farm and suburban manner of life would tend to mingle and merge into a common culture.

IN CONCLUSION

Some Lessons from Abroad. Let us hope that this "rurban" culture will conserve not only the fertility of the soil but also the integrity of the family. Two years ago the writer of this chapter attended a conference of agricultural economists in Germany, and for a week before and a week after the conference the German hosts arranged for a few members of the conference to visit about 100 German farms, mostly "Bauern" or peasant farms. The writer's idea of the European peasant and his farm was greatly changed by this visit. He found the farmer, or "Bauer," a man proud of his ancestors, proud to be a farmer, and one who generally possessed a sense of superiority over city people. Although in many instances the house was built by the farmer's father or grandfather or great grandfather, it was built of brick, had a tile roof, the hall and kitchen floor were generally also of tile, and nearly every house had electric light. The typical bauer farm is 40 to 100 acres in size, but it produces as much as a 100- to 200-acre farm in most of the United States. The barns are generally much better built than in our country—almost always of brick, and frequently the floor that is over the stable and under the hay mow is made of steel I-beams with brick arches.

At each farm the visitors were provided with a page or two of mimeographed information about the farm. Most of the mimeographed sheet told of the acreage of the crops, yield per acre, fertilizer used, crop rotations, number of horses, total cattle, milk cows, swine, chickens, etc.; but always at the top of the page for those farms which could claim the honor, and most of them could, was a statement somewhat as follows: "This farm has been in the family 200 years." Some farms had been in the family for 400 years, some 500 years—one farm had been in the family since the eleventh century. As we considered what had happened during these centuries—wars, economic crises, periods of inflation and deflation, political revolutions—the thought came to us how many times would this family have lost its wealth had it been invested in anything else than land.

This concept of the farm as the hereditary home of the family has profound consequences. We saw practically no soil erosion in Germany, except in the vineyards on the steep slopes of the Rhine Valley. This absence of erosion is owing partly to the cool summer climate, with few torrential rains, partly to the crops grown, but partly also, and perhaps primarily, to the conviction that the land is the foundation of the family, the heritage from the past to be handed on to the next generation undiminished in fertility, and, if possible, with its productivity increased. One could sense among the German farmers the feeling that a man who lets his land erode away was not only dishonoring his ancestors but also depriving his son of the proper heritage. The German farmer is keeping faith with the past and with the future. He is conserving both the natural and the human resources. He has a philosophy of life which one wishes were more common in the United States today.

The influence of a philosophy of life upon the conservation of soil resources finds, perhaps, even better illustration in Japan. Japan proper, excluding Hokkaido, has about the same area as the southern Appalachian region, even less acreage of arable land, less coal, and less water power; but it supports more than ten times as many people as the southern Appalachians, and the productivity of its soils is increasing rather than decreasing. There is a shrine in nearly every Japanese farmer's house, or in the garden, dedicated to the veneration of his ancestors. These family shrines are an important reason for the conservation of the natural resources in Japan.

Should we stop for a moment to think about the things we owe to our ancestors, as the Japanese farmer does every day before his shrine, and as the German farmer does without a shrine, we might be surprised. Many of us owe the house we live in, perhaps also the land we cultivate, and all of us our system of government, our schools, our churches, our own education, indeed, our very lives, and to a large extent our ideals. There would be less need to discuss the conservation of soil resources and better land utilization in the United States, if every farmer had in his garden a shrine to his ancestors.

The Family in Relation to Better Land Utilization. In considering the problems of conserving the soil resources of the United States, the problems of land utilization, and, more recently, the problems of agricultural prosperity and of national welfare, the writer has come to the conclusion that there is no substitute for the institution of the family. The government can buy some of the land that is eroding, or land that has eroded badly, or is otherwise too poor to support a family in a decent manner, and convert this land into forest or grazing reserves. This should be done with millions of acres of land before it washes down into the rivers, causing floods and devastation. Fortunately a start is now being made by the Resettlement Administration and the Forest Service. But a much larger acreage of land must be used to grow crops, and undoubtedly most of these crops will be grown on privately owned land, as in the past.

For the better utilization of our arable land the writer has full faith only in the family farm, and in the family farm only in the case of the family with continuity of life and occupancy of the land. And continuity of family life and of land occupancy is dependent on a philosophy of life. There will not be, he fears, much better utilization of farm land in the United States, until more farmers pass the farm on to their sons. It has been difficult enough in the past for a young man to climb the ladder from hired man to tenant to owner of a farm, and it may be more difficult in the future because of the pressure of rural young people on the land. If the rural youth are unable to find work in the cities or villages, they must work the land. They will tend to work cheaply, and, as tenants, they will try to get as much as possible out of the land, unless it is given to them through inheritance and they can start, so to speak, at the top of the ladder, or unless the government extends a restraining hand.

The German farmer, when old age draws nigh, does not retire to the county seat, as many farmers in our corn and dairy belts did before the depression, and build a house that represents the savings of a lifetime, renting the farm to a tenant. Instead the "Vater" and the "Mutter" retire to a portion of the farm house, which is usually much larger and better built than farm houses in our corn belt, and a partnership contract is entered into with the son, who, with his family, occupies the remainder of the house. Sometimes a new house is built for the old folks or for the son. This son who later inherits the farm does not spend most of his life, nor does his wife, digging and delving and saving to pay off the mortgage on the farm; but in much of Germany he starts without debt, in a house that is usually built of bricks, with a tile roof, and his savings are in turn used to improve the farm and educate the children. The money that the German farmer makes in good times is mostly plowed back into the farm, so to speak—a new house or barn is built or a piece of land is drained, or better stock bought. Each generation climbs from the shoulders of the preceding generation, and wealth and culture accumulate, instead of being dissipated by migration to the cities.[1]

The young man who starts operating a farm in the United States today, unless he inherits it, generally has a harder task before him in acquiring wealth than many pioneer farmers of years ago on the frontier, for he starts with a load of debt. If the youth on the farms could start life free from debt, which is particularly heavy in agriculture because of the high ratio of investment to income, the farmers of the corn belt and the southern counties of the Great Lakes states, and in some of the best counties of the East and South and West, within two or three generations might reach a level of culture and comfort such as the world has never known. For no other nation in the world has so diverse a climate and agricultural production, so extensive an area of fertile soils, and so large a proportion of level or gently rolling land adapted to the use of machinery, with the possible exception of Soviet Russia, climatic condition so favorable to the two most productive feed crops, corn and alfalfa, and a market of nearly 100,000,000 nonfarm people with no tariff barriers between. Nature has been particularly gracious to our central West, and to many counties in the East, South and far West, but man has been taking nature's bounty and

[1] Where the farm constitutes the major portion of the estate and where there are several children, as is usual, the alternatives to debt are the division of the land, which would eventually result in small holdings, uneconomic in size, or in the failure of some of the heirs to receive an equal share of the estate. The writer suggests as a compromise the incorporation of the farm, a division of the shares of stock among the children, but with the heir who operates the farm paid a manager's salary, which should take precedence over dividends. In years of depression, or at other times, should the heirs who have left the farm need to seek shelter and sustenance, the homestead would provide a haven. This proposal has its weaknesses, which might be strengthened by legal provisions.

Some solution of this problem of rural debt and drain of wealth from the farms to the cities must be found. The present trend is toward the proletarianization of the rural as well as of the urban people. Mortgage debt during the recent economic depression probably has transferred hundreds of thousands of farms into the hands of unrelated and absentee owners. The American people are facing the decision as to whether the primary dependence for economic security shall be placed in the family or the state. History indicates that greater dependence, particularly in rural areas, can be placed upon the family. The extensive rural relief in the United States at present cannot be viewed as other than an emergency measure.

building out of it skyscrapers in the cities. Already many of these buildings are a quarter vacant, and unless the birth rate of the nation soon rises, they will be less needed a half century hence than they are now. Nature has provided in the corn belt and the southern portions of the Great Lakes states, in many of the valleys and plains of the eastern and western states, also in certain portions of the South, the basis for as fine a rural yeomanry as the world has ever known, but instead it is becoming a land of tenant farmers living in houses many of which are little better than hovels.

Economic Security. In the United States as a whole the proportion of the total value of farm real estate operated by tenants increased from about one-fifth in 1880 to more than one-third in 1930, and the debt on all farm real estate operated by owners increased from about 10 per cent in 1880 to more than 20 per cent in 1930. After subtracting the value of farm real estate operated by tenants and the amount of debt on farm real estate operated by owners, it appears that considerably less than one-half of the value of farm real estate was really owned by farm operators in 1930.

Can this trend toward loss of ownership of the land by the farm operator and transfer of title to people living mostly in the cities be reversed? Can the apparent trend toward concentration of ownership of urban property also be reversed? Can the people be assured that economic security which prudent men realize should precede the responsibilities of a family? Can the decline in the birth rate be reversed? Not, in the writer's opinion, without a change in the ideals of the people.

The development of science and the advance of invention, which have so multiplied the power of man to produce goods, have not diminished the need to maintain the integrity of the family and exercise the ancient virtues of thrift and sobriety. With a nation, as with an individual, it is not difficult to dissipate great wealth. Probably never in our nation's history has wealth been consumed at so rapid a rate as during the last five years. The soil resources are being depleted by erosion, oxidation of the humus, and removal of the essential elements of fertility—nitrogen, phosphorus, potassium, sulphur, and calcium—in the crops and livestock or livestock products, at an accelerating rate. The houses, factory buildings, and business structures of the nation probably have deteriorated in real value during the depression. The human resources, as measured by the inflow of children, have declined more than 20 per cent during the past decade. The nation's wealth is normally about five times the annual income. Only a few years of economic and social disorganization are required to deplete seriously the wealth of a nation. Nations have fallen in the past not through lack of knowledge of how to produce goods, but primarily because of a short-sighted philosophy of life, and the development of an economic system which undermined the family.

We must recognize that the present economic system and associated social ideals have acquired during the past century almost overwhelming momentum. If the trend toward extravagance, economic insecurity, and depopulation can be reversed at all, it will be among the rural people. And it will come only through the spirit of sacrifice, in the writer's opinion, particularly sacrifice for the sake of children. The past should be recognized as worthy of respect and study, and the future as more important than the present. This is the essence of conservation.

The rapid decline in the birth rate associated with the growth of the cities suggests strongly that land and life are closely related. It is becoming clear that the land is the foundation of the family, and that the family is the foundation of the state.

PART III

CHAPTER X

OUR FORESTS, PAST AND PRESENT[1]

BY J. R. WHITAKER

University of Wisconsin

Forest conservation is a field of vast significance in American life. The services which forests can perform are numerous and their influence far reaching. Moreover, the renewable character of forests makes for a very practical phase of conservation. With sufficient forethought, the nation's resources can be kept at a level more nearly commensurate with its needs for wood products and other forest services, and, at the same time, much of the land which is now unproductive but suited to growing trees may be put to use. In surveying the field of forest conservation, attention will be directed to our forest resources, to forest services and the problems growing out of their impairment, and to essential measures in forest conservation.

THE CHARACTER AND DISTRIBUTION OF OUR FORESTS

The Original Forests. The study of our forest resources and of problems in forest conservation may well begin with a survey of the forest regions, in terms of the original forest cover and of the original features which are still in existence. This survey will outline, directly or indirectly, the original forest wealth and the extent of depletion, the areas where the balance of nature has been most disturbed, and the possibilities each part of our country has for forest growth.

The forests of the United States included and still include an amazingly wide variety of economically useful timber trees. It is true that in the humid tropics the forests are richer in species, and that in Russia there are larger areas of uninterrupted forest, but nowhere else does there exist so vast a forest area combined with so large a number of

[1] For a critical reading of the entire manuscript of Part III, the assistance of Edward C. Prophet, Michigan State College, is acknowledged with gratitude.

useful species. At least 100 species are of recognized economic value, and about 200 may be considered in forest management.

The general distribution of the original forests is easily kept in mind. They formed two broad belts, one extending inland from the Atlantic Ocean to the Mississippi River and beyond, the other inland from the Pacific to the Rockies (Fig. 1). The eastern belt covered highland and lowland alike, whereas the western was and still is interrupted by many areas of non-forest land. The eastern forest is both evergreen and deciduous in composition, the deciduous predominant; the western is

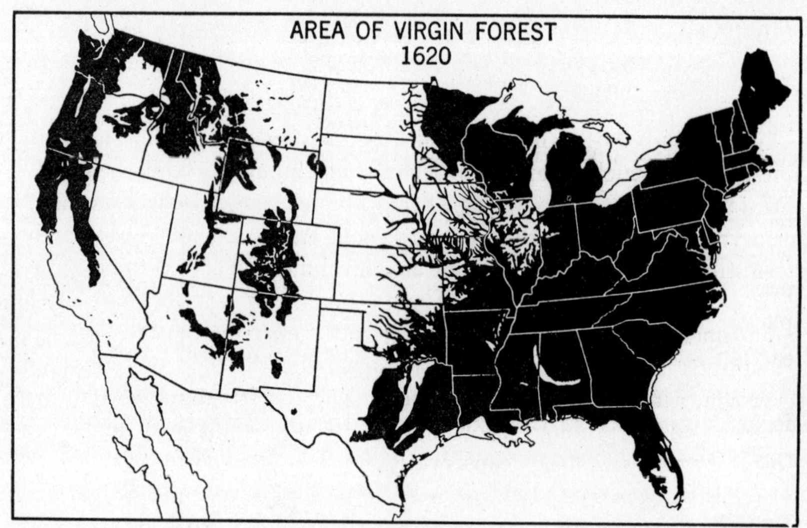

Courtesy, U. S. Forest Service

FIG. 1. The Distribution of Forests in 1620.
Areas of sparse woodland in the Southwest are not shown.

distinctly coniferous. The two meet in the great Canadian forest, which extends in a broad sweep from the Atlantic to the Pacific.

The distribution of the original forest cover and, therefore, of the potential forest land, is understood, in the main, in terms of the amount and distribution of rainfall, although surface configuration, drainage, and soils have played subordinate parts. Trees can grow on slopes far too steep for farming, and most species do not make great demands on soil fertility, but nearly all are rather exacting in their moisture requirements. Long droughts, or rainfall so light as to leave the subsoil dry, may exclude forest growth, and the distribution of precipitation affects vitally the kind of growth that does exist.

That part of the United States occupied by the eastern forest is mainly composed of hills and undulating plains (see Figs. 1 and 2, Appendix), low enough to permit moisture-laden winds to sweep far inland from the Atlantic Ocean and Gulf of Mexico (Fig. 3, Appendix). Precipitation is heaviest during the summer. The favorable rainfall, the long frost-free season, and relatively fertile soils enable the hardwoods to reach their greatest development here, and exclude the conifers almost entirely, or restrict them to swamps, sandy plains, rocky slopes, and mountain heights. The relatively large extent of sandy lands, however, has made for comparatively large coniferous areas, particularly in the northern parts of Michigan, Wisconsin, and Minnesota, and in the coastward parts of the southern states.

In the central section of the country, the rainfall is not sufficient to support forest growth, and grassland becomes dominant, the natural forest being found chiefly along streams. The fact, however, that the rainfall in the eastern part of the prairie region, in central Illinois for example, is sufficient to permit the growth of trees if planted and protected, leads to the conclusion that it is not low precipitation alone which has prevented the growth of trees in that area. West of the prairies, where moisture is insufficient for forest growth, lie grassy plains which have always separated the two great forest areas, the eastern and the western.

In contrast with the original forest cover of the East, the western forests were markedly discontinuous. In the main, they occupy the rainy western slopes of mountains. As a consequence there are two divisions—the mountainous region near the Pacific Ocean, and the Rocky Mountain area. Between are vast plateau areas of grass and desert shrub, interrupted here and there by wooded mountain blocks. On the western coast the rainfall decreases from north to south, and the summer dry season, a few weeks long in Washington, lengthens to several months in southern California. On the lowlands and valleys of the south, the hot dry summers and the winters of scanty rainfall make forest growth impossible, leaving the land to grasses and desert shrubs. On the mountains, where the rainfall is heavier, with a longer rainy season and less evaporation, dense forests occur, extending upward to about 8,000 or 9,000 feet. Above this level, the strong winds and severe winters hinder tree growth, the upper limit being encountered at about 10,000 feet. Sufficient rainfall for forests occurs on both mountain slopes and valley floors in the northern part of the coastal division. Primarily because of the relatively dry summers, hardwoods are of little significance throughout the West, yielding the land to more

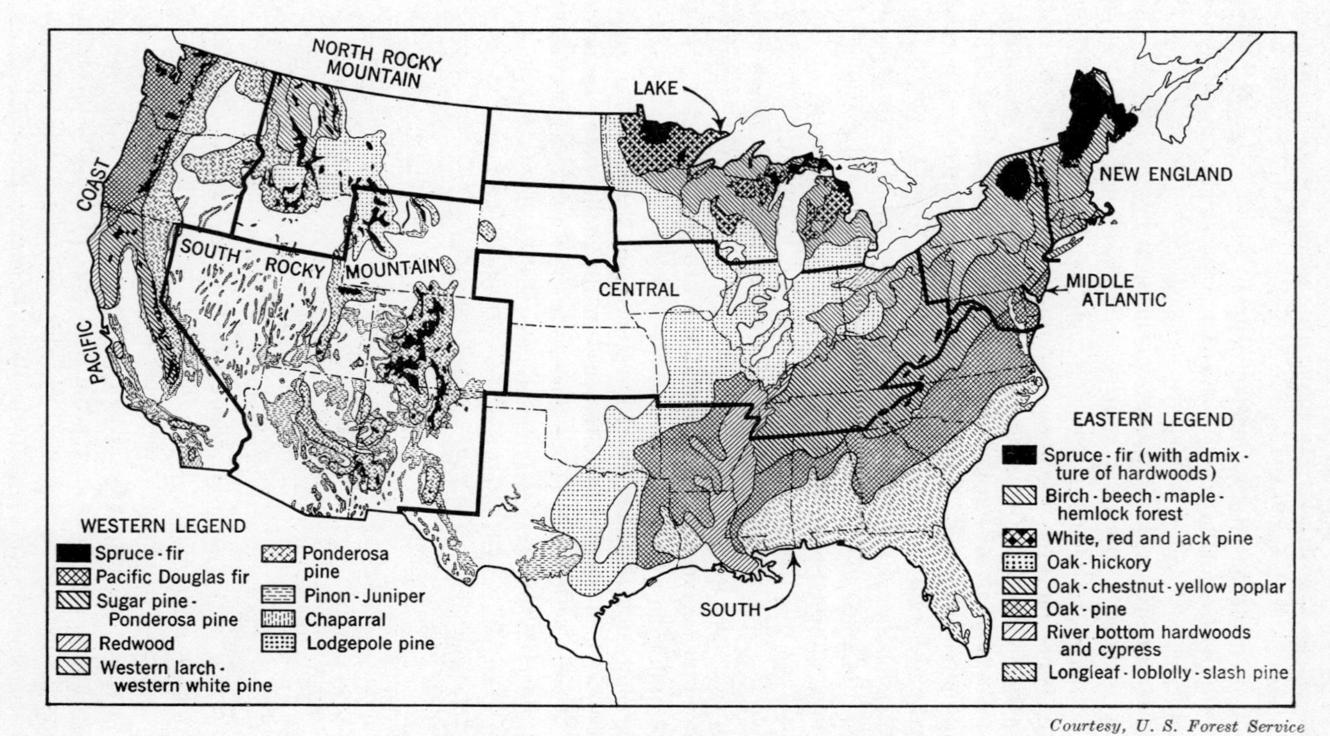

Courtesy, U. S. Forest Service

FIG. 2. Forest Regions and Principal Types of Forest.

hardy conifers. The Rocky Mountain area is likewise predominantly coniferous.

West and east, the original forests covered about 43 per cent of the area of the country, 48 per cent if the open woodland of the Southwest be included.

The Forest Regions. If attention is directed from the general distribution of coniferous and deciduous forests to the traits involved in the utilization and conservation of forests in different parts of our country, it becomes necessary to recognize many different types of forest cover (Fig. 2). The resources and the problems of conservation are distinctive for each type. They are divided by the federal Forest Service into eight groups of states, each group dominated by one, two, or three forest types.

In the Pacific coast division, the ranges of southern California are clothed with an open, drought-resistant woodland, the chaparral, primarily valuable for watershed protection. The chaparral is a mixed woodland of stunted hardwoods and shrubs, ranging from impenetrable thickets to open stands of dwarfed oaks. It covers land of little direct use for agriculture, but of great indirect value as the watershed which supplies a large part of the irrigation and domestic water necessary for man's present use of the adjacent valleys. The chaparral also clothes the foothills of the Sierra Nevadas, grading into dense stands of pine and fir at higher levels. The redwood belt, confined to a narrow strip of the northern coast of California, is of great economic importance, too. Douglas fir is dominant in the coastal belt of Oregon and Washington, and extends eastward to the summits of the Cascades. Northward, the Pacific coast forests are continued in British Columbia and southern Alaska.

Variations in the composition of the Rocky Mountain forests resemble those of the western coast in being closely related to temperature contrasts dependent on differences in altitude. Stunted pines, cedars, and oaks are found at lower elevations, western yellow pine is typical of the next higher belt, and at higher altitudes occur Douglas fir and lodgepole pine.

As a consequence of less favorable climatic conditions, the stands are far less valuable than those of the Pacific coast. Bushwood occupies a large portion of the area, and the stands of pine and fir are open and the trees comparatively small. Here, as in much of southern California, a large part of the value of the forest cover is in watershed protection.

The Lake states region, about 900 miles east of the Rocky Mountains, is a mosaic of coniferous, hardwood, and mixed forests. Being on the climatic transition between the hardwoods to the south and the coniferous forest of Canada to the north, the type of forest is closely related to soil conditions: hardwoods on the better-drained, richer soils, and pines on the sandy, swampy, and stony lands. Chiefly valuable in the past have been the stands of white and Norway pine. The most extensive areas of white pine were found in Michigan on sandy soils. Similar stands, though smaller, were found in Wisconsin and Minnesota, and pines were scattered through the hardwoods in all three states. The New England and middle Atlantic states also have had large areas of pine and spruce similar to that found in the Lake states, though the white pine seldom formed clean stands of large extent, being more commonly mixed with spruce and other conifers and hardwoods. In all three sections, the conifers are set in a matrix of hardwoods, which become predominant toward the southern margin (Fig. 2).

The hardwoods of the central states occupy a humid area of relatively fertile soils. Here oak was dominant in the original forest association, with a background of such species as hickory, elm, maple, and walnut. This was probably the largest hardwood forest in the world, outside of the humid tropics. Easily accessible, early occupied by settlers, destined to be a region of thriving cities, it soon became the chief source of the nation's hardwood supply, though in more recent years a large part has been drawn from the bordering regions, north, east, and south.

The South, like the Lake and New England states, had, originally, vast resources in both hard and soft woods. The oak-hickory and the oak-chestnut-yellow poplar types extend into the southern states; and in addition, they contain extensive oak-pine forests and hardwood areas of the "river bottom" type. More prominent in the lumbering industry of the nation, however, has been the great pine forest known as the Southern Pineries, which stretches from North Carolina to Texas. These southern pines have constituted a major source of saw timber and of naval stores.

Forest Depletion. In this sketch of the original forest resources and regions of the United States are numerous references to forest depletion. Indeed, no more extensive or significant modification of the natural landscape has taken place during the occupation of this continent by the white man, than the wide-spread alteration of the original forest cover.

Clearing the land for farms has been the chief factor in the reduction of the forest area in the United States. To the early settlers, the forest cover was a decided obstacle and had to be removed, by ringing (also called girdling), cutting, and burning, whether a market for timber was available or not. About 24 per cent of the original eastern forest had been cleared for farms by 1880, most of the timber being burned or left to decay in heaps on the ground or in the valley bottoms. Since that time, the timber cut in land clearing has generally been marketed.

The conversion of forests into farms was the chief cause of depletion in the central and middle Atlantic divisions, but in the Lake, southern, and Pacific coast areas, commercial lumbering has been the predominant process of forest removal. With the rail and industrial expansion of the 'seventies and 'eighties, lumber manufacture ceased to be a local industry centering on agricultural villages, and by 1880 large timber companies had systematic production under such headway that lumbering equaled land clearing in the rate of forest destruction. For the last five or six decades timber has been cut chiefly in response to demand for wood products.

Hand in hand with lumbering has gone destruction by fire. Much land that would naturally have reforested itself after logging operations has been burned over, not once but many times, so that together the two are mainly responsible for the large acreage of so-called forest land which now possesses but little forest cover. Although included in the estimates of the nation's resource in *forest land*, the cut-over land is properly referred to as *idle* where the services derived from it are of negligible importance. It should not, however, be referred to as *waste land*, for it is still available for some kind of use, known or yet to be discovered.

These processes of forest depletion have been carried out under a peculiarly favorable set of contributing circumstances. Among the foremost of these has been the attitude that the forests were a barrier to settlement and therefore to be removed as soon as possible, an attitude that persisted long after the barrier quality had disappeared. Hostility to forests became "ingrained in the American spirit," and hastened the removal of forests from land for which there was no competitive use.

Closely related to this attitude was the common assumption that all land humid enough for agriculture (as all forest land is) should be developed as farm land. The literature of the nineteenth century clearly reveals this firm conviction, which persisted through the first two decades of the twentieth century. Nor were Americans alone in this error. The Canadians pushed northward into the vast rocky northland, the Laurentian Shield, in like faith that the plow would follow immediately after the ax. As a consequence, forests were cleared from vast acreages in no wise suited to agriculture under present conditions, both in Canada and in the United States.

Carelessness in dealing with our forest resources and indifference toward their rapid depletion were bred, too, by the firm conviction that our timber supplies were inexhaustible. The early settlers came from countries where woodland was scarce to a land of untold forest riches. It was only natural that they should have firmly believed that the forests of America could never be brought visibly close to exhaustion. The nineteenth century was nearly over before this misconception was seriously challenged. Regional inventories being lacking, it proved impossible even then for anyone, not even the more experienced lumbermen, accurately to estimate the extent of our resources as related to current depletion. Moreover, the decline of production in each region, as in New England, was masked by an increasing output from others. The competition between regions gave a false notion of our total reserves, brought low prices which stimulated consumption, and caused the marketing of high grades at low prices, a condition which tended to exclude the low grades from the markets and to advance the rate of cutting.

Finally, it should be noted that the depletion of our forests has been far more rapid than that called for by an orderly response to market demand. Removal has been hastened by taxes which have placed a disproportionately heavy share of the tax burden on forest property, and by heavy investments plus carrying charges which have practically forced early liquidation through cutting. In addition, the magnitude and the isolation of large timber operations have frequently caused owners to continue production in the face of an overloaded market.

The Present Forest Resources. If the brushwoods of the Southwest be included, the area supporting or available for and capable of supporting a forest cover is 615,000,000 acres in contrast to an original 915,000,000. The area thought capable of producing timber of commercial quality and quantity under present or conceivable future conditions is now about 495,000,000 acres, or one-fourth the land area of the country, in contrast to the original 820,000,000 acres of comparable forest land (Fig. 3). The shrinkage in forest land has occurred chiefly in the eastern part of the Mississippi drainage basin, as a result of the extension of farm land. Although yielding the land to a higher use, this shrinkage of forest area has contributed to the seriousness of the various problems arising from forest depletion.

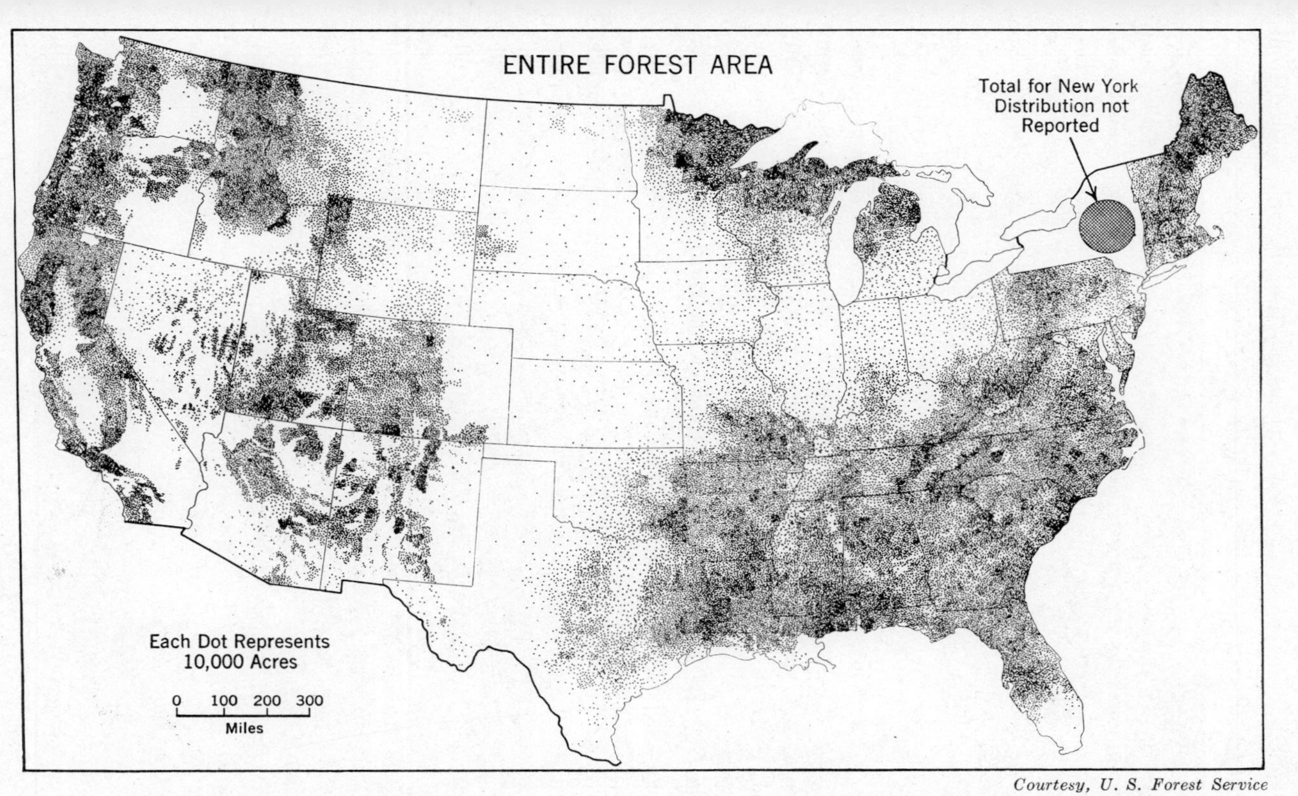

Courtesy, U. S. Forest Service

FIG. 3. Distribution of All Lands Supporting or Available for and Capable of Supporting a Forest Cover.

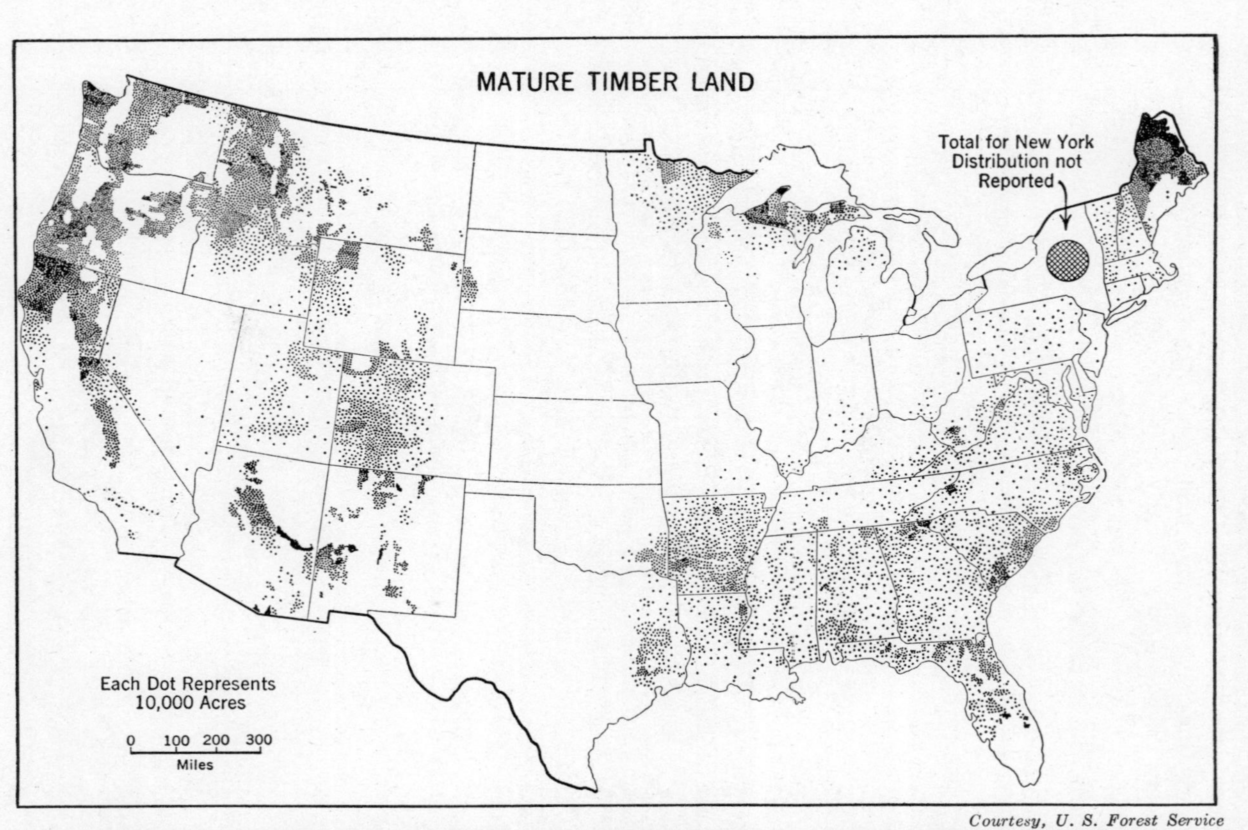

Courtesy, U. S. Forest Service

Fig. 4. Distribution of Land Supporting Timber of such Size as to be Currently Merchantable.

The deterioration of the cover of the remaining forest land is far more significant than the decrease in total area. Instead of all our forest land being in commercial timber of saw-log size, the proportion in low grade cut-over is nearly twice as great as that in saw timber (Fig. 4 and Table 1). Moreover, the second-growth saw timber is commonly far inferior to the original stand. The problem should also

TABLE 1

COMMERCIAL FOREST AREA OF THE UNITED STATES, BY CHARACTER OF GROWTH AND REGION, 1933

Region	Total		Saw-timber Areas			Cord-wood Areas	Fair to Satisfactory Restocking Areas	Poor to Non-restocking Areas
			Total	Old Growth	Second Growth			
	Thousand acres	Per Cent	Thousand acres	Thousand acres	Thousand acres	Thousand acres	Thousand acres	Thousand acres
New England	27,273	6	13,860	7,976	5,884	4,843	6,145	2,425
Middle Atlantic	27,139	5	7,294	26	7,268	10,518	5,998	3,329
Lake	55,895	11	5,095	2,664	2,431	8,880	28,165	13,755
Central	64,249	13	21,224	1,664	19,560	25,592	12,245	5,188
South	190,758	39	57,265	14,338	42,927	52,702	37,236	43,555
Pacific Coast	66,685	13	44,140	38,892	5,248	6,683	6,190	9,672
North Rocky Mountain	32,329	7	17,026	15,172	1,854	5,704	5,933	3,666
South Rocky Mountain	30,570	6	22,741	18,123	4,618	5,959	161	1,709
Total	494,898	100	188,645	98,855	89,790	120,881	102,073	83,299

Source: *A National Plan for American Forestry*, Vol. I, p. 126.

TABLE 2

STAND OF SAW TIMBER IN THE UNITED STATES, BY CHARACTER OF GROWTH AND REGION, 1933

In million feet board measure

Region	Total		Softwoods			Hardwoods		
			Total	Old Growth	Second Growth	Total	Old Growth	Second Growth
		Per Cent						
New England	57,875	3	32,811	18,977	13,834	25,064	10,295	14,769
Middle Atlantic	26,150	2	8,245	144	8,101	17,905	195	17,710
Lake	35,887	2	9,193	7,656	1,537	26,694	13,327	13,367
Central	34,622	2	2,900	1,146	1,754	31,722	6,332	25,390
South	199,297	12	121,449	37,312	84,137	77,848	32,866	44,982
Pacific Coast	1,041,628	62	1,038,909	957,208	81,701	2.719	1,421	1,298
North Rocky Mountain	146,388	9	146,388	142,680	3,708	....	....	....
South Rocky Mountain	125,956	8	125,955	116,215	9,740	1	1	....
Total	1,667,803	100	1,485,850	1,281,338	204,512	181,953	64,437	117,516

Source: *A National Plan for American Forestry*, Vol. I, p. 176.

be viewed in its regional aspects, for averages obscure the critical situation that obtains locally.

With barely half of the forest land of New England in saw timber, and that in relatively inaccessible localities, the region is notably deficient in timber reserves. Less than a tenth of the land available for forests in the Lake states in 1933 was bearing saw timber. The middle Atlantic division has suffered about as severely, and nearly all the remaining timber of the central states is in farm woodlands. Although the forests of the South have been seriously depleted, they remain one of the chief assets of that region and of the nation. Unlike New England and parts of the middle Atlantic states, practically all the timber is easily accessible, except in restricted areas of swamp and mountain. Less than one-third of the softwood saw timber of the Pineries is old growth, however, and restocking is slow and the second-growth timber of relatively low grade.

The western forests have suffered the least depletion, next to those of Alaska. Large areas are inaccessible, however, and all are distant from the eastern market. Even so, forest removal is proceeding at a rapid pace, leaving in its wake local problems, as in southwestern Washington and northwestern Oregon, where restocking is not taking place. The relative abundance and high quality of the forests of the West serve to emphasize by contrast the major fact in forest depletion in the United States—the tremendous reduction of forest resources east of the Great Plains.

The Alaskan forests, not included in the statistical data cited in this discussion, have scarcely been touched. It is the declared purpose of the nation to benefit from the experience gained in three centuries of forest exploitation by applying the lessons thus learned to securing a more orderly development of Alaskan forests, chiefly valuable, it appears, for the production of pulpwood.

FOREST SERVICES AND PROBLEMS RESULTING FROM FOREST DEPLETION

As the forests of the nation have been depleted, the services which they perform for individual regions and for the entire country have been impaired or destroyed. Moreover, changes in the life of the nation, such as the growing need for recreational lands and for wood pulp, have thrown an increasing burden on the remaining forests. Out of this situation have arisen many problems in forest conservation, some of them suggested in the preceding discussion. As the next step toward an understanding of our forest resources and their conservation, the services derived from forests will be examined, together with the problems which their depletion and the increased demand for their services have created.

This analysis of the impairment of forest services through resource depletion is not, obviously, to be taken as a wholesale indictment of forest removal. Even so, it is clear that there has been much needless damage, and that, moreover, a definite program of action is necessary to meet the problems which forest depletion, whether justifiable or not, has brought in its wake.

Supply of Wood Products. Wood products have been used freely if not lavishly throughout the history of the United States. Abundantly supplied with both softwoods and hardwoods of high quality, the people of this country early developed distinct culture traits, such as styles in furniture and in residential architecture, directly related to the quality and quantity of the timber resources. Although the per capita consumption of lumber has declined somewhat since 1906, the tradition of liberal use of wood products has persisted, and the demand for pulpwood has increased many fold since that date. Unquestionably, too, the decline in lumber consumption is a measure, in part, of the rising cost of timber of high quality. We can accommodate ourselves to a marked decrease in use of wood products only by dropping out of American life much that has distinguished it, and by turning to non-renewable resources, a shift highly objectionable from a conservational point of view. The presence of a shortage of desirable woods, the cost imposed by transportation charges, and the threat of still more serious deficiencies in the near future are outstanding phases of the wood-supply problem which now faces the nation.

Only by successive migration from exploited to relatively virgin areas have the forest industries postponed the time when this problem would have to be attacked on a national scale (Fig. 5). The hardwood industry, for example, began in New England and along the Atlantic coast, spread westward through New York and Pennsylvania, and became important in Ohio and Indiana after water and rail transportation developed. It then spread northward into the Lake states and southward into Kentucky, Tennessee, and adjacent areas. Following depletion of these various areas, the industry moved to the largest remaining stand, in the lower Mississippi Valley.

The dominant place in softwood production was held at the middle of the last century by the New England states, then by New York and Pennsylvania, followed by the Lake states, where about one-half of the annual output of the softwood lumber of the country was being cut in the early 'nineties. The industry then shifted to the South and

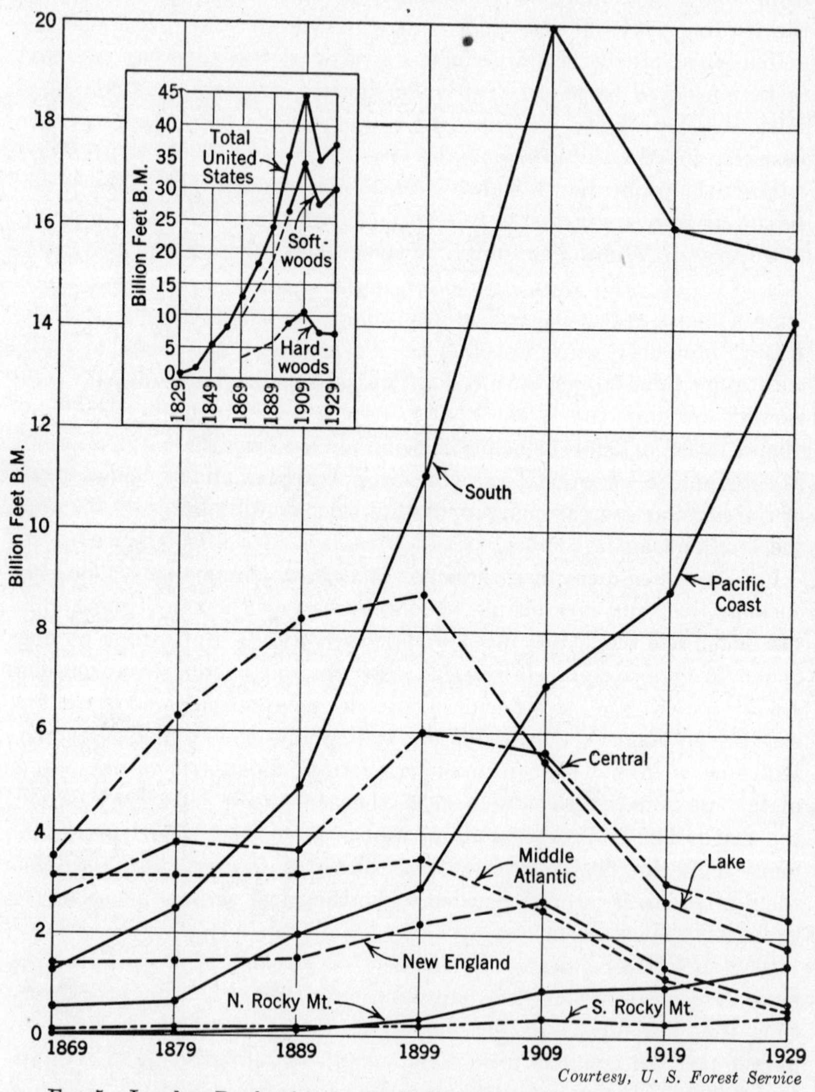

Courtesy, U. S. Forest Service

FIG. 5. Lumber Production in the United States by Regions. 1869-1929.

to the Pacific coast. Southern softwoods reached a peak in 1909 (Fig. 5), though Washington became the leading state in 1905. In 1929, Washington, Oregon, California, and Idaho produced about a half of the total softwood lumber of the country. For more than a decade, Pacific coast timber has dominated the Lake states market, and it is being sold in considerable quantities in the South. Douglas fir is now the leading type of saw timber in the United States, whereas the prized white pine of the Lake states makes up less than one per cent of the stand of softwood. This migration of the dominant source of softwoods across the continent took place in less than seventy-five years.

The last major forest region having been drawn upon, the limited extent of our forest assets has become reasonably clear. Moreover, new aspects of the timber-supply problem have appeared as a result of this sweep of forest exploitation across the country.

As a consequence, the bulk of the remaining timber resources of the United States is far removed from the principal market (Table 2), with more than 60 per cent in the Pacific coast region, and nearly 80 per cent west of the Great Plains. This great distance between producing areas and the principal consuming area, which lies east of the Mississippi and north of the Ohio and Potomac rivers, shows itself in burdensome freight charges, despite special rail-rate concessions to the lumber trade.

On the other hand, the timber in and near this area of maximum consumption has been depleted disastrously without adequate provision for renewal. Most of the old-growth stands are of poor quality or are in remote, sparsely settled areas with poor transportation. The second-growth saw timber consists, in the main, of scattered trees. The growing shortage of hardwoods, for example, is one of the major consequences of this depletion of eastern forests. Contributing one-fourth of the cut of saw timber each year, they constitute only one-tenth of the stand. The end of the virgin supplies is in sight. The impoverishment of the saw-log reserves east of the Great Plains is considered by the United States Forest Service to be the most serious phase of the timber-supply problem.

The depletion of eastern forests has forced the nation to the use, in part, of inferior woods. The remaining old timber is less satisfactory than that already taken out, hemlock instead of white pine for example, and the young growth is commonly inferior to the virgin timber. This change is clearly seen in the furniture industry, which is being forced to rely less and less on such cabinet woods as black walnut. This phase of the problem can be solved only in part by the importation of tropical hardwoods.

A serious problem in pulpwood supply has likewise grown out of the depletion of the eastern forests. As the spruce forests of the northeastern states approached exhaustion, the mills imported more and more pulpwood and pulp from Canada. Inertia, large investments, proximity to markets, presence of cheap water power for making mechanical pulp, and lack of technical knowledge of pulp resources of other areas, all favored importation rather than relocation of plants. Great strides in recent years in the technology of paper manufacture have, however, made practicable the use of a wide variety of species, including yellow poplar, jack pine, and the southern pines. The pines of the South now dominate the market in kraft papers; and a beginning has been made in book and magazine papers, based on methods discovered at the Forest Products Laboratory, Madison, Wisconsin. Full use of the species now available, two-fifths of which occur in the South, would remove much of the necessity for dependence on Canada, where prohibition of the export of unmanufactured pulpwood cut from crown lands is already in force. The expansion to unused pulp resources can be only a temporary expedient, however. Paper mills remain costly investments and consume enormous quantities of wood. To prevent the economic losses from repeated plant relocation and to provide a supply of pulpwood over a period of many decades, it will be necessary to provide new crops of trees on a part of our cut-over land.[1] For some species, this can be done within the relatively short span of twenty years. The production of wood pulp thus becomes one way of meeting the land-use problem created by deforestation.

The timber-supply problem in its various aspects gives promise of becoming far more acute in the near future if the present ratio of consumption to production is maintained. Our forest capital is disappearing at a rapid rate, for the current drain on forests of the country is several times as great as the rate of growth (Table 3). Nor is it possible to meet a major share of our timber needs through imports except at prices much greater than those which have prevailed during the last few decades.

Canada, the United States, and Russia have 80 per cent of the coniferous forests of the world, yet in Canada, as well as in the United States, annual cutting, combined with fire and other losses, greatly exceeds annual growth. Wood-importing countries of western Europe now rely to a large extent on Russia, but recent studies show that

[1] Charles H. Herty, at the Savannah laboratory, has demonstrated that excellent newsprint paper can be made from young southern slash pine that may be grown on the cut-over lands of the Coastal Plain. One large mill is now (1936) being constructed and plans are made for a second. (Editors.)

TABLE 3

THE RATIO OF CURRENT ANNUAL DRAIN TO GROWTH

(1925–1929 Basis)

Region	*Combined Saw Timber and Cordwood*	*Saw Timber*
New England	1.7	2.5
Middle Atlantic	1.3	1.9
Lake	2.1	23.7
Central	2.0	7.6
South	1.5	3.9
Pacific Coast	5.1	10.5
North Rocky Mountains	1.4	4.1
South Rocky Mountains	0.9	1.7
All Regions	1.8	5.1

Source: *A National Plan for American Forestry*, Vol. I, p. 222.

Russia, with two-fifths of the world's coniferous forest area, faces the end of her readily accessible timber supply in Europe in ten to twenty years, and in western Siberia in the next thirty-five years. Russian forests are being recklessly cut, with little or no provision for renewal. The conclusion seems inescapable that the forests of Canada and Russia cannot long continue to meet the demands now being made on them. There are large hardwood areas in the humid tropics on which we are drawing, and shall unquestionably continue to rely, for valuable cabinet woods. It is hardly wise to place great dependence on them, however, in view of their location and of the adverse labor and transportation conditions which exist. Raphael Zon concludes that timber prices will have to go much higher if the Amazon or Congo basins are ever to contribute an important share to the world's timber trade. In view of the world situation, therefore, it seems unlikely that a major part of our timber requirements can be met by imports, without greatly increased costs. A satisfactory solution must be sought within our own country.

Stable Communities Based on Forest Industries. The wood-supply problem has been viewed from the angle of the consumer. From the standpoint of the manufacturer, who is interested in raw materials, and of the public-spirited citizen, who is concerned for the welfare of the local community and of the state, the local exhaustion of timber supply has presented another problem—the migratory character of the lumber industry, and consequent losses in economic and in less tangible values. This problem has not aroused national concern for it has been obscured by the repeated shift of the industry to virgin fields. From the state and local points of view, however, the transient nature of the lumber industry has presented a major problem since

Colonial times, particularly where non-agricultural areas have been involved.

The sequence through which lumber communities tend to pass has been repeated over and over in each forest region. Where agricultural resources prove inadequate to support a thriving farm population, the decline of lumbering is followed by thorough decay of the community and by consequent loss to the state and nation. The rise and decline of lumbering in the northern part of the Lower Peninsula of Michigan furnishes a clear illustration.

While lumbering was flourishing in this part of Michigan, population steadily increased, villages and cities grew up, and thousands of settlers took up farms, marketing their products in the logging camps and milling centers. But after a few decades, logging and fires had destroyed all but scattered fragments of the original forest. The number of employees in camps and mills dropped from many thousands in 1889 to a few hundred in 1929. Many railroad lines were abandoned, leaving farmers without adequate transportation. As the cost of roads, schools, and other government services mounted, taxable rural values declined, and the income of local governmental units was, perforce, greatly decreased. Many farmers, no longer able to find winter work in the woods and deprived of a local market for their produce, left the region, the number of farms in the cut-over northern counties of the Lower Peninsula decreasing 27 per cent between 1910 and 1930. As the forest industry waned and farmers became less prosperous, the villages and towns lost their chief support and dwindled away. A desolate cut-over of barren sands or scrubby second growth, abandoned or poverty-stricken farms, and ghost-like community centers have characterized this final stage in the sequence of forest exploitation of non-agricultural land, a sequence which ordinarily has required but twenty-five to forty years from beginning to end.

The decay of forest communities is not peculiar to Michigan. Stressing particularly the loss in social values, Chambers' account of lumbering in the Pine Woods area of southeastern Texas reveals the same sequence:

> The passing of a large saw mill is a community and sectional tragedy. The company necessarily absorbs heavy losses of "fixed" capital invested in buildings, machinery, railroad, and other equipment that cannot be diverted to another use. Every family in the community is thrown out of economic adjustment. Wage earners and salaried men seek employment in other sawmills, and failing this they must enter other occupations. Local institutions such as the

> church and school decline rapidly. Usually the community does not secure another economic base and undergoes complete disintegration. As families move away houses become vacant. They may be purchased for as little as five dollars each by persons who wreck them to secure lumber. Failing this fate these old dwellings are abandoned to burn in some woods fire or to slowly tumble down with decay. Thus communities of five hundred or a thousand inhabitants disappear from the face of the earth—the homes, churches, schools, and stores perish, government is blighted by tremendous decrease in value of taxable property, and farmers in the district see the local market for produce wither away.[1]

Wherever this sequence runs its course, in the Lake states, in the South, or on the Pacific coast, local political units, such as townships and counties, become practically bankrupt, and the devastated area becomes a heavy burden on the more prosperous parts of the state, contributing little to the state tax funds and requiring large expenditures for schools and roads.

Effect on Climate. As it swept across the United States, the migrating forest industry left a number of problems besides a decreasing wood supply and decadent communities, problems growing out of the impairment of other outstanding forest services. It has been frequently asserted that one of these problems is decreased rainfall resulting from the decrease in forest cover.

Whether forests do actually affect rainfall to an appreciable extent is a debatable question, however, lacking indisputable proof or disproof. A survey by Lowdermilk of the literature dealing with this problem shows considerable contradiction and a decided lack of conclusive evidence. One investigator maintains that forests may increase rainfall 1 to 2 per cent; another reports 10 to 11 per cent excess of rainfall catch in forests over open areas during periods of fog, whereas others insist that deforestation has had no effect whatever. The conclusions reached by the most qualified students are not only somewhat contradictory but are still largely theoretical. There are, as yet, no observational data of unquestioned reliability which would justify the conclusion that deforestation decreases rainfall to an extent that is of practical significance.

Watershed Protection. The removal of the forest cover from vast areas has, however, seriously impaired its service in watershed protection. At the same time, the value to the nation of this service has become greater because of the increase in water-power utilization, the

[1] William T. Chambers: "Pine Woods Region of Southeastern Texas," *Econ. Geog.*, Vol. 10, 1934, pp. 307-308.

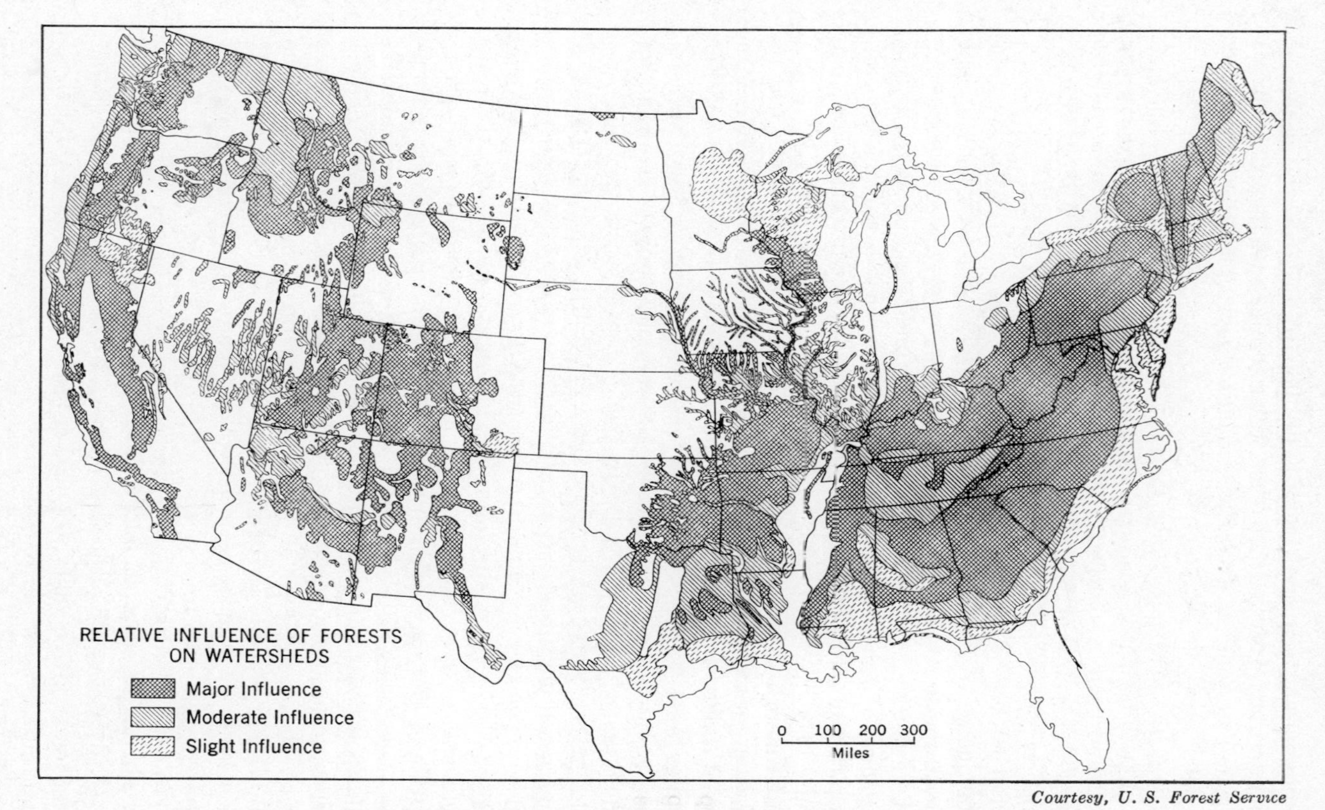

Courtesy, U. S. Forest Service

Fig. 6. Regional Variations in the Value of Forests for Watershed Protection.

occupation by farm and city of easily flooded lowlands, the growth of urban centers with their need for water supply, and the expansion of irrigated acreage in arid and semiarid lands. The management of forested areas in the interest of watershed protection has, indeed, become of great importance in regions of multiple land use and in mountains bordering arid and semiarid areas. About four-fifths of the total forest cover of the nation is classed by the United States Forest Service as valuable for the protection it furnishes. The protective function is exercised in regulating the flow of the streams draining the forested area, in restraining soil erosion of the watershed, and, as a consequence of the effect on soil erosion, in minimizing the sediment load in the streams. (Fig. 6.)

Forests retard runoff during heavy rains and periods of rapid melting of snows, and increase the amount of water that percolates into the ground. By decreasing runoff and increasing percolation, there is a tendency to lower flood levels and to raise low water levels. The immediate runoff from denuded soils is almost invariably greater than from forested areas otherwise similar—three or four times as great on gently sloping lands to more than one hundred times as great on steeply sloping lands of relatively impervious soil. During a heavy rain on sample plots in northern Missouri, for example, 62 per cent of the rain ran off immediately from cultivated fields, 54 per cent from abandoned fields, 2 per cent from scrub oak, and less than 1 per cent from an undisturbed oak forest.

The processes involved in the regulation of runoff by forests are now comparatively clear. The forest litter, leaves, branches, and the roots and trunks of trees obstruct the runoff, absorb water, and form pockets in which water may stand until it can soak into the ground. In addition, percolation is favored by the vegetation cover, for, as Lowdermilk has shown, the sediment in water trickling downward from the surface of bare ground quickly plugs the pores of the soil. The effect of forests on the rate of melting of snow is also significant. The retardation is due in part to shading but mostly to reduction in wind movement. Snow disappears a few days to several weeks later from forested areas than from cleared lands near by.

Denudation of forest lands commonly increases in even more striking fashion the sediment load of the streams which drain them. Soil erosion is vastly greater on open-crop lands than on forested lands, ranging from ten or fifteen times as great on nearly flat land to several thousand times as great on steep lands with easily eroded soils. This sediment is carried into the streams where it silts up reservoirs used for irrigation, for water-power development, and for water supply; impairs the navigability of streams; injures their habitat value for fish; and spoils the recreational qualities of the water.

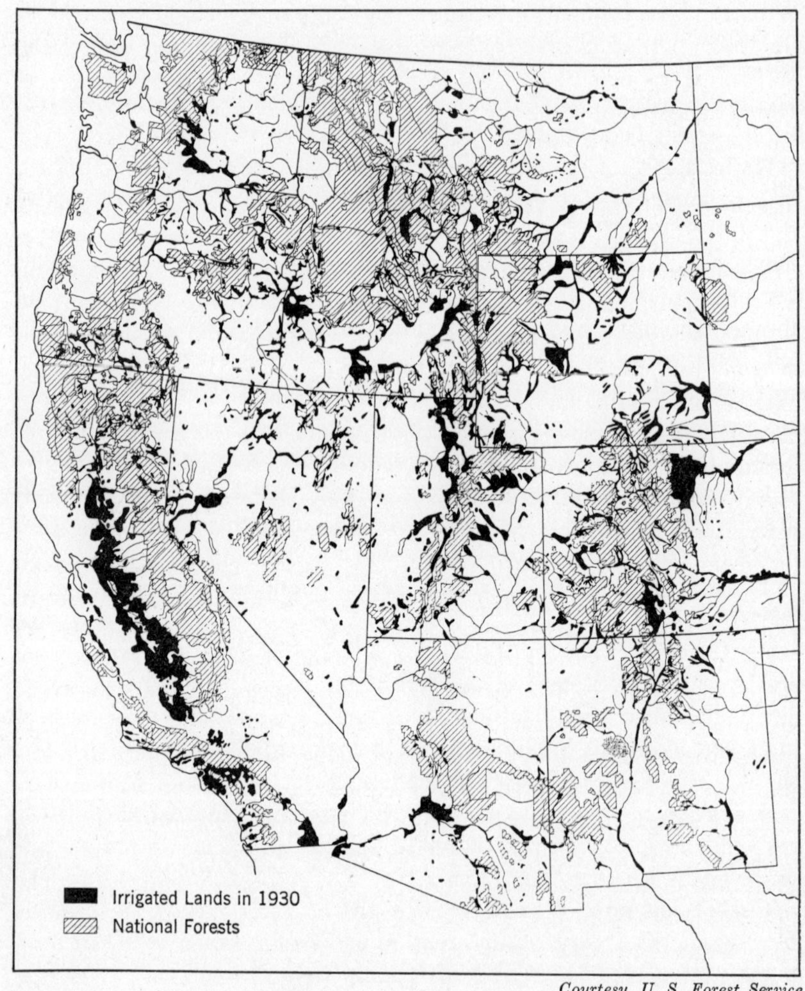

Courtesy, U. S. Forest Service

FIG. 7. Irrigated Lands and National Forests.

By protecting critical watersheds, the national forests help to conserve the water supply of the West.

Fortunately, the protective value of forests seems to be little affected by the exact type of cover. The chaparral of California and the scrub oak of the Ozarks are both highly effective. There appears to be little need for planting, therefore, if commercial production of particular species is not also sought. Brushy growth meets watershed needs quite well if it is protected from damage by fire.

The value of forests for watershed protection is greatest during times of normal rainfall. During an extremely heavy rain, of the kind which may come but once in a decade, their effectiveness is far less, if not actually negligible. And even a fairly complete forest cover is no guarantee against occasional floods, a fact clearly illustrated in the history of the Ohio Valley.

The influence of forests on watersheds varies from region to region. In Fig. 6, in which forests are classified according to their protective value, the forests of major influence include steep slopes subject to heavy or concentrated rainfall; areas of excessive and rapid snow melt; and areas of soils which erode with unusual rapidity, where, in the absence of forest cover, serious damage would probably be done to the soil, to other values of the watershed, or to the streams draining the area. In a number of localities where the demand for water is unusually critical, particularly in the West, the forest cover, even though scanty, is classed as exerting a major influence. Forests are considered of moderate influence on areas of moderate slopes, areas of moderate to scanty rainfall, lands with soils which do not erode readily, and areas where the forest cover quickly reclothes the land after damage by fire or lumbering. Areas where forests are of slight or no appreciable influence include sections of flat surfaces on old lava flows, and deep sands through which precipitation readily percolates and from which erosion is slight. Likewise, the forests on poorly drained and nearly flat lands have been considered of slight importance. The map is highly generalized, including in each type small areas belonging to the other two. In addition to variations in relative influence on their watersheds, there is considerable variation from place to place in the relation of watershed protection to specific problems in water, soil, and wildlife conservation. (Fig. 7.)

Recreation and Wildlife. The use of forest areas for hunting, fishing, and other forms of recreation has been a major satisfaction of mankind for many centuries. Originally casual, unplanned activities, these uses have come to be rather deliberate and planned, particularly during the last six or seven decades. The urbanization of American life has greatly increased the value of forests for recreation, and the development of good roads and low-priced automobiles has placed the forest areas within reach of the city dweller, as well as of rural folk living in natural grassland and deforested areas. The steady depletion of our forests has, at the same time, increased the pressure on the remaining stands.

Many of the more spectacular and heavily used recreational areas have been set aside as national, state, and locally owned parks. It is doubtful, however, if parks are used as much as the vast areas outside of their limits—ordinary forest land possessing no outstanding scenic features, but offering a greater choice of outdoor activities. Ordinary forest land is commonly nearer at hand, moreover, and reached at little cost. If the forest country is within a hundred miles of home, it will be used, even though game is scarce, fishing poor, and the views commonplace.

As a consequence of the tendency to use the recreational areas at hand, a wide distribution of forest land is desired, with particular attention to idle lands near urban centers. In view of the concentration of the urban population of the nation in the central and northeastern states, it is clear that the greatest need for recreational forests is in the part of our country where forest resources are now least abundant, and where the existing stands are being depleted more rapidly than anywhere east of the Pacific coast region. No phase of forest utility has been more disastrously affected by depletion than this one; on the other hand, no phase is closer to the immediate interests of individual cities, townships, counties, and states, nor more easily attacked in a practical way. Wildlife and recreational resources are discussed in later chapters.

The Land-use Problem. Dependent upon the usefulness of forests for recreational opportunities, wood supply, and industrial raw materials is their service in furnishing an income from lands that would otherwise be idle. Income in terms of salable services is desired from each major part of county, state, and nation, and for much land it is "trees or nothing."

The common assumption that all our humid lands would be converted into farms about as fast as the forest cover could be removed blinded the nation to the problem created by wholesale slaughter of forest growth by devastative logging and fires. It is now clear that this was an erroneous assumption, and that vast areas of cut-over land must remain idle unless they are put to other uses than agriculture. To these areas must be added an increasing acreage of farm land—land which was originally unsuited to agriculture, mistreated so badly as to become so, or made so by economic changes. More than 50,000,000 acres in eastern United States belong in this second group.

This idle land is contributing virtually nothing toward the support of the political units in which it lies, for it has slight recreational value, furnishes few raw materials, and commonly pays little or no taxes. In fact, it is actually a heavy burden on the county and state, and in the aggregate, on the entire nation, for its roads, schools, and other public services of less tangible nature are paid for by taxing more prosperous areas. The land-use problem is clearly evident to anyone who travels through desolate cut-over districts, along expensive highways constructed with state and federal funds.

It is certain that a large part of this land can be made productive if the forest cover is re-established. In certain sections of our country the principal income may be from recreational uses. Saw-log production on the better soils is also a possibility, dependent on fire control and other conditions; but of greater immediate significance are the opportunities for the production of wood pulp and naval stores. Importing more pulpwood than we cut, we have a strong market near the cut-over lands for short-time tree crops. In the South, too, are possibilities of land-use through the production of pines yielding turpentine and rosin. At present, that industry is mainly dependent on thrifty young growth in southeastern Georgia and northern Florida. If a sane policy of forest protection and management is adopted, an income from a large part of the cut-over lands of the South is assured.

To assume, however, that all the idle land in the humid sections of our country should be put under definite management for saw-log production, or even pulpwood, appears as erroneous as our earlier assumption that all humid land would be farmed as soon as the trees were removed. Much of our idle land is clearly submarginal for commercial forestry, too. Even large areas that once supported fine stands of timber are now too poor, as a result of repeated fires and soil erosion, to grow trees of commercial value within foreseeable time. Not until these areas have been thoroughly studied and classified will we be able to say what proportion should be put under definite management for commercial forestry. Meanwhile, we should provide adequate protection from fire, and reduce, so far as possible, the cost of maintaining such public services as roads and schools.

CHAPTER XI

ESSENTIAL MEASURES IN FOREST CONSERVATION

By J. R. Whitaker

University of Wisconsin

With the services derived from forests in mind, together with the progressive impairment of those services through forest depletion, we may turn to the chief measures by which further depletion is being retarded, and by which it is clearly possible to increase our forest resources to a level more nearly commensurate with the needs of the nation. Of the various means of maintaining adequate forest resources for the near and distant future, the protection of forests from damage by fire is certainly the most fundamental.

PROTECTION FROM FOREST FIRES

Protection of all forest land from damage by fire is, without doubt, the chief need in forest conservation, for fires not only destroy vast areas of forest each year but may also undo the results of all previous efforts at forest renewal in those areas. A fire of a few hours' duration may set at naught the work of years of careful forest management (Fig. 1), and repeated fires may practically destroy the ability of the land to support tree growth. In tending to prevent *renewal*, fires strike right at the heart of forest conservation.

Extent of Forest Fires. No part of the vast forest area of the United States is immune from fire hazards. Large numbers of fires of local extent occur in every state each year, and occasionally there are truly vast conflagrations. Every forest region has its tradition of a great fire. The greatest in Wisconsin, for example, occurred in 1871, when the Peshtigo fire burned 1,280,000 acres of timber, and more than 1,000 people lost their lives. The total damage from less spectacular fires is far greater, however, than from these occasional fires of vast extent. In recent years, there has been a yearly average of nearly 160,000 recorded forest fires in the nation as a whole, and this despite the initiation of systematic fire control in many forest regions fully twenty-five years ago.

In recent years, the average area burned over annually has been about 64,000 square miles, or more than 6 per cent of the total forest area. If each new year's crop of fires burned over fresh ground, it would thus take only the short span of fifteen years or so for the entire area to be burned over. Fortunately, from this point of view at least, a large proportion of the fires is on land previously burned. In some states where the fire hazard is greatest, as much as 40 to 50 per cent of the forest land is burned over annually.

Courtesy, U. S. Forest Service

FIG. 1. A Recently Burned-over Area in the Flathead National Forest, Montana.

Nature of Damage by Fire. The damage from fires is widespread, touching directly or indirectly every use of forests and of the rivers which drain the damaged area.

Fires destroy large values in merchantable timber and cut down the yield of timber from surviving trees. The growth of the remaining trees is badly stunted, and the fire scars furnish points of attack for fungi and insects. In the virgin pine forests of California, where fires have always prevailed, areas with 35,000 board feet of timber to the acre are considered "exceedingly dense and productive," even for the best sites. These virgin forests represent an average age of two hundred years. In contrast, sixty-year-old second-growth stands in the same region, but where fire has been completely excluded, give 80,000 board feet to the acre. Fires also cut the yield from hardwoods, though they are less liable to damage. It was found in a study of lumbering operations in the Appalachian hardwoods that three-fifths of the total defect in the logs was due to fire injury.

In addition to injury to remaining trees, repeated fires alter the composition of the forest growth. By this means, vast areas of sandy plain in the northern part of the Lower Peninsula of Michigan have been reduced to jack pine and aspen. In Pennsylvania, about 2,000,000 acres have been so wrecked by fire that the land now supports only a cover of ferns, huckleberries, scrub oak, fire cherry, and aspen, where formerly grew magnificent stands of oak, maple, and yellow poplar.

The change in composition is due in part to the tendency of fires to prevent reproduction through the killing of seeds, seedlings, and seed trees. Trees which the forest fire kills without consuming furnish fuel for a later fire. A single fire in pine slash may destroy all the young growth and seed trees, leaving the area incapable of restocking by natural means. The cumulative effect of fires and logging is seen in a part of the Douglas-fir area, cut from 1920 to 1923 and repeatedly burned over. Ten years later, a study of seven counties showed about 40 per cent as non-stocked, 30 per cent as poorly stocked. In the white-pine section of northern Idaho, probably 25 per cent of the cut-over land is non-productive because of fire. Hardwoods are remarkably resistant to complete devastation by fire because of their ability to reproduce through sprouting, but fires in the heavy slash left by clean logging have frequently been so severe as to destroy the sprouting capacity of the stumps. Fire is unquestionably the greatest single cause of forest devastation—of making the land unable to produce a valuable tree crop within a tree generation.

Fire also retards or prevents restocking by damaging the soil, locally, to the point where the productive value is completely destroyed, so far as commercial growth or any other economic use is concerned. The forest litter and humus are burned out, leaving almost pure mineral matter in which higher plant forms such as trees are unable to grow. The destruction of soil has been especially serious on steep slopes where the mantle rock was originally thin. A severe fire followed by a few heavy rains leaves the rock-cored hills almost denuded of their soil cover. This is particularly common in the mountains of the West, on the steeper slopes of the Appalachian hills, and in the Lake Superior and New England uplands. The deterioration of the *site* value of the forest land may make renewal even by planting extremely difficult if not impossible.

The watershed value of forests is, obviously, seriously impaired by this damage to the soil, and by the consequent acceleration of soil erosion (Fig. 2). In a part of the watershed on which Los Angeles depends for its water supply, intense rains on burned-over areas washed down thirty times as much sediment to the square mile as from adjacent areas not burned. This sediment clogs up reservoirs and

Courtesy, U. S. Forest Service

Fig. 2. Destructive Logging and Fires Have Completely Destroyed the Forest Cover.

Deprived of its protective influence, the soil is being rapidly eroded.

irrigation ditches, and covers valuable farm lands. Moreover, the sediment-laden water must frequently be allowed to flow on seaward rather than be diverted out over "spreading grounds" where it may soak into the ground to replenish the supply in wells and springs, for if allowed to flow out over these surfaces, the sediment quickly blocks up the soil passages, thereby interfering with percolation. The destruction of the woody covering also results in a less regular runoff, itself a serious matter. Severe as is the damage to watershed values in the Southwest, where forests are chiefly useful for watershed protection, it is likewise severe in more humid areas, particularly where fires rage through the slash of cleanly logged areas.

In destroying the vegetation cover, leaving a blackened surface strewn with charred limbs and stumps, fire robs forest land, whether plain or mountain, of much of its recreational value. A cut-over area, if protected from fire, is perhaps even better hunting ground than before, and trout streams may have suffered little damage, but repeated fires destroy the wildlife and prevent or retard its reproduction. It has been estimated that forest fires cause more destruction of game than does the total of all violations of hunting and fishing laws. Whether hunting, fishing, or hiking—whatever the reason for seeking recreation in woodlands—the vacationer finds recently burned-over lands repellent rather than attractive. It should be noted, too, that resort areas are subject to serious risks unless adequate precautions are taken to prevent and control fires in their locality. Locally, the forest fire is a calamity ranking with the hurricane and earthquake in the loss of homes and lives. Not only resorters suffer, but also inhabitants of lumber camps and towns, and farmers on adjacent or included lands. Fire is the chief menace faced by all forms of life in and near the forest—whether trees, wildlife, or man.

Besides rendering the land unfit for recreational purposes, fires tend to bring about the abandonment of lumbering operations through destruction of the remaining timber, and they constitute a major obstacle in the way of securing the sustained yield required for stable wood-processing communities. The fire risk is a well-nigh insurmountable obstacle in the way of the private individual who seeks a safe investment in the production of tree crops.

Causes of Fires. The great damage which fires inflict is all the more to be regretted because that loss is largely preventable. Man is primarily responsible through his own acts for starting the fires which yearly ravage an area half again as large as New York state.

Of all the fires on protected land during a recent five-year period, more than 90 per cent were man-caused. In descending order of importance, for the nation as a whole, the known causes were: smokers, incendiary, débris burning, lightning, railroads, campers, and lumbering (Table 1). The rank of these causes is, however, notably different for different parts of the country. Although lightning is the cause of more than half of the fires in the Rocky Mountains, it is accountable for less than 2 per cent in the Lake states. The rapid increase in recent years in the number of tourists has greatly increased the danger from smokers and campers in recreational areas. Attracted to the forests during summer vacations, most tourists come from cities and closely settled farm areas, where they never have occasion during the rest of the year to be careful with outdoor fires. They are not deliberately negligent as a rule, but they are ignorant of the danger, and thought-

TABLE 1

THE PERCENTAGE OF FOREST FIRES DUE TO VARIOUS CAUSES. DATA FOR THE NATIONAL, STATE, AND PRIVATE FORESTS UNDER PROTECTION, 1926–1930

Region	Lightning	Railroads	Campers	Smokers	Débris Burning	Incendiary	Lumbering	Miscellaneous	Unknown
New England	0.69	18.74	2.39	29.16	15.23	4.53	0.69	10.01	18.57
Middle Atlantic	0.54	18.21	6.59	28.03	12.56	6.34	0.61	9.40	17.72
Lake	1.40	12.49	8.03	26.67	15.28	6.66	1.46	12.89	15.12
Central	0.31	7.01	7.70	14.95	18.29	28.24	5.55	6.07	11.87
South	1.10	5.17	8.82	16.51	14.44	30.56	6.62	8.95	7.83
Pacific Coast	23.49	4.94	9.76	23.60	7.31	13.21	4.91	11.28	1.50
North Rocky Mountain	62.53	6.14	7.17	11.38	3.77	3.03	1.64	2.42	1.92
South Rocky Mountain	64.30	2.39	9.72	16.57	1.91	0.88	0.88	3.35	....
Total	9.54	9.05	7.89	21.06	12.54	17.10	3.92	9.20	9.70

Source: *A National Plan for American Forestry*, Vol. II, p. 1404.

less as a result of years spent where forest fires never occur. The deliberate setting of fires is particularly critical only in the Pacific Northwest and in the central and southern states. In the South the turpentine operator has deemed it necessary to burn the accumulating débris in winter to guard against summer fires. Fires are also set by cattle owners to improve the forage value of the wooded areas, despite evidence that in the long run the range is injured rather than improved, through damage to soil and to forage plants.[1]

Both man-made and natural conditions determine the extent of the damage which fires, once started, can cause. Chief among the first is the large amount of slash created by clean logging. If not piled and burned with care, the branches and other unused materials enable fires to start easily and to spread rapidly. Most significant among natural conditions is the weather, both preceding and during a fire. By rendering the forest litter more inflammable, dry weather obviously increases the hazard. Thus the times of greatest danger are the dry seasons of the year. A correlation has also been found between fires and the daily weather, anti-cyclonic conditions being times of greater fire hazard than cyclonic. Wind velocity is critical too—the rate of spread of fire varies as the square of the wind velocity, and shifts of wind direction are also vital in determining the direction in which the fires will spread. Weather conditions are most serious in the West, where a prolonged dry season in summer is the rule.

[1] If set and supervised by skilled foresters, fires may be of some value in the South in controlling certain tree diseases, in discouraging competing vegetation, and in reducing excessive fire hazards during severe droughts. The use of fire for these purposes, however, requires a high degree of technical knowledge and skill.

Protection from Fires. To minimize the damage of forests by fire, provision must be made for preventing unnecessary fires from starting, and for controlling those that do start. It is obvious that the fires set by natural causes cannot be prevented, nor is it likely that those originating from human causes can be entirely excluded. Moreover, fires, once started, are certain to do some damage before they are extinguished. The practical ideal, therefore, is not the complete exclusion of fires from forest land, but the restriction of the damage to what has been termed *allowable burn.* The allowable burn is the burn that may take place annually without seriously damaging a particular forest for the uses to which it is customarily put. Expressed for each region as a certain percentage of the total forest area, it varies with the ease of damage of different forest types, as well as with differences in use. The allowable burn ranges from the minimum of less than one-quarter of one per cent to the maximum of nearly one and one-half per cent, the lowest being found in New England, the highest in the South.

To approach this standard through prevention of unnecessary fires, a thorough system of patrol and inspection in and near forest areas is required. Railroad locomotives need to be equipped with spark arresters, and subjected to frequent inspection. Brush burning may well be carried out only under permit, though if possible the permit system might better be displaced by enlightened public opinion. The patrol of roads, railroads, and the boundaries of forest areas serves to keep roadside fires and fires on adjacent farm lands from reaching the forest.

Fires of an incendiary origin are commonly set by persons who hope to profit from them, either for employment in fighting them or to improve the forage value of the woodland. The first can be corrected, in part, by having available for fire control a crew of men above suspicion of incendiarism; the second depends upon convincing those who run livestock in wooded areas that fires are harmful rather than a help.

Probably the chief means of preventing fires is through an informed and interested public, for smokers rank ahead of all other causes of fires. All who live in forest areas or visit them—lumbermen, farmers, hunters, campers, tourists—should be made aware that only by great care on their part can fires be restricted within the limits of allowable burn. Unceasing efforts to acquaint the traveling public with fire hazards is required, moreover, for every year finds new additions to the group of forest users. Each new generation must acquire a deep sense of responsibility in the matter. Legislation looking toward the reduction of the number of fires set by careless individuals might conceivably be of some value, but to enforce such regulations in the absence of public support would require a fire warden for every tourist. It seems that a far better course is the endeavor to make each forest user actively cooperative in preventing fires.

Fire Detection and Suppression. For the fires which do start despite preventive measures, the object is to confine each to the smallest possible area. Prompt detection is, therefore, of critical importance. The lookout tower thus becomes the "keystone" of the whole fire-detection system. Accurate maps are also necessary if fires are to be located with precision. Once located, speed of attack is the next requirement. Each fire should be detected, if possible, before it covers one-tenth of an acre, and a fire-fighting crew should actually reach the fire before it has covered ten acres. If a fire starts in a forest well organized for fire control, the observer at the lookout tower reports his discovery by telephone to the firemen, who are provided with tools, and with the means of transportation to proceed at once to the fire over roads and trails which have been prepared with this need in mind. Thus men, equipment, and roads are all essential. To build up such an organization requires that men be trained for the task, that roadways, trails, and fire lines be carefully laid out and constructed, and that equipment and plans be ready for any emergency. The supreme test comes in occasional weeks and years when fire hazards are unusually great, when the results of years of protection may be wiped out in a single uncontrolled fire.

Expenses can be kept down and the effectiveness of the organization improved by determining the periods made hazardous by weather conditions. Records of rainfall and relative humidity reveal the seasons when the fire-fighting force should be increased or decreased, and daily forecasts are valuable in focusing the attention on those days when fires are particularly likely to spread. Sunny, dry, and windy days are especially favorable to the spread of fire.

Among the human conditions which should be corrected in furthering fire suppression are the common failure to dispose of slash after logging, and the existence of large areas of tax-delinquent land. The owners of tax-delinquent forest land have little interest in fire suppression, commonly contributing nothing to that end, and, in at least one state, protection by state agencies is withheld from land on which taxes are in arrears. Surely it is sound to conclude that provision should be made promptly to transfer such land to responsible ownership—whether it be private, county, state, or federal. In this, as in all phases of fire prevention, detection, and suppression, the assumption by each state of a large part of the responsibility is essential.

Status of Forest Protection Work. Much has been done to bring forest land under some form of fire protection, but much remains to be done. Of the total area involved, about one-third is still under no form of protection, and for the lands outside the national forests, the actual burn, for a recent five-year period, was eleven times as great as the allowable burn. In the Rocky Mountain states, the ratio of actual to allowable burn was 1 to 1, but in the South it was 14 to 1. This difference is due, in part, to the presence of large areas of national forest in the Rocky Mountains.

Ideal conditions are within reach in the national forests and in the protected state and public forests. For these areas the actual yearly burn is less than 2 per cent of the area, not quite twice that which can occur without serious damage to the usefulness of the forest. This status is maintained, however, only by constant attention, day after day, to the fire problem. A lapse of effort, due to withdrawal of federal and state funds, would be disastrous. On unprotected land, however, the annual area burned is nearly 20 per cent of the total. To expand systematic fire protection to include this land, as well as to maintain and improve the existing organization on protected lands, are the needs of the near future.

Both public and private agencies are contributing funds to meet the expense of fire protection. Through provisions made by the Weeks and Clarke-McNary laws, federal grants of more than $1,000,000 annually assist about forty states in protecting their forest lands. The more forward-looking states have definitely assumed the responsibility for all the forests within their limits except those owned by the federal government, and private owners of forest land are contributing about one-sixth of the total expenditures. Without question, however, these measures of fire protection must be notably increased, or the causes corrected, if fires are to be brought under reasonable control. In the destructiveness of fire lies the chief obstacle to the satisfactory solution of nearly every problem in forest conservation.

The responsibility of society in fire prevention is clear. Although owners of forest land are in part responsible, fires are largely due to the deeds of other persons; the owner can scarcely restrict the fire to the limits of his own land without aid from others; and the consequences affect local, state, and even national interests. On all three bases—causes, control, and consequences—forest fires are a social problem, and therefore a problem the solution of which involves social cooperation.

CONSERVATIONAL LOGGING

Logging practices combined with forest fires are major causes of the deterioration of the tree cover of our forest lands. Logging methods of the past have, moreover, resulted in a failure to use much of the wood in each tree.

Losses in Logging Operations. Loss of wood in logging occurs in various ways. Much wood is discarded in the tops and branches, and left in high stumps. Mistakes are made in cutting log lengths, resulting in pieces too short to be of value. Much merchantable material is cut but remains on the ground unused. Such factors as unwillingness of the consumer to accept odd lengths and competition of other materials are also responsible for much of the non-use. The total amount of wood lost in logging operations averages about 23 per cent by volume of the wood contained in the trees that are felled. How much of this loss is avoidable is not known with precision, for lumbermen have been and still are working under severe economic limitations, but it seems a conservative estimate to put it at about one-quarter to one-half of the total, for that amount of saving has been secured in the national forests.

Deterioration of Forests through Logging. More objectionable than those logging operations which fail to use a large proportion of each tree felled is the practice of logging in such a way as to bring about a definite deterioration of the forest land. More than 90 per cent of the area logged each year in the United States is cut with no serious regard to maintenance and renewal of the forest cover.

Failure to dispose of the slash, the unused tops, and limbs is responsible for the spread of fire and, therefore, for destruction of remaining growth. In clear-cut areas, the slash may cover 25 to 40 per cent of the ground, and the fire hazard is greatly increased for several years after cutting, five to eight years in the long-leaf pine forest of the South. Either fire protection or slash disposal must be increased. The first steps in the protection of slash areas is to pull all tops and logging débris away from the base of seed trees, to lop off the limbs of heavy tops, and to keep fire lanes clear of slash. Further care consists of piling the slash and burning it when fire hazards are low. In this way not more than 10 to 30 per cent of the surface area is burned over. The piling and burning of slash has been a common practice in our national forests for years, and at least nineteen states require some form of slash disposal. Closer utilization would also diminish the amount of slash, a fact clearly illustrated in European forests, where slashings as a fire menace do not exist.

Repeated culling of forests results in marked deterioration. The best species are logged first, thus reducing their seed supply and retarding their rate of reproduction as compared with the poorer species. The effect of repeatedly cutting the best species, large and small, tends eventually to eliminate those trees and to bring about a marked degeneration of the forest cover.

The common failure to leave seed trees is involved in culling, but is an even more serious aspect of clean cutting. If pine lands, for example, are to be kept in pine, enough seed trees must survive to produce a stand in a reasonable time or planting must be done, if the desired cover is to be maintained. In general, four to eight vigorous seed-bearing trees should be left on each acre. Unfortunately, seed trees are commonly among the more valuable timber trees in the stand. Only a very few states have regulations regarding the leaving of seed trees.

Not only must seed trees be preserved if the forest cover is promptly to re-establish itself, but young growth must be protected during the felling of trees and the removal of logs. The practice of dragging logs by motor power directly to a central station from points as much as several hundred feet away may damage more than half the remaining timber. To offset the damage from skidding, the number of seed trees left may well exceed by 50 per cent the normal requirement. In some places it may prove desirable to substitute animals for motor power, for the removal of logs by animal power does little damage to young growth or seed trees.

Young growth suffers, too, from the practice of cutting nearly all the trees, small as well as large. It has been assumed in the past that the smaller trees, if not cut at an actual profit, would bear a share of the general overhead costs of the logging operations. Investigations by government foresters have shown, however, that for each forest area there is a size below which an actual financial loss is incurred in cutting. The "tree that does not yield a profit" is the tree below 16 to 18 inches in diameter in southern Arkansas, 12 to 16 inches in Virginia. A continuation and thorough validation of these studies may go far to prevent cutting of young growth. The preservation of small trees is particularly desirable on steep slopes.

Deterioration by logging is matched by destructive practices in turpentining of the southern forests. It is more or less general for the trees to be chipped too deeply, gutters driven too deep, and too many faces cut on each tree. Trees too small, below 9 inches in diameter, are chipped, and seed trees are not spared. These practices are the more regrettable because the turpentine industry is a vital element in the economic life of the South, many students considering it the key to successful utilization of the forest land of that great area.

Some Basic Causes of Loss of Wood and Forest Deterioration. There is no doubt that a part of the failure to use a higher proportion of each tree felled and to leave the forest in a condition favorable to the production of a new crop of trees may be charged to carelessness. Part of it may also be credited to ignorance—ignorance, for example, of the diameter limit below which cutting is unprofitable. Part of it is due to the fact that the owner does not plan to engage in sustained-yield forestry, a problem to which we shall turn later. But a major reason is the simple fact that these conservational measures are costly, and that society has tolerated and encouraged in the lumber business a degree of competition which alone would have made such measures economically unsound. In prohibiting cooperative agreements and encouraging interregional competition, the public has incurred a large share of the responsibility for anti-conservational logging practices.

Over-production has characterized the lumber industry for many years. It has led to low prices, and low prices to the practice of taking only the best, for it costs as much to cut, log, and saw poor wood as good. Increasing freight costs have, however, obscured the existence of low prices at the mill. Particularly critical in recent years has been over-production on the west coast, where mounting interest charges on investments made during a boom period of timber buying have forced owners to realize something from their holdings. With the failure to utilize much of the wood in the trees that have been cut, there has gone, perforce, little if any regard for the condition in which the forest has been left.

Suggested Remedies. So vital to public welfare is the maintenance of a suitable forest cover on our humid non-agricultural land that there is general agreement that public action of some sort must be taken to substitute conservational logging for forest deterioration.

It is maintained in some quarters that the public should compel, largely through state legislation, the observance of certain minimum requirements in logging practices, including the disposal of slash and the leaving of seed trees, thereby preventing the operator from denuding his land. Laws requiring one or another of these practices exist in many states, although they have fallen short of the desired result, in part because of lack of public support. It must be kept in mind, too, that these requirements do involve an additional expense. This lends support to the suggestion that a law rewarding conservational logging in some way, such as a decrease in taxes, might be more effective. Certainly governmental encouragement of conservational logging of private forests is much to be desired, if for no other reasons than the predominance of private ownership of the nation's forests and the large public interest involved.

Still another course advanced to secure conservational logging is to extend public ownership to a large part of the forest land, thus making it possible to secure a more orderly utilization of the resources of the land so included, to relieve the competitive situation by transferring to public ownership a part of the virgin timber of the west coast, and to enforce conservational logging on the public forest lands through leasing regulations. There is common agreement that our public forests should be greatly extended, though whether to include the over-capitalized forests of the west coast is a highly debatable question. Moreover, public ownership does not of necessity guarantee conservational logging, a truth well illustrated in the forest history of the United States and Canada, but one all too commonly ignored by writers on this problem. Public support of sustained-yield management on public forest lands is also required if public ownership is to result in conservational logging.

The deterioration of forest land, admittedly a process which it is desirable to retard if not to stop, has gone on with public consent, stimulated by an economic set-up which society has definitely encouraged. A major revision of these logging practices must be supported by enlightened public opinion and a citizenry willing to bear its share of the increased costs which must, for a time at least, accompany the desired practices. A matter of public interest for the nation as a whole, it is of even more direct interest to those states with large acreages of non-agricultural forest lands.

EFFICIENT MILLING AND WOOD UTILIZATION

Opportunities. The provision of wood supplies adequate for the needs of society in the near and distant future may be secured not only by forest maintenance and renewal but also by attention to methods of utilization. Recent estimates indicate that about 30 to 35 per cent of the tree is lost in converting the log into lumber, a considerable advance over the 40 to 50 per cent that obtained years ago but still presenting a challenging opportunity. Losses also take place at later stages in the manufacturing process, so that only about one-third of each tree enters the finished products.

Advances in Milling. Marked advances have occurred in recent years in the more efficient mills. The amount of sawdust has been greatly reduced by using band saws for the older circular saws; some of the lumber is cut to required dimensions at the mill, thus eliminating small pieces; and methods of curing have progressed greatly, resulting in less splitting and warping of seasoning lumber.

Utilization of Wood "Waste." Material formerly discarded, such as sawdust, slabs, and odd lengths, is being utilized. The sawdust is being used as a sweeping compound, and as a raw material in the manufacture of linoleum, dynamite, and a great variety of plastic materials. Much waste is devoted to making alcohol, tannic acid, charcoal, fiber board, and paper. Built-up construction is a means of using low-grade wood and small pieces. Research is providing new outlets for materials that otherwise would be discarded, and these advances are being applied quite promptly in the industry. The integrating of a variety of wood-using industries under one ownership or around one population center is another development making it possible in some places to reduce the losses involved in manufacture. It is more difficult to find use for the wood waste produced by small mills, but, on the other hand, these mills make sustained-yield management of woodland possible in localities where the supply of logs is far from sufficient for the larger, more efficient mills.

Wood Preservation. Much progress has likewise been made in wood preservation. Preservatives, such as zinc chloride and creosote, prevent ravages by decay and insects, thereby increasing the life of timbers three to eighteen years, according to method of treatment and the uses to which the treated wood is put. Preservatives not only greatly lengthen the life of wood for such employment as railroad ties, but also make it possible to use inferior species, trees that normally decay too rapidly to be used without treatment.

Wood Substitutes. Closely related to economies resulting from wood preservatives is the use of wood substitutes. Although this is a partial solution to the timber supply problem, it is doubtful if it should be encouraged by the state; in fact, there is much reason for holding to the opposite view, that substitution should be counteracted by research aimed at making wood more serviceable for the uses where competition is met, for substitution commonly displaces wood, a *re-*

newable resource, with *non-renewable* resources, such as iron. The long view in conservation dictates that renewable resources displace non-renewable resources wherever economically feasible.

Efficient Utilization versus Renewal of Forests. Although avoidable loss should never be condoned, and unavoidable loss should be decreased by research directed toward the discovery of profitable ways of utilization, inefficiency in the manufacture and use of forest products is not as regrettable, from the viewpoint of the social group, as waste and loss in the mining and utilization of coal. Efficient utilization is desirable, but the crux of forest conservation is *renewal* of the basic resource. The responsibility of each generation is particularly that of doing all it can to encourage the preservation and renewal of forests, thereby making the most of the fundamental resources of land and water, decreasing the drain on non-renewable minerals, and providing for the great variety of services which forests can render.

FOREST PLANTING

In forest planting and management, the purpose is to secure renewal at a rate commensurate with our needs for the various forest services, from wood supply to game cover. Planting is being done where a tree cover should become established, but is being renewed at too slow a rate, or not at all. It is questionable if extensive planting for lumber production is feasible as yet in this country, natural reproduction assisted by fire control and conservational logging being a superior method by far, but it may well be justified on other bases, such as the control of soil erosion.

In the eastern part of the United States are lands which were cleared for farming but which are now unsuited to agriculture. Where restocking is not taking place with sufficient rapidity to check erosion, planting is recommended, particularly in parts of the Piedmont, the inner margin of the Atlantic-Gulf coastal plain, and the Ohio drainage basin. Burned-over or cut-over forest lands which are not suited to agriculture but on which new timber is not establishing itself also require attention, particularly if they are critical watersheds. Some forested areas on which the stand is too thin may require planting, also belts of land on prairies where the trees are needed as windbreaks. It should be remembered, in considering a planting policy, that reproduction of some kind of a tree cover will normally take place in humid areas if there is adequate fire control, and that all too frequently fires and soil erosion have so damaged the soil that it is not now fertile enough to support the more valuable species of trees. A thorough land classification in terms of the productive capacity of the land, and its potential services if forested, should precede planting wherever extensive areas are involved.

SUSTAINED-YIELD FORESTRY

If the forest resources are to be kept at a level commensurate with the needs of the nation, sustained-yield forestry is required. With a yearly consumption several times yearly growth, some such provision against the needs of the future seems absolutely essential. Moreover, sustained-yield management is the only satisfactory solution to the problems presented by the migratory character of the cut-out-and-get-out type of lumbering. In developing the forest to a productive stage, full-time or part-time employment is given to many families to the square mile, and after the forest is on a sustained-yield basis, two to three families are required for each square mile, in protecting the forest from fire, thinning, cutting, and so on. A permanent source of raw materials for wood-manufacturing centers and a local market for farm products are also provided.

A rough application of the sustained-yield principle involves the control of fires, protection of young growth in logging operations, leaving uncut the trees which are too small to yield a profit, some attention to keeping the better species in the stand, slash disposal, and prevention of injurious grazing. Intensive management may well be restricted to timber growing on the most favorable areas in order to produce large trees of high quality. It includes various methods to secure maximum growth of the best species, such as girdling, thinning, pruning, and planting.

Plans and Opportunities. Various plans involving our forest land have been prepared by the United States Forest Service. One which would approximately meet the estimated timber needs postulated for some sixty years hence would place 15 per cent of our forest area under intensive management, 60 per cent under extensive management, and the remainder under simple fire protection. If Nelson C. Brown is correct in holding that we must be content with an extensive rather than intensive system of management until wood is more valuable, the percentage under extensive management would have to be increased.

Of the various forest regions, there is much reason to believe that the South is destined eventually to lead in sustained-yield management. The South contains about two-fifths of the forest land of the country;

tree growth is relatively rapid, far more rapid than in more northern areas; the flatness of the plains makes for cheap logging; the region is strategically located with regard to the more important markets; and saw-log production can be carried out alongside other ventures—grazing, thinning for poles, turpentining, and paper making. The Pacific coast region likewise ranks high in potentialities for continued timber production.

Most progress has been made in farm woodlots, which constitute more than one-fourth of the commercial forest land of the country. Nearly all this land is in eastern United States, near the great consuming areas. It is easy to protect from fire, and from insect and disease pests, and selective cutting is adapted to farm management. The ease with which logs can be hauled by truck long distances to milling centers is another advantageous factor. Increasing the production from farm woodlots is one of the most practical measures looking toward renewal of our forest resources. Widely dispersed, these woodlands serve as game cover, recreational areas, watershed protection, a local supply of firewood, and so on, and their development strengthens rather than injures the farm economy, and puts a premium on local initiative. A carefully planned extension service in forestry comparable to that available in most states for agriculture should make available to all farmers the information necessary to the wise location and efficient utilization of farm woodlands. Any trend toward a decrease in tenantry is also in the direction of more effective use of woodlots. Here, as in all phases of land utilization and conservation, the tenant system existing in America is found to be highly anti-conservational in its effects.

In large-scale commercial forestry, a satisfactory beginning in sustained-yield forestry has been made by paper companies. For short-time tree crops suitable for paper manufacture, conditions are more and more encouraging, for it is an industry with large investments in plant equipment and therefore not easily moved from place to place. On the other hand, private capital has not as yet found sustained-yield management for the production of saw-log timbers economically feasible outside of farm woodlands. Whereas practically all the farm woodlands are under some form of sustained-yield organization, less than one per cent of the remaining private forests are so managed. The major accomplishments in sustained-yield management of commercial forests outside of farms are found in the national forests.

Private capital has met serious obstacles to sustained-yield forestry for timber production. There has been much uncertainty as to cost and markets; the fire hazard has been great; the time element involved has vastly increased the element of risk in timber production besides making it unattractive to men who required income from their investments at frequent intervals; the existing methods of taxation have been a burden and an element of great uncertainty; and competition with virgin forests which cost nothing to produce have, heretofore, debased prices below a level at which trees could be grown at a profit equal to that realizable in other forms of investment. It is likely that large-scale, sustained-yield forestry as a private business will eventually be restricted to the more favorable areas tributary to permanent industrial centers; but even there, unfortunately, handicaps still exist.

It appears that the public must assist in correcting these conditions, if private initiative, in line with the American tradition, is to bear a large share in the growing of new tree crops. Greater security from fire is desired, and some maintain that adequate fire insurance should be provided. The extension service, which provides expert counsel and planting stock, should be extended to all forest-land owners. Some students maintain that there should be public loans to private interests at low rates, contingent on the operation of the forest property on a sustained-yield basis. And certainly major tax revisions are required. If our needs for forest services are to be met in a generous way during the next three or four generations, we must get a "continuing forest condition" under way before our virgin forests are exhausted. The nation does not face timber starvation, though a considerable decline in national cut in the near future seems inevitable, but it does face the need for planned production of timber on a part of its present agricultural lands.

MINIMIZING DAMAGE FROM DISEASES, INSECT PESTS, AND OVER-GRAZING

Among the conservational measures which rest, in part, on public agencies are the control of insect pests and plant diseases, and the minimizing of damage from over-grazing.

Plant Diseases. The damage done by fungi to forests is appreciable but difficult to control. Some kinds attack the wood, destroying its commercial value; others the living tissues, weakening and killing the tree. Of the two outstanding tree diseases to date, the chestnut blight, which attacks the living tissues, appeared in the East in 1904, and soon spread to the entire range of chestnut in that part of the country. It dooms the chestnut to a minor place, for no practicable means has yet been found for checking its spread. The white pine blister, also imported, is wide-spread in the East and has reached the Northwest. The disease spends part of its life cycle on such plants as the currant and gooseberry; hence, by destroying all such hosts in the neighborhood of the trees, the disease can be brought under control. It is the outstanding practical problem in the control of forest diseases today.

Being widely dispersed, diseases are controlled with difficulty. In the main, control is effected by the elimination of hosts and by cutting defective and mature trees. An inspection service to detect outbreaks before they become epidemic and investigations to further the knowledge of such matters as control methods and disease-resistant species of trees are needed.

Insect Control. Like tree diseases, insect pests are widely dispersed, and also require unceasing vigilance and cooperative action in their control. Insects lower timber yields and retard growth. They frequently change the composition of the forest and create serious fire hazards. Generally the damage is so scattered that little can be done, but occasionally there are infestations that permit concentrated attack, such as that of the tree-killing bettles in the lodgepole pine of western Montana.

Here, too, the best methods in sustained-yield management are involved in control—destruction of infected trees, the harvesting of mature trees, clearing of forest litter, and constant inspection to detect outbreaks of insects in their early stages. Also, a more careful regulation of imports would aid in excluding harmful insects, and the preservation of bird life would assist in the control work now under way.

Over-grazing. The damage to forest lands from grazing animals is large. More than half of the forest land of the country is grazed by domestic livestock. Over-grazing, which is quite common, seriously damages both the tree growth and the capacity of the land to grow trees.

The problem has three phases: in the farm woodlands of the central, northeast, and Lake states, the range lands of the South, and those of the West. The forest ranges of the West are vital in the livestock industry of that area. The flocks and herds graze on the forest ranges for a part or most of the year, and are wintered on forage crops grown on the valley bottoms and adjacent lowlands. The millions of acres of range land in the national forests of the West are essential to the agricultural utilization of many areas. The problem thus centers on the use of large areas of publicly owned land by private owners of ranch property and livestock. On many ranges the forage has been seriously depleted through over-grazing, and destruction of small trees and seedlings has prevented reproduction of the forest. Serious erosion has followed this destruction of the ground cover. Much headway has been made in correcting these conditions on the forest ranges within the national forests, though control of over-grazing is still inadequate. In the northern part of eastern United States, over-grazing of woodlots is quite general, and in the South the damage has been especially serious. Hogs, in particular, can prevent restocking by devouring pine seeds and the roots of the seedlings. In general, fencing against hogs is as necessary as fire control in the protection of young forest growth in the South. Here, as in other parts of eastern United States, the damage from grazing will undoubtedly decrease with a wider dissemination of proper methods of woodlot utilization.

RESEARCH

In the control of damage to forests by insects, diseases, and domestic animals, as in every phase of forest utilization, programs of action are hampered, if not rendered ineffective, by the need for more knowledge about forests, their character, and use. Much of the waste and deterioration of our timber lands has resulted from ignorance. In addition to lines of needed research already indicated, others may be added here.

Adequate Inventory. A basic need for truly guiding our efforts toward maintaining sufficient forest resources is a thorough survey of the forest areas as they exist today. Only by keeping track of the balance in our bank account can we plan wisely. The national forest survey, authorized by Congress in 1929, is under way, and the results are proving their utility in the hands of foresters, county assessors, state tax commissioners, and others.

Land Classification and Zoning. Here, as in other phases of land use, land classification is imperative. In the absence of such a survey, we cannot know, except in a fragmentary way, where forestry will pay. In view of current trends, this task of providing land classification may well be cared for by the individual states as well as by the federal government. Both state and federal agencies are at work upon it. Once known, the land that is primarily of value for forests may well be zoned for that use. The employment, through zoning, of the police power of the state to bring the use of privately owned lands into harmony with public interests is a major forward step in forest conservation.

Forestry. In the actual work of growing and harvesting trees, there is a promising field of research. More study of methods of sustained-yield forestry is required. In the field of plant breeding and selection, the development of new varieties of trees with more desirable traits than those in existence has scarcely begun. Problems such as these are being attacked in their regional setting at the forest experiment stations, one of which is located in each of the major forest regions. These stations are expected to become to the new industry of timber growing what the agricultural experiment stations have been for agriculture.

Utilization. There is wide room for improvement in wood utilization, a field of research being carried forward at the Forest Products Laboratory, Madison, Wisconsin. As an outstanding accomplishment of practical value, the establishment of this federal research laboratory is unique. Despite the long use of wood, little was known about it when the laboratory was opened in 1910. Since that date, it has been the leading agency in this country in the investigation of problems dealing with wood utilization. The laboratory seeks to develop more economical methods of converting standing timber into finished products; to make the growing of timber more profitable by increasing the possibilities in the utilization of both used and unused species; to find ways of utilizing materials that would otherwise be wasted; and to find new uses for old materials, and new materials for old ones.

TAX REFORM

The public interest is clearly furthered by research which aids in the efficient utilization of our forest resources and in the establishment of sustained-yield forestry as an income-producing enterprise. Perhaps even more vital for the present is the need for a reform in our general property tax as applied to forest land. It is commonly agreed that taxation has the power to affect the business of timber growing and the future of forests in a peculiarly unfavorable manner. Heavy taxation has undoubtedly tended to force premature cutting and to make selective logging unprofitable; and, above all, the uncertainty regarding future tax exactions has stood as an unsurmountable obstacle to the investment of capital in forests grown for timbers of saw-log size. In spite of the many-sided public interest in forestry, the public, through the property tax, has been subjecting the forest business to an influence directly opposed to conservation.

Forest property is sometimes assessed for more than its worth; and if not, it is very commonly assessed at a higher ratio to its true value than other classes of property. This discrimination against forest property in the administration of the property tax has been quite general. The Forest Taxation Inquiry stresses, too, the well-known fact that the property tax takes a larger proportion of the income from an investment that does not yield a yearly income, than from one that does. The longer the period of waiting, the greater the inequality. In other words, the necessity of paying taxes on forests for several years in advance of the receipt of income is the discrimination present in the nature of the property tax. If the property tax were so modified that it fell due only when the income was obtained and in proportion to the income received, it would then correspond to the "income tax" and to the taxation of all property which yields an annual income.

No magical results in forestry can be expected from tax reform, but a revision would unquestionably help. More nearly correct assessments should be secured, based on accurate maps and inventories, and on a comparison with sales from areas of comparable stands. The tax-collection procedure should be revised to prevent the accumulation of delinquent taxes, a condition which throws additional burdens on the forest owners who do pay their taxes. These changes look to more efficient tax administration.

As regards changes in the tax measures, three plans are selected by the Inquiry as giving most promise. The *adjusted property tax* levies on each forest property for which income is deferred more than a year a tax somewhat less than the usual property tax. The longer the deferment of income, the greater the reduction. This seems to be the most nearly perfect plan. The *deferred timber tax* postpones all payment until income is realized through cutting or sale of products. The loss in local tax revenue is made good from a timber-tax fund provided by the state. Into this fund go taxes assessed on a fixed percentage of the value of the forest products when cut or sold. This plan gives almost immediate relief, but puts a burden on the state until the timber-tax fund accumulates. The *differential property tax* grants for all timber land a state-wide reduction below the current assessments, a reduction based on the average period of deferment. Much like the first plan, this one is more easily worked out. After years of study of the problem, both in this country and elsewhere, the Inquiry concludes that these are the most practicable solutions. Unlike the yield-taxes provided for in certain states, these taxes would apply to all forest land instead of being restricted to the holdings of those owners who apply for consideration under the new tax regulations.

ENLARGEMENT OF PUBLIC FORESTS

Ownership of Forest Land. Four-fifths of the forest land of the United States is in private ownership, and as such, is subject to taxation. The remaining fifth is in public forests of various types.

In more than half the states, tax-delinquent lands revert to the townships and counties. In addition, municipal and township forests have been acquired to protect water supplies, and are administered for this purpose. Many forested areas have also been secured for their recreational value. The county, municipal, and town forests constitute about 1,000,000 acres, as compared with about 5,000,000 acres in state-owned forest lands. More than 85 per cent of the state-owned forest land is in the northeastern and northwestern parts of the country.

The national forests greatly exceed all other public forests in area, consisting of about 140,000,000 acres in continental United States (Fig. 1, Chapter XX), and containing one-third of the remaining saw timber. Ninety-five per cent of the national forests were set aside from the public domain; the remainder was secured by exchange or purchase.

Evolution of National Forest Policy. As a consequence of a series of notable advances in our forest policy since 1890, the legal basis for the enlargement of our national forests is now practically complete. In 1891, Congress, as stated in Chapter I, passed an act authorizing the president to set aside portions of the public domain as forest reserves, later to be known as national forests. Harrison, Cleveland, McKinley, and, in particular, Theodore Roosevelt, set aside large areas in western United States. The next great step was the passage of the Weeks Law in 1911. It provided for the extension of national forests by purchase, thus making it possible to establish forests in eastern United States; but, unfortunately, all purchases were limited to lands of unquestioned value in protecting or promoting the navigability of streams. This defect was remedied by the Clarke-McNary Act of 1924, which extended the right of purchase within the watersheds of navigable streams to include land of value for the *production of timber.*

Why Enlarge Our Public Forests? Various objections to the extension of public forests have been advanced. The withdrawal of these lands from private ownership cripples the local governments for a time, for public lands pay no taxes. Public lands must be concentrated in fairly large blocks, a requirement which seriously impairs their value for erosion control, game cover, and recreational use, and the ease with which wood waste can be kept at a minimum. It is maintained, also, that to enlarge public forests is to place on society a task which, in line with American political traditions, had better be undertaken by private initiative.

Even though the validity of these arguments be granted, they do not alter the conclusion that our public forests should be greatly enlarged. Private initiative should be given all possible encouragement, but the fact remains that there are public interests in forests which are not and, apparently, will not be safeguarded by private ownership alone, for the simple reason that private owners cannot afford to do so.

It is fairly certain, for example, that, if the next few generations are to be adequately supplied with timber of saw-log size, much of it must be grown on public lands. To wait until the economic reward to private owners is more certain is to delay provision against a future need. A necessary crop which requires one to two hundred years to mature must, it appears, be the concern of society if it does not at present offer adequate inducements to private business. Private individuals find it hazardous to take the financial risks involved, but society can ill afford not to take them. In the extension, by the Clarke-McNary Act, of the right of federal purchase to include lands needed for the promotion of timber production, the nation accepts the challenge and makes provision for meeting it. For this reason, if for no other, this act stands as a major advance in our national forest policy.

Even clearer at the present, though possibly no more certain in the long run, is the need for an enlargement of public forests in order to guarantee those services for which it is difficult to make compensation to private landowners—scenery and recreation, wild game cover, and watershed protection. The private owner generally finds it difficult to secure a full return from the recreational use of his forest land; he has no direct interest in furnishing flood protection for the agricultural and urban property which lies downstream, and he gains nothing by providing a regular, sediment-free water supply for some city perhaps a hundred miles away. To meet these needs alone, there should be a great increase in public forests.

CONCLUSION

The enlargement of our public forests is but one of several essential measures in forest conservation. In these measures are involved four major lines of constructive action—an accurate stock-taking or resource inventory, the preservation of certain portions of the resource, the discovery and prompt employment of more and more efficient means of utilization, and systematic provision for renewal. Interest is focused particularly on renewal, however, for no matter how freely our forests are used, the needs of the future can be adequately met if proper provision is made for growing new crops of trees. With sufficient forethought, there appears to be no reason why the American people should ever be without an abundant supply of the services which forests can render.

Basic to all considerations of policy is the fact that our country, a "forest nation," is nearing the end of its supply of virgin timber. A shift from dependence on natural forests to reliance on forests grown under some measure of human control is required in the years that lie ahead. This new industry, silviculture, will not depend on the original vegetation of our country, but on its soil and water resources. Thus, as our original forest wealth disappears, the problem of supplying forest services becomes more and more nearly identical with the problem of utilization and conservation of our humid lands.

PART IV

CHAPTER XII

WATER SUPPLY FOR DOMESTIC AND INDUSTRIAL USES

By Robert M. Brown
Rhode Island College of Education

THE IMPORTANCE OF OUR WATER RESOURCES

One cannot imagine man separated from water any more than one can imagine him separated from land. Water is an essential part of his being. He uses it in innumerable ways; and because in areas of dense population he has been favored with it, frequently he spends it recklessly, thinks of it as he thinks of air as an unlimited requisite of existence, and gives little heed to its value. In drier regions water is held of greater value, and stringent laws governing its use are formulated.

The place of water in the lives of people in arid lands may be partially realized by the frequent rain ceremonies of the Hopi Indians and by the repeated references in the religious literatures of desert peoples, as the Bible and the Koran, to water as a blessing and to paradise as a place where there is abundant water.

Our water comes from precipitation, and the average rainfall for the United States is about 30 inches per year. This average will lead us easily to the total amount of water received by the country in one year but it tells nothing about distribution. East of the 95° W meridian, with a rainfall increasing from 20 inches per year in central Kansas to about 50 inches per year on the Atlantic coast, is the humid belt. This area receives about 60 per cent of the rainfall of the United States. A small area in the Northwest including western Washington, western Oregon, and northwestern California is also humid. These two areas are best favored with water resources. Between the 95° W meridian and the Rocky Mountains, with annual rainfalls between 10 and 20 inches per year, is the semiarid belt which receives about 17 per cent of the rainfall of the United States. Between the Rocky Mountains and the Cascade-Nevada Range is an arid belt with less than 10 inches of rain per year where crops will grow only in such areas as are peculiarly favored with water.

In regions of scant water supply, conflicts are likely to arise over water rights, and frequently in densely settled regions there must be a choice between uses. It is more essential, for example, that mankind have drinking water than that mankind have water for transportation. One arrangement of the uses of water in order of influence or importance is as follows:[1] "(1) atmospheric moisture indispensable to organic life; (2) drinking water for man; (3) water used in agriculture and animal husbandry; (4) water as a habitat of fish and seafood; (5) water used for generation of power; (6) water used for mechanical and chemical processes in industry; (7) water as a means of transportation; (8) water as a medium for the removal and purification of wastes; (9) water as a recreational asset; (10) water as a determinant of political boundaries; (11) water used as ice."

For all these manifold uses, the United States must depend upon its rainfall. The 30 inches of annual rainfall cannot be applied to all these. About one-half of the rainfall is evaporated and goes back into the atmosphere as water vapor; about one-third of it forms the runoff, draining by rill, brooks, and rivers to the sea. This is the visible water supply, and the greater percentage of the uses in the above list arises from this portion of the water. One-sixth of the rainfall sinks into the ground and forms ground water; this is a less well known but very important reservoir of water which acts as a stabilizer of lake levels and stream flow and a source of water supply for plant growth.

The problem of the manipulation of the enormous amount of water which falls on the United States varies with the humidity or aridity of the area. Evaporation, runoff, and ground soakage are not uniform, and unwise practices may increase runoff to a danger point and destroy the balance set up by natural agencies. Among the many problems of water are the control of floods, which, for example, have caused great losses of life and property in the Mississippi Valley; the control of low water stages which have hindered navigation, as on the Mississippi River, or have caused losses of crops, as in the Imperial Valley; its use for navigation, power, water supply for cities and towns, and the removal of refuse from houses and factories; the erosive tendencies of rain and streams; the silting of streams and consequent deposition

[1] Thorndike Saville, "Planning for Water Resources Development," *Scientific Monthly,* Vol. 41, No. 2, p. 170, August, 1935.

when stream flow decreases; its use for irrigation; the maintenance of the ground water supply and the stabilization of the water table; and the use of water as a recreational appeal. A water policy of the country should be so established as to yield the greatest benefit possible from our water resources and be so regulated as to serve the greatest need. At all events, one needs take the stand that water is a highly valuable resource, too precious to be wasted.

IMPORTANCE OF WATER FOR DOMESTIC PURPOSES

Water is one of mankind's most essential needs. Primitive settlements were located around springs and watercourses, and when the water failed the people were driven from their homes. Palmyra, once a city of possibly more than 150,000 people, vying with Damascus for the trade between Egypt and Babylon and reaching great prominence under the reign of Queen Zenobia, consists today of a few ruins in a desert landscape while Damascus still exists. Both were oasis cities, but the drying up of the oasis at Palmyra spelled its doom. Later peoples learned how to build aqueducts and transport water from distant springs and rivers. When gold was discovered in the Australian desert in 1892 and the towns of Kalgoorlie and Coolgardie were founded, the district was practically waterless. For a while the railroad transported water to the towns at a cost of about $5,000 a day. In 1903, a water line was completed from the Darling Range, 350 miles away, and a delivery of 8,000,000 gallons daily resulted. So long are the pipes that they contain a month's supply of water; in other words, the water takes one month in traveling from Mundaring to Kalgoorlie. In some states of the arid West where an insufficiency of water exists, water commissioners demand applications for the use of water and the requests are granted according to the essential needs of water up to the limit of the available supply. Preferential rights are frequently stated, as for instance in Arizona where first choice is given to domestic and industrial uses, second to irrigation and stock watering, and third to water power and mining uses.

Residents of humid areas, especially in the United States where the growth to dense population has been recent, have not really appreciated the value of water as the dwellers in more arid regions have. In the eastern United States, only a few years ago, a moderately dense population was adequately supplied with water and the problem of water had not appeared above the horizon. The idea that there was an ample supply was inherited, and it has been passed on by inference to the present generation. Today it is necessary to combat the idea and treat water as a natural resource of limited though perhaps of inexhaustible amount which must be conserved so that the supply at any one time may be adequate for our needs and particularly so that its misuse may not be a burden to future generations.

SOURCES OF WATER SUPPLY

Cities and towns in the United States obtain their water supply for domestic purposes from many sources.

Lakes. In the glaciated parts of the United States thousands of lakes exist, and these near cities and villages may serve as sources of domestic supply. The Great Lakes yield water to their large riparian cities: Lake Michigan to Chicago and Milwaukee; Lake Superior to Duluth; Lake St. Clair to Detroit; and Lake Erie to Buffalo and Cleveland. In New York state a number of lakes serve the neighboring large cities as Skaneateles Lake, Syracuse, and Hanlock and Candice lakes, Rochester. Many of the glacial lakes, however, have to be deepened by artificial dams before enough water can be impounded to yield a sufficient supply. Reservoirs, artificial lakes, are made by some cities by the damming of rivers. Many lakes are enlarged by damming.

Wells. Most rural towns and many urban localities depend on ground water for their domestic supply, and this comes to them in part through springs but largely through ordinary wells. Lowell, Massachusetts, obtains its water from wells averaging 50 feet in depth; Tacoma, Washington, 25-75 feet; Schenectady, New York, 40-44 feet; and Dayton, Ohio, 50-70 feet. In every rainfall where there is a surface mantle over the rocks, a certain percentage of the water is absorbed by the soil (estimated average about 16 per cent). This forms ground water. Its upper surface is known as the water table. The amount of ground water is much greater than is commonly supposed. It has been said that[1] there is enough water under ground so that, if it were brought to the surface, it would form a layer probably 500 to 1,000 feet deep. The depth of the water table varies; in swamps the water table reaches to the surface, and in arid areas it may lie a hundred feet below the surface. Frequently, in humid areas, water is struck before one digs to thirty feet. The water-table depth in any single locality varies with the rainfall. A long period of drought, such as was experienced in some localities during the summer of 1934 and

[1] Salisbury, Barrows, and Tower, *Modern Geography*, pp. 205-206, Chicago, 1913.

in others during the summer of 1935, takes a serious toll of the ground water, and the water table may be so lowered that it falls below the level of the well bottoms and the wells become dry. If the drain is not overly heavy the water table is generally brought back to its normal level by succeeding falls of rain. An extended drought, however, may bring serious damage by killing off the vegetable cover and subjecting the soil to wind and later rain erosion. In some localities, the water table has been lowered beyond the level of efficiency by stripping the vegetation cover, as in excessive deforestation, and in the processes of extensive cultivation, soil erosion, and ditching. For example, it is estimated somewhat roughly that the water table over large areas in the United States has been lowered from ten to forty feet by these methods.

The yield of the well is in a large degree determined by the texture of the water-bearing layer (aquifer). Wells in gravel which permits a ready flow will yield more than an aquifer of gravel and clay. To be of value a well should yield at least a few gallons a minute, and a maximum yield for wells may be a thousand gallons a minute. Rapid pumping from a well will lower the level of the water, but as the amount of ground water feeding the well is frequently enormously greater than that of water in the well, after a short period of rest, the well generally regains its level.

Springs. These are more primitive than wells. They have determined the location of early settlements as in the Plymouth Colony. In semiarid lands where grazing is the industry, the spring was of first consideration, and ranch warfares frequently resulted over the possession of the water right. In arid lands they have determined the courses of travel. Many oases are depression springs, depressions which tap the water table, and these areas cause exceptions to the nomadic characteristic of desert people since they permit a sedentary population. In many springs the flow though persistent is not rapid and the yield is not large. Rare yields are reported from Silver Spring, Florida, of 368,000 gallons a minute, and Warm Springs, Oregon, of 116,500 gallons a minute. A scarcity of rainfall may diminish and even stop the flow of a spring. It is probable that this is what happened at Palmyra and resulted in the abandonment of the site.

Artesian Wells. These tap a porous layer (the aquifer), generally sandstone, which lies between two impervious layers of rock or below an impervious layer. The porous layer should have an exposure for the intake of water at a higher level than the land about the well, and the impervious layer or layers imprison the water. Boise, Idaho;

Houston, Texas; Memphis, Tennessee; San Antonio, Texas; and Baton Rouge, Louisiana, are some of the cities that obtain their domestic water from this source. The rock layers are particularly favorable for artesian wells along the Atlantic and Gulf coastal plains and on the Great Plains. On the semiarid plains they have been used as a source of water for household and for stock. Large parts of Nebraska, South Dakota, eastern Colorado, and northwestern Kansas obtain their artesian waters from the Dakota sandstone, the collecting area of which (intake) is around the base of the Black Hills in South Dakota and along the eastern foothills of the Rocky Mountains. Many artesian wells have been drilled to great depth, as 3,843 feet at St. Louis, Missouri; 4,625 feet at Pittsburgh, Pennsylvania; and 3,071 feet at Galveston, Texas. In these wells the water is tepid, ranging in temperature from 70° to 80°. In South Dakota so many wells have been drilled that the artesian water is greatly diminished in amount and other sources of water supply have to be sought.

When the intake is higher than the mouth of the well and the aquifer is full, flowing wells may result. One such well in France has been flowing for nearly 800 years. There is likely to be a great waste of water from flowing wells as originally there was loss of oil in gusher wells. In some states laws are passed forbidding certain practices which lead to waste. California protects her ground water by legislative enactments. Not infrequently artesian waters are charged with gas or contain mineral matter in solution so that their uses are limited; sometimes they are unadapted for household purposes, and sometimes altogether unfit for many industrial applications.

Streams. Surface water furnishes the source of domestic water to a large number of cities. If only large cities are listed, this would seem to be the largest source of water supply, but the *National Resource Board's Report*[1] states:

> About a third of the people of the United States live in 90 cities of more than 100,000 population, another third in smaller towns and villages, and the remainder on farms. The latter two-thirds depend extensively on ground water. Waters obtained from underground sources generally do not require filtration and are suited to the public systems when available in sufficient volumes. The use of ground water is reflected in the analysis of statistics of water systems supplying 67,000,000 persons. A fourth of this total use ground water, but more than half of these are in the populous area east of the Mississippi and north of the Ohio, where surface supplies are also abundant. Ground water serves four-fifths of the consumers in

[1] Washington, 1934, p. 331.

> Florida, and one-half to two-thirds in the other states around the Gulf of Mexico. These sources are still more important in the dry Southwest.
>
> Two and a half million consumers in 18 of the larger cities (population over 100,000) use ground water.

Nevertheless, many of the large cities in the United States obtain their water supply from surface sources: Atlanta, Georgia, from the Chattahoochee River; Bismarck, North Dakota, Kansas City, Kansas, Kansas City, Missouri, and Omaha, Nebraska, from the Missouri River; Minneapolis and St. Paul, Minnesota, St. Louis, Missouri, and New Orleans, Louisiana, from the Mississippi River; Cincinnati, Ohio, and Louisville, Kentucky, from the Ohio River; and many others from smaller streams. Where large streams serve as the source of supply the question of storage does not arise, but when small streams are used storage reservoirs have to be constructed to concentrate the waters and furnish a head. As cities grow, the reservoir constructed at one period is inadequate for the next. Boston, a few years ago, had for its supply the Framingham Reservoir some twenty-five miles away. When this became inadequate it built the Wachusett Reservoir, at Clinton, Massachusetts, forty-five miles away. This in turn has become inadequate, and the city is building a dam in Enfield, Massachusetts, a hundred miles away, tapping some of the tributaries of the Connecticut. New York has had similar experiences, as is shown farther on.

The Rain Barrel and the Cistern. In some localities the runoff from roofs is collected in cisterns or barrels as a source of wash water. This device was originally quite extensive where the source of water was an unpiped well and the drawing of water somewhat of a chore. In semiarid lands it has the advantage of furnishing an additional supply, and in areas where the ground or surface water is hard of yielding a soft water.

Sea Water. It has been suggested that the ocean water might be distilled, and thus yield an unfailing supply to coast cities. The expense involved, however, is so large that it is forbidding when other sources are available. Baku in Transcaucasia and Aden on the Arabian Peninsula, situated in very dry regions, resort to this method. With an abundance of oil at Baku the process is much less expensive than at Aden, where coal must be brought from a distance.

TRANSPORTATION OF WATER

In many localities water is carried by hand from well or spring to the house. In a survey of 1,139 homes in northern Rhode Island it was found that in 292 water was carried by hand, and in 164 the water was obtained by a hand pump in the dwelling. In many lands it is a familiar scene to see women with jars on their heads going to and from streams or fountains. The vender of water may be seen in many eastern settlements.

The supplying of water was once considered a private affair, and in 1800 in the United States there was but one public water works company in comparison with fifteen private works. In 1652 the Water Works Company of Boston introduced the first public water supply in America. It consisted of a reservoir about twelve feet square to which water was conveyed through wooden pipes from near-by springs. This supply was drawn upon for both domestic and fire purposes. By the end of the nineteenth century there were 1,690 public works and 1,489 private works, and the trend toward a public ownership has grown rapidly since 1900. Bringing water into the house to be tapped by a faucet was a great achievement, but it is so commonplace in many localities today as almost to forbid comment. To accomplish this, miles of pipes must be laid through city streets; New York in 1915 had in excess of 3,000 miles of water mains, Chicago 2,500 miles, and Los Angeles 3,800 miles, a greater distance than from San Francisco to Boston.

Furthermore, as cities grew it was necessary to bring water from increasingly greater distances. The proposed Los Angeles supply from the Colorado River is about 270 miles long, the Owens Valley supply to Los Angeles is 238 miles away and with the Mono Basin addition 350 miles, San Francisco's new source in the Hetch Hetchy Valley is 170 miles away, and New York City brings water 125 miles.

CONSUMPTION OF WATER

The average consumption of water per day per capita for two hundred cities in the United States is about 140 gallons. In listing these cities according to population, there appears a suggestion that the smaller cities have a less per capita consumption than the larger. Cities having a population of 500,000 or above had a daily per capita consumption of 150 gallons; those between 300,000 and 500,000, 149; those between 50,000 and 100,000, 118; and those between 30,000 and 50,000 rose again to 123.

A study of the individual cities, particularly in the group of 30,000 to 50,000 population, leads one to conclude that the smaller city will have a less per capita daily consumption of water than the larger wherever the industrial uses decrease commensurately with the decrease in population. Cities with excessive per capita daily consumption include: Tacoma, 430 gallons; Buffalo, 324; Pittsburgh, 253; Albany, 230; Chicago, 270; and Salt Lake City, 203. Cities with low per capita daily consumption are: Fall River, 48; Hartford, 64; Oklahoma City, 53; Providence, 65; and St. Paul, 70.

The public water works of the United States deliver water to approximately 80,000,000 people at the rate of over 1,000,000,000 cubic feet of water a day, or 7,500,000,000 gallons. The average daily per capita use of 110 cities of the United States with a population above 100,000 is 140 gallons. New York City is very close to this average, with 142 gallons. The excessive use of water is due to waste, and metering appears to be the only remedy. A flat rate for water permits the householder to be reckless, extravagant, and wasteful. An investigation of the water consumption of the cities of New York state shows the difference between the consumption of water with metered service and partly metered service. Seventeen of these cities had 75 per cent, or less, of their systems metered. The average per capita consumption of these was 234 gallons a day. Six of these reported a per capita consumption above this average. Fifteen cities in New York state which had more than 75 per cent of their systems metered reported an average daily per capita consumption of 96 gallons. The daily average per capita consumption of New York state cities whose systems are 100 per cent metered is 98 gallons, and the average of American cities all of whose services are metered is 85 gallons. The city of Tacoma, which stands at the head of the list of excessive per capita usage, admits that there is a large wastage by overflow, and but 8 per cent of the water is metered.

In ancient Rome the daily consumption was at the rate of 300 gallons per capita, so insistent were the inhabitants upon the use of water for luxurious baths and constantly flowing fountains. The building of aqueducts was one of Rome's great engineering achievements.

ADEQUACY OF SUPPLY

As one would expect, in arid regions the density of population is small because of the lack of water. Nevada as a whole is our driest state, and its density of population is 0.7, the smallest of the states (109,821 square miles with a population of 77,407). The most densely settled part of the state is in the extreme west where from the Sierra Nevadas a few mountain streams flow for water supply and irrigation. Here are situated Carson City, the capital, and Reno, the largest city. Most of Utah is dry, but a large city such as Salt Lake City will thrive because of neighboring mountain streams fed in part by mountain snow.

Denver to the east of the Rocky Mountains is in a semiarid belt, and for a while the mountain streams supplied her needs for water; but later the city came to use the pioneer bore of the Moffat Tunnel to secure water from the headwaters of the Colorado.

In humid areas where many people reside, the problem of water supply becomes acute particularly if the source of supply is drawn from secondary streams. Great Lakes cities have an abundance, and cities drawing water from large rivers are practically immune from shortage. However, in a period of extended drought such as occurred during the summers of 1930 and 1934 a serious shortage of water was experienced in the basins and the main streams reached such low stages that the quality of the water was affected. Along the eastern seaboard during the drought of 1930, a wide-spread limitation of the use of water was evoked in order to preserve the supply. Water-supply boards prohibited the use of water for lawns and for the washing of automobiles. In some areas schools were closed, Monday washday banned, and tub baths limited, so serious was the shortage. Rural communities dependent on wells saw the drying up of this source of supply and were forced to transport water from afar.

Thus, in most sections, the supply is adequate if rains are fairly regular, but a serious deficiency of water is the experience of too many communities during a long dry spell.

COMPETITION IN THE USE OF WATER

The use of land and the preservation of the ground water are reported[1] in conflict in parts of the Mississippi Valley. First, the increased tillage of the land causes an increased runoff and thus less ground water, and, second, the stress for more cultivable land leads to the drainage of swamp and fen lands which in turn lowers the water table. Thus the expansion of arable lands in these regions has a disastrous effect on ground-water storage and will in time affect the agricultural efficiency of the region.

In the eastern densely populated district, towns and cities are competing for drainage areas, the protection of the present supply and need of a future supply are bringing out new problems.

[1] *Report of the Mississippi Valley Commission of the Public Works Administration* 1934, p. 71.

Conflict over Withdrawals from the Connecticut River. The construction of the new reservoir to supply the City of Boston caused the State of Connecticut to file a bill of complaint with the Supreme Court during January, 1928, against the Commonwealth of Massachusetts for planning to divert the waters of the tributaries of the Connecticut River—the Swift, Ware, and Miller rivers—from their natural flow into the Connecticut. Briefly, the State of Connecticut made the following charges: (1) The navigability of the Connecticut would be impaired by any diminution of the natural flow of the river which would result in a flow too slow and sluggish to free the bed from sandbars. (2) The flood stage would be lowered, and the inundation of floodplains which gives the soil its great fertility would be lessened. (3) The pollution of the stream by Massachusetts and Connecticut industrial plants and cities was large, and unless the full flow of the Connecticut was maintained this would not be removed but remain as a detriment to health.

Conflict between New Jersey and New York. Again in 1930 the State of New Jersey sought to enjoin the State of New York and the City of New York from diverting the waters of the Delaware River for an additional water supply for New York City. New Jersey alleged that the proposed diversion would transgress its rights in many respects. These are stated below, not as arguments upholding the truth or falsity of the claims, but merely to show in how many ways a river may be affected when the waters are used for water supply: (1) Interfere with navigation. (2) Deprive the state and its citizens who are riparian owners of the undiminished stream. (3) Affect water power and the ability to develop it. (4) Injuriously affect the industrial use of the river. (6) Increase the salinity and thus injure the oyster industry of Delaware Bay. (7) Injure the shad fisheries. (8) Injure the water supply of New Jersey towns and cities. (9) By lowering the level of the water injure the cultivation of adjoining lands. (10) Injuriously affect the river for recreational purposes.

Both these petitions were denied, the Court holding that a state could claim a fair share of interstate waters but could not do so to the material damage of another state.

Conflict over the Colorado River. In the case of the Colorado River a more serious problem arises. The river has an average annual flow of 16,000,000 acre-feet. The Colorado Compact allocated 7,500,000 acre-feet to the Upper Basin and a similar amount to the Lower Basin with 1,000,000 acre-feet surplus. The United States Geological

Survey[1] estimates that at Parker, where the water is first turned from the river for use, the annual supply available will be about 9,593,000 acre-feet. Irrigable lands below Parker and within the bounds of the United States total 2,304,000 acres and will demand 9,909,000 acre-feet of water. In Mexico at least 1,000,000 acres are irrigable and will require 3,357,000 acre-feet. Requirements of southern California for domestic uses are placed at 2,000 second-feet of water, equivalent to an annual flow of 1,448,000 acre-feet. Thus the total amount which the present-day conditions anticipate is 14,714,000 acre-feet. Using the estimate of the United States Geological Survey there will be an annual shortage of 5,121,000 acre-feet of water in the Lower Basin, or using the allotment of the Colorado Compact, an annual shortage of 6,211,000 acre-feet. Thus the entire annual flow of the Colorado River is inadequate for the needs of the Basin, yet it must be tapped as a water supply for cities in southern California which lie outside of its basin.

Los Angeles. Los Angeles is a city in a semiarid region where plant growth must be stimulated by irrigation. Settled in 1781 on the Los Angeles River, the town obtained from King Carlos III of Spain by royal decree the ownership to all the waters of the river in perpetuity. Until 1914 this was practically its only source of water, and it was considered sufficient to supply a population of 250,000.

When Los Angeles passed the quarter-century mark in population, and the Los Angeles River, described as a stream whose bed must be sprinkled regularly to keep down the dust, became inadequate, the city tapped the Owens River, 238 miles away. Owens Valley, about 150 miles long, lies between the Sierra Nevadas on the west and the White Mountains on the east.

Practically all the drainage is from the Sierra Nevadas between Mount Lyell and Mount Whitney. The river empties into Owens Lake, which has no outlet. Previous to 1905 the valley had a population of about 3,500, who gained a livelihood by farming on lands irrigated by the river, since the rainfall of the valley is light—probably not more than five inches a year.

In areas of limited precipitation, conflicts frequently arise over rights, and it is not strange that, when Los Angeles went beyond her borders for water, trouble followed. The intake of the Los Angeles system on the Owens River was below the head gates of the lowest irrigation ditch, and consequently the city could not deprive the farmers

[1] E. C. LaRue, "Water Power and Flood Control below Green River, Utah," *United States Geological Survey, Water Supply Paper* 556, Washington, 1925.

of water, but on the contrary it took at the beginning only such water as would have gone into Owens Lake and eventually evaporated. In reality Los Angeles benefited the Owens Lake farmers by connecting them by rail with the outside market. This boon acted as a boomerang, since it offered inducements to settlers, and the population by 1920 had doubled and a tourist trade had been inaugurated. With this increase in population and a corresponding withdrawal of more water from Owens River by the settlers, Los Angeles found in 1923 that the leavings were not sufficient for the city's needs and began to buy land of the farmers to lessen the irrigation drain. Altogether 80 per cent of the irrigated lands of the valley were purchased. In 1924 there was an outbreak by the farmers, aqueduct waste gates were opened or dynamited, and about 200,000,000 gallons of water were turned into the desert.

Today Los Angeles, beyond the million mark in population, is looking forward to a city of 2,000,000 people and must have more water than can be derived from the Los Angeles and Owens Rivers. She has already surveyed an aqueduct route to the Colorado River—270 miles away—to carry 1,500 second-feet of water, and construction has already begun. This will be the greatest distance that water is carried for domestic purposes in the United States but it will be exceeded when Los Angeles takes Mono Lake. The 1,500 second-feet of water will supply 1,500,000 people with domestic water. A score or more of other municipalities of southern California besides Los Angeles will share in this supply. As shown above, this subtraction of a domestic supply from the Colorado River hampers other though less important enterprises in the Valley itself.

New York City. The domestic water supply in humid regions of dense population is obtained perhaps with greater ease than in arid areas but is beset with difficulties no less acute. New York City's water supply is able to yield about 1,200,000,000 gallons of water a day. This water comes from a number of sources: the Catskill system, the latest addition to the city sources, has a maximum of 600,000,000 gallons a day; the Old Croton source of 1842 yields 336,000,000 gallons a day; the Ridgewood system, an extensive underground supply developed on Long Island, adds 90,000,000 gallons a day; old borough sources in operation before their incorporation furnish 30,000,000 gallons a day; and private water companies which hang over from earlier days are estimated to yield 44,000,000 gallons a day.

Soon after the completion of the Catskill system the city was using about 850,000,000 gallons daily. It was estimated that within ten years there would be a serious shortage of water. This condition repeats the history of the water supply of New York beginning with the wells and springs that served 1,500 people in 1664 until late in the year 1915, when the Catskill water was turned into the distributing pipes. Until the Old Croton Dam was constructed (1837-1842) the city was not large enough to demand a water supply from outside her boundaries. The various units of New York's water system represent in part the development of her constituent parts before their union as Greater New York, and in part old contracts by private water companies in the days before public water companies were much in vogue.

New York's first publicly owned water works were constructed in 1830 and yielded 21,000 gallons of water a day. This was an almost insignificant amount in comparison with the Manhattan Company, a private concern, that had a maximum capacity of 700,000 gallons a day. It was a beginning, however, and the additions to the water supply were made more and more by the city itself. In the meantime the boroughs, as they in turn faced the demand for water, developed independent systems of their own.

Whereas New York is built on a rocky island and therefore has a limited water table, Brooklyn is situated on glacial sands and gravels which extend eastward throughout Long Island. The underground water about Brooklyn in 1926 yielded 104,000,000 gallons a day; 73,000,000 gallons of this was taken from wells from thirty to several hundred feet deep; 34,000,000 from infiltration galleries laid for six miles ten to fifteen feet below the water table; and in addition Brooklyn received 20,000,000 gallons a day from surface supplies.

New York City covers an area of 315.9 square miles and has an average rainfall of 44.63 inches. If the entire precipitation of an average year over the city was impounded it would amount to 204,125,707,138 gallons or an average fall of 550,000,000 gallons a day. Only a meager percentage of this is available, since with paved streets the runoff is excessive. The watershed of New York's water system, not counting the Queens and Richmond supplies, is 1,136 square miles—an area equivalent to the State of Rhode Island. This is a little in excess of two square miles for every 10,000 people. The Queens and Richmond areas would probably bring it to three square miles, which is the average amount of drainage space per 10,000 people, utilized by cities dependent on surface water.

In 1925 New York used 847,000,000 gallons of water daily. The yield from her water works was 1,100,000,000 gallons, a safe surplus of 253,000,000 gallons daily. The city is increasing in population each year by about 250,000, and this makes an increase in water consumption of 31,000,000 gallons daily a year. By 1930 New York City was using 1,002,000,000 gallons daily, and the safe surplus had diminished to 98,000,000 gallons daily: in 1935 with the same rate of increase New York City consumed 1,157,000,000 gallons daily and the safe surplus had gone. The new reservoirs to be constructed from the headwaters of the Delaware River will divert 440,000,000 gallons daily, at a cost of $273,000,000, and will probably last the city until 1955 when new sources of supply must be found.

QUALITY OF WATER

Factors Affecting Quality. Not only must settlements have sufficient quantity of water but also it must be of good quality. The quality, however, must be determined in terms of its use: the quality suitable for sewage disposal may be greatly different from that desirable for drinking purposes.

Rain falling on the surface of the earth and flowing over the land cleans it of all loose particles of mineral materials and animal and vegetable refuse. It is a great natural scavenger.

Most surface supplies and wells if they are open to rain wash are contaminated. Furthermore, drainage from populous districts is particularly liable to contamination. Water for household purposes should be: (1) Clear. A roily water may not be harmful for drinking but it is objectionable to the eye and to the mind. It may be disastrous to use it for washing clothes and for some cooking, and the industrial use of some of it may be costly. Many water works have settling basins in which the water remains motionless for a period of time to allow all matters in suspension to be dropped. Sediment in streams, known as turbidity, is common in surface streams and rare in underground waters. A turbidity of ten parts to the million would be considered objectionable. (2) Tasteless and odorless. It is at times not easy to get the taste from water. At certain seasons of the year a taste is more evident than at others, owing probably to growing organisms. One frequently gets accustomed to the taste of the water served over a long period of time and objects to the taste of the water of another locality. Odors may arise from water from growing organisms when such water is not harmful and also from decaying organisms when it is harmful. A water with a disagreeable taste and odor is considered likely to be unwholesome. (3) Have a low degree of mineralization. Ground water may contain a variety of dissolved mineral products. The mineral content varies in different parts of the United States, depending on the character of the soil. The glacial soil of New England originating from the insoluble granitic rocks has a low mineralization, and the soil of some midwestern areas has soluble compounds and a high mineralization. Water of low mineralization is soft and is desirable in industries. (4) Free from harmful bacteria. Bacteria are probably the most dangerous features in a water system. Others, as turbidity, taste, odor, and mineralization, may be observed, but the bacteria content gives the ordinary consumer no indication of its presence. Water boards go to great expense to make a water supply safe. It is said that, in China, the natives' preference for tea has saved the people many a scourge.

Mineral Salts in Water. Hardness is a measure of the calcium and magnesium salts present in the water, and it may be considered for ordinary purposes in three stages: soft water with less than 60 parts of salts to the million (p.p.m.), water with temporary hardness with 60 to 120 p.p.m., and water with permanent hardness, in excess of 120 p.p.m.

Water with temporary hardness may be rendered soft by simple processing, but water with permanent hardness cannot be made soft without an extensive and expensive operation. Hard waters do not permit the proper detergent action of soap and are thus not desirable for household use, for certain industries as laundries, or for boilers where they produce a crust or scale by the deposition of the salts present.

Other undesirable salts which may occur in water are those of iron and manganese. Frequently their presence in water used in the textile and paper industries is harmful.

The Catskill water supply for New York City is well suited for business and household purposes, for it is very low in iron content and corrosive constituents. The city authorities sum up the advantages of a soft water: A soft water reduces the amount of soap required in laundries and in silk dyeing, and affects favorably the operation of power houses, breweries, and photographic establishments. A soft water with low corrosive action eliminates to a great extent scale in boilers and corrosion of tubes, thereby reducing the cost of steam production and the probability of accident. The use of softer waters means the aggregate savings of hundreds of thousands of dollars affecting many classes of consumers in Greater New York.

The Camden, New Jersey, water-supply board speaks of its soft water in this way: "People taking a bath have here no difficulty in getting soap to lather. In the Middle West it is a hard job."

A stream of hard water will have its hardness greatly magnified under low water stages.[1] For example, the Missouri River with a flow of 180,000 cubic feet a second has a hardness of 145 p.p.m.; but, when the flow is reduced to 8,000 cubic feet a second, its hardness becomes 315 p.p.m. The fall of 1930 was a very dry period in the Delaware River Basin. At Philadelphia the flow fell, between January, 1929, and September, 1933, from 80,000 to 5,000 cubic feet a second and the hardness increased from 35 to 165 p.p.m. This change is estimated to have cost the water consumers in the Philadelphia district at least $6,500,000.

Pollution of Water. Lakes and streams are polluted by sewage, waste from industrial plants, and by surface drainage; wells and underground waters are polluted by cesspools and barnyards; wells with unprotected openings by surface wash and animals; and frequently springs and sources of streams are polluted by surface wash and cattle.

Large cities depend on surface streams to carry off their sewage. Many cities are located on large streams, and the pollution becomes dangerous particularly if a downstream city desires to use the river as a source of water supply. On the Great Lakes, the cities turn their waste into the lakes and in turn draw their water supply from it. A way out of the difficulty is to treat the raw sewage chemically before turning it into the river; but though this may protect from the bacteria of human waste, it adds an impurity to the water that must be removed. Again, when the river reaches a low stage the waste is carried by a smaller body of water and the flushing value of the stream is at a minimum, the pollution is magnified. Another great source of pollution to streams lies in the industrial plants which line the banks and discharge their waste into the rivers. The material discharged varies with the industry, but chemicals, dyestuffs, and oils are found in large amounts. In the Appalachian region mine drainage wastes make up the bulk of the discharges. The National Resources Board reports that mine drainage is costing the railroads running east from Pittsburgh $12,000,000 to $20,000,000 a year in corrosion and scales in locomotives as a result of the depreciation of the quality of the water.

Many examples of pollution may be discovered by the investigation of the streams in the locality where one lives. For example, Narragansett Bay, Rhode Island, receives at its head the waste of three streams. One of these, the Blackstone River, brings the sewage of Worcester, Massachusetts, and the waste of many mills to the Bay. The city of Providence discharges its treated sewage into the head

[1] *National Resources Board Report.*

of the Bay, and along the upper shores are three or four great oil concerns. The Bay is tide water and therefore not of value as water supply, but the polluted waters have spoiled the character of the Upper Bay or Providence River as a recreation ground, have caused diseases from bathing in the Bay, and for a number of years have led to a decline in the oyster fisheries.

Results of Pollution. The Report of the Mississippi Valley Commission of the Public Works Administration gives a pictorial graph in illustration of the statement that the typhoid-fever death rate in the United States is largely caused by unsafe water. Briefly this shows that, in 1900, 36 out of every 100,000 persons died of typhoid fever; in 1910, 24; in 1920, 8; in 1930, 5; and in 1932, 4.

Thus the change in water from a pestilence-bearing medium to a purer supply has been of recent origin. This is further illustrated by gleanings from water-board reports.

In Richmond the death rate from typhoid fever in 1908 was 49.7, and it averaged 59.4 per 100,000 persons for the ten years previous to that date. Settling basins were put into operation late in 1908; the death rate due to this disease fell to 24.1 in 1909 and averaged 12.2 during the next fifteen years. In 1924 a filter plant was put into operation, and the death rate again fell to 5.4 for 1925 and 1.1 for 1926. The typhoid death rate in Los Angeles for the year ending June 30, 1925, was 1.07, and in New York City 2.0. Now New York traces typhoid to oysters, milk, uncooked vegetables, ice cream, and carriers from outside the city; Los Angeles claims that 50 per cent of the typhoid fever comes today from outside the city. Wilmington, Delaware, reports a 26.9 per cent reduction in the typhoid death rate after purification processes were instituted for the water supply.

The Denver report on its water system says that the death rate in all cities from typhoid fever is greatly reduced when filter plants are installed, and that there is a second reduction in the death rate when the practice of sterilization of the water with chlorine is adopted. The typhoid death rate in St. Louis diminished from 47 per 100,000 persons in 1903, to 17 in 1913, 4.2 in 1923, and 3.8 in 1924.

Again in Jersey City in 1891, using the Passaic River as its source of water, the typhoid-fever death rate was 101.3 per 100,000; in 1898 from the Pequannock it was 40.6, and 1906 from the untreated Rockaway River, 21.6. In 1913 hypochlorite of lime was used, and the death rate fell to 10.3, and finally, in 1926, subsequent to the use of chlorine, it fell to 1.57. New Orleans, which originally used raw water with disastrous results, reported a death rate for typhoid fever of less than

2 per 100,000 persons in 1925. Today urban water supplies can be practically absolved as carriers of diseases, and only negligence of the most flagrant character or breakdowns in the water system will make the water supply of a city dangerous.

PURIFICATION OF THE WATER SUPPLY

The character of raw water varies greatly. The Great Lakes waters in their natural state are ideal potable waters, but they are disagreeably polluted by the cities located on them. Topographic conditions at Chicago and Milwaukee compel the cities to dump their sewage, and some of it is untreated, into their sources of water supply. This is overcome partly by placing the intake of the water system far out into the lake—6,565 feet in 67 feet of water for Milwaukee and from two to four miles offshore for Chicago—and partly by sterilization.

Buffalo has its intake a mile and a quarter from shore. Chicago's attempt to solve the problem was to reverse the flow of the Chicago River, but this did not settle the difficulty, for other Illinois towns and neighboring cities continued to contaminate the waters of the lake.

New Orleans has experienced great difficulty with its water supply. Up to the time the present system was put into operation the city depended in part for its water on cisterns which stored the rainwater drained from its roofs, and from a private company which served the raw Mississippi River water. Since 1909 a carefully treated river water has been served the city which is advertised as "a clear, pure water of the most desirable quality." The long journey of the waters of the river from other valley cities which pollute it is in itself a cause of self-purification, and apart from its turbidity—650 p.p.m. of suspended matter—it is usable.

A few localities are fortunate in obtaining water without treatment, believing with Worcester that "clean watersheds, impounding reservoirs which are kept free from pollution, and long storage of water, are the best agents for purification."

San Francisco has its water basin carefully excluded from contamination and neither purifies nor filters its supply. Portland, Oregon, has nothing to pollute its supply and claims that filtration will never be necessary. New Bedford uses no artificial purification.

The process of cleansing polluted water has reached so high a degree of perfection that almost any raw water may be rendered clear, palatable, and safe. An early stage in the process is *sedimentation*. Some of the water used is very turbid. The river water at St. Louis averages 1,430 parts of suspended matter in a million, but the settled water averages but 25 parts; at Atlanta the turbidity runs at times as high as 5,000 p.p.m., but at other times it falls as low as 100; at New Orleans the Mississippi River averages 650 parts; the Missouri at Kansas City 3,100 parts.

To a large degree, because of little movement, lakes are settling basins and can normally be expected, if not agitated, to have a low turbidity. The Detroit supply is as low as 35 p.p.m.

Later, various operations are carried on which are necessitated by the character of the water. *Coagulation* is effected by the introduction generally of sulphate of alumina; this coagulates organic matter in the water and entangles bacteria. It is a finer stage of *sedimentation*. *Filtration* is both mechanical and bacterial, reducing turbidity and removing harmful and undesirable bacteria. *Aeration* makes good a deficiency of oxygen and is helpful in removing odor and taste due to destroyed bacteria. *Chlorination* is an efficient germicide, and is introduced as a safeguard specially when the other processes are not used. *Coppering* is used to prevent algae growths that tend to cause a taste and odor.

Investigations promise in the near future an absolutely tasteless water. Thus the waters of the land may be brought to the household clear, tasteless, and sanitary, and to the factory soft and clear.

The great problem that remains is the quantity of water in view of growing populations. Systematic investigation, not of a city's possible resources, but of the water resources of an extensive area containing many urban groups, so that a proper and satisfactory distribution of surface waters may be made without infringement on the rights of others, is the need of the immediate future.

ANALYSIS OF USES

Primary Uses of Water. The distribution of water to the various uses differs in cities and towns, and few estimates have been made. In Los Angeles an investigation[1] reached definite figures, as follows: the congested business district used approximately 78.5 per cent of the water; the industrial area, 5.5 per cent; first-class residential area, 6.5 per cent; second-class residential area, 5 per cent; and third-class residential area, 4.5 per cent. In Pasadena the business district used 45 per cent; apartments, 18 per cent; de luxe residences, 16 per cent; high-class residences, 13 per cent; and moderate-priced residences, 7 per

[1] D. M. Baker and H. Conkling, *Water Supply and Utilization*, New York, 1930.

cent. It is hardly safe to draw conclusions from these figures, yet, as was instanced in ancient Rome, water seems to have a place among the luxuries.

Secondary Uses of Domestic Water. Most water systems are the sources of water for fire protection, and occasionally cities have separate mains, as is reported by Detroit, Michigan, and Milwaukee, Wisconsin. In these cities the water source is the same, but in the fire mains the expense of purification is eliminated. The possibility of pumping water into the mains by fire boats on the lake makes this a feasible project in these and similarly located sites. Purification costs range from a few cents to a number of dollars per 1,000,000 gallons. Columbus, Ohio, a few years ago reported $17.46 per 1,000,000 gallons, and Grand Rapids, Michigan, $10; on the other hand, in many cities the cost is less than a dollar for 1,000,000 gallons.

In many localities the lessening cost of insurance when hydrants are favorably located will in time pay for the installation of water mains.

Again, the water supply is used frequently as a sewer flush. It had been feared that, when the natural flow of streams was diverted for water supply, the use of the stream for the removal of sewage would be hampered. This was in part the contention of the State of Connecticut against Boston for diverting the headwaters of the Connecticut River and that of the State of New Jersey against New York for diverting the headwaters of the Delaware River.

Chicago has turned its sewage into the Chicago River which drains into Lake Michigan. Since this contaminated her water supply, the City has cut a channel from the Chicago River to the Des Plaines River, a tributary of the Illinois and thus of the Mississippi River, reversed the flow the Chicago River, and diverted its sewage to the Mississippi River. In order to carry this off, the City received the right to divert 10,000 cubic feet a second of water from Lake Michigan to serve as a flush. The diversion of this great amount of water was at first thought to have a deleterious effect on the level of the water in the lakes. A period of low lake levels was experienced, but later the lakes returned to their normal level and the fluctuation is today believed to be the result of a scanty rainfall rather than the withdrawal of water.

STOPPING WASTE

Water is expensive. As population increases, water has to be brought from greater and greater distances, and this in turn increases the expense. In New York City the construction of water works cost up to January, 1933, $497,306,000, and the proposed plan of adding to the present (1936) inadequate supply waters from the tributaries of the Delaware River will cost $273,000,000. Operation costs of the New York system during 1932 were $9,670,000, and interest and sinking fund charges, $25,285,000. The revenue from the sale of water during 1932 was a little more than $25,000,000. With this great outlay and in the face of threatening shortages it is necessary to stop waste.

This may be done in a number of ways: (1) Preventing waste in the system itself due to leakage. Cities are realizing this and are taking every means to make the system perfect. The Memphis authorities, for example, have a man under contract for the sole purpose of locating underground leaks. (2) Metering. New York City has about 26 per cent of its water metered. The interpretation of the present law permits the authorities to install meters in business houses only and not in private houses unless the owners apply for one. Thus in New York City practically all the waters used for commercial and industrial purposes are metered, and but 18 per cent of the meters are on domestic service. It is the belief that if all the water of the city were metered enough wastage would be avoided so that the need for the new development of the water system could be postponed a number of years. (3) Raising water rates. New York City has the same rates that were in operation fifty years ago, although practically every other form of public utility charge has advanced. No one likes to have water rates advanced, but it appears to be an easier thing to do than to make people realize that water in the home costs money, that it is a valuable resource, and that it ought not be wasted.

CHAPTER XIII

WATER POWER AND ITS CONSERVATION

By Frank Williams

University of Pennsylvania

INTRODUCTION

Importance of Power. "Mechanical power is the heart of modern civilization." Until means of mechanical power were developed, man was unable to gain any definite control over the elements. Lack of power in *large* amounts delayed the coming of comfort and the high standard of living generally prevalent in the United States. The power-driven machine and its accompanying division of labor have almost entirely replaced the self-reliant workman of former decades. Man's welfare and comfort depend on a continued and uninterrupted supply of power. Power is as essential a part of the necessities of modern life as are food, clothing, and homes. Indeed, without the use of mechanical power man's necessities and luxuries would be limited to the products of his immediate locale. The use of power allows him to live where he desires, to have his wants carried to his home, and to be transported to and from his work.

Power Resources of the United States. The United States is more fortunate than most nations in its abundance of power resources. Not only are there extensive supplies of coal, oil, and gas within its boundaries but there are vast water-power resources at its command. This non-expendable source of power has been rapidly developed, but there are many potential possibilities of tremendous importance.

Early Development of Water Power. Settlements had hardly become permanently established in the early colonies, particularly from Pennsylvania to New England, before rapidly flowing or falling water was set to turning wheels which would make the work of man easier or enable him to accomplish more with the same amount of effort. In these early days, flour and grist mills and sawmills were the most important. But soon there followed paper mills, powder mills, woolen mills, cotton mills, rolling and splitting mills, nail factories, factories for tilt, blade, and edge tools, oil mills, and snuff mills. Industry at first was extremely primitive—only the smallest streams that were little more than rills were the source of power; but as capital accumulated and skill was developed, larger and larger streams were harnessed. The increased population and the demand for goods made the construction of larger mills necessary. The handicap of the restricted site, near the stream, with the danger of recurring floods, was a serious drawback.

The Coming of Steam. But in a world so limited as to means of producing energy, and at a time when factories were reaching their limits in size because of the necessarily restricted conditions, came the discovery of the power of steam. This break from "muscle, wind and water to steam as a source of energy was an epochal change." The revolution brought about by the discovery of steam was especially notable in areas where coal was near at hand as in Pennsylvania. Although small mill units persisted in the use of direct water power (and there are a few even now in existence) the large industrial output was due to coal-generated power.

The Dawn of Electricity. The change from steam to electricity threatens to be quite as revolutionary as that from water to steam. There have been striking gains in the development of electric power in our country. A little over fifty years ago the electric industry of this country had its beginning. From its small start in New York City (in 1882) it has spread to nearly every portion of the country, penetrating every part of our social and economic life.

> Operation of the first Edison central station distribution system was begun in New York City on September 4, 1882, the prime movers being steam engines. A few days later the second Edison station began operating at Appleton, Wis., the electric generator in this case being driven by water power. These two plants were the nucleus of the electric power industry which now has a total generating capacity of 45,000,000 horsepower. The two methods of power production, by falling water and by steam, represented in these primitive plants, have continued to be the principal methods used in the production of electrical energy. . . ."[1]

Of prime interest to us then is: How shall this electricity be developed?

Revival of Interest in Water Power. The attention of the public has again been focused upon the development and use of water-power resources. This interest has often led to such enthusiasm on the part of those who favor the development of these resources that rash state-

[1] Federal Power Commission, National Power Survey, *Interim Report,* Power Series 1, United States Government Printing Office, Washington, D. C., 1935.

ments concerning hydroelectric possibilities abound. Many have even gone so far as to predict that hydraulic power might be able to supply all our needs for power, heating, and light. If it can be shown that this permanent source of power can be made to satisfy all our needs and that it can be developed in comparative economy with other sources of power, then there will be a sound basis for such claims. It is pointed out that there is a continuously increasing demand for power delivered in the form of electricity. But this does not necessarily mean that electricity so used must be made through hydroelectrical energy rather than by means of coal- or oil-driven machinery. A survey of resources and an analysis of economic conditions pertaining to methods of production of electricity are necessary to determine the part to be played by each in the development of our power requirements.

THE WATER-POWER PLANT

Types of Water Wheels. When man first used water power is unknown. Crude devices were developed to help lighten man's labors in ancient times. In order to take advantage of a common source of power, wheels were placed in stream currents for the purpose of raising water for irrigation, or by means of a connecting shaft for turning stones in order to grind corn, and for driving other simple machinery. Probably the first type to be used was the "current wheel." This consisted of a large wheel with paddles which dipped in the current of the stream. Of such a type is the noria, which is made of bamboo with woven paddles and is still used by the Chinese. These devices had a very low efficiency and could use probably not more than 3 or 5 per cent of power available in the current of the stream.

An improvement on the "current wheel" was the undershot wheel which was so constructed that the water was conducted to it in a confined channel, or flume, and utilized under a head or fall. Thus was acquired a greater velocity, and since there was but small clearance at the sides and bottom nearly all the water in the channel was made available for driving the wheel. This type of wheel gave an efficiency in the neighborhood of 30 per cent. A further improvement of the gravity wheel was made when the flume was raised so there was but a very small clearance at the center of the wheel. This was known as the "breast wheel" and had an efficiency of 50 to 70 per cent. Sometimes large wooden pitchback wheels having enormous buckets were used. These turned inward toward the fall; thus the impact of the falling water was lost.

Of the early gravity wheels, the "overshot" was the most efficient (Fig. 1). This wheel was built with buckets which were filled with water at the top and turned in the direction of the flow. Thus the impact of the falling water aided the weight in turning the wheel. Efficiencies of 80 or 85 per cent were obtained in this wheel. This type of wheel was extensively used up to about 1850, and a few are still in existence in isolated areas or where but a small amount of power is desired. In nearly all places where these simple wheels were used there was plenty of water, so wasteful methods were not a serious problem.

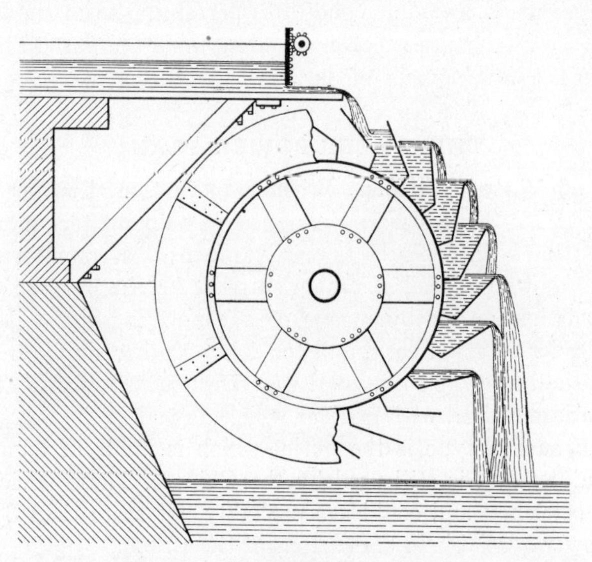

Fig. 1. Overshot Water Wheel.

About the middle of the nineteenth century the turbine was developed and it soon almost completely superseded the overshot wheel. The latter, though efficient, could not be used for large power development. These wheels, being of large diameter and low speed, limited the head of water from 10 to 40 feet. This was the chief reason why the overshot and its predecessors soon became obsolete after the introduction of the turbine. In 1844 Boyden designed a 75-horsepower wheel for a mill at Lowell, Massachusetts. Many improvements have been made, so that common working wheels now have efficiencies of well over 90 per cent (Fig. 2). Accompanying the development of the water-power wheels, there has been a marked increase in the head of water until it has reached about 1,000 feet in this country and about 1,200 feet in Italy. The Pelton, or the bucket and nozzle type, which was developed especially for use where high head is desired, is commonly utilized where there are drops of more than 800 feet.

Functions of the Dam. Ordinarily the primary purpose of a dam is to give a head of water great enough to operate the wheel or turbine. However, its function may be of great importance in producing pond-

Courtesy, Philadelphia Electric Company

Fig. 2. Generator Room. Conowingo Project.

age or storage, particularly in streams of decidedly uneven flow. The dam, therefore, is one of the most important considerations as costs of construction and safety are of prime significance. Careful estimates are required so that the structure will withstand the attacks of the forces of nature, such as erosion and pressure of both water and ice, and at the same time keep the cost as low as possible. The types of dams commonly used are earth, timber, masonry, and concrete with various combinations of two or more of these at any one site (Fig. 3).

Other Required Equipment. In addition to the power house and its machinery, many other forms of equipment are required either to control the flow of water or to fulfill federal and state laws which govern the use of streams. These include channels, forebays, penstocks, gates, valve houses, trash racks, and, in many cases, chutes and fishways. On navigable streams it may be necessary also to build and maintain locks of specified capacity.

Courtesy, Philadelphia Electric Company

Fig. 3. Conowingo Dam and Power House on the Susquehanna River.

ECONOMICS OF WATER-POWER DEVELOPMENT

Restrictions of Direct Water Power. The necessity of placing the factory at the source of power was one of the chief reasons why the steam engine so rapidly replaced a large part of the water power. Water power is handicapped, in comparison with coal or oil, in that it cannot be transported until it has been converted into electricity. Unfortunately the distance to which the current can be economically transmitted is rather definitely limited. Several factors must be considered in determining this distance, but under ordinary conditions of technical development at present, it is limited to 200 or 300 miles. This means that hydroelectric energy must be consumed relatively near its place of production, and that the probable near-by market is as much (or more) of a factor in considering development as the physical factors of the area.

Effect of Electrical Transmission. Although electricity is still comparatively limited in distribution, the development of the means of electrical transmission allows water power to be brought from the isolated mountain area, with its sparse population, to the busy and densely populated metropolitan areas. The use of the early direct water power required that the mill or factory be placed on the bank of the stream. If the stream was large enough to have considerable volume, or had considerable head, it was often difficult to find convenient factory sites on the banks that were not endangered by disastrous floods.

With the transmission of electricity from plants of large capacity to distances of 275 or 300 miles, it is possible for water again to be a major factor in the country's sources of power. Thus has come about a revival in the interest in water power with a consequent construction of large hydroelectric plants and extensive transmission lines. Such has been the revival of popular interest that exorbitant claims have been made that "free" or "cheap water power" would supply all the electricity needed. But is water power "free" or is it always cheaper than other means of developing electricity?

Competition from Other Sources. And what of other means of developing electricity? Did the steam engineers abandon the field to the revived contestant? Not at all. Their answer was to perfect new and better methods of steam-electric development particularly along lines of lessened fuel consumption. The result is that in many localities electricity can be produced more economically by using coal than it can be transmitted from distant sources of "cheap water power." A recent report of the Federal Power Commission says:

> In some sections of the country, particularly certain sections in the Middle West, conditions unfavorable to economical development of water power have resulted in systems comprising for the most part fuel-burning plants, where large power loads exist, steam-power plants predominate; while, in case of smaller isolated communities internal-combustion-engine plants have been found best adapted to service. In other sections, such as those served by the Washington Power Co., and Montana Power Co., the sole source of power is from water-power generating plants.[1]

Where large loads exist, it has been found quite generally that low costs result from a combination of steam and water-power plants. In such combinations, all variations of relative amounts of the two sources of power are found. It is almost impossible to evaluate any water-

[1] Federal Power Commission, National Power Survey, *Interim Report,* Series 1, 1935, p. 43.

power project except for a definite set of conditions. Sites that would be unprofitable for hydroelectric power if developed now might be successful if developed at some future period.

> The value to a system of any additional source of power lies in the dependable capacity in kilowatts which that source will add to the system and its capability to produce kilowatt-hours which can be absorbed by, and will meet the requirements of the load to be served. Aside from matters of broad public policy, the determination of whether water-power or steam plants should be constructed to meet the requirements of a given territory, necessitates the evaluation of many factors involving the characteristics of the load, and the resulting relative net costs. The definite answer to the question of which source of power should be developed requires, therefore, detailed knowledge of the facts in each case.[1]

Isolation of Water-power Sites. Unfortunately a large number of the undeveloped water-power sites are situated in areas where there are but few people. If such power is used, long and expensive transmission lines are required to carry the electricty to the industrial and commercial centers. Suitable sites are seldom found near large centers of population. Most of the developed and potential water-power sources are from 50 to 250 miles from the power market. The Pit River plants of the Pacific Gas and Electric Company are 220 miles from San Francisco, and the Leevining Creek plant of the Southern Sierras Power Company is 330 miles from San Bernardino. Boulder Canyon is 270 miles from the market that it is now ready to serve. Even in "New England the Comerford plant of the New England Power Association is 150 miles from its principal markets in Massachusetts." Similarly extensive transmission lines are necessary in the Southeast to care for the output of the major developments. In order to develop hydroelectric plants economically there must be found favorable conditions of stream flow, head, geological conditions, and topography. The best streams for water power are free from silt and have uniform flow, which is maintained by a natural reservoir such as a swamp or a lake.

Irregularity of Stream Flow. It would be difficult to find a stream more nearly approaching the ideal than the Niagara River. With Lake Erie as a natural reservoir it has a large volume of clear water with uniform flow, and where it plunges over the recessed escarpment at Niagara Falls it has high head. Furthermore, it is unusual in being in a well-settled region with several metropolitan centers near by. Such conditions are rare, however. Commonly, streams are subject

[1] *Ibid.*, p. 43.

to wide variations in volume and in silt content. These variations may be yearly, seasonal, or non-periodic and must be taken into account in designing an economical plant.

Available water supply determines the output characteristics of a hydroelectric plant. Nowhere is precipitation in the form of rainfall or snowfall uniform throughout the year, and often there is wide variation in precipitation from year to year. This condition leads to unequal flow of the streams with a tendency to high water in the spring and fall, and low water in late summer and winter, because of light precipitation and freezing, respectively. Market conditions, however, generally require a more or less regular supply of power throughout the year, and if there are variations they do not often correlate with fluctuations in stream flow. How can these conditions of variable stream flow be met? There are several possibilities, but not all are practicable or economical.

1. *The stream might be developed only to minimum stream flow.* But the cost of the dam and additional necessary equipment to provide for floods and other conditions would be too great relative to the small amount of power that could be developed.

2. *A site might be developed to use the maximum flow and provide for the sale of excess seasonal power to customers who could use it intermittently.* Such a method may be possible theoretically, but seldom could conditions be found where it would be practical.

3. *Steam auxiliaries might be established.* This is sometimes feasible, but market conditions and prices must be carefully considered.

4. *Reservoirs may be constructed to regulate the flow of the stream.* This has the same general effect as the steam auxiliaries in increasing the power, but costs and markets may not justify this procedure.

5. *Hydroelectric plants of two or more drainage basins may be interconnected or correlated with steam plants.* Widening of the market area through such a system may make possible a more economical production of power.

6. *A combination of plans 3, 4, and 5 may be developed.* Seldom is it possible to provide for adequate seasonal storage. Therefore, some form of auxiliary service is necessary to make the production of the necessary power economically feasible. Several companies have made use of this procedure, and it has resulted in notable savings. In a larger way, such a plan was worked out by the United States Geological Survey, several years ago. This project was known as the "Superpower System for the Region between Boston and Washington." The plan contemplates a primary electric line (connecting the two cities)

into which electricity would be fed by isolated power plants in the region. This would allow transfer of power from stations of surplus production to peak markets and allow more even distribution, and thus do away with a large amount of excess equipment. If this plan were followed out enormous savings in fuel and hydroelectric equipment would result.

Costs and Field Surveys. The cost of a hydroelectric project is hard to determine unless a detailed and exhaustive field survey is made. The cost per kilowatt has wide variation: the lower limit is seldom below $100 and the upper limit is determined by the value of the power produced. Much of the investment in a water-power project consists of expenditures necessary for land, dam, regulating works, and access to site and rights-of-way. All these are independent of the size of the installation. Water conduit, power house, and generating equipment are generally in proportion to the installation. To these costs must be added the preliminary investigation necessary to obtain information required for application for license, promotion and organization expenses, and interest charges during construction. In general, the initial costs necessary in the construction of a hydroelectric plant are much greater than those of a steam plant having the same capacity. The operating costs may be much less, however, since the operating force is smaller and fuel is eliminated. Transmission is generally a high cost in hydroelectric plants, as many of them must be situated at considerable distances from the market. From the above brief discussion it is clear that careful investigation is necessary before deciding whether, in any one region, it is more economical to develop electricity by steam or by water power. It takes time to establish a new power project, whether it be steam or water. The problems to be solved are many and complex. The type and size of the plant necessary to serve most economically both the present and the increasing power requirements of the area must be determined. The plant must be designed and built. The time required varies greatly, but a large steam plant would take two years or more, and a water-power plant three or more years.

AMOUNT OF AVAILABLE WATER POWER

Estimates as to the amount of water power available in the United States vary greatly—usually from about one hundred to two hundred million horsepower. Of this about fifty million is believed to be available without any special provision for storage. Owing to marked differences in precipitation and topography there is a correspondingly wide variation in estimates of potential water power in different parts of the country.

The total capacity of water wheels at water-power plants in the United States on January 1, 1936, according to the annual report just released by the Department of the Interior through the Geological Survey, was 16,079,407 horsepower, an increase of only 4,100 horsepower during the year.

The following table shows the total capacity of water wheels in water-power plants in the United States at different dates and the increase between dates:

TABLE 1

Date	Horsepower	Increase	
		Horsepower	Per Cent
1921 (November)	7,927,958		
1924 (March)	9,086,958	1,160,000*	14.6
1925 (March)	10,037,655	958,697	10.5
1926 (January 1)	11,176,596	1,138,941†	11.3
1927 do	11,720,983	544,387	4.9
1928 do	12,296,000	575,017	4.9
1929 do	13,571,530	1,275,530	10.4
1930 do	13,807,778	236,248	1.7
1931 do	14,884,667	1,076,889	7.2
1932 do	15,562,805	680,930	4.3
1933 do	15,817,941	255,136	1.6
1934 do	15,913,451	95,510	.6
1935 do	16,075,307	161,856	1.0
1936 do	16,079,407	4,100	0

* About 2.3 years. † About 0.8 year.

An estimate based on the present practice of installation of water wheels at fully developed water-power sites indicates that water wheels with a capacity of about 80,000,000 horsepower would be required to make use of all the potential water power in the United States. Therefore 20 per cent of the nation's resources of water power is developed at the present time.

Zonal Distribution. In order "to study, analyze and report intelligently on the power problems of the country,"[1] the National Power Survey, under the direction of the Federal Power Commission, decided to divide the country into seven major zones. These are shown in Fig.

[1] *Ibid.*, p. 3.

4. Since many transmission-line systems cross state boundaries it was thought advisable to include several states within each zone. Three of the zones, Northeast, Middle West, and Southeast, have been divided into subzones. In all cases but two the zone boundaries follow state lines. Pennsylvania is divided by a north-south line near the center and the Upper Peninsula of Michigan is included in a subzone[1] with Wisconsin.

Although adequate field studies have not been made and some records of stream flow do not cover a sufficient length of time, a tentative

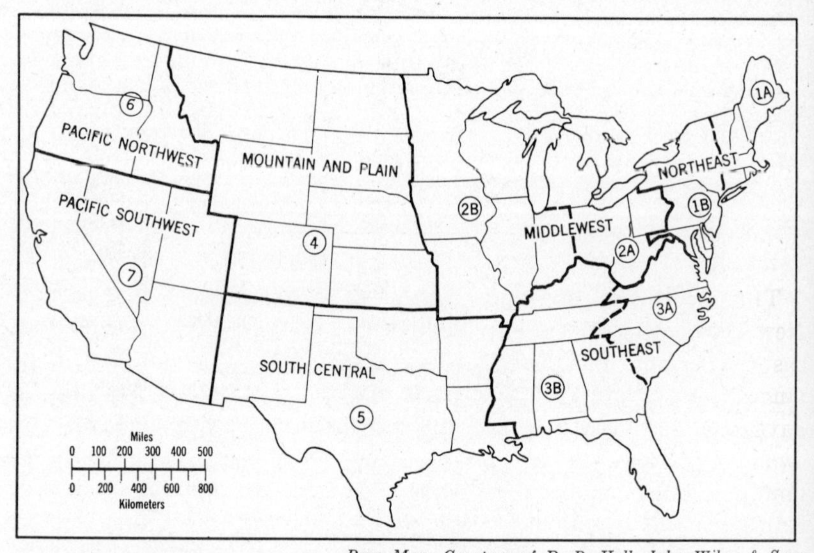

Base Map, Courtesy of R. B. Hall, John Wiley & Sons

FIG. 4. Power Zones of the United States. (Adapted from report of Federal Power Commission.)

summary of the undeveloped water power of the United States has been made by the National Power Survey. This is shown in the accompanying table.

According to these estimates, 64.6 per cent of the undeveloped water power of the United States is found in the two Pacific zones and 22.5 per cent in the combined potentialities of the Northeast and Southeast. This leaves but 13 per cent, which is found scattered throughout the other three zones and includes the upper Mississippi Basin and much of the area adjacent to the Great Lakes.

[1] *Ibid.*, p. 3.

TABLE 2

UNDEVELOPED WATER POWER IN THE UNITED STATES*

Zone	Region	Number of Sites	Estimated Average Annual Output, Thousand Kilowatt-hours	Estimated Installed Capacity Kilowatts
	1	2	3	4
1.	Northeast	327	21,075,000	5,886,100
2.	Middle West	234	13,203,000	3,604,600
3.	Southeast	369	41,112,000	10,826,000
4.	Mountain and Plain	93	15,992,000	3,431,300
5.	Southwest	83	6,301,000	1,522,900
6.	Pacific Northwest	528	114,200,000	15,664,000
7.	Pacific Southwest	249	63,800,000	11,694,000
	Total	1,883	275,683,000	52,628,900

* *Ibid.*, p. 3.

The Northeast Region. This zone is divided into two parts—New England makes up one subdivision, and New York, New Jersey, eastern Pennsylvania, Delaware, and Maryland the other. New England, most of New York, and parts of Pennsylvania and New Jersey have been glaciated. This accounts for the large number of lakes and swamps which act as natural reservoirs producing a rather uniform flow in a large number of streams. Coupled with this condition is a rather even distribution of adequate precipitation and a fair amount of forested areas which aid in the retention of water and retard runoff. Falls and rapids are numerous as a result of inequalities in the igneous and metamorphic rocks and the superimposed stream courses following glaciation. In the unglaciated portion there are many rapids and cascades due to inequalities in the rocks found in the beds of the streams.

In this area are many streams which have water-power possibilities. The ten most important are shown in Table 3.

The figure given to the St. Lawrence is estimated for the International Section which would be allocated to the United States. In the 113 miles from Lake Ontario to St. Regis there is a fall of 92 feet, but it is very unevenly distributed—91 feet is in the lower 48 miles. The estimate for Niagara Falls pertains to the energy which could be utilized by additional developments in the flow of water now allocated

TABLE 3

River	*Estimated Average Annual Output, Thousand Kilowatt-hours**
St. Lawrence	5,724,000
Susquehanna	3,366,000
Delaware	1,530,000
Connecticut	1,274,000
Kennebec	1,082,000
Potomac (in Maryland)	1,053,000
Niagara	870,000
Penobscot	742,000
Androscoggin	734,000
Black (New York)	680,000
Total 10 streams	17,055,000
Total for zone	21,075,000

* *Ibid.*, p. 35.

to the United States by treaty. The importance of nearly all the potential sites on the above streams lies in their geographical position, as they are within practicable transmission distances of load centers. These power sites are located almost in the heart of our most important industrial and manufacturing area. The large population and the extensive manufacturing facilities demand a large amount of power. In this zone are found almost 30 per cent of the people of the United States as well as a large proportion of the trade and industrial development.

The Middle West Section. A great deal of this zone is quite uniform as to surface and lies at a rather low level above the sea. Furthermore, there is considerable homogeneity in the rocks, and this combined with low stream gradient permits a relatively small number of rapids and falls. Exceptions to these general conditions are found in the eastern portion which is made up of part of the Allegheny Plateau, in the southwest area which has part of the Ozarks, and in the northern part which has one of the largest areas of late continental glaciation in the United States. Here streams have been diverted and have not yet reduced their beds to grade, and falls and rapids are numerous. Here also are found thousands of lakes, ponds, and swamps which act as natural reservoirs and maintain a more uniform flow.

Part of this Middle West section is underlain by or is near to coal. Only the more favored sites, particularly in the western and northern parts of the area, will probably be developed in competition with low-cost, steam-generated power. Some of the best or most easily developed power sites are already occupied by dams and power houses. However,

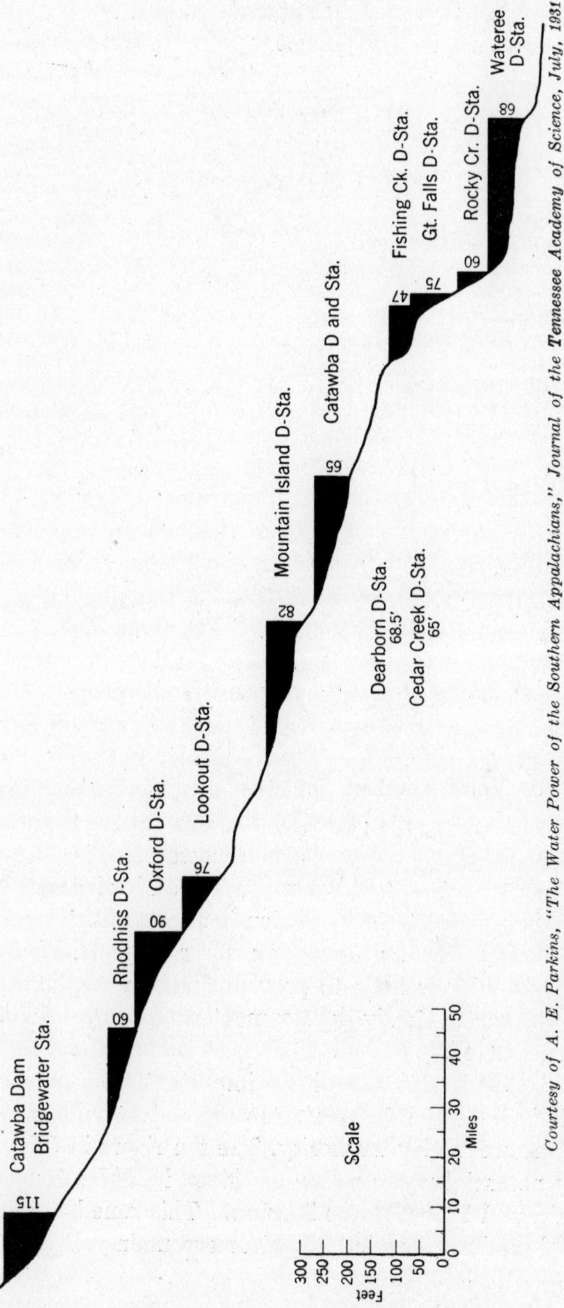

Courtesy of A. E. Parkins, "The Water Power of the Southern Appalachians," Journal of the Tennessee Academy of Science, July, 1931

FIG. 5. Profile of the Catawba-Wateree River. D., dam; Sta., station.

the hydroelectric power that has been developed in the three states of Illinois, Wisconsin, and Minnesota probably does not exceed the equivalent of two million tons of coal annually.[1] The ten rivers best favored for potential water power are listed in Table 4.

TABLE 4

River	*Estimated Average Annual Output, Thousand Kilowatt-hours**
Kanawha (in West Virginia)	4,743,000
Cheat (Monongahela Basin)	1,525,000
Potomac (in West Virginia)	801,000
Clarion (Allegheny Basin)	629,000
Wabash	472,000
White (in Missouri)	448,000
Iowa	383,000
Menominee	376,000
Gasconade (Missouri Basin)	360,000
Upper Mississippi (above Cairo, Ill.)	357,000
Total, 10 streams	10,094,000
Total for zone	13,203,000

* *Ibid.*, p. 36.

The Southeast Region. Parts of this zone are low-lying, flat, and without water-power possibilities. In the southern Appalachians, however, is found the most rugged region in the eastern part of the United States. Streams flowing westward and northwestward from the divide, such as the Tennessee, are long but frequently have interrupted gradients as at Muscle Shoals. In addition they have many rapid-flowing tributaries with power possibilities. The eastern slope of the southern Appalachians is much steeper than the western, hence the streams flowing to the southeast have many rapids and falls where high-head plants may be constructed. The region is almost entirely lacking, however, in natural reservoirs for storing water (Fig. 5). With the exception of forests there is little to prevent rather violent fluctuations in stream flow, and for steady development of power artificial reservoirs must be constructed.

The Tennessee Basin is the most important, and the figures given below include the estimated projects proposed and under construction by the Tennessee Valley Authority. The ten rivers in this region with the largest potential water power are given in Table 5.

Mountain and Plain States Region. This zone has a fair amount of potential water power but the sites are mainly in the western or

[1] Walter H. Voskuil, *The Competitive Position of Illinois Coal in the Illinois Coal Market Area,* Bull. 63, Ill. State Geol. Survey, 1936, p. 14.

TABLE 5

River	*Estimated Average Annual Output, Thousand Kilowatt-hours**
Tennessee	23,800,000
Cumberland	3,350,000
Savannah	2,015,000
Santee	1,416,000
New (Kanawha Basin)	1,332,000
Roanoke	1,315,000
Potomac (in Virginia)	1,163,000
Warrior and Tombigbee	1,137,000
Yadkin—Peedee	1,032,000
Chattahooche	755,000
Total, 10 streams	37,315,000
Total for zone	41,112,000

* *Ibid.*, p. 36.

mountain portion where the population is scarce and few important centers of consumption are found. The eastern portion with the greater market has but few power sites, and the distance from the West is too great for economic transmission of electricity under present development. The most important streams are listed in the following table:

TABLE 6

River	*Estimated Average Annual Output, Thousand Kilowatt-hours**
Upper Missouri	4,788,000
Upper Columbia	3,804,000
Yellowstone	3,275,000
Upper Colorado and Green	2,157,000
Platte	1,239,000
Snake (Columbia Basin)	571,000
Arkansas (above Wichita)	103,000
Cheyenne	55,000
Total for 8 streams	15,992,000
Total for zone	15,992,000

* *Ibid.*, p. 36.

South Central Region. This is the least important of the zones in potential water power, having but 2.3 per cent of the total undeveloped in the United States. Much of the area is level and the rainfall is light. Many of the most important sites are in the West, far from existing load centers. When water power is developed in this section in the future, much of it will undoubtedly be in connection with irrigation and water supply, flood control, and navigation. The following streams are the only ones of importance potentially:

TABLE 7

River	*Estimated Average Annual Output, Thousand Kilowatt-hours**
Red	2,391,000
White (in Arkansas)	1,739,000
Arkansas (below Wichita)	770,000
Rio Grande (above El Paso)	603,000
Ouachita	325,000
Brazos	295,000
Guadalupe	136,000
Calcasieu	42,000
Total, 8 streams	6,301,000
Total for zone	6,301,000

* *Ibid.*, p. 37.

Pacific Northwest Region. This is the outstanding zone of the nation with 41.4 per cent of the undeveloped water power of the country. Here are the physical conditions which make for high potential hydro energy—high, rugged mountains and abundant, relatively uniform precipitation. Five large streams have the major portion of this undeveloped power, but several small streams are important. Some power has already been developed in this area, and plants with large capacity are now being constructed in the Booneville and Grand Coulee projects. The major basins with estimated undeveloped power follow:

TABLE 8

River	*Estimated Average Annual Output, Thousand Kilowatt-hours**
Columbia, including tributaries above Portland	62,700,000
Snake River and tributaries	17,570,000
Puget Sound Basin	10,760,000
Willamette Basin	6,530,000
Cowlitz River	3,270,000
Total, 5 basins	100,770,000
Total for zone	114,200,000

* *Ibid.*, p. 37.

Pacific Southwest Region. From the standpoint of undeveloped water power this zone is the second most important in the United States with 23.2 per cent of the total for the country as a whole. Included in the estimates given is the output of the development on the Colorado River generally known as the Boulder Canyon project. This dam has just been completed, and the ultimate capacity of the development is about five billion kilowatt-hours per annum.

The major basins with undeveloped resources are given below:

TABLE 9

River	*Estimated Average Annual Output, Thousand Kilowatt-hours**
Colorado Basin (outside of Grand Canyon National Park)	21,900,000
Colorado Basin (inside of Grand Canyon National Park)	7,300,000
San Joaquin—Sacramento Basin	17,470,000
Klamath and Trinity Basin	10,150,000
Total	56,820,000
Total for zone	63,800,000

* *Ibid.*, p. 37.

Consumption of Electricity. The following table shows how wide-spread and inclusive the use of electricity has become.

TABLE 10

ANNUAL CONSUMPTION OF ELECTRICITY IN THE UNITED STATES, 1929–1933, BY CLASSES OF CUSTOMERS*

(Data Taken from Reports of 215 Systems; Thousand Kilowatt-hours)

	1929	1930	1931	1932	1933	Estimated Consumption upon Return of Pre-depressional Industrial Activity
Farm	1,503,000	1,666,000	1,787,000	1,448,000	1,502,000	2,069,000
Residential and domestic	7,957,000	9,157,000	9,904,000	10,120,000	9,971,000	13,093,000
Small light and power	10,636,000	11,312,000	10,852,000	9,987,000	9,727,000	13,014,000
Large light and power	40,255,000	38,021,000	34,850,000	29,606,000	32,153,000	43,800,000
Municipal street lighting	1,556,000	1,696,000	1,824,000	1,748,000	1,592,000	2,335,000
Municipal light and power	1,443,000	1,612,000	1,709,000	1,738,000	1,748,000	1,966,000
Street railway and interurban railway	4,833,000	4,629,000	4,386,000	4,020,000	3,815,000	4,265,000
Electrified steam railroad	520,000	551,000	572,000	544,000	698,000	1,390,000
Miscellaneous	2,730,000	2,725,000	2,550,000	1,680,000	1,793,000	3,415,000
Total	71,433,000	71,369,000	68,434,000	60,891,000	62,999,000	85,347,000

* *Ibid.*, p. 12.

It is evident that in most of the groups using electric power there was a marked falling off after 1929. This is especially noticeable in production for industrial purposes, which reached a low point in 1932. Though still below the demands of 1929 there has been a remarkable recovery in the years since 1932. The estimates made by the Federal Power Commission of the amount of electricity required in the near future are important. No definite date can be given, but since the estimate shows an increase of 20 per cent over the previous maximum, it presents a current problem. Hydroelectric plants cannot be of mushroom growth. Plans must be made now so that intelligent foresight may be exercised in choosing sites best suited to serve the public of the future.

Accordingly special investigations were necessary in relation to residential power consumption, rural electrification, commercial and industrial demands, and probable new requirements for power in electrochemical and electrometallurgical processes and the increased demands for railroad electrification. Certainly with anything like resumption of pre-depression conditions the domestic load will increase, particularly as there is an ever-increasing sale of electrical appliances which are considered necessities in the modern home. With prosperity on the farm would come a much larger demand from the agricultural group. Approximately 725,000 farms now receive electric service from central stations. Since there are 6,300,000 farms it seems that an increase to 1,000,000 farm users would be a conservative estimate. Electrical consumption in industry will be greatly increased not only for power-driven machinery but for the modern devices, such as air conditioning.

Although the amount of power required by street railways and interurbans may increase slightly above the 1932 level, it is doubtful whether it will ever reach the level of 1929 because of inroads from other means of transportation. However, the loss from this form of transportation will probably be more than met by expansion in electrification of railroads.

Production of electric energy in 1929 and estimates of future demands by districts are shown in Table 11.

Table 12 shows the annual production of electricity by the major plants of the United States, 1929-1933. The 215 systems here represented produce and handle more than 93 per cent of the total energy reported by the United States Geological Survey as made available for use in 1933 (generation by electric railways and railroads is excluded).

As might be expected, the preceding table shows that the electric power development is greatest in the most densely populated and most highly industrialized sections of the country. It also shows a wide variance as to the relative part played by water and fuel in the production of electric power. Water-power plants produce 41 per cent of the electric power, but most of this is developed in four zones or districts—Northeast, Southeast, Pacific Northwest, and Pacific Southwest. This is easily explained by reference to the discussion of streams in the different zones and the map which shows location of electric

TABLE 11

PRODUCTION OF ELECTRIC ENERGY AND MAXIMUM DEMANDS IN 1929, AND ANNUAL REQUIREMENTS UPON RESUMPTION OF PRE-DEPRESSION INDUSTRIAL ACTIVITY*

(Data Taken from Reports of 215 Systems)

Zone	Power Region	1929		Resumption of Pre-depression Industrial Activity			
		Generation†	Sum of Maximum Demands	Generation	Sum of Maximum Demands	Increase over 1929 Generation	Increase over 1929 Maximum Demand
	1	2	3	4	5	6	7
		Thousand Kilowatt-hours	*Kilowatts*	*Thousand Kilowatt-hours*	*Kilowatts*	*Per Cent*	*Per Cent*
1	Northeast	26,030,000	6,305,000	33,816,000	7,869,000	29.5	24.8
2	Middle West	30,747,000	6,732,000	36,163,000	7,969,000	17.6	18.4
3	Southeast	8,292,000	1,839,000	10,002,000	2,273,000	20.6	23.6
4	Mountain and Plain	2,996,000	534,000	2,964,000	569,000	− 1.1	6.6
5	Southwest	5,221,000	1,058,000	5,984,000	1,222,000	14.6	15.5
6	Pacific Northwest	4,680,000	923,000	5,226,000	1,066,000	11.7	15.4
7	Pacific Southwest	8,829,000	1,730,000	10,550,000	2,071,000	19.5	19.8
	Total	87,295,000	19,121,000	104,705,000	23,039,000	19.9	20.7
	Increase over 1929			17,410,000	3,918,000		

* *Interim Report*, p. 13.

† Individual items in this column differ slightly from those given in the table on page 321 as the boundaries of the selected power districts do not in all cases conform exactly to the zone boundaries.

generating stations (Fig. 6). Many of the rivers of the country have a very low gradient—6 to 8 inches per mile. It is generally not feasible to utilize, for power purposes, grades of much less than 10 feet to the mile. When this is considered in connection with the unequal distribution of rainfall and the location of coal and other sources of fuel it can be understood why some areas have but little hydroelectric development and others have much.

Hydraulic Developments Are Not Always Cheap. In former years when small water-power plants were developed the costs were as low as $70 and $100 per kilowatt. By 1900 the average cost had risen to $150 per kilowatt, and by 1920 it had reached $200 to $250 per kilowatt; recent estimates on undeveloped sites have varied from $300 to $600 per kilowatt. This cost includes real estate, water rights, and a large number of other costs which have to be met. This means that the fixed charges are high although the operating costs may be small.

Furthermore, whereas the hydro plant seems to have very nearly reached its highest efficiency, the steam plant has not approached its ultimate efficiency. Thus with relatively higher costs for hydroelectric

TABLE 12

ANNUAL PRODUCTION OF ELECTRICITY BY MAJOR PRIVATE, MUNICIPAL, AND PUBLIC DISTRICT ELECTRIC UTILITY PLANTS IN THE UNITED STATES, 1929–1933*

(Data Taken from Reports of 215 Systems)

Zone	Region	Type of Prime Mover	1929		1930		1931		1932		1933	
			Thousand Kilowatt-hours	Per Cent of United States Total	Thousand Kilowatt-hours	Per Cent of United States Total	Thousand Kilowatt-hours	Per Cent of United States Total	Thousand Kilowatt-hours	Per Cent of United States Total	Thousand Kilowatt-hours	Per Cent of United States Total
1	Northeast	Hydro	8,795,080		8,390,311		8,443,586		9,813,507		10,120,853	
		Steam	17,667,549		18,100,565		17,541,394		14,486,498		14,682,012	
		Internal combustion	624		1,361		2,379		2,335		2,387	
		Total	26,463,253	30.3	26,492,237	30.8	25,987,359	31.5	24,302,340	32.4	24,805,252	32.2
2	Middle West	Hydro	3,511,415		2,935,548		2,903,032		3,334,498		3,218,066	
		Steam	27,146,590		26,918,510		25,171,763		21,474,784		22,462,412	
		Internal combustion	9,255		15,507		24,257		27,564		23,462	
		Total	30,667,260	35.1	29,869,565	34.8	28,099,052	34.1	24,836,846	33.2	25,703,940	33.4
3	Southeast	Hydro	6,830,733		5,780,329		5,749,126		6,130,019		6,243,838	
		Steam	1,900,150		2,345,203		2,273,977		1,459,821		1,695,541	
		Internal combustion	27,175		30,896		30,595		14,921		11,467	
		Total	8,758,058	10.0	8,156,428	9.5	8,053,698	9.8	7,604,761	10.2	7,950,846	10.4

4	Mountain and Plain...	Hydro..............	1,788,010		1,492,514		1,108,854		780,134		1,065,794	
		Steam..............	1,585,429		1,667,702		1,612,606		1,475,377		1,470,893	
		Internal combustion..	18,784		25,923		21,992		19,476		18,450	
		Total............	3,392,223	3.9	3,186,139	3.7	2,743,452	3.3	2,274,987	3.0	2,555,137	3.3
5	Southwest...........	Hydro..............	66,805		57,757		62,578		144,713		156,040	
		Steam..............	4,348,009		4,464,308		4,127,798		3,597,642		3,664,974	
		Internal combustion..	99,729		66,807		32,177		19,685		15,399	
		Total............	4,514,543	5.2	4,588,872	5.3	4,222,553	5.1	3,762,040	5.0	3,836,413	5.0
6	Pacific Northwest.....	Hydro..............	3,472,967		3,645,668		3,689,855		3,551,100		3,523,456	
		Steam..............	765,398		710,051		513,803		155,552		165,010	
		Internal combustion..	36		52		....		....		....	
		Total............	4,238,401	4.9	4,355,771	5.1	4,203,658	5.1	3,706,652	4.9	3,688,466	4.8
7	Pacific Southwest.....	Hydro..............	6,713,394		7,157,799		5,404,606		7,385,925		7,287,492	
		Steam..............	2,547,509		2,168,583		3,727,867		1,023,577		1,054,516	
		Internal combustion..	376		359		222		207		203	
		Total............	9,261,279	10.6	9,326,741	10.8	9,132,695	11.1	8,409,709	11.3	8,342,211	10.9
	Total, United States...	Hydro..............	31,178,404		29,459,926		27,361,637		31,139,896		31,615,539	
		Steam..............	55,960,634		56,374,922		54,969.208		43,673,251		45,195,358	
		Internal combustion..	155,979		140,905		111,622		84,188		71,368	
		Grand total........	87,295,017	100.0	85,975,753	100.0	82,442,467	100.0	74,897,335	100.0	76,882,265	100.0

* *Interim Report*, p. 9.

development and decreasing costs for fuel generation of power the former will be used largely only in especially favored areas or in border-line areas after careful consideration (Fig. 7). Water power, then, is not always "a free gift from God" nor does it represent so much "velvet." There are many places in the country, however, where

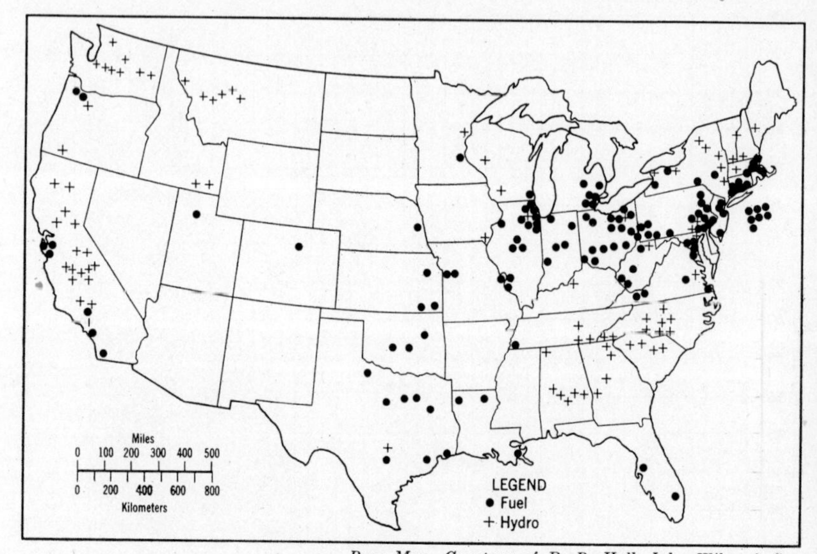

Base Map, Courtesy of R. B. Hall, John Wiley & Sons

FIG. 6. Location of Electric Generating Stations in the United States. (Adapted from report of Federal Power Commission.)

natural conditions favor water-power development, especially when such favored areas are relatively inaccessible to coal or other fuel.

CONSERVATION AND CONTROL

Maintenance of Power. "Control of power is a social as well as an engineering and economic problem."[1] A sudden cessation of the flow of electricity of the country would be a national catastrophe. Homes, streets, roads, and public and industrial buildings would be in darkness, and in our modern dependable era there would be no adequate substitute even to approach present lighting conditions. Electric signals, so necessary in all modern transportation, would fail and transportation would be at a standstill. Street cars, subways, elevators, and conveyors in general would stop if current ceased to flow. Practically all factories would have to close for lack of light, and many

[1] *Ibid.*, p. xi.

would stop for lack of power to run the machines. A large amount of food would deteriorate for want of refrigeration, bakeries would cease to turn out bread and pastry, and many sources of water supply would fail when the electric pumps failed to function. In fact, practically all

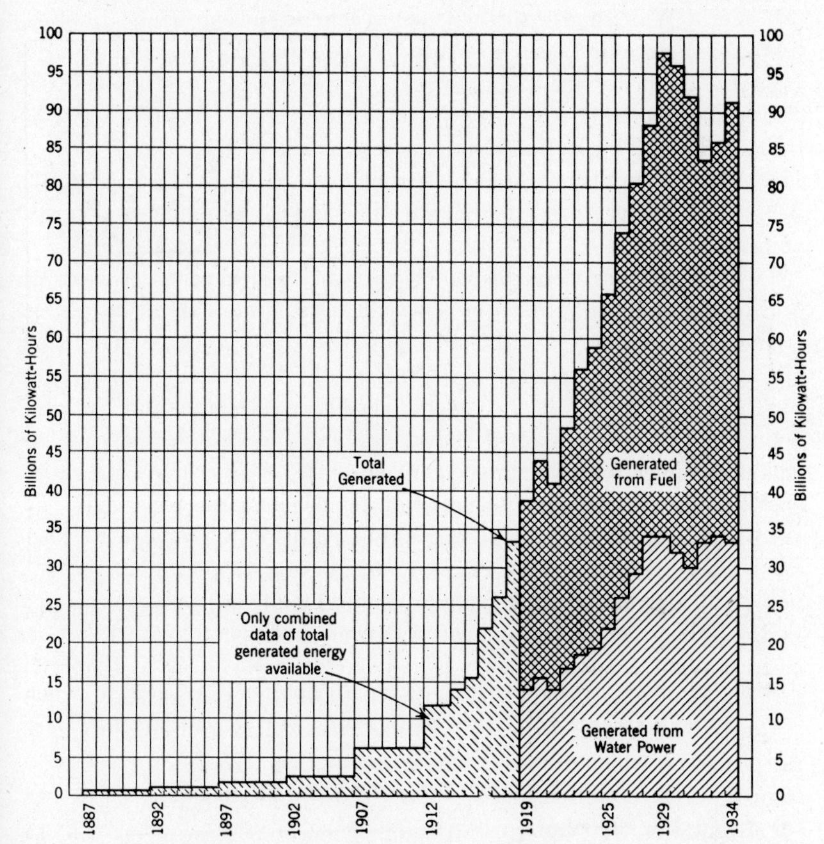

FIG. 7. Annual Production of Electricity for Public Use in the United States, 1887-1934 (Federal Power Commission, 1935).

activities of modern life would collapse if there should be a failure in the supply of electric current.

The output of our industries, the comfort of our homes, offices, and workshops, the welfare of our people, and even our national safety depend on a plentiful supply of electricity at all times and at reasonable rates. It is not only necessary that electric power in sufficient quantities be supplied now but provision must be made for continued improvement and expansion in order to supply the probable future requirements.

Power and National Defense. "While it is difficult to say that any single resource is fundamental, it might well be argued that power supply comes very close to being so."[1] When the United States entered the World War almost all the surplus generating equipment that was available before had been absorbed by the rapid expansion of industry brought about by the requirements of the Allied governments. The power shortage was not seriously felt in this country until the winter of 1917-1918. The Buffalo-Niagara region felt the deficiency particularly, as the supplemental power from Canada which had previously been used was required in the war-time industrial expansion in that country.

Power shortages were due to lack of fuel and generating capacity, and to the deficiency in water power. The last was caused by the extreme cold weather in 1917-1918 and the light precipitation in the spring and summer seasons of 1918. Partial relief for the shortage was obtained by shutting down old and inefficient factories and by interconnection of power plants. The maximum utilization was secured by the interconnection of water-power plants. Water-power plants have a specific place in the plan for national defense since they are independent of fuel supply and the accompanying transportation facilities, and since they require a very small amount of man power. A national policy of defense should include a survey of the requirements of hydroelectric power because of the time necessary to complete an electric plant. Muscle Shoals is a good example of a hydroelectric development which could not be constructed in a short time.

Control of Water Powers. Unlike the conservation of most natural resources, which are often extractive and expendable, the conservation of water power is more concerned with the use of a permanent force and the distribution of the resulting electricity to the largest number at the most economical rate. With this end in view there has been a decided development in this country of the opinion that water power should be controlled by the public. This does not necessarily mean that it should be owned, developed, or operated by the public. The amount of control which may be advisable or required is different in different places and under variable conditions.

In the North American Conservation Conference held in 1909, commissioners from the United States, Mexico, Canada, and Newfoundland agreed upon principles pertaining to the control of water power.

[1] *Ibid.*, p. 49.

"We regard the monopoly of waters, and especially the monopoly of water power, as peculiarly threatening. No rights to the use of water powers in streams should hereafter be granted in perpetuity."[1] These commissioners further expressed themselves as being in favor of giving grants only upon conditions of prompt development and with guarantees of proper compensation to the public.

The Federal Power Commission. The principles as set down by this conference were the basis of agitation and activity on the part of a group of conservationists who were encouraged by President Theodore Roosevelt and led by Gifford Pinchot, then Forester of the United States. The activity of this group resulted in the creation of the Federal Power Commission in 1920. This Commission found its work greatly hampered by lack of funds and a trained personnel. Its activity has continued, however, and in recent years has increased. One of the important results of the Commission's work is the *Interim Report* of the National Power Survey.

State Commissions. In addition to the Federal Commission the states have provided commissions, bureaus, governor's boards, or some other bodies which deal more or less directly with state control of water power. Many of these bodies have little or no facilities for obtaining the facts concerning water power and in the past have generally depended upon the Federal Power Commission for data. Considerable resentment at federal interference has often been expressed, however, as there is fear of infringement upon states' rights. Recently there has been a decided movement toward some form of state planning.

Why Water-power Plants Should Be Controlled. If water-power resources are to be controlled, what is the fundamental principle upon which the procedure is based? It would seem that a resource, such as falling water, which originates over a wide source but is available only at one or more particular points, should be the property of all the people rather than that of a few who happen to own land at the favorable sites. As an illustration, the waters of the Great Lakes (excluding Ontario) cover 88,360 square miles, and the contributory drainage area is 241,560 square miles. The rainfall of this vast region flows through the narrow outlet of the Niagara River, and the water is available for the first time at one place, the Niagara Falls. If adjacent lands were owned by private parties, and if the owners were allowed to develop the water power fully, the income would be fabulous. Yet it is clear that such a condition would not be favored by the

[1] As quoted in C. R. Van Hise, *The Conservation of Natural Resources in the United States,* The Macmillan Company, New York, 1918.

public. Nor would defense of such a procedure be proposed by the most rabid believers in private enterprise. The same principle applies to lesser streams where the concentration is not so obvious but is nevertheless similar. The public owned the water power in the first place. If, in certain localities, laws and judicial divisions have allowed it to pass into private hands it should still be subject to public control.

Advantages of Public Control. Public control seems necessary in order to insure reasonable rates. A large proportion of the best and largest water-power sites are owned by a small number of corporations. By controlling adjacent power sites and by coupling up a large number of plants a higher use of power is made possible. Such a concentration is economically advantageous, and conservation demands that we encourage this consolidation for the most efficient use of water. Under such conditions, however, the consumers can be protected only by public control. Otherwise monopoly in water power will develop in many districts because of isolated sites and the limited distances over which electricity can be economically transmitted. Cheap and reliable supply of power which is widely distributed and accessible to all should be the possession of the American public. The manufacturer desires it in order to lower his costs of production; the purchaser of the goods will share in the resulting lower prices; and the domestic user may have more electrical conveniences in his home which he can operate at costs within his capacity to pay.

It is further suggested by Van Hise in his *Conservation of Natural Resources of the United States* that, since water power is a public right, a tax should be levied when a franchise is granted for a hydro-electrical development. Such a tax is only fair in order that all the public may have the "advantage of a national or state resource." This contention is sound and is based on the principle mentioned above. The waters which flow through a single stream have fallen on a large part of any one state or on parts of many states. Hence it is equitable and just that a tax be placed on the franchise of the water-power company. Such a tax would, of course, be imposed upon the consumer, but he could well afford to pay this additional charge in order to obtain the cheaper rate which would follow because of public control.

Public control of stream sites, if properly supervised, would also lead to a more complete development. The importance of available power is so great that we cannot afford to have potential resources needlessly wasted. Quite often, when private companies locate dams on streams, they do so with little or no regard to the major possibilities of the area. In order to derive the utmost from the power potentialities of a stream or drainage basin it is necessary to have a careful investigation by a group of competent engineers. Public regulation seems the only possible way that this can be accomplished.

In order to have full development there must be control of reservoir sites so that a system of pondage may be developed. Each reservoir in a system is more or less dependent on those farther upstream. A single owner cannot, ordinarily, afford to construct a system of reservoirs. Since the control and supervision of an interrelated system of reservoirs should be a unit, it is necessary that it be under government or state control.

Furthermore, in order that the water-power resources be developed to meet the needs of the people, the public has a right to require that a sufficient amount of power be developed for the purpose. Otherwise power sites might be acquired and held undeveloped in order to prevent their being used in competition, or in order to gain a monopoly over the area supplied. Public control would prevent this and would insist that there should not be a large amount of unused water flowing over dams while an excessive rate for power is charged. The recognition that the public had its rights in the matter of water power was early expressed even in the Colonial period. In "An Act for the Encouragement . . . to build Water Mills" passed by the Assembly of Maryland, on September 5, 1704, in order to "insure the public that the acquisition of a mill site was not for speculative purposes," the grantee was required to "Enter into Bond" that he would begin the building of "Said Water Mill within One Year." The toll to be charged was also fixed.

Finally, public safety often requires that dams be under public control. Much loss of life and property has resulted from destructive waters let loose from reservoirs by bursting dams. Poor construction, slack supervision, careless estimates, insufficient spillways, or obstructions (any or all) may cause a disaster such as that at Johnstown in 1889. Although such catastrophes are possible even under public supervision, it is generally believed that the element of safety would be greater if dams were built under the direction of state or government engineers.

Legal Basis of Control of Water Powers. The Constitution gives Congress the power to enact legislation concerning water power on public lands, on reservations of the United States, on navigable waterways, and on streams along the national boundaries. Several regulations which pertained to navigable waters and irrigation were passed by Congress in the last century. In the present century several acts have been passed by Congress which have dealt particularly with water power, either in general or in relation to specific areas. Previous to 1920, laws pertaining to water power were administered by the War Department, if navigable streams were involved; by the Department of the Interior, if water-power sites were found on public lands, reservations, national monuments, etc.; and by the Department of Agriculture, if in the forest reserves. Under such divided administration much confusion was inevitable. In order to correct this condition Congress in 1920 passed an act creating the Federal Power Commission. This commission is composed of the Secretaries of War, Interior, and Agriculture. It has jurisdiction only over water-power development.

Controversies over Rights of Control. In recent years several controversies have arisen between the federal government and some of the states concerning permits and leases for water-power plants on non-navigable streams. The Federal Power Commission, acting for the federal government, has jurisdiction over all navigable streams. The question for controversy arises when developments on non-navigable streams affect commerce on navigable streams. The Federal Power Commission has served notice on power companies that the companies must apply to the Federal Commission rather than the state authorities. It is claimed that this has delayed developments by power companies, and several states have filed protests. The actions by the states have come about largely because they have recognized that in these stream sites, when developed, they have a resource to be taxed. In all probability there will be greater cooperation between the states and the federal government, and the difficulties relating to water power will be amicably ironed out.

Interstate Compacts. Controversies between states often arise where water-power sites are found on streams which form boundaries or where several states are involved in a single drainage basin. In order to overcome some of these difficulties the interstate compact has been used. A specific example is of interest—the Colorado River Agreement. Five steps are usually taken in negotiating and concluding an interstate compact. (1) Congress authorizes the negotiation of the compact and outlines its purpose. (2) The state legislatures authorize commissioners representing them to meet and negotiate a compact. (3) The commissioners meet (under the chairmanship of a federal representative) to negotiate and sign the compact. (4) The state legislatures ratify the compact. (5) Congress ratifies the compact.

The above procedure is followed, in general, in all interstate compacts, but it had to be modified in the Colorado River Agreement. Arizona failed to ratify, and Congress ratified the compact before approval had been given by all the state legislatures.

Manner of Public Control. Water power may be developed according to one of three general policies: (1) unrestricted private development; (2) private development under regulation; or (3) public ownership. Anything like a conservative estimate concerning the viewpoints of the people in relation to these three policies would be hard to make. As expressed through legislation, both federal and state, public opinion seems to favor private development under regulation.

Most of the regulation of hydroelectric plants has concerned itself with determination of rates and types of service. A much more comprehensive public control of the utilities has been proposed in recent years. There have been various propositions, but in general they include: supervision of financial policies, and supervision also of the location and construction of hydro plants, and the distribution of transmission lines. Public ownership in water-power development has been before the public in the last few years. Government activities in the Tennessee Valley, in the Far West, and in some other areas has recently caused wide comment. At present there are seven federal projects and five public district projects involving electric power production which have either just been completed, are actively under way, or are scheduled for the near future. The decision of the Supreme Court giving the government authorities at Muscle Shoals the right to sell surplus electricity has opened up new questions. Do other government developments on streams in general created primarily for navigation, irrigation, or flood control have the right to produce and sell hydroelectric power in competition with private utilities? This will have to be settled by the Supreme Court.

SUMMARY

Water power was early developed and for many years was practically the only mechanical power available to man. Sidetracked for a long time by steam, it again gained an important place when man learned to produce and transmit electricity. Hydroelectric power will play an increasingly important rôle in the economy of American life. With the growing demand for electric power in the home, on the farm, in the city, in the factory, and in transportation facilities greater sources of energy for the development of electricity will be utilized. Water power will have to compete with the fuels in the demand for energy. In some parts of the country, as in the Northeast, a considerable portion of the available water power is already in use. In others, as the Southeast, Pacific Northwest, and Pacific Southwest there are vast potentialities which will be developed as the demand for power increases. In others, as the Middle West and Southwest, the amount of potential water power is small, and of that very little is now used.

In some districts, although water power is available, it is more economical to use coal or some other fuel in the development of electricity. Much more hydroelectric power should and will be developed. It should be the purpose of an American public to insist that the water power of the United States shall be intelligently produced and regulated so that the people, at all times, shall have available plenty of cheap hydroelectric power.

CHAPTER XIV

OUR WAYTERWAYS AND THEIR UTILIZATION[1]

By A. E. Parkins

George Peabody College for Teachers

INTRODUCTION

Water bodies—oceans, seas, gulfs, bays, sounds, straits, lakes, and rivers—supply man his cheapest "ways" for travel and transportation, if used in their natural condition. They are nature's gift. Man has but to supply the carrying agent. His greatest contribution to navigation is the modern carrying agents. From log to leviathan represents thousands of years of mechanical development. Man has made the water carrier swifter, more capacious, and more efficient, thus greatly reducing the cost of transportation. He struggles still with storms, currents, and ice, much as did his savage ancestors. He has deepened channels and basins, constructed canals and locks about rapids and falls, built protecting breakwaters, directed the courses of rivers at will, but always at the cost of time and labor and materials. The extent to which the "rectifying"—we call such, "improvements for navigation"—should be carried, economically, is roughly proportional to the commercial demands. In densely populated industrial regions that have large volumes of commerce, costly improvements are economically possible. In pastoral and forest regions, even in most agricultural regions, man, if he is wise, will use the waters much as nature made them.

In making improvements, whether in the carrying agents or the navigated waters, man must adapt his work to:

1. The physical condition of the water bodies.
2. The types of commodities to be carried.
3. The ever-increasing commercial demands resulting from an increasing population and a changing economic order.
4. The mechanical developments and improvements that are continually being made under the spur of competition.

[1] This chapter has been read critically by J. E. Switzer, Geography Department, University of Indiana, W. W. Spellings, Peabody College, and J. W. Reid, Jr., Tallequah Teachers College, Tallequah, Oklahoma.

In the United States water improvements for navigation are hardly more than a century old. It is mainly in the last quarter century that large sums have been appropriated by Congress. In late years the annual expenditures for the maintenance and improvement of harbors and river works (not including flood control) have been about $100,000,000. In 1876 the sum appropriated was $6,000,000 and in 1902, $20,000,000. The total spent for such improvement and maintenance up to June 30, 1934, amounted to nearly $1,800,000,000.[1] The value of water-borne commerce of our country for the calendar year 1933 was nearly $12,600,000,000.[2] Therefore mighty stakes are involved in this water transportation. To spend $100,000,000 a year on public works that make possible the movement of commerce worth $12,600,000,000 seems a good investment, yet are we certain that every one of the 969 projects supported is yielding suitable returns?

Conservation demands that each project or related project measures up to the expenditures. If reports show that harbor improvements on our seaboard or lakes pay reasonable returns this is no justification for supposing that river improvements, or canals divorced from harbor improvements, will pay. Water transportation must measure up with land transportation in efficiency and cost, when and where these two types compete. What taxpayers of our country want is the cheapest type of transportation possible consistent with modern demands. *They pay the entire transportation bill,* whether by water or on land—*the cost of the "way" and its maintenance, the transportation vehicle and its operation, and the administration.*

OUR WATERWAY RESOURCES

In its navigation resources the United States ranks high among the nations. The types of "waters" used for the movement of commodities are:

1. Ocean waters, for ocean and coastwise navigation.
2. Intracoastal waters—bays, sounds, lagoons, tidal rivers. Two types: deeper waters for ocean and coastwise vessels; shallow, for small intracoastal vessels.
3. Lakes. Only the Great Lakes are discussed in this chapter.
4. Rivers (gravity flowing). We will call improved rivers, riverways.
5. Canals.

Ocean Waters. The length of the "general" coastline of the United

[1] *Report of Chief of Engineers, U. S. Army,* Part 1, 1934, pp. 3, 13, calculated.
[2] *Ibid.,* Part 2, p. 3.

States is as follows: of the Atlantic Ocean, 1,888 miles, of the Gulf of Mexico, 1,629 miles, and of the Pacific Ocean, 1,366 miles; total, 4,883 miles. The tidal shoreline (reaching into harbors to points where such waters narrow to a width of three statute miles) is 7,314 miles. The shorelines of islands are not included. Our jurisdiction over coastal waters, of course, extends only to the three-mile limit, except by special agreement with other nations. We can thus include the ocean waters contiguous to our coast as a part of our waterway resources. Improvements for ocean and coastwise navigation—lighthouses and lightships, life-saving stations, and coast guard patrol boats and airplanes—are for the safety of vessels and men. These, though contributed by our federal government, are international in their benefits.

Seacoast Harbors (the Deeper Intracoastal Waters). The effectiveness of a coastline is measured more by the number and usableness of the harbors than by length. The Atlantic Coast harbors of our country are numerous. Those north of and including Chesapeake Bay are capacious. From Sandy Hook northeastward they are largely the result of glacial action and drowning. Shifting bars are uncommon, for the currents are strong, the offshore waters deep, and the supply of sands meager. The southern shore of Long Island is an exception. Boston Harbor is separated from the ocean by drumlins. New York Harbor is largely the drowned lower Hudson Valley.

From Sandy Hook southward to the tip of Florida and all around the Gulf, the harbors for the most part are estuaries, the result of the drowning of valleys carved in the unconsolidated muds, sands, and gravels of the Coastal Plain. At Philadelphia, Baltimore, and Richmond the estuaries cut completely across the Coastal Plain to the Fall Line. Most estuaries are ill adapted, in their natural condition, for modern commerce. They are shallow and thus require much dredging to provide navigable channels for modern vessels. Moreover, they call for continual attention owing to the tidal shifting of materials.

The Pacific coast harbors, though excellent in general, are few in number. The harbor at Los Angeles is largely man-made. Two shallow, marsh-bordered sheets of water have been dredged into a very serviceable harbor, that ranks high in commerce among the great ports of our country. San Francisco Bay and Puget Sound are most excellent natural water bodies. They require only a minimum of improvement. Both are classed as drowned harbors. San Francisco Bay is a drowned mountain valley; Golden Gate that leads out to the ocean is a drowned mountain pass. Puget Sound besides being drowned has been glaciated. The lower Columbia River is also drowned. There are shifting bars at the mouth that require constant attention even with fairly permanent improvements. It was the shallow water of these bars that deterred Vancouver from claiming the Columbia a British river. Gray, shortly after, in a smaller vessel, sailed many miles inland from the ocean and took possession in the name of the then young United States of America.

Seacoast Harbor Improvements. The limited space available will permit only a general discussion of harbor improvements for ocean commerce. The Port Series listed in the bibliography will supply an abundance of material. The series includes studies of ocean ports and of lake ports, as of June 30, 1934.

A harbor to be serviceable should be spacious enough to meet the demands for anchorage space and freedom of movement of the vessels visiting the harbor. Since anchored vessels shift their position with changes in the wind each vessel must have a space allotment greater in radius than the length of the vessel. The additional space demanded is proportional to the length of anchor chain paid out. Deep harbors are not essential, but the depth should be at least 5 to 10 feet deeper than the draft of the vessel at the lowest tide. Most American harbors in their "original condition" are too shallow to meet the demands of the large sea-going vessels of today. Until well into the nineteenth century the depth demands of ocean vessels were modest and little dredging of channels and anchorage space was called for. The large harbors today have 25- to 30- and even 40-foot channels with a width of 300 to 600 feet. The map, Fig. 1, shows the depth of channels and anchorage space in the more important harbors. Harbor improvements that have to do with serviceable channels, anchorage space, and turning basins are, as a rule, provided by the federal government. State, city, and private companies ordinarily provide the freight piers and channels to state, city, or private wharves or to dry dock and ferry slips.

Harbors with broad mouths on low coasts call for breakwaters or piers to form protecting "headlands." The artificial harbor produced is commonly known as a "harbor of refuge." Ice harbors also, employing breakwaters, are needed in some northern rivers. Delaware Bay has both a harbor of refuge and an ice harbor.

Lagoon harbors like the one at Miami, Florida, require much dredging of the lagoon to secure the requisite depth and also frequent dredging in the entrance through the barrier beach, because of active tidal scour and wash and deposition. Most estuarian harbors are shallow in their original state. At Baltimore at the head of the Patapsco

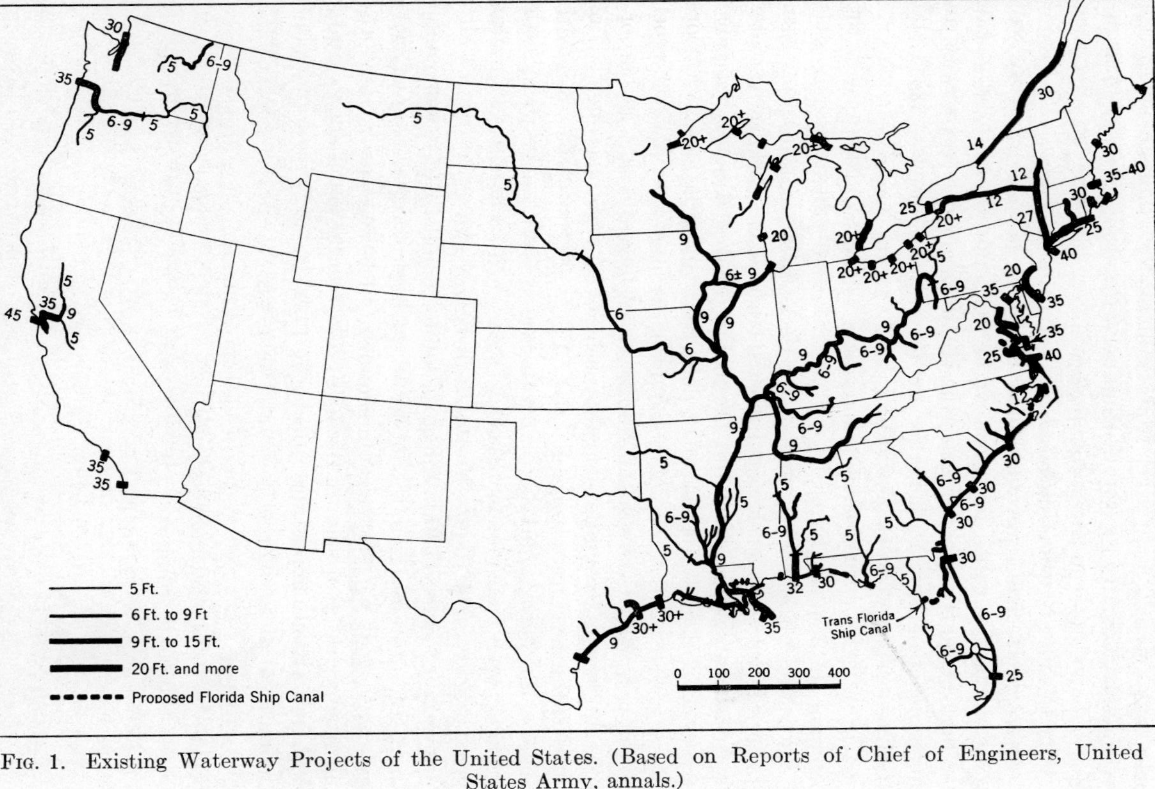

FIG. 1. Existing Waterway Projects of the United States. (Based on Reports of Chief of Engineers, United States Army, annals.)

estuary, a channel 20 miles long has been excavated from the city harbor to the 35-foot contour in Chesapeake Bay. Far down the Bay near the mouth of York River another channel 4.5 miles long has had to be dredged to give 35 feet of water needed for the large ocean-going vessels bound to or from Baltimore.

As cities like New York, Philadelphia, Baltimore, and others expand their overseas commerce, additional wharf space, anchorage basins, and channels are called for. For several years the federal government has been making a new harbor in the shallow Jamaica Bay to expand the facilities of New York harbor for the transshipment of commodities. Numerous other channels have been, or are being, provided to connect wharves on the Jersey and Long Island sides of New York Bay and the Hudson River.

The silt-laden Mississippi makes the maintenance of a deep channel (35 feet deep) for ocean vessels from the Gulf to New Orleans a costly project. It is at the head and at the mouths of the channels, "passes," as they are called, of the bird-foot delta that silting is a problem that calls for continual supervision and frequent dredging. Jetties[1] have not entirely solved the problems of providing a usable channel.

An interesting harbor development in late years on the Gulf Coast is the Houston Ship Canal that extends 50 miles northwesterly from the ocean across Galveston Bay, and thence along Jacinto River and Buffalo Bayou. This channel is 30 feet deep with a varying width of 150 to 250 feet. The channel ends in a turning basin.

Even San Francisco Bay, though a large natural harbor in which, a Spanish admiral declared, the navies of the world could ride at anchor, has had to have some federal improvement. The existing project provides for a dredged channel through San Francisco Bay, on the line of the main ship channel, to a depth of 45 feet and a width of 2,000. The removal of submarine rocks and shoals is also provided for. This work is being financed by the federal government. The state of California also has made large contributions to fit San Francisco to handle large volumes of commerce. It has provided "43 piers, 15 passenger and automobile-ferry slips, 5 car-ferry slips, a large union passenger

[1] This device was used by Eads in South Pass in 1879 (jetties completed). He and some associates contracted to maintain the channel 26 feet deep and 200 feet wide at the bottom for a term of 20 years. The total sum paid them by the government was $8,000,000. Although the jetties are probably more effective than any other method known, other devises are needed to control the silt (400,000,000 tons a year) that is deposited where river currents meet tidal gulf waters.

The Mississippi from New Orleans to the Gulf is treated by the engineers of the United States Army as a harbor, that is, a deeper intracoastal waterway.

depot, and 5 miles of bulkhead wharves parallel to the sea wall, providing an aggregate of 17.2 miles of berthing space."

To cross the bars at the entrance to the Columbia River, jetties and frequent dredgings are necessary to maintain a 40-foot channel at mean low tide. The lower Willamette and lower Columbia are here considered intracoastal. From Portland to the ocean is 110 miles. This in its original condition had controlling depths of only 10 to 15 feet at low water. The present project provides a 30-foot channel from Portland to the head of the estuary.

Intracoastal Waters, Other than Harbors. Besides the major harbors just discussed, the meeting points of land and ocean commerce,

FIG. 2. A Barge on Albemarle Sound, 1930.

there are several other conspicuous deep intracoastal water bodies in the United States, namely Narragansett Bay, Long Island Sound, Delaware Bay, Chesapeake Bay and several of its estuaries, Tampa Bay, Mobile Bay, Galveston Bay, San Francisco Bay, Puget Sound, and others that have required but little improvement to fit them to handle ocean and coastwise traffic. The drowned portion of the Hudson River tidal waters to Albany, and the Mississippi to New Orleans, may rightfully be classed with these deeper intracoastal waters just discussed.

There are many hundreds of square miles of lagoons and estuaries, shallow intracoastal waters, that have been improved to meet the needs of shallow-draft crafts, too small, for the most part, to brave the coastal waters (Fig. 2). These lagoon waters are almost continuous from New York Bay southward to the tip of Florida and also border almost the entire Gulf coast. Most of these shallow intracoastal waters, and several deep intracoastal water bodies have been connected by short canals, here and there, to form the great Intracoastal Waterway that extends from Cape Cod Bay to Key West. The Gulf Coastal Waterway is completed only in part. These waterways are shown in Fig. 1.

The Great Lakes. The connected Great Lakes form the greatest inland body of navigable waters in the world, measured by area of water surface, depth of water, and volume of commerce. This great waterway, in its original condition, had two distinct barriers to continuous navigation, one between lakes Superior and Huron and the other between lakes Erie and Ontario. Lake Superior is connected with Lake Huron by the St. Mary's River, but at the St. Mary's rapids (the Sault of the Ste. Marie) there are only two or three feet of water plunging over resistant red sandstone ledges. The current is so strong that even skiffs and canoes must be cordoned upstream. The first American ship canal (with one lock) at the St. Mary's rapids was completed in 1855. A canoe and batteau canal, however, had been constructed on the Canadian side of the river in 1798. It was destroyed by Americans in 1814. There are now four locks on the American side of the St. Mary's River at Sault Ste. Marie, in two canals. The depths of water at the locks are 12.6 feet, 18 feet, 34.5 feet, and 24.5 feet, respectively. The Canadians have a ship canal (and lock) that accommodates the largest of lake vessels. All the locks are free to either domestic or foreign vessels in either country. The St. Mary's River has been improved. Two channels 20 and 24 feet, respectively, have been provided, one for upstream the other for downstream navigation. In the St. Clair and Detroit rivers, the connecting waters between lakes Huron, St. Clair, and Erie, much dredging and blasting of hard rock has been necessary to provide a 20-foot channel. About 1829 the Canadian government constructed the Welland Canal between lakes Erie and Ontario. The chambers in later years were deepened to 14 feet and lengthened to 270 feet, and recently the Welland Canal has been greatly improved to accommodate large lake and ocean freighters. This canal is several miles to the west of Niagara River. Lake Ontario is distinctly a Canadian lake in its commercial activity. In the others, United States commerce dominates.

Lake Michigan, the second of the Great Lakes in size, is connected with Lake Huron by the broad, deep Strait of Mackinac.

There are few natural harbors on the Great Lakes. Every harbor has had some improvements, which, in general, are similar to those of ocean harbors.

Navigation improvements of the Great Lakes in comparison with those of the Mississippi and ocean harbors are fairly permanent features. Tides are scarcely discernible even with a tide gauge. The lake levels are fairly constant, varying not more than one or two feet during a year and three or four feet in a decade or two. The changes in the level are correlated fairly closely with the relative amount of rainfall of the Lakes Region. The velocity of the currents in the connecting waters varies but little from season to season. The connecting waters carry little silt, hence bar-forming is not active in these channels. Nor is bar-forming as active in the harbors of the Great Lakes as on the south Atlantic and Gulf coasts. River harbors, like those at Cleveland and Toledo, however, do call for close attention to maintain a uniform channel depth.

The total shoreline of the Great Lakes, in American waters, is nearly 4,700 miles (8,345 miles, total length). As a result of navigation improvements in the channels connecting the lakes and the numerous harbors, large vessels (many 600 feet long drawing 17 to 18 feet of water) can sail 700 miles from Buffalo to Duluth-Superior, and about the same distance to Chicago, carrying loads larger, in tons of cargo, than those in most ocean carriers. Some of our largest cargo carriers can transport 12,000 to 15,000 tons of iron ore to the load and an equal volume of coal or grain. The commercial possibilities of the Great Lakes, however, are not measured by the length and width of each of the lakes. Were the demand great enough, hundreds of traffic routes, rather than a few as at present, could be developed, so vast is the expanse of water.

Up to June 30, 1934, there had been spent on the harbors of the Great Lakes (American waters) about $166,000,000. Maintenance during this period had amounted to about $45,000,000.

The Rivers of the United States. The navigable rivers of the United States may be grouped as follows: rivers of the Atlantic slope, rivers of the Pacific slope, the Mississippi and its tributaries, and the Gulf slope rivers. All the rivers of the Great Lakes basin are short. The Red River of the North in the Hudson Bay basin drains northward into Lake Winnipeg.

Most of the Atlantic slope rivers were, in their original condition, navigable[1] for only short distances from their mouths. The navigable

[1] Navigable bodies of water are bodies that are navigated in fact. "They are navigable in fact when they are used, or are susceptible of being used in their

sections of New England rivers measure but a few miles, for the rock of the upland comes nearly to the ocean's edge. The only exception is the Connecticut, which has a 12-foot channel (improved) to Hartford, 52 miles from the mouth. Southward from New York Harbor the navigable sections lie between the Fall Line and the intracoastal waters, and it is largely in these sections that improvements have been or are being made under "existing projects." The riverways (to be distinguished from intracoastal shallow waters) are very short in Virginia and North Carolina. Fayetteville on the Fall Line in North Carolina is 115 miles from Wilmington; and Augusta on the Savannah is 219 miles from the ocean. The Alabama is navigable to the edge of the Piedmont, 364 miles from Mobile Bay. In the past, some of the west Gulf slope rivers have been used to float commercial products, and now and then there is some agitation to canalize the Trinity (to Dallas), but today water navigation is restricted, largely, to intracoastal waters, natural or dredged.

Only a few rivers on the Pacific slope are navigable. The Sacramento is considered navigable to Red Bluff, 261 miles from Suisun Bay, and the San Joaquin for about 100 miles. River crafts, since the region was settled, used the Columbia from Portland to the Cascade Water Gap about 160 miles from the mouth, or 50 miles above Portland. Canals and locks at the water gap and The Dells open up long stretches of shallow water for navigation, as Fig. 1 shows.

The Mississippi and Its Tributaries. The greatest of all river systems of the world, in certain respects, is the Mississippi. The Missouri-Mississippi from the Rockies to the Gulf is 4,200 miles long, the longest river in the world. It is 2,475 from Lake Itasca, the source of the Mississippi, to the Gulf of Mexico. The Missouri is 2,945 miles long, the Arkansas 1,460 miles, the Ohio (including its longest headwater tributary) 1,283, the Tennessee nearly 1,000, and the Cumberland more than 700.

There are some 15,000 miles of riverways that have been navigated within the Mississippi River Basin. Figure 1 shows the mileage of the "existing projects," however, to be far less than this. It is more than a thousand miles from Cairo, near the mouth of the Ohio to the Gulf, and nearly a thousand miles from Pittsburgh to Cairo. St. Paul, at the head of navigation on the Mississippi, is 874 miles by river from the

---

ordinary condition as highways for commerce . . ." This definition is mainly for purposes of defining ownership of land and water and the right of the public to use the waters as possible highways. Exactness demanded in scientific writings calls for a statement of the minimum depth for navigation.

Ohio's mouth. Fort Benton in Montana, once the head of navigation on the Missouri, is 2,285 by water from the Missouri's mouth; Sioux City, Iowa, once an active river town, is 807 miles; and Kansas City, now the head of the federal barge line traffic, is 390 miles from the mouth.

When forest and grassland were still dominant and men too few to construct roads, and railroads were unknown, many of the tributaries of the Mississippi now but little used were active arteries of trade and travel. The navigable lengths of the rivers were far longer than now —not that there is less water but the present standards of efficiency, and even necessity, are higher. Many of the rivers listed as navigable in the past were navigable only during seasons of high water, three to seven months of the year. The Ohio, for example, in low-water periods had only one to two feet of water in portions of the navigable channel. Boulders and snags were common. Work of removing some of these obstructions was begun about 1825. The first locks and dams were provided for by Congress in 1879. Other dams were constructed at later dates by special appropriations. No consistent plan of river improvement was followed. Improvement to fit the river to handle modern barge traffic began about 1910, at which time a general plan was adopted by Congress.

The Mississippi, just below Cairo, before improvements were made, had a minimum depth of only 4 to 4.5 feet. Above Cairo the Mississippi was about as navigable, before improvements were made, as the Ohio. Even though the fluctuations in depth of water are not great in the upper Mississippi (most of the tributaries flow out of the lands covered by the ice in the Wisconsin glacial epoch and thus abound in lakes and marshes), navigation was frequently interrupted, if not suspended, during the dry season. Intermittent service was discouraging to shippers and led to loss of patronage and finally to complete cessation of traffic. An attempt is now being made to modernize the transportation facilities. Later in this chapter the "existing project" rivers and canals will receive attention.

MAN'S USE OF THE WATERWAYS

His Use of the Riverways. Explorers, fur traders, colonizers, farmer-settlers, all in their turn, have found our waterways almost indispensable. Our ocean harbors welcomed the first explorers and colonizers. On some of them were founded the first settlements from which began the conquest of the land now included in the United

States. The fur traders, the advance guard of civilization, used the Hudson, the Connecticut, several of the Maine rivers, and the St. Lawrence for their operations. Up the Hudson, the Mohawk, and on to the Great Lakes went British and Dutch fur traders. The St. Lawrence and Ottawa led the French in their birch bark canoes to the same Great Lakes, once the greatest fur-producing region on the continent. The low divide between the Mississippi tributaries and the Great Lakes favored the wide wanderings of the French voyageurs in their trading operations with the Indians. After them into the heart of the continent went the British and British-American trader along the same routes. Navigable waterways to them meant rivers and creeks of a foot or so of water as a minimum.

The birch bark canoe was the carrying agent, particularly in the Great Lakes Region. It could be carried over portages and even pushed through marshes in wet seasons. On the Great Lakes and the St. Lawrence as commerce expanded bateaux, pushed, cordoned, or sailed, carried European commodities to the French trading posts at Detroit, Mackinac, and elsewhere, and returned laden with furs.

Both the canoe and the bateaux were used on the Ohio, Mississippi, and Missouri by fur traders. When the farmer-settler began the conquest of the Mississippi Basin, larger craft were employed to carry them westward to new homes on or near the many rivers and afterward transported their products downstream to markets. These primitive crafts were the raft, the flatboat, and the keelboat. Some flatboats, suitable only for downstream navigation, were 50 to 60 feet long, and 20 feet wide. They could carry 250 to 300 barrels of flour or an equal weight of other products. The journey from the Ohio's mouth to Natchez or New Orleans took 25 to 30 days. The flatboat used the cheapest form of propulsion—the river currents. Since the marketable products were ready for shipment during the off-season on the farms, the farmers or farmers' sons generally manned the boats, and thus the cost of transporting the products to market was low, so low, indeed, that flatboat traffic continued long after the coming of the vastly superior steamboat. Stern necessity forced the majority of farmers to transport their own products to market, but there developed rivermen who carried products on commission or bought them outright much as auto-truck men do today.

The keelboat, fewer in number and much smaller than the flatboat, and therefore in downstream navigation not as efficient a carrier, could, with much labor, be poled, "bushwhacked," or cordoned upstream. It was the "express boat" of the Mississippi. The journey from New Orleans to Louisville took from 70 to 90 days.

Sailing boats were not adapted to the meandering forest-bordered rivers where in the course of 20 or 30 miles the boat must sail toward every point of the compass. Besides, the tall trees tended to check the winds, and strong currents interfered.

All forms of river carriers were eclipsed by the steamboat when it appeared in the early part of the nineteenth century. The first steamboat on interior rivers was the *New Orleans,* built in Pittsburgh, which made its first trip in 1811. But it never returned, for its boiler and engine were not powerful enough to cope with the strong currents of the Mississippi and the Ohio. It was used for many years in the trade on the quiet waters between Natchez and New Orleans. Effective steamboat navigation on the Mississippi and its larger tributaries dates from about 1815-1820. The first river steamboats had hulls like the *Clermont* on the Hudson. In time the designers of river steamers found that the hull of their vessels must be patterned after the flatboat—long, broad, and thus enabling a shallow draft. In reality the river steamers were flatboats with engines added. They sailed *on* not *in* the water. Someone jokingly declared that they could sail in a heavy dew. As time went on the engines and boilers of the steamboats were improved and the speed increased. In 1815 the *Enterprise* steamed from New Orleans to Louisville in 25 days and 2 hours. In 1828 the *Tecumseh* ran the same distance in 8 days and 4 hours, and in 1852 the *Eclipse,* in 4 days and 18 hours. The fastest time ever made—even to date—on the Mississippi was by the *Robert E. Lee* in 1870. This steamer made the 1,200 miles between New Orleans and St. Louis in 3 days, 18 hours, and 14 minutes.

Most of the river steamers on the interior rivers between 1840 and 1870 (about) were excellent passenger and packet boats, large, spacious, grand, veritable floating palaces. The keelboat, as previously stated, took from 70 to 90 days to cover the distance that river passenger and packet boats did in 5 to 9 days. No wonder, then, that the steamboat in its maturity was treated with respect, for to the people of that time it did actually "annihilate" space and greatly reduced the costs of transportation. Besides, it was the only comfortable and speedy means of travel for long distances. It served, except in low-water seasons, a large part of the Mississippi Basin within 50 or so miles of navigable rivers. Ice gave no trouble south of the Ohio and very little on that river. The steamboat hastened the settlement of the basin. It carried settlers westward and afterward kept them in touch with the friends, relatives, and markets they had left behind. The increasing population in turn called for more steamboats.

In 1820 there were 72 registered steamers on the Mississippi, by 1842 the number had reached 400, and five years later there were 1,200. It was estimated that in 1840 some 40,000 men were employed in river transportation—some of course ran the flatboats—and that from six to seven million people were dependent on the rivers for transportation. The steamboat brought many economic advantages to the people served. The Mississippi Basin for the first time was brought into connection with national and international channels of trade. The producers received more for their products, and consumers paid less for their merchandise. There was a rapid increase in wealth. Products that heretofore had been considered worthless now came to have economic value. The merchants were benefited. Their money turn-over was more rapid than before and they were not obliged to carry so large a stock as formerly and thus less capital was tied up in goods. Formerly the replacement of stock was a matter of six or eight months; after the steamboat came, only a month or so. That there ever could be greater efficiency in transportation, greater speed, and greater luxury in travel was undreamed of in the 1840's.

The Decline of the Steamboat and Riverway Transportation. By about 1850 a new form of transportation began to dispute the supremacy of the steamboat. Railways using steam locomotives were first used in the United States about 1830; in England about 1825. At first the railroads in most states were not thought of as competitors of the steamboats on the rivers. Many of them were laid out to supplement steamboat transportation, to fill in the gap here and there between rivers and lakes and tidal waters. In Michigan, for example, the earliest railways projected were to extend from the head of navigation of rivers flowing eastward into Detroit River or Lake Erie and the head of navigation of those flowing into Lake Michigan. The Baltimore and Ohio was projected to connect the Ohio River with the Patapsco at Baltimore.

Some people as late as 1829 doubted their efficiency as compared with canals. In the *Federal Gazette* of Baltimore, a doubter in 1829 expressed himself as follows:

> If a railway can be constructed in any country where a canal could be made, and in many situations where canals are impracticable, through want of water—if loaded boats and wagons have been raised and let down 220 feet on some of them—if they can be completed and kept in repair for far less expense than canals, and

> do not occupy one-fourth part of the room—if they cause no bilious or intermitting fevers in a country through which they pass—and if five or six wagons, each loaded with 20 cwt. can be impelled with a velocity of 10 or 12 miles per hour by means of one of Perkins' steam engines, expending two or three bushels of coal from Pittsburg to Baltimore; if these things be so, and they can be demonstrated, is it not time to abandon impossibilities and think seriously on a subject of greatest importance?

In the late 1830's railways became a subject of such importance that many state government and private corporations projected lines to connect navigable rivers or to extend from seaports to interior navigable rivers. Railway planning and building were active in New York, Pennsylvania, Maryland, South Carolina, Illinois, and elsewhere. But the panic of 1837, caused partly by the "boom" in railway construction, checked railway expansion in many states and stopped it entirely in others. It was not until the 1850's that railway building was resumed. At first all the lines were short and in few instances competed with steamboats. It was not until consolidation and the building up of through lines took place and the paralleling of rivers as the extension continued that the struggle for supremacy between steamboats and railways became active. Not always did the railroads fight honestly. They often cut freight rates to starve out the boat lines. The autocratic (so considered by the railways) Interstate Commerce Commission, empowered to supervise railway rates and finances, is the public's reaction to such unfair activities. The practice of lowering rates on lines competing with waterways and advancing them on others became so common that the public in general today accuses the railways of such unfair methods even where investigations show that they no longer exist. The railways frequently purchased large urban tracts of land with river frontage that they did not and could not use.

Undoubtedly the greatest factor, however, in the decline of river transportation from the 1860's on to recent decades was the changing conception on the part of the public of what constitutes efficient transportation. Standards of transportation were advanced. The railways were able to improve their service and meet the more exacting demands of the public. The river craft did not. The old generalized passenger-packet boat had reached its highest stage of development in speed, carrying capacity, efficiency in loading and unloading, and operation. A spirit of conservatism seemed to have become ingrained in the managerial personnel. It had lost the ability of adaptation. The river steamer of 1920 differed but little from that of 1840. But what an improvement in the transportation equipment of the railways! New blood with new ideas was needed on the riverways.

Apparently, several adverse natural conditions were operating to cause the decline of river transportation on the Mississippi and its tributaries.

1. There were many adverse physical conditions—strong currents, seasonal variations in depth of water, ice in the northern rivers, snags, and lack of uniformity in depth of channel.

FIG. 3. Loading Cotton, Alabama River, about 1840.

2. The flow of commodities was variable. The steamboat for the most part served agricultural regions whose marketable products moved mainly in the fall and winter. For most of the year "return cargoes" were not available. Passenger traffic yielded large returns before the railways came. Riverways today are successful only in densely settled industrial regions or connecting industrial regions and areas producing raw products for manufacture.

3. The area served by the riverways was small indeed, strips not more than some fifty miles on either side.

4. It was more difficult and costly to provide "branch lines" (or feeders) of riverways than of railways.

5. Terminal facilities were inadequate. The cost of handling freight

at terminals or between boats and railways was expensive. Wharf boats were few (Fig. 3).

It was these adverse conditions and many others that brought about the near extinction of the old-time passenger-packet steamboat on our rivers. Only a few are now engaged in the transportation of freight. Many river cities have one or more that are in the excursion business (Fig. 4). Though the grandeur of these century-old (in hull, appointment, and architecture at least) steamers may attract excursions they are wholly unfit to function in modern transportation.

Again it is these adverse conditions that have had to be recognized and avoided or eliminated in the new era in river transportation that is

FIG. 4. An Old-Time River Steamer, and a Wharf Boat at St. Louis, 1935.
Most of this type are now used in the excursion business.

now upon us, before river transportation can hope for success. Not all people who know the riverways and their shortcomings are certain that they can stage a "come back." The railways which were so successful in the struggle of the nineteenth century are still with us, and moreover improved; and in addition are auto-trucks and good roads which in certain types of traffic are even more serviceable than the railway.

In an investigation made in 1928 at Nashville, Tennessee, to discover why shippers did not use the Cumberland River, a large number of business men were interviewed. Forty-three per cent ascribed the lack of use of the river facilities to "the speed and convenience of truck and railroad," 16 per cent to "requests of customers for shipment by truck or rail," 13 per cent to "slowness and irregularity of river service," 14 per cent to "reliability of truck and rail service," 6 per cent reported that "trucks saved drayage and storage." Other reasons given were "lack of improvement in river transportation" and "changed commercial conditions." Said one, "Buyers no longer place advance orders as was the case forty or more years ago." Merchants in small river towns who formerly maintained a stock worth $15,000 to $20,000 now need carry only $5,000 or $6,000 worth. They can get deliveries from wholesale houses at Nashville within a few hours in summer or winter, high water or low, by truck or rail.

A similar investigation at Memphis about the same time brought similar replies. On both rivers many improvements in channels and terminals had been made, and at Memphis newly designed carrying agents were in operation.

Man's use of the other navigable rivers of the United States, the rise and decline of the steamboat, was similar to the story just sketched. The Cumberland had its first steamboat in 1818. A steamboat reached Arkansas Post on the Arkansas in 1820. A steamer on the James River that ran between Richmond and Norfolk was described in 1818 as being "a floating hotel, fitted up with much taste and neatness, with accommodations for both board and lodging." Steamboats on the James, Potomac, and other Virginia rivers "were crowded with passengers." The Roanoke, Cape Fear, Savannah, Alabama, and other rivers in the South were the main arteries of commerce. The Savannah about 1835 had 20 steamboats of large size and 50 steam tow-boats with scores of barges. The river towns and nearby farming sections of most of the tributaries of the Ohio were served by steamboats. The Missouri at times was navigated as far as Fort Benton. Sioux City, Omaha, and Kansas City had more regular service. On the Pacific slope the Columbia, Snake, and Sacramento were used actively after the frontier reached the Far West, two decades or more after the beginning of the steamboat era on the Mississippi.

Riverway transportation on the Mississippi was at its highest in 1859, just before the hostilities between North and South severed commercial relations and the trade of the upper Mississippi Basin turned eastward (Fig. 5).

Man's Use of the Great Lakes. The Great Lakes have never experienced the decline that characterized the history of navigation on the rivers. Railways for the most part tend to increase lake traffic. They act as feeders from the farming regions to the west of the lakes and connect the lakes with the Atlantic. With the present 20-foot channel the railways—even if the cost of navigation improvements are considered in determining "real" rates—can hardly compete with the large lake vessels. The great size and specialization of the carrying agents, their speed and lack of interruption en route, and the numerous labor-saving devices used in loading and unloading at the lake terminals make for efficiency in modern transportation equivalent or superior to that of ocean transportation. The story of lake navigation previous to the era of steam has already been noted briefly.

Steam navigation on the lakes began in 1818 when the steamer *Walk-in-the-Water* made its first trip between Buffalo and Detroit. As with the steamboats on interior rivers to the south, the *Walk-in-the-Water*, and the scores of crafts that followed in the years after, stimulated the western movement. Travel from Buffalo to Detroit was reduced from 5 to 10 days to 48 hours, and the journey was accomplished with much greater comfort. By 1826 there were six steamers on

FIG. 5. The Mississippi River at New Orleans, about 1850.

Lake Erie. As on the rivers great improvements were made as time went on in size, speed, and efficiency, and improvements are still going on. From Lake Erie steamers entered the commerce of Lake Huron and Lake Michigan, though the sailing vessels long continued to carry a large part of the commodities of these lakes where the services of tugs were scarcely needed. Sailing vessels found some difficulty in navigating the St. Clair and Detroit rivers unassisted, but a large percentage did use these waters. In 1852 there were 80 steamboats, 50 barges, and 270 schooners on the Great Lakes. The completion of the Soo Canal in 1855 extended the active traffic lines into Lake Superior, and soon iron ore became one of the important articles of lake commerce.

The increase in the size of lake vessels has kept pace with the increase in the depth of navigable channels. The first waterway improvements were made in the harbor at Erie, Pennsylvania, in 1825. By 1851 nearly $3,000,000 had been spent on harbor and river channel improvements. For many decades improvements were desultory as to time and location. A "20-foot channel" project was adopted by Congress in July, 1892. In 1905 Congress authorized a preliminary examination and survey with a view to enlarging the channel to 22 or 25 feet. The board of engineers suggested after careful consideration that the enlargement be deferred. Subsequently, however, appropriations have been made to deepen channels to 25 or 26 feet. This work is now being carried on. In certain channels where the currents are strong, and especially where fogs are frequent, as in the St. Mary's River, two channels are provided, one for upbound and one for downbound vessels.

Today the greatest physical obstacle to navigation on the Great Lakes is ice. The season of navigation varies from 225 to 240 days. For 125 to 140 days each year, or about a third of the time, all movement, except for the ice crushers that operate across Lake Michigan, the Straits of Mackinac, and Lake Erie, must cease. The long period of inactivity after all is not so serious to the continued success of water transportation as such a period would be on the Lower Mississippi, for the great bulk of the commodities carried are iron ore, grain, and lumber. The grain can be transported to eastern markets in the fall before the navigation season closes. Iron ore and coal and lumber can be stored readily. The great importance of the Great Lakes in the domestic and to some degree in our foreign commerce lies, as previously stated, in the large dimensions of the channels provided by the federal government, the large size of the lake carriers, the efficiency of the loading and unloading devices,[1] and the location of the Lakes between great mineral deposits, forests (now about depleted), and large grain-producing areas on the one hand and a densely settled industrial region on the other. In the industrial region are produced large quantities of coal. Its blast furnaces consume most of the iron ore produced in our country, and its demands for the grain of the West are great. Moreover, the industrial region extends to the Atlantic seaboard and thus has contacts with the world traffic routes.

[1] In 1921, 12,500 tons of iron ore were dropped into the steamer *Kerr* in 16.5 minutes, and this was unloaded at Conneaut in 3 hours and 5 minutes. This record has not been broken so far as the writer knows. The usual time is from 1 to 2 hours to load and 6 to 8 to unload. In 1830 the sailing vessel *Osceola* took 7 days to unload 1,678 bushels of wheat at Buffalo. This was considered a record at that time. With present devices that many bushels would be lifted into an elevator in 2 or 3 minutes.

In no other region of the world is man utilizing and thus conserving navigation resources as in the Great Lakes Region.

RECENT DEVELOPMENTS IN RIVER TRANSPORTATION

In a previous section some of the possible causes for the decline of transportation on our rivers were sketched. Transportation on the Mississippi reached its lowest point, measured by tonnage moved, some time between 1900 and 1920. There was roughly a half century or more of rise followed by a half century of decline in riverway transportation.

Our harbors, the deeper coastal waters, and the Great Lakes show a fairly steady rise in traffic movement. No matter what improvements were made in land transportation, they "carried on." There has been a gradual and profound advance in the capacity and efficiency of their carrying agents and freight and passenger terminals. The growth in importance of railways aided overseas commerce and also, to a certain degree, coastwise and lake commerce. Deep-water transportation like that of our Great Lakes or coastal waters has little to fear from railway competition.

The Experimental Barge Line. The new era in river transportation was ushered in about 1918 when the federal government took over the railways and the director general of transportation appointed a committee to study the possibilities of reviving or increasing commerce on the rivers, canals, and deep waterways. The committee in 1918 recommended that a fleet of modern river carriers be created on the lower Mississippi River and another on the Warrior-Tombigbee-Mobile riverway. Congress that year authorized the War Department to proceed with the development, and thus the Mississippi-Warrior River Barge Line was created. Large appropriations were made to develop efficient water carriers, and the work in channel improvement was speeded up. By 1920 the beginning of a fleet of modern tugboats and efficient barges was in operation on the Mississippi and the Warrior-Tombigbee riverways. The Inland and Coastwise Waterways Service, under the direct control of the War Department, was created to operate the steadily increasing fleet.

This venture was far from successful. The federal government lost on the average $1,000,000 a year between 1920 and 1924. Congress was informed by Major General Ashburn that in his opinion "this loss could be stopped under certain conditions and a net income accrue within five years of corporate activity, failing which it would become the duty of the Secretary of War to inform Congress that the whole project of creating navigable streams to afford the people of the United States cheaper transportation was a colossal failure."[1] To give the experiment further trial Congress in 1924 created the Inland Waterways Corporation, a quasi-independent organization, with Ashburn as director. The federal government purchased capital stock in the corporation from time to time and made donations or special appropriations so that by 1930 its total investment in the I.W.C. was about $24,400,000.[2]

The major function of the Inland Waterways Corporation is, as the articles of its creation state, to demonstrate to private companies the feasibility of inland water transportation; and when success has been demonstrated and private corporations show a willingness to utilize the waterways, the federal government is to retire from the field. The I.W.C.'s engineers have exhibited much enterprise and intelligence, in developing efficient carrying agents. The freight barges are of steel. They vary in size, the large number on the lower Mississippi being 230 feet long, 47 feet wide, and 11 feet deep, and drawing 3 to 6 feet of water when fully loaded. They have a capacity of 2,000 tons of freight each. Some of the larger have a capacity of 3,000 cargo tons, the smaller 400 to 1,000. They have water-tight compartments that make them as unsinkable as ocean vessels. The barges may be loaded or unloaded either through top hatches or side doors. The towboats are among the most powerful ever constructed on inland rivers. The largest are of steel, twin-screw tunnel type, powered by Diesel engines with an indicated horsepower of 1,800. The corporation also owns several car floats, a few oil tankers, some derricks, and terminal and landing barges. The numbers in the various types are increasing. No money has been spared to provide the most efficient equipment. The federal government through the I.W.C. now maintains federal barge lines on the lower Mississippi (New Orleans to St. Louis), the Warrior-Tombigbee (New Orleans to Port Birmingham), the Illinois River (St. Louis to Chicago), the upper Mississippi (St. Louis to Minneapolis), and the Missouri River (St. Louis to Kansas City). Congress has empowered the I.W.C. to extend services to any waterway which, it is thought, can bring favorable returns. The equipment on the upper Mississippi, the Missouri, and the Warrior River divisions is smaller than that used on the lower Mississippi. See map, Fig. 1.

[1] *Report of Inland Waterways Corporation,* 1928, p. 1.

[2] In 1927 the paid-in capital stock was $3,000,000. A "barge line users committee" in 1927 appealed to the Secretary of War to have the capital stock increased to $50,000,000.

Terminal facilities, the most efficient, have been provided at most large river ports (Figs. 6 and 7). Loans were made by the I.W.C. to

FIG. 6. Old Method of Handling Package Freight, 1916.

FIG. 7. The I.W.C. Terminal at St. Louis; Rail and River Transportation Coordinated, 1935.

many cities to provide the necessary terminal equipment. New Orleans secured a loan of $400,000, Memphis $450,000, Vicksburg $20,000, and

Helena, Arkansas, $60,000. Usually, if not invariably, the I.W.C. pays a heavy rent to the cities for the use of the river terminals.

In 1929 the I.W.C. achieved what it had been desiring for some time —the coordination of river and rail transportation. The Interstate Commerce Commission ordered the railways connecting with the barge lines "to establish a sweeping system of barge-rail and rail-barge-rail rates and routes" for shippers who desired to combine water and rail facilities.

Waterway Improvements. Since the middle of the last century, but chiefly since about 1875, desultory improvements have been made in various rivers of our country. Sometimes improvements in one part of a river bore no relation to those in another. The appropriations secured depended largely upon the initiative and activity of the congressman, or congressmen, in whose district or districts the waterways lay.

As a general statement it may be said that even moderate federal appropriations were not asked for until a decade or two after the decline in river transportation set in. This decline supplied the argument for seeking public money. The lower the traffic figures sank on the riverways the more insistent became the demands. If a few locks and a three-foot channel did not bring the desired results in increasing traffic, then more locks and a five-foot channel were demanded. All the time the railways were extending their lines and improving their service. The good roads movement got under way in the last two decades or more, and the auto truck has entered as a serious competitor with the railway.

One may make the generalization that the more the money spent on most of our rivers the less the movement of commodities on them. This state of affairs is due largely to the public's turning away from waterways to railways and trucks, which give more efficient and speedier transportation.

Existing River Projects. Only a few of our scores of rivers now being improved will be considered here. Nearly every river in our country that in recent decades has been navigated, if by nothing more than motorboats, is included in the list of rivers receiving federal funds. The waterways map, Fig. 1, shows most of the larger "existing projects." The following table shows some important details of the more important riverways. (Table 1.)

The works and improvements necessary to provide navigable riverway channels vary, of course, with the nature of the channel. In previous projects when the appropriations were small improvements consisted largely in narrowing the channel by dams of loose rock extending

TABLE 1

DETAILS OF IMPROVEMENTS ON THE MORE IMPORTANT RIVERWAYS*

Riverway	Length of Improved Channel, Miles	Depth of Channel, Minimum	Size of Locks: Length, Width, Water on Sill	Number of Locks and Dams
Lower Mississippi }	1931	9	No locks	
Upper Mississippi }		9	600 x 110 x 10	26
Ohio	981	9	600 x 110 x 11	50
Illinois	326	9	600 x 110 x 10	7
Tennessee	648	9	600 x 60 x 9	27
Missouri (to Sioux City)	769	6	No locks	
Cape Fear	115	8	300 x 40 x 9	2
Savannah	201	6	No details	1
Warrior-Tombigbee	343	8	282 x 52 x 8.5	17

* Data, *Report of Chief of Engineers, U. S. Army*, 1934, various pages.

from the bank or shallow water to the edge of the channel, snagging, and the removal of rocks, and at places devices to protect the caving of the banks were necessary. When large appropriations became available more permanent works were possible. Dredging and the construction of substantial dams and locks are now the order of the day. These provide much slack-water navigation. The slope of the river and the number of rock ledges determine the number of dams and locks required. On the Ohio and the upper Mississippi immense sums have been spent, or are being spent. The medium cost of such works on the Ohio is from $2,500,000 to $3,000,000. The navigation improvements at Louisville required $7,600,000. The average cost of locks and dams on the upper Mississippi is about $4,000,000. The expense of constructing the Alton Dam will be $10,000,000. The lift of the lock varies from a few feet to 38.

It will be noted in the above table that there is an attempt to standardize the depth and the size of the locks, thus making it possible for boats of standard size to operate on several of the rivers if traffic so demands.

THE FEASIBILITY OF RIVER AND HARBOR IMPROVEMENTS

Costs and Returns on the Various Types of Waterways Compared. The question of the feasibility of waterways involves a consideration of, first, the total (past and future) cost of improvements and the returns; and, second, a comparison of the relative costs of providing water and rail transportation, where such comparison is possible.

The total cost of the several types of waterways, the sums of money needed to complete existing projects, and the cost of maintenance to June 30, 1934, are shown in Table 2.

TABLE 2

COSTS OF TYPES OF WATERWAYS COMPARED*

	Total Expenditures† to June 30, 1934, Millions of Dollars	Amount Needed to Complete, Millions of Dollars
Seacoast harbors and channels........	673	55
Lake harbors and channels..........	213	10
Mississippi River system.............	536	155
Intracoastal canals and other waterways...........................	134	12
Operating and care of canals‡.........	133	

* *Report of Chief of Engineers, U. S. Army*, 1934, p. 13.
† Includes maintenance.
‡ Separate from maintenance.

The total sum spent on our waterways (to June 30, 1934) was approximately $1,800,000,000 and it will take more than $232,000,000 to complete present projects. In addition to this huge sum, cities, states, and port districts have appropriated more than $1,000,000,000 and private corporations $1,300,000,000 for local improvements, making a total of $4,000,000,000.

And the returns? Statistics are not available to present a complete picture of the domestic and foreign commerce of our country that moves by water. The following "scraps" of information, nevertheless, will give us some idea of the immensity of the commerce, at least, on some of our waterways. The total "water-borne commerce" of the United States, foreign and domestic, in normal times, is valued at more than $20,000,000,000. There moved through the ports of our lakes and seacoasts in 1933 a foreign trade ("water-borne" exports and imports) valued at more than $4,000,000,000 (adjusted for duplications), and a domestic of $7,500,000,000. The value of freight, foreign and domestic, passing through the St. Mary's canals in that year was more than $534,000,000. The total for the Great Lakes ports was $2,100,000,000.

The freight moved on the Ohio River is valued at about $110,000,000 and that on the entire Mississippi system at $990,000,000.[1]

As intimated in previous pages there certainly is little question in the minds of most students of navigation and water transportation about the feasibility of improvements that the federal government has made in most of the ocean and lake harbors on which have grown up our great cities. The expenditure of $673,000,000 on ocean harbors and channels to fit them to function for scores of years—commodities worth $11,700,000,000 moving through annually—is certainly good business, though there are, no doubt, many ports at which the expenditures can hardly be justified. For a large part of this commerce no carrying agents except vessels can function. One must certainly agree that the $213,000,000 used on the harbors and the channels connecting the lakes that carry a commerce valued at $2,100,000,000 is money well spent. But there are many voters in our country who question the feasibility of spending (up to December 31, 1934) $536,000,000 on the Mississippi River system for construction and maintenance, $133,000,000 more for operation of canals (most of which are on the Mississippi and tributaries), and nearly $200,000,000 more to complete existing projects to move freight valued at $990,000,000 (1933). Such voters declare also that the improvements of the Missouri between Kansas City and the mouth which cost $69,000,000, maintenance $2,000,000 a year, that in 1934 had a freight movement of $3,500,000, can hardly be considered feasible. The Illinois riverway cost about $113,000,000, exclusive of terminals. Its commerce was valued at $9,000,000 in 1934.[2]

Real Costs of Transportation, Riverway versus Railway. Riverway advocates without exception in their plea for federal expenditures claim that the riverways give shippers far lower rates than do the railways. The Federal Barge Line arbitrarily cuts its rates to 80 per cent of that of competing lines of railways, and the Interstate Commerce Commission in 1929 sanctioned such a cut in barge-rail or rail-barge-rail rates. That a lower rate by river carriers than that of the railway is given *the shipper* is thus a fact.

But river carrier rates, anyone will agree, are *not* based on the same complex of items that railway rates are. The railway company must purchase its rights-of-way, construct its roadbed and tracks, and provide its own depots and terminals (many of which are very ex-

[1] *Statistical Abstract,* 1934; *Report of Chief of Engineers, U. S. Army,* 1934, Part 2, various pages.

[2] Data from *Report of Chief of Engineers, U. S. Army,* Part 1, 1934, p. 3; *ibid.,* Part 2, 1931, pp. 5 and 31.

pensive and are adornments to the cities in which they are located). It must provide, of course, its own traffic equipment, a large part of which is idle many weeks each year because of the seasonal variation in the flow of traffic; pay immense sums in taxes on its tangible properties; and hire a veritable army of employees to keep the right-of-way in perfect condition, to man the traction equipment, and keep the proper records demanded by efficient operation and the Interstate Commerce Commission. It also pays heavy attorney's fees to fight the numerous suits brought by persons who look upon the railways as easy picking. *All these items are reflected in the rates the public is called upon to pay.* We know that these rates are not exorbitant, for one of the functions of the Interstate Commerce Commission is to see they are reasonable.

The waterway rates on the Federal Barge Line, on the other hand, are based only on the cost of the operation of the powerboats and barges. With privately owned common carriers the shipper pays for the craft. The *way* is provided and maintained, the locks (if there be any) are operated, and the channel lighted to make navigation safe and reduce insurance rates, all by the federal government at no cost to the carrier. Cities usually furnish terminals. Only the traffic equipment is taxed. The very expensive "way" pays no taxes. *Some one must recompense the federal government. If the shipper does not, the general public must.* The taxpayers of the United States pay *the entire cost of transportation, directly or indirectly, whether by rail or water or air.* They have the right to demand the cheapest form of transportation available, consistent with adequate service. Their representatives in Congress are obligated to give them the most for their money.

If the common carriers on the Ohio, for example, were operated on the same basis as the railways, that is, were they called upon to meet these hidden costs and amortize the capital investment ($125,000,000) through a 50-year period, they would need to charge 0.86 cent a ton-mile in addition to the posted rate of 0.8 cent. Their actual rate would thus be 1.66 cents. The "freight revenue" of the railroads in the eastern district of the United States in 1933 was 1.01 cents a ton-mile, and in the southern 0.85 cent. In fact, the freight moved on the Ohio River costs *the public* annually from $8,000,000 to $10,000,000 more than if the railways paralleling the river handled it.

The commodities carried on the Ohio, by class and percentage, are coal and coke about 44 per cent; gravel, and stone 43 per cent; logs, lumber, oil, gasoline, metallic ores, metals, and manufactures 11 per cent; and package freight 2 per cent.

Is it not more than likely that if the $132,000,000 (the capital investment of the federal government in the Ohio riverway) had been spent in the building of roads more people would be benefited and benefited directly? The $132,000,000 would build four parallel, two-lane, $45,000-a-mile roads from Pittsburgh to Cairo. If to this capital investment of the government in the Ohio we add the money spent to improve navigation on the Mississippi from Cairo to New Orleans ($156,000,000, or one-half the total spent on flood control and navigation) the four roads could be extended on to New Orleans. They would pass through every one of the major cities on the Ohio and the Mississippi touched by riverway craft.

This sum, $288,000,000, would construct two parallel, $100,000-a-mile, double-track, de luxe railways, completely equipped, between Pittsburgh and New Orleans and in addition build a similar double-track line from Cairo to Chicago by way of St. Louis. The total distance that freight would have to travel by railway would be only about two-thirds to one-half that by river. The speed of the modern Mississippi River steamer pushing a "tow" is about 4 miles upstream and 8 miles with the current. Freight-carrying land vehicles, railway trains or auto trucks, move 30 miles an hour either way. A round trip by train or truck, between Pittsburgh and New Orleans, could be made in less than 4 days. It would take the modern tug and barges 30 days with no delays or stops. Four days at least, however, would need be added to pass the 100 locks in the up and down voyages on the Ohio. One argument made by the friends of the riverway is that it is a "multiple-track" way. Measured on the basis of time the hypothetical railways mentioned above, as movers of freight, are equivalent to sixteen "tracks" on the Ohio and Mississippi.

In this discussion of the relative costs of riverways, roads, and railroads, no consideration has been given the possible allocation of some of the costs of navigation dams, to flood control and power development. The reason for not considering these other uses is that, so far, federal appropriations on the Ohio, Illinois, upper Mississippi, and the Missouri have been made specifically for navigation.

Has the Federal Barge Line Been a Success? In a previous section in this chapter the activity of the federal government in advancing riverway transportation through the I.W.C. has been discussed. Between 1920 and 1924 about $1,000,000 a year were sunk, as Senator Warren once remarked, into "the deep black mud of the Mississippi." Even Congress developed a resentment to appropriating further money, and so in 1924 the Inland Waterways Corporation came into being, as previously discussed. For some years it operated at a loss.

In 1934 the net operating loss of the I.W.C. was $985,368.50. There was a net profit, however, in 1935 of $651,802.83, leaving a net profit to the I.W.C. at the end of twelve years of about $781,000.[1]

As stated previously, the federal investment in the I.W.C. was gradually increased. In 1927 it was $24,400,000. Some of this money was loaned by the I.W.C. and paid interest to the I.W.C. The I.W.C. paid no interest on the loans from the Federal Government.[2] It paid no taxes except indirectly in the rents to municipalities for the use of their terminals; it paid no corporation taxes, no insurance, and no office rent.[3] These costs private operators would be called upon to meet. These are facts that friends or enemies of the Federal Barge Line must accept. The managers of the Federal Barge Line find solace in the vast amount of money that has been saved (?) the shipping public by offering rates lower than the railways. The controller of the corporation estimated that from June 1, 1924, to December 31, 1933, the direct saving to the public had amounted to $20,664,000. "This is the difference," he reports, "between the charges paid by shippers on traffic routed via Federal Barge Lines and what the charges would have been if the traffic had moved by rail."[4]

The reader should also understand that the "way" over which the Federal Barge Lines boats travel is also a federal contribution. The railways that compete with the Federal Barge Line have no such advantages. The friends of the riverways insist that the money spent on the navigation improvements should in no way enter into the calculations that are testing the feasibility of the Federal Barge Line. The president or director of the I.W.C., General Ashburn, contends that "the money which has been spent to create these navigable streams to provide flood control, to maintain channels, and so forth, has already been spent, and the only possible way in which to get return upon the money so invested is to utilize the water rights-of-way so created, in the manner for which they were created and free of any charges. The utilization of what has been created adds nothing to the cost of crea-

[1] *Annual Report of Inland Waterways Corporation,* 1935, p. 13.

[2] The annual interest on the capital stock of the I.W.C. in 1927 and since at 4 per cent amounts to $976,000. If bonds had been floated to finance the corporation this sum would need be earned to keep the corporation a "going concern." For the twelve years between and including 1924 to 1935, the total interest would be more than $11,700,000. The net profits for this period (interest not considered) as just stated, were only about $781,000.

[3] *Annual Report of the Inland Waterways Corporation,* 1933, pp. 16-18.

[4] *Annual Report of the Inland Waterways Corporation,* 1933, p. 45.

tion, of maintenance, taxes, or other charges. In order to reap the full benefit of all the money which has been spent, this school holds, it is necessary to carry to completion the main arteries in the order of their importance, in accordance with sound economic and sound engineering principles, and to build outward from the main arteries as sound business judgment dictates, and any agency, other than the one which destroyed water transportation, should be allowed their free use so all the benefits of such cheaper water transportation shall be available to all the people."[1] In another report we find this question, "Would they have us throw these carriers into the discard with a billion and a half dollars (the total cost of all waterways, harbors, lakes, canals, and rivers up to 1931) they advocate throwing away by abandoning our waterways policy? Should not this matter receive consideration?" The author of this chapter leaves the answering of the question to the readers.

Apparently, the public has a "white elephant" on its hands, donated by Congress through the earnest solicitation of hundreds of shippers who profit by federal operation of the barge line, and who would object strenuously if the beast were permitted to die. What should be done? It is not the province of this chapter to suggest a course of action.

Certainly the facts just presented lead the readers to conclude that the Federal Barge Line has *not yet* demonstrated that private corporations can successfully operate common carriers on the Mississippi riverway. But possibly the Federal Barge Line may be a failure because of the times. During most of the period the line has been operating we have been in a depression. There has been a slump in all types of domestic commerce. In normal times the Federal Barge Line venture might have been more successful. Many investigators, however, seem to think otherwise. They say that during a depression shippers are more likely to see the cheaper forms of transportation, and the riverways provided by the federal government and the barge line financed and operated by the federal government do offer a cheap type of transportation *to the shippers*. Riverways are more costly than railways, however, *to the general public* who, as previously stated, *must pay all costs of transportation.*

The Feasibility of the Intracoastal Waterway or Canal. The location and depth of the various parts of this waterway are shown on Fig. 1. Cape Cod Canal, Long Island Sound, and Chesapeake Bay belong, in our classification, to the deeper intracoastal waters. It is on

[1] *Annual Report of the Inland Waterways Corporation,* 1933, p. 15.

these that most of the commerce of the Intracoastal Waterway is carried. These deeper sections, without a doubt, as previously stated, represent feasible investments. The 12-foot channel of the Chesapeake-Delaware Canal carries a fair commerce mainly between Baltimore and Philadelphia. The cost, about $5,000,000, is far less than the annual value of the commodities moved annually, namely $45,000,000. The 12-foot channel from Norfolk to Beaufort, North Carolina, has much less traffic. Commerce on the shallower channels to the south is largely local. Only a small amount of through-freight could be expected, for the larger ports are served by large, deep-draft coastwise vessels and are also connected with three very efficient railways on the Coastal Plain and the Piedmont. The chief beneficiaries of the shallow Atlantic Intracoastal Waterway as a "through-route" are owners of private yachts who migrate between northern ports and Florida resorts, fall and spring. Parts of the Gulf Intracoastal Waterway in Louisiana and Texas carry a large commerce. Oil and oil products bulk the largest in quantity and value. The total cost of the Atlantic and Gulf Intracoastal waterways is about $134,000,000. They are not yet completed.

CANALS OF THE UNITED STATES

Just about a century ago the United States was in a canal-building boom. The Middlesex Canal in Massachusetts was opened for service in 1808, the Erie in 1825, the Pennsylvania about 1840, and the Chesapeake and Ohio about 1840 (Fig. 8). The favorite pastime of many dreamers of transportation in the early nineteenth century was to connect rivers with canals, no matter where, over plateaus or mountains, without a thought of the topographic difficulties, the supply of water at the crest of the watersheds, cost of operation, and amount of traffic that would tend to flow to the artificial waterway. "Astonishing as it may seem," wrote one enthusiast about 1820, "75 miles of canal are all that is necessary to give water communication between Market Street bridge (Philadelphia) and the Pacific Ocean at the mouth of the Columbia." By the time the railway mesh had become quite thoroughly spread over American landscapes east of the Mississippi, many states and private corporations had constructed about 4,000 miles of canals. Figure 9 shows the location of the more important canals about 1850. New York and Pennsylvania, Maryland, and Virginia, each projected canals in the latter part of the eighteenth century from the Atlantic seaboard cities westward to the Great Lakes and toward the Ohio.

New York's canal is the only one that has survived to our day, and that only after two expensive enlargements. Topographic conditions were more favorable than in most states, and the New York canal occupied a natural strategic traffic route. Pennsylvania had to use portage railways to connect east-flowing and west-flowing canalized rivers. Neither Maryland nor Virginia got its canal over the bold Allegheny Front and Plateau. The Chesapeake and Ohio Canal in Maryland went no farther than Cumberland, and the James River Canal only a few miles west of Buchanan, both towns being in the Great Valley.

The Chesapeake and Ohio Canal was being used but little in 1890 to float coal to Tidewater. The James River canal went into disuse

FIG. 8. The Delaware River Canal, 1935.

more than a half century ago; and the Pennsylvania Canal shortly after the early 1860's. Since the 1870's, 4,000 miles of canals that probably cost upward of $200,000,000 have been abandoned.

In the early part of this century the state of New York greatly enlarged the Erie Canal[1] and some of its branches at a cost of more than $120,000,000.[2] It is toll free. It was estimated that the enlargement would enable the canal to transport 20,000,000 tons of freight a year. In 1931, 3,722,000 tons were moved. Fredrick S. Green, superintendent of public works, in his report to Governor Smith in 1926, stated that the operation and maintenance of the canal (including amortization charges) in the single year 1925 had cost the taxpayers of the state $10,600,000 or $4.51 for each ton carried. The railroad rate from

[1] The title now is the New York State Barge Canal—Erie Division.
[2] The capital cost to the state, as of June 30, 1933, was $173,500,000.

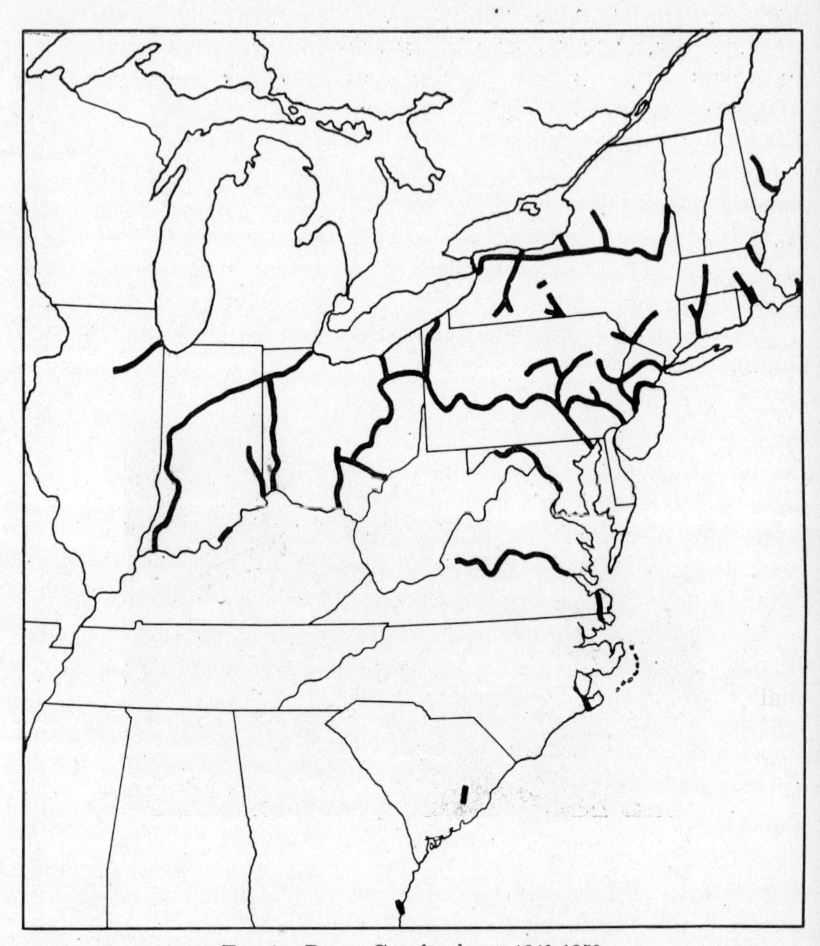

FIG. 9. Barge Canals about 1840-1850.

Maine—Cumberland and Oxford; Massachusetts—Middlesex, abandoned about 1850 or before; Rhode Island—Blackstone Valley, soon abandoned; Connecticut—Farmington, by 1850 filled in to make roadbed for New Haven-Northampton R.R.; New York—state canal system: Erie with branches to Lake Champlain, to Oswego, up Black River, from Chenango to Binghamton, to Cayuga and Seneca Lakes, and along Genesee Valley, also Delaware-Hudson; New Jersey—Morris Delaware-Raritan; Pennsylvania—Pennsylvania Canal and Portage Railway, Delaware River Canal to Easton, Lehigh Navigation, Schuylkill, Beaver and Erie, N. Br. Susquehanna, Susquehanna to Tidewater; Delaware—Chesapeake and Delaware; Maryland—Chesapeake and Ohio; Virginia—James River-Kanawha, Dismal Swamp, Alexandria Canal; North Carolina—Clubfoot-Harlow, Dismal Swamp; South Carolina—Santee and several short canals; Georgia—Brunswick; Alabama—Muscle Shoals, Huntsville, Louisiana—several short (not shown); Kentucky—Portland-Louisville; Ohio-Miami-Maumee, Ohio and Erie (Portsmouth to Cleveland) and branches; Indiana—Wabash and Erie (Evansville to Lake Erie), White Water; Illinois—Illinois and Michigan; Wisconsin—Portage Canal. (Data from R. S. Tanner, *Canals of the United States,* 1840, and Coulton's *Atlas of the World,* Vol. 1, 1856.)

Buffalo to New York was $3.70 a ton.[1] In 1925, 2,344,000 tons were carried. If the canal had been used to its capacity—20,000,000 tons—the cost would have been only 52.8 cents a ton. But in spite of many attractions and benefits, and much publicity, the New York shippers prefer to use the railways.

The only other barge canal (except canals as parts of riverways and the intracoastal waterways) now in operation is the 7-foot Hennepin Canal in Illinois that connects the Illinois River with the Mississippi. Its construction was authorized by Congress in 1890. The total cost to June 30, 1934, was about $11,500,000. The annual cost of operation is about $148,000. The annual interest on the capital investment and amortization amounts to $700,000. This plus the $148,000, or $848,000, would have to be reckoned with each year if the canal were a private venture. The total value of the commodities carried on the canal varies from $105,000 to $370,000 a year. The median value is about $250,000. This means that the public of the United States is spending $848,000 a year to move $250,000 worth of commodities for the shippers along the waterway!

Ship canals, like the one in St. Mary's River, because they accommodate large carriers, are in an entirely different category from the almost "extinct" barge canals. The Soo canals carry more tonnage annually than either the Suez or the Panama Canal.

There is some doubt of the feasibility of the proposed trans-Florida Canal whose construction was begun on September 19, 1935. Some doubt the saving of time that is claimed—two and a half days between the Atlantic and the Gulf. It should be remembered that the speed of vessels will need be reduced to 6 or 8 miles an hour and insurance charges will be increased. Numerous expensive bridges must be provided ready for servicing vessels day and night. The freedom of movement on land will be greatly curtailed and the water table lowered in the section of the state crossed. Florida is divided in opinion as to the feasibility of the canal. Congress early in 1936 refused to vote money to continue the project.

ARE THE RIVERWAYS AND BARGE CANALS OUTMODED?

From the scooter-roller skate-tricycle-bicycle stages in life on to the ride we make in the auto hearse, we move and have our being on wheels. A century or so ago men thought of wheeled vehicles as supplementary to the river steamer. We are living in quite a different age.

[1] *Special Report, N. Y. State Department of Public Works,* 1927.

River and canal traffic is slow. Man and goods now move by modern means of land transportation as far in an hour as they did a century ago in a long day. The river was dominant when there was no other form of "rapid transit." It was dominant when speed and efficiency were measured by the ox-cart and the Conestoga wagon. It now is economically possible only where immense quantities of heavy freight with an all-year movement are available and the cost of channel improvement is low. The railway brought about the decline of river transportation because the former was more efficient. Today on short hauls, and on long hauls under certain conditions, the truck and bus are more efficient than the railways, and a large part of our population is turning to them. The river steamboat now has to compete with two modern means of transportation more efficient than it is, as actual experience shows, even considering the new type of river carrier.

Speed is a dominant condition of our age. The speed of locomotives has been materially increased in recent years in the face of competition offered by fast-moving automobiles, auto buses, auto trucks, and airplanes. The rate of movement of freight has been increased. Fast freight express trains that handle package freight have been put on many railways leading out of the great distributing centers. Inexpensive adjustments in design of power units and the widening of the tracks will enable railways greatly to increase their speed. "Streamlining" is an aid. Since water is 800 times as dense as air, it is quite evident that increase of speed of freight carriers on the riverway can be obtained only at a tremendous increase in the consumption of power.[1]

The writer leaves to his readers the answering of the question that heads this section.

THE CANADIAN-AMERICAN ST. LAWRENCE SEAWAY PROJECT

The section of the St. Lawrence involved in this project extends from the eastern end of Lake Ontario to deep water in the harbor of Montreal, a distance of about 250 miles. In it are several stretches of deep water, separated by three groups of rapids, the total length of the rapids being about 43 miles. The Canadian Government long ago constructed canals, six in number, about these rapids, thus making a 14-

[1] The dominance of railways over other "ways" in American transportation is clearly shown in the following data for 1930: freight movement by rail, 2,179,-000,000 tons; through ocean ports, 320,000,000; on the Great Lakes, 125,000,000; on riverways and canals, 50,000,000. (Data from *Statistical Abstracts; Report of National Resources Board,* p. 354.)

foot channel, minimum, for lake and ocean vessels. Most of the locks are only 270 feet between the gates (Fig. 10). The Seaway project involves the enlargement of these canals and locks and the dredging of channels here and there to give a navigable depth of 27, 30, or 33 feet (which depth is not yet decided on). The improvement will require 25 miles of canals in which there will need be 8 or 9 locks.

The new Welland Canal, nearly completed, has lock chambers 859 by 80 by 30 feet and a channel depth between the locks of 25 feet.

Every summer a score or more of European freight boats seek cargoes at the head of Lake Superior. In 1933, 24,000 Canadian and for-

FIG. 10. The La Chine Canal and a Lock, near Montreal, 1935.
Dimensions of lock: 270 feet by 45 feet by 14 feet.

eign vessels passed through these Canadian canals carrying nearly 19,000,000 tons of freight. (Figure 11.)

Canada has spent nearly $130,000,000 on the Welland Canal, and on all its canals for deep-water navigation about $250,000,000. A country with only 11,000,000 population, which has already spent many hundreds of millions on several great railway systems, finds it impossible at present or in the near future to appropriate the money to enlarge the St. Lawrence canals to the dimensions of the new Welland. It cannot spend money profitably on its waterways so long as its railways are in need of more freight to meet their costs of operation.

Shortly after the World War there began an agitation in the Middle West of the United States for better transportation facilities to the seaboards, south, west, and east. Railway rates were too high for profitable agriculture, it was claimed; besides, at times the railways were unable to meet American standards for the rapid movement of commodities. It was then, as stated in previous pages, that provisions were made to increase water transportation facilities. It was under such

FIG. 11. Lake Vessels Unloading Wheat at Montreal, September, 1935.
The size of lake steamers docking at Montreal or ocean vessels entering the Great Lakes is restricted to the dimensions of the St. Lawrence canal locks.

conditions that a St. Lawrence waterway large enough to float the majority of freight-carrying ocean-going vessels was called for. "Make every lake port an ocean port," was the slogan. These conditions and the agitation still prevail.

CHAPTER XV

FLOODS AND FLOOD CONTROL

By Guy-Harold Smith[1]
The Ohio State University

INTRODUCTION

Rivers come into existence as a result of precipitation falling upon the earth's surface, and have as their chief function the drainage of the excess waters to the sea. The lands receive their precipitation at very irregular intervals, and as a result the river with a uniform discharge does not exist. If all precipitation could be absorbed into the earth to become a part of the ground water and then discharged more or less evenly the streams probably could be confined to their channels. But an important proportion of the precipitation never becomes a part of the ground water but flows quickly to the water courses, swelling the streams beyond their constraining banks. The placid stream fed largely by underground waters becomes in times of flood a raging torrent. With its capacity and its competency greatly increased, the river in flood becomes a powerful agent of destruction. Streams vary greatly in their capacity for destruction, but none is without its flood problem.

The fertile alluvial lands of the Nile, the Tigris-Euphrates, the Hwang Ho, and the Mississippi, the creation of their respective rivers, are repeatedly inundated, bringing death to millions and destruction to the works of man. The great rivers are, at the same time, the giver and the destroyer of life and property. In the song, "River Stay 'Way from My Door," are epitomized the fear and the respect of a people for the power of a great river. Smaller streams suffer from recurring floods, and the damage done is locally very great. The flood problem may be said to have its beginning when waters derived from runoff and underground sources spread beyond the restricting channel of the

[1] The author wishes to acknowledge the kind assistance of Professor C. C. Huntington, Ohio State University, who read this chapter and offered a number of constructive suggestions and criticisms.

stream. Actually, torrential rains may produce flooding of local areas by the runoff from highland areas to adjacent lowlands without the water having reached the channels of either permanent or intermittent streams. Usually such floods due to sheet wash are of short duration and cause little water damage. The principal damage is done by rill erosion and by burial of crops by sediments carried down from the adjacent higher ground. But the rapid runoff representing an important proportion of heavy rains is the chief cause of floods, though there may be complicating circumstances.

FLOOD DESTRUCTION

The damage from floods, which appears to be increasing, must be evaluated in terms of rainfall changes, increase in runoff, and the value of the dollars in which the damage is expressed. It appears that the floods are becoming more destructive in the United States, the average anual loss amounting to at least $35,000,000. In 1913 the damage from floods along the Mississippi and Ohio rivers was computed to be in excess of $162,000,000. The unprecedented flood of 1927 within the Mississippi basin caused a total loss of more than $284,000,000. Within the Missouri basin the yearly loss is estimated at $2,800,000. Most of the damage is confined to the headstream areas and particularly along the Kansas River and the lower Missouri. Disastrous floods are not confined to the Mississippi and its major tributaries but are characteristic of practically all the major streams in the United States. Occasionally flood damage is particularly heavy west of the Cascades, within the Sacramento-San Joaquin basin and in the Los Angeles area. In 1927 New England suffered from one of the most disastrous floods of recent years, and in the spring of 1936 heavy rains, falling upon the frozen ground in northeastern United States, locally produced extensive damage. The Atlantic slope from New England to Florida is subject to occasional floods which damage riverine property to the extent of millions of dollars annually. Along the coast of Florida flooding commonly results from the disastrous hurricanes which produce tidal waves along the coast as well as bring heavy rains to the interior.

The predisposition of our people to preempt the rich riverine lands for both agricultural, industrial, and commercial purposes subjects them to the hazards of recurring floods. Railroads annually suffer enormous losses from floods. The railroad builders found the water courses nicely graded and therefore very well suited for the railway lines. Furthermore, many of the engineers, while giving careful consideration to the problems of bridge construction and the location of the tracks, could hardly anticipate the great unprecedented floods. Data on floods and normal stream discharge were lacking or, in many instances, covered such a limited number of years as to give little indication of the flood hazards. As a result the railways have spent millions to replace and relocate bridges and tracks destroyed by floods.

Many of our large cities such as New Orleans, St. Louis, Cincinnati, Nashville, and Pittsburgh were founded upon rivers when the water courses were the principal highways of commerce. The use of the lowlands for industrial and commercial purposes has caused excessive damage at times of flood, due both to the destruction of property and the suspension of business for periods varying from a few days to several weeks, as along the Mississippi in 1927. Lands once used for private purposes are not easily relinquished, for the owners, especially if individual land holders, can hardly afford to abandon the properties to the use of the river. In such areas the recurring floods cause increased damage due to an increase in property values through the years. Urban areas subject to floods are abandoned only with great difficulty, for both industries seeking low land values and people of the low-income class seeking low rentals are likely to locate on these cheaper lands along the river. Protection against floods is sought before abandonment is considered. If protective levees, usually built at public expense, prove adequate, property values increase and the utilization of the land is intensified. Then an unprecedented flood which overtops or breaks through the levees causes enormous damage. The increased property damage in many cities is due to man's encroachment upon the rivers.

In agricultural areas the amount of damage depends upon the season and whether intensive economic use is made of the land. A winter flood may cause little damage to farm lands, but in summer the inundation of the crop lands may greatly reduce the yield or completely ruin the crop. In southern California where the winter season is important for the production of vegetables the occasional winter floods may be very destructive to the intensively cultivated lands. The losses in rural areas are offset in part by the enrichment of the lands by the deposition of silts. The fertile topsoil eroded from the slope lands within the drainage basin is deposited in part along the alluvial plains of the master stream and the major tributaries if they are aggrading streams. In some areas the spreading of coarse sands and gravels along a floodplain may depreciate the value of the land for crops.

PHYSICAL CONDITIONS AFFECTING FLOODS

Causes of Floods. Floods are the result of many conditions working singly or in combination. Usually no single cause can be assigned the whole responsibility. The immediate cause of most floods, however, is the excessive runoff from precipitation of high intensity, though many other conditions may be necessary to cause a great flood. Although most floods are related directly to heavy precipitation and the immediate surface runoff, floods are also caused by dam failures, ice obstructions, high tides, and gales.

Precipitation Features. Rainfall is not a continuous but a recurrent phenomenon. In the United States the results of the occasional rains can be combined into several distinct types. The long-time averages give us the normal annual rainfall régimes for the several sections of the United States. Ward[1] resolved the thousands of individual rainfall records to fourteen major types, but these may be further reduced in number.

In northeastern United States the annual precipitation of 40 to 45 inches of rainfall is quite evenly distributed throughout the year. During each month sufficient precipitation is received to maintain a continuous flow of water in the streams, though occasional droughts may reduce some to insignificant trickles. This is the New England type and is characteristic not only of New England but also of much of the northeastern part of the country.

To the westward the quantity of precipitation is reduced and the régime becomes characterized by a late spring-early summer maximum. Since this distinguishing feature is common to extensive areas within the Missouri basin it is known as the Missouri type. Westward toward the Rocky Mountains the quantity of precipitation is reduced to 10 to 15 inches annually, but the régime remains the same.

Along the Gulf coast the annual precipitation of 55 to 60 inches is so distributed as to produce a monsoon-like maximum in the summer with two periods of minimum rainfall in May and October. This is the north Gulf coast type, which is modified along the south Atlantic coast by the late summer-early autumn hurricanes which displace the summer maximum forward toward the early autumn.

In much of the semiarid and arid interior of North America the seasonal régime of the precipitation is of little significance as a flood factor, for the quantity is so small. The floods are due chiefly to melt-

[1] Robert De C. Ward, *The Climates of the United States*, New York, 1925.

ing snows or to torrential downpours falling upon barren ground or upon steep slopes.

Along the Pacific slope of western United States the numerous rainfall records may be resolved into the north Pacific type and the south Pacific type. Both are characterized by a winter maximum and a summer minimum. Along the north Pacific the months of July and August are usually so dry as to be deficient in moisture, though irrigation is not necessary for general agriculture. In the south Pacific area the winter precipitation is much less than in the north and the summer minimum becomes an extended dry season. Agriculture requires irrigation, and the limited moisture is inadequate for agricultural needs. Floods are generally confined to the rainy season or to the spring and early summer months.

Runoff Characteristics. Every drainage basin has a characteristic runoff pattern, but from year to year there is considerable variation due to the amount and seasonal distribution of precipitation, the rate of melting of the snow cover, and many other conditions. In much of eastern United States the maximum runoff comes in the spring months chiefly because the winter snows upon melting add their contribution to the spring rains and the frozen condition of the ground prevents sink-in. The runoff is usually least in late summer when occasional droughts and high evaporation reduce the amount of water which reaches the streams, and in the mid-winter when sub-freezing temperatures maintain a snow cover, thus delaying runoff until the spring. The winter minimum is quite characteristic of the more northern states because of the severity of the winter season. In the interior of the country where the late spring-early summer maximum is a characteristic feature of the rainfall the maximum discharge of the streams becomes more sympathetic with the rainfall régime. In spite of these variations much of eastern United States is susceptible to spring floods.

In New England, where the precipitation is quite evenly distributed throughout the year, the runoff shows both a spring and an autumn maximum. The most disastrous floods are associated with the melting snows of spring, as illustrated by the floods of early March, 1936, and with the occasional but heavy rains of autumn (Fig. 1).

In the western part of the United States the maximum runoff comes chiefly in the early summer. Along the Pacific coast the winter precipitation may produce floods immediately as was true within the Sacramento basin during the winter of 1936, but usually the precipitation falls as snow in the mountains and is not released until spring and early summer. As the snow fields are reduced the discharge of the streams is greatly diminished by late summer and early autumn except for a few major rivers such as the Colorado, the San Joaquin, the Sacramento, and the Columbia which tap never-failing sources in the mountain areas.

The Intensity of Precipitation. The surface runoff which is the chief source of flood waters is dependent not only upon long-continued precipitation but also upon heavy storms of short duration. A two-inch fall of rain would hardly produce a flood if it fell in a drizzle extending over several days, but if it were concentrated within an hour or two the resulting runoff would in areas of steep slopes produce local

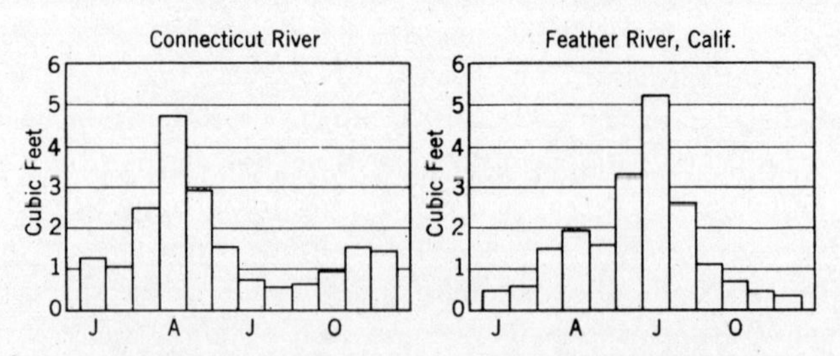

FIG. 1. Runoff Hydrographs for the Connecticut and Feather Rivers.

The ordinates show the average monthly runoff in cubic feet per second per square mile. The Connecticut River shows the spring maximum so characteristic of northeastern United States, and the Feather River illustrates the discharge of rivers along the Sierra Cascades where the melting snows from the high mountains produce an early summer maximum. (After the National Resources Board, Part III, Report of the Water Planning Committee.)

flooding. In a large section of eastern United States a ten-minute rain of more than an inch may be expected once in twenty-five years.[1] Such heavy rains of short duration are the cause of considerable flood damage in limited areas (Fig. 2).

In the Rocky Mountains the floods are of two principal types, namely, those which are due to heavy general rains and those due to the so-called cloudburst type of rainstorm. Rains of the first type are infrequent, and the resulting floods are confined to the principal streams which receive the waters of large drainage areas. The long-continued rains accompanied by rapidly melting snows cause a steady rise in the streams until the flood stage is reached, and then follows gradual retreat to the water course. Such floods are characteristic of the major tributaries of the Missouri such as the Yellowstone, Milk, North and South Platte, and Big Horn rivers. The cloudburst type seems to localize principally in the open basins along the front of the Rocky Mountains and along the valleys within the mountain mass.

[1] David L. Yarnell, "Rainfall Intensity—Frequency Data," United States Department of Agriculture, *Miscellaneous Publication* 204, 1935, p. 33.

The high intensity of the rainfall results in rapid runoff, swelling the local streams to flood proportions. Such floods quickly subside, but their suddenness usually causes heavy damage particularly to roads, railroads, and reclamation projects.

Occasionally the two types are combined into a single flood, for there is no sharp distinction between the two. In the Big Horn Basin the heavy rains of July 21 to 27, 1923, produced an unprecedented flood on the Big Horn as recorded or measured at Thermopolis, Wyoming. The local but heavy showers of July 21 and 22 were followed by veritable cloudbursts on the twenty-third and twenty-fourth. The total fall for the seven-day period is estimated at several inches. The result-

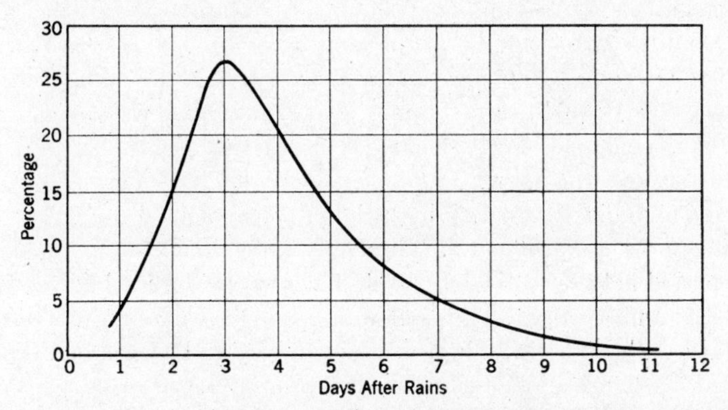

Fig. 2. A Composite Distribution Graph for Eight Storms in the Muskingum River Basin above Dresden, Ohio.

The surface runoff, as shown by the graph, produced the greatest rise in the river on the third day following the precipitation in the tributary area and then gradually declined to normal by the twelfth day. (Data from W. G. Hoyt and others, *Studies of Relations of Rainfall and Runoff in the United States*, United States Geological Survey, Water Supply Paper, No. 772, 1936, p. 141.)

ing flood caused enormous damage, the railroad alone sustaining a loss estimated at more than $1,000,000.

Forms of Precipitation. When precipitation falls as rain we may expect the streams to reflect in their discharge the increased supply of water. But when the precipitation comes in the form of snow there will be no immediate response in the runoff unless the snow is quickly melted. A heavy snow cover lying upon deeply frozen ground or upon well-saturated ground is a potential flood hazard particularly if the melting is rapid and accompanied by a heavy rain.

The impending floods from a dangerously heavy snow cover may be prevented by recurring cold periods which check the runoff. If the night temperatures fall well below freezing the runoff may be so delayed as to give ample time for the flood crest to flatten out. Also short cold periods may be very effective in delaying the runoff set in motion during the warm periods.

In northern United States and in the higher areas in the west, having a cold winter season with temperatures held well below freezing for long periods, spring floods may be expected annually. The severity of the floods may be lessened somewhat when the snow cover is particularly light and when the rate of melting is regulated by periodic freezes which hold the flood waters in check. In New England the winter snows are particularly heavy, and yield upon melting sufficient runoff to cause devastating spring floods. In the period between 1880 and 1933 there were 153 floods recorded for the Merrimac River at Lawrence, Massachusetts. Of this number 44 were in March, 56 in April, 17 in May, and the remaining 36 in the months of June, July, October, November, December, January, and February. Since the precipitation of northeastern United States is quite evenly distributed throughout the year, it is evident that the floods of the Merrimac are due in a large measure to melting snow.

The Columbia River deriving a large proportion of its waters from melting snow was in flood at The Dells, Oregon, 120 times in the 57-year period between 1878 and 1934. The month of June had 51 floods; May, 31; and April, 21. The remaining 14 floods came in the months of January, February, March, July, November, and December. The increased discharge of the Columbia River in late spring and early summer is due very largely to the progressive melting of the snow in the mountain sections of the drainage basin.

Configuration of the Terrain within the Watershed. On relatively flat lands each field becomes to a limited extent a catchment basin retarding the discharge of water to the water courses. Water drains slowly from the lands of low relief, giving time for the stream to discharge its waters continuously within its confining channel, unless successive storms fall upon the saturated ground. The excess water from these later storms cannot be absorbed and quickly seeks the water course endangering the riverine property when the stream passes flood stage. In areas of low relief and gentle slopes runoff is delayed sufficiently to permit infiltration, but in regions of steep slopes there is a rapid streamward movement of the surface water unless precipitation is light and spread out sufficiently to give time for infiltration to the subsurface reservoir of underground waters. In rugged areas with steep slopes torrential rains usually are accompanied by rapid runoff and a flooding of the low lands along the water courses. A heavy protecting cover of vegetation may somewhat reduce the runoff and consequently the flood damage, but forested areas are not free from floods. All other factors being equal, the steeper slopes in a drainage basin yield the greater surface runoff.

In the Red River basin as measured at Grand Forks, North Dakota, the annual precipitation averages approximately 21 inches and the surface runoff is only 1.25 inches. The light rains in the area no doubt are partly responsible for the low runoff, though the chief consideration is the extremely flat terrain. For the Mississippi basin above Keokuk, Iowa, the precipitation averages 29.51 inches, of which 6.98 inches or approximately 23 per cent are lost by surface runoff. Here the slightly more rugged terrain and the increased precipitation are conducive to a greater runoff than is characteristic of the nearly level Red River plain. As illustrated by the Tennessee River, the steeper slopes of the southern Appalachians cause even greater runoff. The proportion escaping to the streams without having become a part of the ground water reaches nearly half of the average precipitation of 50.36 inches.

Shape of the Watershed. By *a priori* reasoning a circular watershed with the several tributaries joining the main stream at or near a common point would be conducive to floods at times of wide-spread and heavy rains. In eastern United States general rains covering extensive areas are common enough to be an important cause of floods. Recurring storms in a more or less circular drainage basin would result in a simultaneous discharge of the tributaries into the master stream, probably resulting in flood damage. The Ohio drainage basin, though not circular in area, is commonly subjected to extensive storms which produce floods along the master stream. The several major tributaries contribute to the Ohio enormous quantities of water which on occasion inundates the low lands along the river.

If the whole drainage basin of any river system is subject to general and recurring storms, floods may be expected along the master stream no matter what the shape of the watershed. In long linear basins a single storm of high intensity may produce a flood in a limited section of the stream, and unless there are reinforcements from other sources the flood crest might flatten out sufficiently to recede to the channel in the downstream section of the main stream (Fig. 3).

Also, floods on such major streams as the Mississippi, the Missouri, the Ohio, the Columbia, and the Susquehanna may be caused by a number of storms so distributed within the watershed and spaced at the proper time intervals as to result in the coincidence of crests in the lower course of the master stream. This was true of the 1933 flood

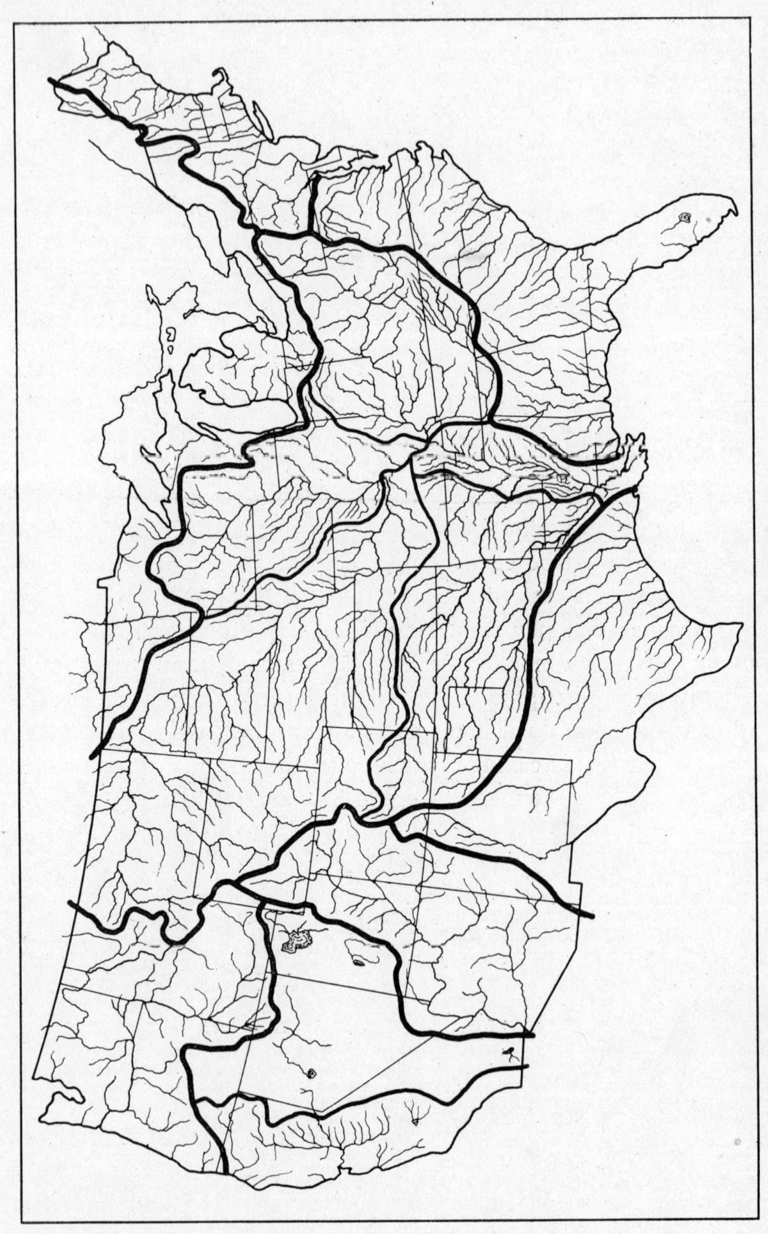

Fig. 3. Major Drainage Regions of the United States. (After National Resources Board, Part III, Report of the Water Planning Committee.)

of the Ohio River[1] when general rains over the drainage basin had saturated the ground and filled the channel. An earlier storm of March 13 to 15 moving eastward across the Ohio basin yielded its greatest precipitation in the Wheeling area. A few days later a second storm followed, accompanied by heavy rains centered over the lower Miami valleys and the Cincinnati area, and as a result the flood crests from the two areas reached Cincinnati simultaneously.

Soil and Rock Conditions. Floods occur because the soil is unable to absorb the precipitation as fast as it falls or before it escapes as sheet wash to the water courses. This failure to absorb the water depends upon the nature of the soil, slope, degree of saturation, the amount and intensity of the precipitation, and other conditions. Where the surface soil consists of coarse sands and gravels which permit a high proportion of the precipitation to infiltrate to the underground reservoir, floods seldom occur unless the ground is saturated or frozen, or the intensity is so great that excessive runoff results. In the coastal plain of the Atlantic and Gulf coasts where the underlying formations are particularly porous, there is little danger from floods of local origin. Though much of the area receives an annual precipitation of 40 to 60 inches, the surface materials readily absorb a high proportion of the rainfall.

In the Great Lakes states where the glacial drift consists of sand and gravel the danger from floods is not great. Here also the slight relief of the glacial landscape is conducive to infiltration. These sandy and gravelly areas are particularly characteristic of Michigan, central and northern Wisconsin, and northeastern Minnesota.

Where the surface soil is clayey and more or less impervious to infiltration, the runoff will be heavy in all storms of great intensity. Usually such areas suffer extensive denudation from sheet wash and rill erosion, and great quantities of soil are carried to the water courses. In the Piedmont and the southern Appalachians both the surface soil and the underlying crystalline rocks have limited storage capacity, and, as a result, the many rivers are subject to flood. The heavy rainfall of the Appalachian Mountains throughout the year results in a continuous discharge of the many streams, so that at times of heavy storms destructive floods spread beyond the protecting channels and progress seaward causing damage in the Coastal Plain, where floods of local origin are rather uncommon. The most disastrous floods are in-

[1] Wallace T. Buckley, "The Ohio River Flood of March, 1933," *Ohio Journal of Science*, Vol. 35, 1935, p. 75.

herited from the Appalachians and are confined to the major streams which rise in the crystalline areas to the west and north.

Orientation of Rivers. The orientation of streams is a significant factor in the flooding of the adjacent flood plains. In Siberia the northward course of the Ob, the Yenisei, and the Lena result in flooding because spring comes to the head stream areas while the northern and downstream sections are still frozen. In North America the Mackenzie presents a similar situation, except that the larger lakes tend to flatten out the crest of the floods. This condition causes the inundation of extensive areas along these streams in late spring and early summer. To a limited extent the Red River of the North is affected in a similar manner because of its south to north orientation. Fortunately very few major rivers in the United States are so oriented as to suffer from the type of floods so characteristic of the great Siberian rivers.

In much of continental United States the general rains of cyclonic origin and the local thunderstorms move from the west toward the east. Stream courses such as the lower Ohio, the lower Missouri, and many others which are so oriented as to receive the torrential rains successively in different parts of their course suffer from the resulting floods. Water courses which are oriented transverse to the path of the local thunderstorms may escape serious damage, for the flooded area would be somewhat restricted.

Physiographic Aspects of Floods. Streams which are lowering their courses into bedrock usually are bordered by rather steep slopes and the flood waters do not inundate extensive areas. And many streams which flow on more gentle gradients are commonly bordered by narrow alluvium-covered flats which are subject to limited flooding when the river rises above the protecting banks. Along such streams little damage results from inundation, but bridges, roads, and other structures which lie close upon the river suffer from the rush of the flood waters.

The recent erosional history in northeastern United States, disturbed as it has been by glacial and post-glacial changes in level, has been characterized by a Pleistocene filling of once deeper valleys. This partial filling was terminated at the close of the glacial period, and a reexcavation of the valleys began. The erosion of this alluvial material has produced a series of terraces along many streams with the main stream confined to a meandering channel within a low floodplain. In the lower sections of a valley the terraces are most numerous and upstream may converge to only one, or in some instances be non-existent. In the upstream section the incision made in the alluvial plain may have served to limit the flooded areas at times when the stream spread beyond its confining channel. The single but low terrace was a haven of refuge from the flood waters. With the settlement of the land and the clearing of the forest, runoff has increased, carrying with it sufficient soil to fill the shallow incision in the alluvial plain thus setting the stage for more extensive damage in times of subsequent floods. Along the lower sections of such terrace-bordered streams the narrow floodplain is frequently inundated, but the flood damage is confined to the lower plain, the terrace areas being high enough to escape inundation.

The efforts of the Soil Conservation Service and other agencies to check runoff by the construction of weirs across gullies serve the dual function of preventing and reducing soil erosion and rapid runoff at the same time. The checking of the runoff should also prevent the deposition position of coarse débris over the near-by alluvial plains. In many rugged areas the best agricultural land is to be found along the alluvial lands of the master stream and its major tributaries. When the forests were cut from the adjacent slope lands runoff was increased and as a result the capacity and the competency of the streams were increased. Sand, gravel, and even large boulders were carried downstream in torrential currents and strewn across the alluvial lowlands, thus reducing if not destroying the agricultural utility of the land. A protective cover on the slope lands will do much to prevent the despoliation of these limited areas of agricultural lands.

Rivers such as the Mississippi, Missouri, Red, Illinois, and many others flow seaward on a broad alluvial plain. Where the gradient is very low the stream follows a meandering course. The most notable example of such a stream in the United States is the lower Mississippi, though meanders are characteristic of streams of all sizes.

The large streams which flow along broad alluvial plains are commonly bordered by important natural levees of their own creation. The streams in time of flood spread beyond their banks, and as their velocity is checked a thin veneer of sediment is deposited in a narrow strip along the water course. By repeated floodings this river-side strip is built up into a protecting natural levee. The river is then confined, except for the major floods, between the protecting levees. The land slopes away from the river to low-lying back swamps partially drained by smaller rivers which flow more or less parallel to the master stream. Such streams are known as the Yazoo type, the name being derived from the stream of that name in the alluvial plain of the Mississippi above Vicksburg.

Since the natural levees which border the streams are made by the rivers it may be expected that in times of great flood the flood waters will rise above the levees and inundate extensive areas between the levees and the back swamps. Where the levees are low or weak the flood waters may break through to the back swamp areas by way of crevasses.

The system of meanders is continually shifting as the river erodes the banks on the outer bends. This weakens the protecting levee, and in time of high water there is always the danger that crevasses will be formed. By this process of levee building and silting of the back swamp areas the alluvial plain is built up with the main stream swinging slowly across the plain and the meanders moving progressively downstream.

The seaward extension of the delta of the Mississippi results in a gradual lengthening of the stream. As a consequence the river bottom is built up slightly to maintain the necessary gradient. Subsequently floods will build up the adjacent levees, confining all but the greatest floods to the levee-bordered channel. A great river flowing seaward is a powerful physiographic agent ever changing the configuration of its alluvial plain.

FLOOD CONTROL

To escape from the danger of floods various control measures either singly or in combination have been utilized to provide the necessary protection. Probably one of the earliest methods used to escape from floods was to evacuate the area at the first warnings of impending danger. Flight to safe areas could hardly be interpreted as flood protection, but it did mean the protection of life and a limited amount of property. This method still is used when there is a failure of other protective measures. Throughout the history of civilized man the fertile alluvial lowlands have been preferred areas of habitation; and, as high water menaced periodically the homes of the people, the protecting dike or levee became one of the first methods of defense against floods.

Channel Improvements. One of the simplest and most individual methods of flood protection is channel improvement. Along relatively small streams riparian owners may without a great deal of expense improve a stream channel by clearing out obstructions such as brush and trees. Accumulated débris from previous floods may be removed, facilitating the discharge of flood waters, thus preventing the stream from overspreading its banks and inundating adjacent lands. This simple method is usually accompanied by a straightening of the channel by cutting across meanders and other sharp bends in the river. The clearing and straightening of the channel make for a rapid discharge of the flood waters, preventing inundation of riverine properties.

Such local flood-prevention methods are effective unless the stream is aggrading its channel and building up its floodplain. In such cases the puny efforts of man may be wasted in a futile attempt to prevent flood damage. A stream that is building up its course will continue to do so in spite of local protective works. The control of such a stream will require preventive works in the headstream areas and perhaps along the lower course of the stream as well.

Along the streams which are not aggrading, improvements along the water course are most effective. Channel straightening has the effect of steeping the gradient, thus increasing the velocity. The stream is then able to carry along its course both a larger quantity of sediment and larger fragments. Unless it is loaded to capacity it will deepen and perhaps widen its channel sufficiently to carry the water of subsequent floods if the course is not allowed to become clogged by débris and to revert to its former circuitous condition.

Local improvements in the channel planned to protect only the adjacent property may actually increase the flood hazard downstream. Improvements designed to facilitate the rapid downstream movement of water along the tributaries will contribute to the flood crests along the master stream. It is because of the conflicts of interests within a drainage basin that all flood-control works should be coordinated, so that preventive measures applied in one area may not nullify the works in another.

Protection by Levees. Levees are very commonly associated with other local preventive measures used along the smaller streams as well as along such major streams as the Mississippi and the Missouri. Short levees are usually constructed where the banks are low to maintain a uniform channel height. Channel straightening will require fill-ins and protecting levees to make sure that the stream in time of flood is confined to its new channel. Along streams which have been gauged over a long period of time the flood crests may be so well known that protective dikes may be constructed to contain all floods between them. In such cases the levees or dikes should not be placed too close to the river's edge, but set back somewhat, leaving room for other preventive works along the stream and providing a safety margin in anticipation of unprecedented floods. Such a system of protecting dikes will require a correlated system along the tributaries and a series of gates to provide for the drainage of the lowlands outside of the dikes in time of low water. In times of flood the gates will have to be closed, preventing drainage of the lowlands. To avoid local inundation it may be necessary to install pumping machinery to lift the water over the levee to the main stream.

The confinement of a river between closely spaced levees creates a dangerous situation because the flood waters, no longer having access to the floodplain, rise above former crest levels, increasing the danger of breaks or crevasses. This danger may be lessened somewhat by a scouring and a deepening of the channel which becomes a restricted floodway in time of high water. At the time a river is in flood and restricted to a levee-protected channel the increased velocity, while it scours and enlarges the channel, eats away the banks, forming crevasses through which the flood waters may escape to the low back swamps. Temporarily at least levees give protection to riverine property, but not all students are agreed upon the effectiveness of the method.

Levees as a protective device have been most extensively used along the lower Mississippi, but they are necessary along many of the major tributaries such as the Red, the Arkansas, and the Illinois. Many of our principal cities are located upon the larger rivers, and wherever there is likely to be extensive damage to valuable urban property by inundation protecting levees are constructed. Though rather inexpensive, the levees, if properly constructed and maintained, may give adequate protection against all floods except those classed as the great and unprecedented floods.

It is estimated that the flood damage along the Illinois River averages more than $2,000,000 annually. The water course is protected by a costly system of levees which in many places are located too close to the river, resulting in disastrous breaks and extensive inundation. The fertility of the plain invited settlement of lands which should have been dedicated to the river. Because of the high cost involved in the maintenance of the system of levees, limited areas once used for farms have reverted to their former condition and now are used for floodways and game refuges. What is true of the Illinois is also true of the Mississippi, except that the scale is greater both in the levee system required and in the destruction of property when the levees fail.

Along the Red, the Arkansas, the White, and the Ouachita rivers the construction of levees has given inadequate protection to more than 2,000,000 acres of alluvial lands. The system of levees needs to be reorganized and coordinated into a unified project not only for the sake of the 2,000,000 acres now receiving partial protection but also to give increased security to the 7,000,000 acres subject to inundation in times of high floods.

Levees along the Mississippi River. Levee construction along the Mississippi was begun at New Orleans in 1717.[1] The first single mile of levee was gradually extended upstream, the individual planters assuming responsibility for their respective sections along the river. Since the early settlers along the Mississippi were interested in navigation as well as flood protection, the levees were so placed as to serve the dual function of facilitating commerce and of giving protection to the rich alluvial lands.

Recurring floods along the river called for additional levees constructed chiefly by riparian land holders, by counties, parishes, levee boards, and the several states. But it soon became evident that adequate protection was beyond the means of the local organizations. There were many acres which, because of sparse population and limited resources, were unable to assume their full share of the responsibility, and as a result flood waters overtopping the natural levees spread downstream inundating farm lands locally well protected. As a result of the lack of coordination of the levee systems and the absence of protective works in the sections still remaining in the public domain, there developed very early a movement for flood control by the federal government. Government aid came first somewhat indirectly by two acts of Congress, the first in 1849 and the second in 1850, by which the swamp and flooded areas were ceded to several states with the provision that the revenue derived from the sale of such land was to be used for drainage and for flood protection.

The ever-growing levee system was severely tested by the disastrous flood of 1859, which destroyed important sections of the system. Before adequate repairs could be made the Civil War, like a series of destructive floods, had as one of its unfortunate consequences a deterioration of the levees. And during the reconstruction period recurring floods culminating in the great flood of 1882 aroused the nation to the need for adequate protection. In 1879 Congress created the Mississippi River Commission which became the federal agency for carrying out the program of flood control, though the first money appropriated for use by the Commission was for the improvement of the river for navigation, and flood protection was only an incidental matter.

The Commission after careful study of the problem, established the standards for levee construction and otherwise cooperated with local

[1] Andrew A. Humphreys and Henry L. Abbot, *Report upon the Physics and Hydraulics of the Mississippi River,* War Department, Washington, 1874, p. 150.

agencies, such as levee boards, in providing the necessary protection. Specifications for levees and other control works have been revised from time to time, but its continual efforts toward standardization and coordination of systems have resulted in constructive though inadequate protective works, as was demonstrated by the great floods of 1922 and 1927.

Spillways and Floodways. The natural history of a river confined to a levee-protected course includes not only an overtopping of the levees in time of flood but also the breaking of wide gaps in the levees permitting the flood waters to escape to the back swamp areas. It seems logical to conclude that a similar method as an adjunct to the levee system would be a recognition of the natural behavior of a river. The creation of breaks or crevasses in the natural levee permits the river to use the back swamp area to lower the flood crest.

Recognizing that a large river may at times need more of the floodplain than is available between the levees, an additional floodway may be provided in the lower back swamp areas. Such floodways should be protected by dikes and coordinated with the levee system of the master stream and its major tributaries. The use of well-protected floodways should be an effective method of lessening the danger of breaks in the levees where too much water is confined to a narrow water course. Old crevasses might be used for the spillways through which the waters may be diverted to the floodways. This adaptation of the man-modeled water courses to the natural courses of the river is a recognition of the natural behavior of the river.

In the lower section of the Mississippi the river is held in between high natural and artificial levees. The water which seeps through or overtops the levee does not return to the river but flows to the Gulf of Mexico by way of the Atchafalaya River and the Bayou Lafourche. The latter is a levee-guarded channel extending from Donaldsonville, Louisiana, to near the Gulf. This condition along the lower Mississippi illustrates how the diversion of waters from the main stream may lower flood crests in the downstream section of the river and for a limited distance upstream.

The Mississippi River Commission from its inception in 1879 to 1927, when the greatest flood known in the history of America inundated 23,573 square miles,[1] stood rather rigidly for a system of flood control consisting of levees only. One important reason for this plan was the matter of cost. After the 1927 flood the Commission's policy was broadened to include a more comprehensive scheme of levees as a

[1] *Monthly Weather Review,* Supplement 29, 1927, p. 34.

first line of defense to be supplemented by spillways, and perhaps reservoirs, and other protective measures.

Retarding Basins. The problem of flood protection may be partially solved by the use of preventive works in the headstream area of a drainage basin. If the runoff could be checked sufficiently to prevent the waters resulting from torrential rains from reaching the water courses too promptly, flood danger could be reduced greatly. To check the runoff sufficiently to prevent or even reduce materially the danger of floods is almost impossible under present methods of land use. Since the staying of the runoff is almost beyond control, retarding dams may be used so to flatten out the flood crests that damaging floods may be averted. The retarding dam is usually constructed of earth except for the spillway or the gateway and so designed that local flood waters accumulate behind the dam and are discharged automatically, maintaining a bank-full condition along the water course. A series of retarding dams functioning in such a manner may be a very effective means of preventing floods. If such retarding basins are equipped with outlet structures and control gates the normal emptying progress may be arrested. This use of control gates increases materially the effectiveness of the retarding reservoir as a flood-control measure.

After the Dayton flood of 1913 the Miami Conservancy District of Ohio was organized to protect the valley from such disastrous floods. This was accomplished by the construction of a series of five retarding dams across the Great Miami River and its tributaries. Two of the dams are on the Miami and Loramie Creek above Dayton, two are on the Mad and the Stillwater which join the Miami at Dayton, and the fifth is on Twin Creek, which enters the Miami above Middletown. This flood project with its retarding dams, levees, and channel improvements has been regarded as one of the most successful flood-control methods, though there has been no flood equal to the 1913 inundation to test its effectiveness.

The success of the retarding dams in the Miami basin has resulted in the adoption of a similar method of flood control in the Muskingum Watershed Conservancy District, though storage reservoirs to impound the flood waters are provided for in the latter plan.

Storage Reservoirs. The construction of storage reservoirs for flood prevention alone is a rather costly method of control unless the reservoirs may be used for other purposes such as water supply, power, recreation, and the regulation of the low water level of the master stream. The reservoirs which now serve as flood-prevention works were in most instances constructed for other purposes and flood control was a secondary though important consideration. For example, the Wilson Dam on the Tennessee was constructed for power purposes, but it also regulates the flow of the lower course of the river. In the Cascades and the Sierras the many dams constructed for power purposes and for the storage of irrigation water minimize somewhat the flood hazards resulting from melting snows. Such dams not only reduce the flood crests but may also improve the low-water stage of the river.

The construction of many small dams in the headstream area of certain of our major streams not only will serve as flood prevention but provide recreational opportunities as well. The public preference for waterside facilities for recreation is based upon the benefits derived from a refreshing swim in water decidedly cooler than the hot, stifling air of summer. If the stored water is not needed for drinking purposes these numerous reservoirs might be used by a large number of persons if they are easily accessible to the public.

The construction of a sufficient number of reservoirs for adequate flood control by prevention is beyond the means of the nation, but where the reservoirs may serve other purposes there may be some justification for the expenditures of public moneys. The use of a reservoir for more than one purpose introduces commonly a conflict of interests; for example, to serve best in the prevention of floods a reservoir should be empty, but for the production of power it should be maintained as nearly full as possible. Also for recreation purposes the water level should be maintained near the maximum level in order that beaches and recreational facilities may be kept in good condition. The reservoirs used principally for the storage of irrigation waters serve very effectively for flood-prevention works for the reason that when the danger of spring floods is greatest the reservoirs are being filled. Usually at the beginning of the period of excessive runoff either from rains or from melting snows the reservoirs are empty and their capacity for additional storage is greatest. As the rainy season begins to wane, the reservoirs become filled, and the water is then discharged for irrigation purposes. Thus two important functions are served by the same reservoir without either making concessions to the other.

In order that reservoirs may have a long life and serve the function of flood prevention, efforts should be made to prevent their silting up. The drainage basin above a reservoir should be so protected from erosion that maximum capacity of the reservoir can be maintained. If the runoff carries great quantities of sediment into the ponded waters of the reservoir, the capacity may be greatly reduced. Not all sedimentation can be prevented, but if the watershed is forested or grass covered the load of silt carried by the stream is reduced to a minimum.

To be most effective reservoirs should not be placed too far upstream, for such placement will require more dams and will intercept only a small proportion of the runoff. A downstream location as near as possible to the area to be protected is to be preferred. One major dam across the master stream just above the area subjected to floods will give greater protection probably than ten smaller dams in the headstream area. It is not recommended, however, that the large dams be substituted for small dams in the tributary areas but that a coordinated system of reservoirs be considered not only for flood prevention but for other water needs as well.

Forests and Floods. It has been often stated that a forest cover in a drainage basin materially reduces floods but forested areas are not free from the hazard of flood damage. There is conclusive evidence that the eastern tributaries of the Mississippi and the lower section of the master stream suffered from great floods before the land was settled and the forest was largely removed. Although the effect of forests upon runoff has often been overstated their effectiveness should not be depreciated.

Adequate flood protection is largely dependent upon engineering structures, but the forest cover should be considered as a supplementary protective measure. A closely forested area with its absorptive leaf-litter delays runoff somewhat and gives greater seasonal uniformity to the discharge of the streams.

> The litter-covered forest floor is generally recognized as the best protection against erosion of soil. . . . A mere comparison of the forest soil made porous by these agents and by the penetration of tree roots, with the packed soil of adjacent fields will convince any one of the value of this cover in retarding runoff.[1]

This slight retardation of runoff may serve to reduce floods provided the subsequent rains are delayed a sufficient length of time to permit the lowering of the water table and a drying out of the litter. If the absorptive capacity of both the litter and the soil is reduced because of saturation heavy recurrent storms will cause floods. Probably the most important effect of the forest cover is not in its effect upon surface runoff but upon its protection of the soil, which in rugged areas is susceptible of removal, and when both the forest cover and the absorptive topsoil have been removed, all rains, no matter what their

[1] E. F. McCarthy, "Forest Cover as a Factor in Flood Control," *American Society of Civil Engineers, Trans.*, Vol. 93, 1929, pp. 718-719.

spacing, yield rapid runoff. These indirect results are of major importance in the prevention of floods and in the maintenance of reservoir capacity whether the reservoirs be used for flood prevention or for other purposes.

THE RESPONSIBILITY FOR FLOOD CONTROL

Introduction. The control of floods is a responsibility which extends beyond the limits of the inundated areas. The calamitous floods of the Mississippi and other major streams of the United States always arouse wide-spread public interest in the causes of floods and their control. To charge the whole cost of protective works to the immediate beneficiaries would burden them with taxes beyond their capacity to pay. Obversely, to charge the cost to people who in no way receive any of the benefits directly from flood control is to misplace the responsibility for control. These two conflicting concepts can be harmonized by expecting the local beneficiaries to accept a share of the costs in proportion to their capacity to pay and charging the remaining costs to the general public by means of federal and state taxation. In this way the per capita cost of flood control is so small that the individual willingly assumes his share of the national responsibility.

Floods have no respect for political jurisdictions, just as political boundaries show little relation to hydrographic boundaries. Since flooded areas seldom coincide precisely with political areas the existing minor civil divisions such as townships and counties are unable individually to cope with the flood problem. This inadequacy of the political units as originally delimited has led to the organization of levee boards, conservancy districts, water control boards, reclamation districts, and other legally constituted bodies for the practical solution of many water problems including the control of floods. In the case of the lower Mississippi the magnitude of the problem transcends the local jurisdictions and consequently becomes invested with a public interest national in scope.

Individual Responsibility. The flood problem begins with the formation of a tiny rivulet in the farmer's field. Its control is both a personal and a social responsibility. His personal interest is not confined to the hazard of floods on his farm but to the associated loss of soil as the runoff gathers into rivulets which converge into larger and more devastating streams, producing both water and soil damage.

The individual landowner, though he may have a humanitarian interest in the flood hazards of the drainage basin in which he lives, can do little toward the solution of the problem, especially if he lives beside a large stream. In rural areas where streams are small individual farmers may by channel improvements and the construction of levees give protection to their low-lying lands. The clearing of a stream channel of driftwood, trees, and other obstructions may so facilitate the flow during high water that the channel is widened, thus increasing its capacity.

The individual interest may be inimicable to the public interest, however, in the matter of flood control. The farmer who hastens the downstream movement of water across his farm may be contributing to floods in the lower section of the river. With an understanding of his individual responsibility the farmer may by altering his farm practice so delay runoff as to contribute toward the solution of the flood problem, and all farmers working collectively may materially reduce flood crests in downstream areas.

Imperceptibly the personal responsibility of many individuals enlarges to a regional responsibility coextensive with each important drainage basin. If the whole watershed lies within a single state the flood-control agency or conservancy district might be organized under the laws of the state, and if the problem be of sufficient moment might deserve the blessing of the state in the form of financial aid.

Regional Aspects of Flood Control. Planning for the best use of water resources is essentially a regional responsibility, the region being coincident with the drainage basin of the streams concerned. This concept of the planning region cannot be adhered to rigidly, for the transmission of water power in the form of electricity and the distribution of water for irrigation and municipal purposes extend far beyond the limits of the drainage basin, and require a modification of the hydrographic region to include adjacent areas which constitute the peripheral sections of an economic region (Fig. 3).

The problem of flood control, however, is rather strictly confined to the drainage basin. So long as control measures involve only riverine works the plan would require the cooperation of river-side communities, but as control is extended to include preventive measures the whole drainage basin should be organized into a unit. The obstacles which make difficult the realization of this ideal are many, and probably will stand in the way of a strictly regional organization based upon the hydrographic basin. Practically this ideal may not be necessary, for levee boards, conservancy districts, and other water control organizations may serve as the legally constituted agencies to deal with state and federal authorities.

The Responsibility of the States. Where a drainage basin lies entirely within a single state a conservancy district or flood control board may be authorized by the legislature or by a conservation board charged with the responsibility of handling the many water problems of the state. The State of Texas has recently provided for the Brazos River Conservation and Reclamation District in order that the several water problems may be solved under a single authority.

Flood problems which involve two or more states may require interstate cooperation in order that a flood-control program may be extended to all parts of the drainage basin. The cooperation should include not only an interstate agreement but also a uniformity of laws to facilitate the work of the organization charged with the responsibility of flood control. Such interstate pacts are rather difficult to secure for the reason that the benefits to be derived from flood-protection works are not equally distributed among the several states. The apportionment of costs in a manner which appears equitable to one state will not be acceptable to another. Flood-prevention works such as storage reservoirs may be located in one state and the area thereby protected from floods may lie to another. An interstate compact which would provide an acceptable distribution of costs is difficult to attain. In addition to the economic difficulties the legal requirement of authorization and ratification of interstate compacts by Congress and the legislatures of the states concerned practically precludes their wide use. One of the most notable interstate agreements is the Colorado River compact involving the interests of seven states. Flood control was, however, a minor consideration in the negotiations of this interstate compact. The engineering aspects of this problem are relatively simple. The placement of engineering works and other preventive measures can be determined without unnecessary conflicts of opinion, but an equitable distribution of benefits and a fair apportionment of costs are very difficult matters to adjust.

Conservancy districts authorized by a single state may be empowered to borrow money to carry out a flood-control program and levy assessments against the benefited properties to finance the project. The state's responsibility extends to a supervision of the financing operations and the retirement of the outstanding bonds. Where the cost of protecting bottom lands is so high that farmers have difficulty in making payments the state should maintain a conservative policy in authorizing flood-control projects. Only those projects which are self-liquidating or in which there is an important public interest should be authorized. It may be necessary to appropriate what appear to be unduly large sums to protect such utilities as water-supply plants in order that there be no interruption of the service. For such purposes excessive expenditures may be justified, but there should be a careful scrutiny of all flood-control plans to make certain that the benefits to be gained equal or exceed the cost of the protective works.

In those projects in which the federal government is a participant the responsibilities may be shared by the two jurisdictions. Whatever may be the share assumed by the federal government, the state can best undertake the purchase of right of way, flowage rights, the relocation of roads, and the settlement of damage claims. The representatives of the state can negotiate with local property owners to better advantage than can the federal government. The landowners are disposed to accept the evaluation of their property as fair and just if made by their neighbors and friends who are familiar with local values, and at the same time the government benefits both by lower costs and by the resulting good will created by fair evaluations.

Federal Responsibility. During the early history of the United States the many functions of the federal government did not extend to the construction of flood-control projects, partly because such works were not considered within the jurisdiction of the government. Flood damage was restricted in area, and, so far as protection or control was regarded as a public responsibility, the costs were shared locally by the beneficiaries of the protective works. But as recurring floods inundated an increasing acreage of valuable farm lands along the lower Mississippi there developed a strong sentiment in favor of the federal government's assuming a share of the financial burden.

Where state boundaries transect a watershed, interstate cooperation becomes necessary to control floods. Federal responsibility begins first with the government's control of legally navigable streams where state and national cooperation are essential to an effective control program. The navigation needs and the flood-control requirements should be welded into a common program. The collateral uses of water should also be given careful consideration in any flood-control project. Though there may be some conflicts in purpose as represented in the construction of reservoirs, the essential unity of the flood-control problem and that of the conservation of water must be recognized.

It required many years for the concept of national responsibility to develop, but the magnitude and recurrence of the Mississippi floods kept the question before the public. After each great flood the people of the lower Mississippi appealed to Congress for aid. Among many people there was some doubt as to the constitutional authority for the federal government to undertake the building of levees for the protection of private property. With the creation of the Mississippi River Commission in 1879 the United States government began to participate actively in the program of flood control, though the first moneys expended were primarily for the improvement of navigation and flood protection was an incidental consideration. Therefore the federal government entered upon a program of flood control under the guise of the constitutional authority to promote navigation.[1] With the settlement of the rich alluvial lands along such rivers as the Mississippi, the Sacramento, and other major streams, and the development of our complex system of railroads, highways, and postal system, the federal government became empowered under the commerce clause to build flood-control works to maintain and facilitate interstate commerce. The early doubts on the constitutional authority have largely been removed and the government has extended its jurisdiction to include flood-prevention projects in the headstream areas.

After the great Mississippi flood of 1927 the people of the United States were awakened to the need for a comprehensive plan of protection against the recurrence of such a disaster. The limited participation of the federal government of the period immediately after the establishment of the Mississippi River Commission has been extended. From this limited participation responsibility has been expanded to an assumption of 100 per cent of the costs of labor and materials in the construction of levees and other protective works.

As the question of constitutional authority has been settled and as engineers have come to recognize that flood control involves also flood prevention, government participation has moved upstream from flooded areas to the headstream areas. Every great flood on the lower Mississippi is related to a flood of major proportions on the Ohio, though a flood on the Ohio does not always cause a flood on the lower Mississippi.[2] With a recognition of the importance of the Ohio as a contributing cause of floods on the lower Mississippi, there has developed a sentiment for flood-prevention works in the headwater area of the Ohio Basin, and the federal government is participating in the control works.

The Tennessee Valley Authority, though it is a plan involving multiple objectives, will by its system of reservoirs control the flow of the Tennessee River. In a similar manner the Muskingum Watershed Con-

[1] National Resources Board, Part III, *Report of the Water Planning Committee,* Washington, 1934, p. 378.
[2] *Monthly Weather Review,* Supplement 29, 1927, p. 7.

servancy District with its several reservoirs and retarding dams is primarily a flood-control project, though other water uses are included in the plan. The Tennessee Valley Authority is chiefly a federal project, but the Muskingum Watershed Conservancy District is being financed jointly by the federal government, the State of Ohio, and the District. In these two projects is epitomized the government's participation in the flood-control works now being constructed in the headstream areas.

In order to circumvent the extravagant use of federal money for flood-control works the Water Planning Committee of the National Resources Board recommended

> . . . the policy of requiring appropriate contributions from localities benefited as a most satisfactory general test whether a particular project is meritorious.

The Committee further recommended

> . . . that federal contributions be made (*a*) only where there is reasonable protection against maximum floods; (*b*) only where the total benefits justify the expense; (*c*) only where there are responsible and legally constituted authorities with which to deal; (*d*) to an extent not greater than 30 per cent of cost of labor and materials where the benefits are chiefly local; (*e*) to an extent greater than 30 per cent only in proportion to benefits definitely applicable to recognized national interests; (*f*) to a full 100 per cent only where the benefits are almost wholly of national interest.[1]

The above recommendations refer only to the construction of flood-control works during normal times and cannot be applied rigidly during an economic emergency when public-works projects must be authorized to give work to the unemployed.

International Control of Floods. Fortunately the boundaries of the United States are so located that the problem of floods is not beyond the control of man. An important section of the Canadian boundary lies within the Great Lakes-St. Lawrence system which is relatively free from floods. Our conflicts with Canada have involved the low-water stages of the Great Lakes rather than high levels. The diversion of water from Lake Michigan for the purpose of sewage disposal at Chicago has at times of low-water stages on the Great Lakes drawn vigorous protests from Canada.

Another section of the Canadian boundary, from Lake of the Woods to the Rocky Mountains, lies across a region of slight rainfall where

[1] National Resources Board, Part III, *Report of the Water Planning Committee,* Washington, 1934, p. 273.

the problem of floods is very local and minor. Also a long section of the boundary from the Red River to the Rockies lies very near the water parting between the Missouri River and the Assiniboine River which joins the Red River at Winnipeg.

The Red River of the North rises within the United States and flows northward across the Canadian boundary to Lake Winnipeg. Spring advancing from the south sometimes opens the headstream area while the northern and lower course is still blocked by ice. These occasional spring floods overspread the flat alluvial plain across which the river flows, damaging the adjacent farm lands and a number of small urban centers. The drought conditions of the period between 1930 and 1936 turned the attention of people to the problem of water deficiency, though floods such as the inundations of 1882, 1897, and 1916 may occur again when the wet phase of the climatic cycle recurs. In 1912 a treaty between the United States and Canada created the International Joint Commission which serves for the adjudication of the many water problems of interest to the two countries, and if the problem of floods becomes critical the Commission stands ready to facilitate negotiation and arbitration.

Along the boundary between the United States and Mexico there are two areas requiring international cooperation for the control of floods and the apportioning of the water resources. The lower course and the delta of the Colorado were long subject to recurring floods, but the construction of the Roosevelt Reservoir on the Salt River and the Coolidge Reservoir on the Gila River somewhat reduced the flood hazard, and the completion of the Boulder Reservoir should practically eliminate the danger of inundation in the delta. Now that the hazard of floods has been prevented by the construction of three large reservoirs for irrigation purposes the apportionment of water remains as the critical unsolved water problem of the Colorado.

More than 800 miles of the Mexico-United States boundary lies along the Rio Grande. The water of the upper course is derived exclusively within the territorial limits of the United States. Above El Paso the control of the river is essentially an American problem, though Mexico is vitally concerned with the quantity and the quality of the water which enters Mexican territory. Below El Paso additions to the Rio Grande are drawn chiefly from the Sierra Madre of Mexico. Floods in the lower course so far as they are the result of increments from the south can be controlled only by the cooperation of the Mexican government. The construction of the Elephant Butte dam across the Rio Grande at Hot Springs, New Mexico, practically prevents the danger of floods in the 125-mile section above El Paso.

The water problems of Mexico and of the United States are not so susceptible of arbitration as the Canadian-American problems. In the dry regions of southwestern United States the shortage of water has often precipitated disputes over rights under the doctrine of prior right, and an equitable distribution of the limited water resources. It has been suggested that a commission similar to the Canadian-American International Joint Commission be provided for the solution of Mexican-American water problems.[1]

[1] *Ibid.*, p. 382.

PART V

CHAPTER XVI

OUR MINERAL TREASURES[1]

BY WILLIAM H. HAAS
Northwestern University

GENERAL RELATIONSHIPS

Minerals[2] and Civilization. Mineral deposits are among the most highly prized treasures of any nation. They are the basic resources through which nations achieve industrial greatness and through which they are able to maintain their supremacy. With them the national foundations are laid for a rich industrial evolution; without them no nation can hope for a sustained industrial and commercial advance. The country without the basic minerals is inevitably destined for a lesser rank and is almost sure to be outstripped in economic progress by others more favorably supplied. Indeed, the cultural complex of a nation is, to a very high degree, mirrored in the per capita consumption of minerals, both as to quantity and variety. The extensive use of minerals, and metals particularly, is also the element which most clearly differentiates the complexity of the highly developed nations of today from the simplicity of long ago. Moreover, it is the metal world that makes possible the modern, high-precision measurements necessary for the highly technical products which add so much to our well-being, comfort, and satisfaction. We are definitely living in a

[1] The writer claims little originality of material. The chapter could not have come into being without a rich literature from which to glean, none of which is more illuminating than the writings of Dr. C. K. Leith. For personal help, acknowledgments must be made to Dr. C. H. Behre, Jr., and especially to Dr. W. H. Voskuil.

[2] Minerals are classified as metallic and non-metallic. The most important of the non-metals are the mineral fuels—coal, petroleum, and natural gas. In this chapter Dr. Haas centers his attention especially on metallic minerals. Dr. Bengtson in the chapter following discusses the conservation of our mineral fuels. (EDITORS' NOTE.)

mineral age, and our cultural development is definitely a mineral civilization.

Mineral deposits assume an international importance also, greatly out of proportion to their intrinsic value. In periods of war, when the ready transfer of goods is hampered and commerce becomes disorganized, certain minerals develop a strategic value wholly unappreciated under peace-time conditions. The industrialized nations of the world are all alike, however, in that not a single one of them, perhaps fortunately for the world at large, has within its confines a sufficient amount and variety of minerals to maintain its present culture even in times of peace. It is because of this international interdependence especially that minerals have such a disturbing tendency to undermine the good will among peoples.

In many respects western civilization has gone well beyond that of the Orient. The main difference between the Orient and the Occident is in the stage of industrialization reached and all that such a stage carries with it. It is quite possible that the so-called progressiveness of western nations is more the result of a fortunate possession of natural resources than of innate native abilities. It may be regarded as an accident that by far the world's finest deposits of basic minerals[1] are so favorably placed tributary to the North Atlantic basin; but it is not an accident that in this basin have arisen the progressive, industrial centers of the world. Nowhere else is there an area so rich in high-grade material so compactly and favorably placed. Had opportunities been reversed, cultural progress would unquestionably have been far different. As long as the white race is in the possession of this region, it may be expected to remain dominant even if not most populous.

The Three Great Iron Centers of the World. The industrial superiority of the nations in the North Atlantic basin is indicated by the world's pig-iron production. There are only a few great iron and steel centers or units in the world. The United States, as one, normally produces approximately 43 per cent of the world's total. The Franco-German, acting in the main as a unit (France, Germany, Belgium, and Luxemburg), comes next with an output of about 35 per cent, and

[1] In terms of relative importance, minerals may be divided into two groups: basic and contributory. The basic minerals—coal, iron, and copper—by the coordination of distinctive properties lay the foundation of our modern machine technology. The contributory group of metals and non-metals make up all the rest. For other purposes, minerals may be known as the alloy metals, the nonferrous metals, the mineral fuels, the fertilizer minerals, and the like.

Great Britain, generally a weak third, produces about 9 per cent.[1] The North Atlantic, therefore, accounts for about nine-tenths of all the pig iron produced, not including production of smaller units in other parts of the world under its control. The remaining production is in small units maintained to supply local demands. It may safely be predicted also that, discounting great cultural upheavals, the present

Courtesy J. T. Stark

FIG. 1. Open-pit Mining. Biwabik Mine. Mesabi Range, Minnesota.

The estimate of merchantable ore reserves in the Mesabi Range alone is more than 1,150,000,000 tons. The reserves of low grade ore are many times this figure.

set-up will continue indefinitely.[2] The contributory metallic resources of the world will be drawn to these centers. One plant in the United States is already importing iron from Chile with a world record haul of 5,000 miles in spite of a heavy payment of toll through the Panama Canal.

Possession versus Exploitation. The mere possession of huge mineral deposits does not in itself assure a high state of economic

[1] In recent years, the U.S.S.R. has forged ahead of Great Britain in pig-iron production, but most of the Soviet output is also tributary to the North Atlantic.

[2] C. K. Leith, "The World's Iron Ore Supply," reprint of paper read at the World Engineering Congress, Tokyo, Japan, 1929, p. 37.

prosperity and advancement. Metal ores have been in the earth throughout the history of man, yet they had slight significance to the early peoples, and they mean little to backward nations of today. It is the *utilization* of minerals that lays the foundation for material prosperity. The general scarcity of wealth and the hopeless state of poverty of a non-industrial England at the time of American colonization are mirrored in the system of indentured servants under which many immigrants bound themselves to serve as laborers in order to get a transatlantic passage. Records indicate that approximately one-half of the colonial population came in under such arrangements. This picture was changed with the exploitation of two of the basic minerals, coal and iron, and England eventually became the great creditor nation of the world. What the exploitation of exceedingly rich mineral deposits has meant also in American development can scarcely be overestimated. The Indian, though in possession of these riches for thousands of years, derived no benefit therefrom for the simple reason that he never learned to make use of them.

Minerals in International Trade. In the cultural development of nations, the place of minerals in international trade is not always fully appreciated. Modern industry calls on all parts of the world for the materials used in industrial processes. "If a country is a large mineral producer and large exporter, it is almost sure to have a positive international trade balance and to be a receiver of gold or an importer of international bonds."[1] No nation can long exist on a negative trade balance, and few nations are so favorably placed as to have much of a positive trade balance on non-mineral activities. The British commonwealth of nations, which now includes approximately one-fourth of the habitable globe, is founded upon the exploitation of England's two key minerals, coal and iron. It was the export trade in coal and the productivity of coal and iron that made England, insignificantly small in area, the proud "Mistress of the Seas" and the "Creditor Nation" of the world. Coal had been in use some two thousand years, but it was not until this energy had been harnessed and directed by the use of iron that England blossomed forth. Likewise, the United States remained a debtor nation in spite of all her rich agricultural lands until she learned to use her vast mineral resources in making exportable products. Argentina, at the other extreme, with scant mineral development has found it necessary to import large amounts of mineral products, which in certain years have been sufficient to change a positive

[1] J. Terry Duce, "Mineral Trade, Exchange and Security," *Elements of a National Mineral Policy,* prepared by The Mineral Inquiry, 1933, p. 43.

into a negative trade balance. Venezuela, as another example, paid the last instalment of her national debt in 1930 and is the only country in South America without a foreign debt. Money has been accumulating from her large oil sales, giving her a favorable export as of 617,547 bolívars over an import in 1930 of 143,587 bolívars.

Minerals and Depressions. If the exploitation of the mineral resources by a people brings about cultural advancement, there is also the unfortunate side during periods of depression. During such periods of stress, the consumption of food and clothing, even if somewhat restricted, goes on nevertheless. This is not so true with minerals, for they enter another function of life. The metals go mainly into the construction of durable goods, the manufacture of which can be postponed during hard times. Skyscrapers are not built when "For Rent" signs are increasing; machines and tools are not replaced in the face of uncertainty of demand; nor, at such times, do railroads replace equipment or people buy new cars. With the demand shut off, the decline in consumption is faster than the decline in production, stocks accumulate, and prices fall. When prices drop, marginal producers are forced to shut down, perhaps with large debts unpaid. The larger corporations with great reserves may weather the storm, finding it more profitable, in some cases, to produce at a loss, thereby adding to an accumulating surplus. As one plant after another closes and others more and more restrict their output, employees who are let out are unable to keep up their part in economic relationships, the business man cannot meet his payments, and ultimately the whole community collapses. Such is the common lot of the marginal mining camp. Probably no group of people is more quickly and severely affected by economic ups and downs than those engaged in this basic industry. The need for conservation of human well-being is perhaps greatest here.

The Demand for New Minerals and Mineral Products. In this evolution of industrial nations since about 1850, with coal as an "energizer" and iron as the "harnesser" of energy, there has arisen an ever-growing demand not only for the older and better-known minerals and mineral products but also for the rarer and less well-known ones. This demand has long since outrun the available supplies, and new metals or alloys have been created, each with its own special characteristics. All these alloys, including steel, serve purposes so specific that modern industrial civilization would break down without them. The most important of these are the alloys made with "tonnage" steel in producing "special" steels. Such essential steel alloys are being made with chromium, nickel, cobalt, molybdenum, silicon, tungsten, vanadium, and others. Industry has even gone beyond alloys in creating metal-like products from the non-metallic field which prove more or less effective substitutes for metallic products. This seeking for a greater variety of products than the metals can supply has assumed great commercial importance only during the more recent decades. The alloy industry is still only in its beginning, and the possibilities in the field are limitless. The great variety of alloys, some five thousand of them,[1] and the many composition products emphasize particularly the fact that the metallic world is not able to meet the demands made on it by industry and that this stringency is likely to be felt still more as time goes on.

With the possession of our modern alloy steels, it is difficult to picture the restrictions placed, in other days, on machines made from cast iron or simple carbon steel. The present high-pressure, internal-combustion engine would then have been impossible. The cooperative use of metals in the making of industrial machinery arose out of necessity and became more involved with each onward step. The development of electrical machinery added copper, as a "carrier" of energy, to coal and iron in the list of basic, industrial minerals. The need for steels with special properties of toughness, hardness, and resistance to abrasion and impact, with greater tensional strength, and the like, brought forth the development and use of the ferro-alloy metals. As needs have arisen, special steels have generally been developed to meet the exigency of the demand. The contributory minerals have also taken an important rank. Many of these are now key minerals in the spheres of their activities, and without them the industry would become stagnant, at least for a time. The interrelationship of minerals, functionally, cannot be overemphasized. It is not that one is more important than another, but each has its particular niche to fill in the modern, highly integrated industrial world.

SOME ASPECTS OF MINERAL CONSERVATION

Minerals Not Reproducible. Minerals differ from the other great groups of resources in that they are not only exhaustible but are also not reproducible. Worn-out soils may be rejuvenated, forests regrown, reservoirs refilled by rains; only in the mineral world does nature rarely replace. Man can have no part in their formation, only in their exhaustion. Neither are any substitutes available on a large scale. The metals are basic in this respect. They may replace wood, but

[1] Zay Jeffries, "Modern Uses of Non-ferrous Minerals," *A.I.M.E. Series,* 1935, p. 7.

wood is never likely to replace any of the metals in industry. Wood, which man can produce, is being replaced to an appreciable extent by metals or other minerals which man cannot grow. Although synthetic organic compounds such as rubber are produced successfully, there is no hope for synthetic iron or even copper, gold, or platinum except as a laboratory curiosity. Surprising as it may seem, one or more of the basic elements in nearly all synthetic products has a mineral origin. The marvelous durability of the modern automobile tire over the old is due not to a new kind of rubber but to mineral compounds which have been added to the rubber. All industries and activities are demanding more and more metals in building better and more efficient products, not only because of the greater strength but especially because of the greater refinements possible. Substitution of one metal for another is possible and of common occurrence, but, if forced, it results invariably in decreased efficiency or an upward revision of costs.

Metallic Minerals Recoverable. There is, however, one encouraging element in the use of metals. In their exhaustibility they are radically different from another important group of minerals, the fuels. The millions of cubic feet of natural gas that daily have been pouring into the air unchecked are gone, never to be regained. A ton of coal which may have served its useful purpose in propelling a fast train is at the same time dissipated in heat and energy, never to be brought together again. Our superlatively rich deposits of petroleum, exploited and consumed at an unprecedented rate, are rapidly vanishing. Yet a half ton of metallic iron made from a ton of iron ore may be in constant use for a century or more before it finally disappears. In its history, the iron may be used over and over again and during this time may serve an almost infinite variety of purposes. Because gold has become a monetary standard, the national treasuries of the world have some gold that may have been mined in the pre-Christian era. It is highly probable, too, that even some of the more common metals like lead, copper, and others, that were smelted a thousand or more years ago, are in part still in use.

The Distribution of Ores. The distribution of ores is limited areally because the rocks in which they have had their origin are limited geologically. Most metallics are located in regions where once deep-seated molten rocks are close to the surface, and this condition is most commonly found in mountainous areas. Thus topography and, still more, the geology of a country, to a very great degree, indicate the probable metallics available. According to the geologic history, therefore, one nation may be rich in possibilities of one or many metals and another nation may find all exploratory work ending in disappointments. Thus, the world's metallic resources are fairly definitely known. Although they are buried within the earth, there is relatively little uncertainty as to their whereabouts. The laws of ore deposition are so well known that no large corporation could be induced to do blind exploratory work unless so directed by a competent geologist. This does not mean that all metallic deposits are definitely blocked out and their metal content established. It does mean, however, that

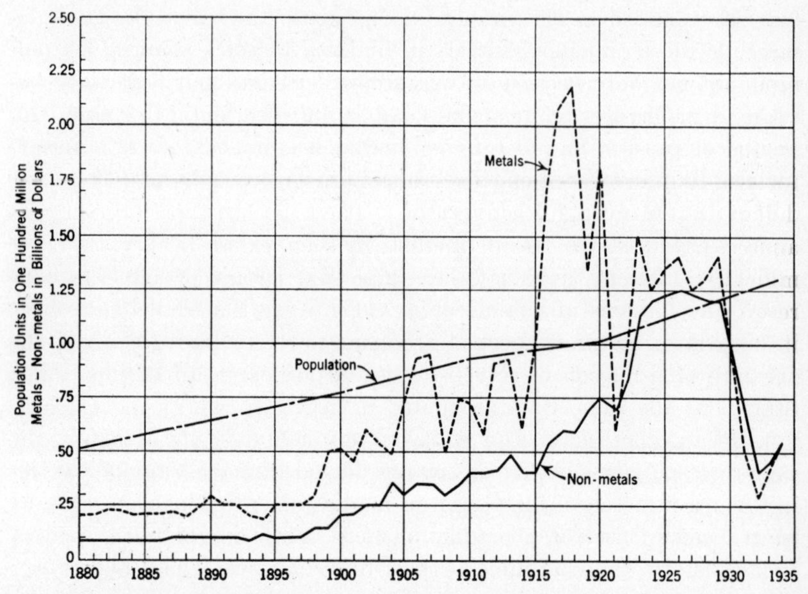

FIG. 2. Production of Metals and Non-metals in the United States, as Related to Population, for the Years 1880-1934, Compiled from United States Publications.

the leading nations such as the United States, England, France, Germany, Italy, Japan, and others have no illusions about discovering some huge metallic storehouse in the future. In the United States, the possibilities of finding another Tonopah, or Comstock, or another Leadville, or Cripple Creek, or a Mesabi, or a Butte are regarded as extremely improbable. Of the great nations Russia offers the greatest possibilities of new finds. Taking the world as a whole, much geologic exploration is yet to be done before the mineral resources can be established with certainty.

The Increase in Mineral Production. In spite of definitely set limits of reserves, exploitation goes on apace at an increasing tempo.

The rate at which the mineral industries have developed in the United States is unlike that of any other country.[1] Since the beginning of this century, our country has produced more than 1,000,000,000 ounces of gold, about 12,000,000,000 ounces of silver, 40,000,000,000 pounds of zinc, 100,000,000,000 pounds of copper, 136,000,000,000 pounds of lead. The major part of the metal production has been since the beginning of the present century. In 10 years, 1921-1930, lead production was 21 times as great as during the full 50 years of the first half of the nineteenth century. For the same periods, copper production was 52 times, zinc 96 times, gold 24 times, and silver 11 times as large. More silver was produced in the last 30 years than in the previous 105 years; more gold in the last 26 years than in the previous 107 years; more copper in 18 years than in the previous 115 years. Our annual production has risen to astounding heights, and for all minerals for the 10 years preceding the depression it was around 5⅓ billion dollars on the average. By way of contrast, in the past 25 years the annual production of farm products has increased 17 per cent, but minerals 77 per cent, about 4½ times as fast. Yet a shortage of mineral reserves will be felt, unquestionably, long before the land has reached its maximum productive capacity. In many of the industrial nations, the rate of depletion of reserves is much greater than in the United States.

In peace time, the United States is very definitely the leader in this field—not only in the rate of increase but also in the total production of the major metals. Of the eighteen major metals produced, the United States ranks first in the production of eight. The only other political unit in any way comparable is the British Empire. These two control the bulk or about two-thirds of all the minerals produced. The United States is not only the greatest producer but also the greatest consumer: from 1921 to 1930 we, 7 per cent of the people of the world, consumed 50 per cent of the world's copper production, 40 per cent of the zinc, and 39 per cent of the lead. Our share in the consumption of the world's production of coal was 37 per cent; pig iron, 47 per cent; and petroleum, 75 per cent.[2] Surely there is a limit to our mineral-producing capacity, and the production curve must sometime turn downward.

World Distribution and Control of Minerals Limited. In spite of the world-wide distribution of metals, it is rare that the ores of any

[1] John Wellington Finch, "The Age of Mineral Utilization," American Mining Congress, Chicago, 1935, mimeographed copy, p. 3.

[2] Finch, *op. cit.*, pp. 4 and 5.

one metallic mineral come from more than three or four countries, except in very insignificant amounts. Thus the United States and France account for 62 per cent of the iron ore; China and India 76 per cent of the tungsten; United States and Chile 64 per cent of the copper; Peru and southwest Africa 79 per cent of the vanadium; Malay and Bolivia 62 per cent of the tin; Spain and Italy 80 per cent of the mercury; Canada and New Caledonia 96 per cent of the nickel; France and Hungary 49 per cent of the bauxite; United States and Mexico 51 per cent of the lead; United States and Australia 51 per cent of the zinc;[1] and Chile practically all the nitrate. It is scarcely ever appreciated that the United States and the British Empire control 70 per cent of the world's supplies of sixteen out of seventeen metals and minerals essential to present-day civilization. The one exception is potash.[2]

Dominance of the United States. It has been a natural evolution that corporations in industrial countries should attempt to gain control of valuable ore deposits both within and without the national domain. It is largely a matter of self-preservation. Thus the United States, even though producing from its own mines 37 per cent of the pig iron of the world, goes far afield for more iron and gets a commercial control of 38 per cent. With only a little manganese mined within the United States and that under sufferance of a relatively high tariff, 20 per cent of the world's manganese is mined under American control. The United States produces no nickel, yet has a commercial control of 39 per cent; it produces only 17 per cent of the vanadium, yet has commercial control of 76 per cent; it mines 23 per cent of the silver, yet controls 66 per cent; it produces 23 per cent of the bauxite, yet controls 43 per cent.[3] In no other field of production have American capital and energy and skill scoured the earth for profitable investments as they have in the mineral world. With such rich possessions of her own, it is not surprising that many of the weaker nations look upon the United States with considerable trepidation, fearing this commercial peace-time penetration more than aggression by war, for America is recognized as a peace-loving nation. The penetration is largely the result of a highly developed technique learned in the development of domestic deposits.

Examples of commercial penetration of American capital in the

[1] H. Foster Bain, "World Mineral Production and Control," *Foreign Affairs*, July, 1933, pp. 706-710.

[2] Arthur Notman, "International Aspects of the Mineral Industry," *Elements of a National Mineral Policy*, prepared by The Mineral Inquiry, 1933, p. 9.

[3] Bain, *op. cit.*

search for minerals could be greatly multiplied. No other nation is comparable. The industrial nations of Europe under the guise of colonization and protectorates have extended their political control over mineral resources but have lagged behind in commercial penetration. The United States, on the other hand, has added little by political control. Thus the British commonwealth of nations, covering one-fourth of the inhabited part of the globe, has great wealth widely distributed. Although Canadian mines produce 89 per cent of the world's nickel, yet British capital controls only 50 per cent and United States capital 37 per cent; Malay produces 37 per cent of the world's tin, yet the British have commercial control of only 33 per cent. France is the leading producer of bauxite with 31 per cent of the total, yet has commercial control of only 11 per cent, and the United States 43 per cent. In another category is China, mining and having commercial control of 55 per cent of the world's tungsten; and Spain, which, in the same way, mines and controls 44 per cent of the world's mercury. That, in the future, the United States should maintain this overwhelming ratio in actual commercial control without political control, in the face of rapidly dwindling supplies of the better-grade ores, does not seem possible or probable, perhaps not even advisable, for the good of the world as a whole. The whole story is only another example of the extraordinarily rapid evolution of the American mineral industry. This means also that the United States is using up minerals faster than any other nation in the world.

INTERNATIONAL RELATIONSHIPS

Nationalism in Control of Mineral Resources. Political measures may affect the use of minerals both favorably and adversely, constructively and destructively. Taxes, license fees, tariffs, and royalties are only a few of the means used by nations to make known their points of view. Post-war tendencies have emphasized the importance of minerals and their control, and unfortunately a strictly nationalistic point of view is growing. In general, control has become centralized in the hands of a relatively few countries. Throughout a greater part of the world, governments are aiding their industries more and more in order to secure a greater national security. The international steel combination of western Europe, the Continental Steel Pact,[1] is an example of an international agreement for the strengthening of world position. So effective has this cartel been that the percentage of steel

[1] C. K. Leith, "The World's Iron Ore Supply," reprint of paper read at the World Engineering Congress, Tokyo, Japan, 1929, p. 34.

exports from the region has been increased at the expense of both the United States and Great Britain. If England should join this group, it would greatly strengthen the cartel's competitive position with the United States. The major world units which have survived the keen trade competition of the last few decades would thus be reduced to two, western Europe and the United States (to three, if the Soviet

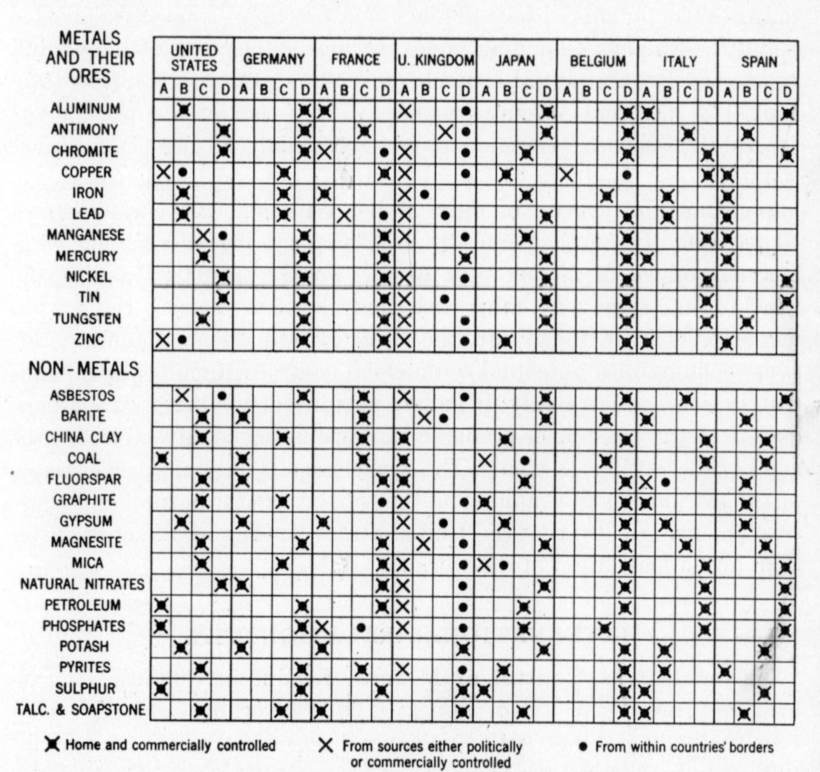

FIG. 3. Indicated Ability of the Principal Consuming Countries to Supply their Needs of the Leading Industrial Minerals.

After a chart prepared by the Minerals Division, Bureau of Forestry and Domestic Commerce, June 1, 1934, in *Report of National Resources Board,* Dec. 1, 1934, p. 443.

Republic be included and counted separately). That new steel centers or units may arise in India, the Far East, Africa, or South America is possible, but only in a secondary way. Competitively, the handicaps for those regions are too great for them to become even a threat to the established centers in the United States and Europe (Fig. 3).

The Relation of Minerals to National Ambitions and Fears. Many political assumptions are based on the fallacy that where there is a will there is a way. It assumes that an early start, militant aggressiveness, organizing ability, or some other cause has made certain nations the leaders in the industrial world. These qualities may be factors, but no people can achieve great material objectives without adequate natural resources. The cultural development of ambitious nations must necessarily follow quite different lines, according to the resources which they possess. It is therefore absurd for the leading nations to aim for the same type of industrial leadership, for the simple reason that there is no economic equality of resources among them. The political power accruing from the exploitation of the world's mineral resources will continue to be related mainly to the North Atlantic countries and centers involved, because these are the centers of the basic resources. For nations which lack minerals to waste their limited resources in an attempt to shift industrial control from the more fortunate countries to themselves is suicidal. In the present set-up of nations and distribution of mineral resources, certain nations must forego certain industrial and nationalistic ambitions.

The jingoism of the "yellow peril," or the dread of Chinese man power under the control of efficient, warlike Japan, disregards the fact that modern wars are won with materials rather than with men as "cannon fodder." The enormous quantities of scrap iron imported into Japan are a mere bagatelle from the standpoint of world production of iron. The total reserves of iron ore in Japan would supply the United States for not more than six months, and all China could supply the world for only one year. However, with the rich mineral deposits of the Philippines, Japan would be at least ten times better off than she is now. Steel mills with their accessories, blast furnaces, finishing plants, rolling mills, and so on, take a tremendous amount of capital, and no nation without basic resources is wealthy enough to develop a great steel unit for peace-time activities and to remain in competition with more-favored nations. Nor can a great steel unit be built up as an emergency measure during time of war.

The Relation of Control of Minerals to World Peace. A nation or state consists primarily of a group of individuals organized for self-government, and secondarily of a certain territory over which control is asserted. That one group of peoples is more aggressive, more industrious, and of higher cultural attainment than another is everywhere recognized. To evaluate all the factors that bring about these differences is practically impossible, but there is a growing appreciation of the importance of minerals, especially by the nations less well supplied. The importance of a rich store of essential minerals can scarcely be overestimated; yet no nation by any zeal or effort of its own can raise its assets one iota in this respect. Their presence, a priceless treasure and a purely fortuitous accumulation, has no relation whatsoever to any efforts of the possessor. To make up for any deficiency, the only recourse is through commercial penetration or by the conquest of war. Nations rich in their own right, as history well shows, are the ones best equipped on a competitive basis for such penetration, and the nations less well supplied, it appears, accept the inevitable. It is not strange, however, that nations poor in metallic resources should feel justified in making war on still weaker peoples whose mineral resources are lying fallow. For the sake of international good will it would seem that countries having a monopoly or a preponderance of certain essential minerals (1) must permit minerals to flow freely in international trade, and (2) must consider such minerals in trust, not so much for furthering nationalistic aims as for furthering a greater well-being of all peoples.

CONSERVATION RELATIONSHIPS

Mining a "Robber Industry." The transitory character of the mining industry may be read in the shifting of production centers. When one deposit is worked out, another must be found to take its place. Thus already numberless areas where deposits were once worked have been abandoned and with them dependent activities have also disappeared. This abandonment of production centers is, of course, more evident in the older mining countries than in the new. In Great Britain there are many abandoned mining units of copper, lead, iron, and tin, as also iron and lead in Spain, and silver in Germany. The United States is not too young to have its "ghost cities" also, such as Comstock, Tombstone, Breckenridge, Central City, Mercur, and many others. Not only has the United States worked out many of its great deposits, but in others peak production has been reached, and, in still others, the decline will come soon. The Mesabi Range has reached its peak and—it now appears—will be a minor element in the production of iron after the 1940's. Zinc production in the Mississippi Valley is on the decline, and soon the region will be only a minor source for the metal. The Keweenawan copper district is largely only a memory, and Butte will likely become so within the next few decades. Gold production reached its peak about 1915, and the decline since has been rapid.[1]

[1] C. K. Leith, *World Minerals and World Politics,* McGraw-Hill, 1931, p. 24.

Conditions Affecting the Exploitation of Ore Bodies. That there are many undeveloped mineral deposits is true; yet most statistics do not tell the full story. There can be no certainty or definiteness as to the amounts or the length of time such reserves will suffice in industry. It is an easy matter, relatively, to determine the cubic contents of an ore body and to estimate by analysis the amount of this or that metal available to the ton of ore. But the answer to the question, can the ore be worked *profitably* in our present state of knowledge and equipment, has so many unknowns and variables that the conclusions can be little more than mere personal opinions even of those most capable of judging. How soon specific deposits can be worked profitably is another question even harder to answer, as still more unknowns are involved. The elements of uncertainty are legion. Is the chemical combination of the ores such that they will yield under known processes and equipment available? What is the cost of getting the ore out? Is the tonnage large enough to warrant expenditures? What are the smelting or concentrating facilities? What labor supply is available, and what expenditure is necessary to make a healthy camp site possible? What are the possible food and water supplies? What are the transportation possibilities? What is the market price of the product now, and what is it likely to be five or ten years hence? What political changes are in the offing? As profit is the only motive, except with government subsidies, any change in one or more factors may make a venture an ignominious failure or an outstanding success. Probably in no other industry are there so many hazards to be overcome as in metal mining. Fortunes have been won, but fortunes also have been lost, and many a lifetime of labor spent in prospecting has been left unpaid. All this, however, emphasizes the fact that statistics may be most misleading, and result in gross misinterpretations. No one knows or can know precisely how long a certain mineral will be commercially available at reasonable prices.

Unquestionably, new mineral districts will be discovered, and others now known but inactive will come into production sometime. Many rich, undeveloped deposits in Bolivia and even in northwest Argentina remain undeveloped for no other reason than the unprofitableness of the venture under present cost conditions. Chile is known as the "land of ten thousand mines," and yet has relatively only a few mines in active operation. Thus complete exhaustion of any one of the minerals is far in the future; but equally certain is the fact that there is a gradual shifting to deposits with leaner and leaner content and in more and more inaccessible regions. The geologist is convinced that, by and large, the cream of the richest, low-cost producers has been feasted upon and that their equals will never again be found.

The Effects of Technological Discoveries. The great discoveries in the mineral world may well be, therefore, not so much in the location of new "El Dorados" as in the invention of means of greater efficiency in using what we have already found. Research has already done much in the aiding of conservation, and it may be taken for granted that only beginnings have been made. Mechanical improvements now make possible the extraction of ore at a cost hitherto regarded as unprofitable. There have been great improvements in the concentration of ores; especially has the flotation process recovered large quantities of metal formerly wasted. The record is an impressive one. The technical advances in the mining industry in favor of the conservation of metals have probably not been exceeded in any other industry. The advance, in general, has kept pace with economic conditions. This technological skill, in fact, has proceeded so rapidly that sometimes huge plants have become outmoded before actually being put into use. The American mining industry has led the world in making possible the lowest unit prices available anywhere.[1]

Examples of technological advance and mechanical skill are legion. Probably the most far-reaching changes in recent years have come in the production of copper. Before about 1907 the copper-lead-zinc camp at Bingham, Utah, produced high-grade ore chiefly from vein and replacement bodies located within the main igneous mass. The normal annual production from this high-grade material (1901, for example) was 14,000,000 pounds of copper. The ore was rich enough to yield about 61 pounds of copper to the ton, or approximately 3 per cent. With an advance in the technology of ore recovery, the Utah Copper Company began to apply steam-shovel methods on a large porphyritic mass, so lean as to be considered unworkable in the past. In the development of the much leaner ore body, production rose to more than 140,000,000 pounds, from material carrying about 18 pounds of the metal to a ton of ore, or a richness of only 0.7 per cent. Thus, in a short space of years, a large mass of worthless rock had become an economic ore body. The experience gained at Bingham changed the estimate of ore reserves not only in the United States but in other parts of the world as well.

It is a mistake to think that a single piece of mechanical equipment, such as the diamond drill or steam shovel, can bring about revolu-

[1] C. K. Leith, *Second Report of the Science Advisory Board,* September 1, 1935, Washington, D. C., p. 362.

tionary changes. The steam-shovel method at Bingham was only secondary to greatly improved technological processes. The ore is crushed and leached with sulphuric acid, and the copper is precipitated from the solution with iron. These advances in technology also made possible the development of the famous Chuquicamata deposits. Here a hill, once tunneled and cross-tunneled for the richer ores by the Spaniards and long abandoned, now became a great ore reserve. Chuquicamata, profiting by the development in other mining centers, developed its own sulphuric-acid plant and used electricity as a precipitant. The copper is plated on a base, peeled off, and reaches the market as electrolytic copper, as fine as any made. A far-reaching effect of such technical advance is the cheapening of the product in comparison to what its price probably would be had the new process not come into being. Such advances have the same effect ultimately as enriching the ore, were such a thing humanly possible. Other industries have also profited by these methods. Without them the electrical industry unquestionably could not have its record of progress, for they have made a large supply of copper available at reasonable prices.

The Problem of Impurities in Ores. Impurities may be a great handicap in the processing of some ores; yet, with improved technology, they may be turned to good account. Thus, the Alabama iron ores are a little too high in phosphorus for the basic open-hearth furnace and not high enough for the basic Bessemer process. The large reserves of lateritic ores in Cuba are more cheaply available to the Atlantic seaboard than the Lake Superior ores, but their impurities of chrome, nickel, and alumina bring about certain metallurgical complications that make the mixing of these ores with others necessary. The very large reserves of iron in Newfoundland, most favorably located on Great Bell Island, Conception Bay, are yet so high in phosphorus content as to be unusable in the United States, except as mixtures, without making radical changes in the smelting plants at great expense. In the United States the early demand was for ore very low in phosphorus. With the growing scarcity of such ores, the open-hearth process met the problem in a measure. Ore high in sulphur was at first considered worthless, but larger and larger amounts of such ore are now used. Small amounts of manganese were considered most detrimental in earlier stages; now, ores containing up to 6 per cent are at a premium. The possibilities for high-silica ores are also gaining. It is inconceivable that ultimately any otherwise good ore should be rejected because of certain impurities.

The Lake Superior iron ores of standard high grade suitable for present smelting practices in either Bessemer or basic open-hearth furnaces are very limited and probably will not be mined extensively beyond the middle of the century. This may bring about a radical change in the American industry. For more than fifty years, the main reliance has been upon these ores, which have furnished about 84 per cent of the total production. The American industry is built upon these rich, low-phosphorus ores, and it may become more profitable to import low-phosphorus ores than to beneficiate the low-grade, domestic ores or to rebuild American plants. Thus, Germany with its basic process can use large quantities of very high-phosphorus Newfoundland ores, whereas the United States cannot. It is inevitable, though, that in the United States low-grade ores, of which we have large reserves, will ultimately come into use supplemented by increasing importations. Already this country is importing some ores from Cuba, Chile, Sweden, Spain, and North Africa for use on the Atlantic seaboard.

The Profit Motive and Conservation. To a patriotic citizen thoughtful of the future of our country it is scarcely possible to consider metals in any aspect aside from the element of conservation. In the production of minerals as a profitable venture, the idea of waste is repugnant. Under our present economic system, it is the hope for profit that induces the prospector to endure the hardships necessary in his search for ores, the individual miner to leave on the dump the less rich ore because he cannot afford to pack it out, or the big corporation to set its engineers at work to devise means for the utilization of leaner and leaner ores. Rarely is an individual or a corporation so oblivious to sound practice as deliberately to allow needless waste. It is not reasonable, however, to expect the individual or corporation to give up the idea of profit for the sake of saving. When the miner finds he cannot make a reasonable wage by taking his second-grade ore to market, he either tries to eliminate certain expenses or abandons the ore altogether in the full realization that the ore is now being wasted as far as he can see. He is so placed that it is more profitable to him to waste than to save, and he takes the normal course. This, however, is not necessarily needless waste. That needless waste does occur through ignorance, some of it due to inexcusable mental inertia or uncertainty of results, or to a host of other reasons, is surely so. Most of the waste is caused by conservatism, where present gain is a stronger urge than the uncertainty of the future. It is, therefore, very commonly the question of *the present against the future,* whether this interim is one year or a century, which is the determinant of proper use or waste.

Labor Costs a Factor in Utilization. In the profitable utilization of ores and metals, the human element must not be considered a negligible factor. Production costs in no small part are labor costs. Every effort in successful enterprises is and should be made to lower labor cost as well as any other cost. This is done in a host of ways, mainly through greater efficiency in handling materials. A reduction of wage scales with the same output also reduces the cost per unit product. The question that frequently confronts the producer is, Is it wise to save 50 cents' worth of material at a cost of 60 cents for labor? An answer only too frequently is: Cut the wage scale to 40 cents. Where public opinion permits, even women and children have been and are pressed into such service and exploited. Few conservationists, however, would insist that it is worth while to save at the price of the exploitation of human life. The development of all resources is for the improved well-being of all the people. Where the problem of lowering costs arises, the human element, although replaceable, is more important than the resource which, if not utilized then, may be gone forever. As there is a conflict between present dividends and future possession, so there is an equally pressing conflict between present dividends and human responsibilities.

The Need of Wisdom in Conservation. In the conservation of metals, the policy of reducing waste to a minimum in both mining and extraction ought to prevail. This waste, in the cases of some of the metals, seems not only needlessly but wickedly high. The mania "to make a showing" in big present profits leads frequently to unsound practices. It is the large corporation, whose existence, in time, extends beyond the present management personnel, that gives the most thought to the future and may even operate for a time at a loss to assure a future commensurate gain. Conservation is a long-term and humanistic conception, and any principle or attitude that extends it and breaks down the all-too-common notion of present gain at all costs is sure to be helpful to the conservation of our national treasures. Commonly, the small concern, the hardest to regulate, is also the greatest transgressor. Conservation, therefore, is a matter of education in points of view, unfortunately a slow process at best.

The "there-ought-to-be-a-law" attitude may be commendable as well as highly pernicious. The effect of legislation without the process of education is rarely wholesome. Legislation which helps to quicken education is justified. To force a copper smelter to appreciate the advantages of controlling the sulphur gases may be most desirable, especially when it proves to be profitable to the smelter as well as to the country at large; but to pass legislation to force all smelters, no matter where situated, to collect their sulphur gases and convert them into sulphuric acid would be an act not only of gross injustice but also of far-reaching evil economic consequences. The cost of production of the acid in regions without a market would add to the cost of the production of the copper, forcing the company to abandon the leaner ores which then presumably would never again be worth the development necessary for their use. All such smelters might conceivably produce more sulphuric acid than the world could consume. The flooding of the markets would bring about a lowering of the price and general chaos in the industry. Thus legislation would have forced the saving of sulphur (not a critical element) in smelters at the cost of the conservation of the copper, which is fairly critical. Gain in one direction is commonly counterbalanced by losses in another, and the abhorrence of waste in most up-to-date corporations is sufficiently great as to lead to the choice of the right side. Such specific examples, however, must not becloud the issue, nor lead to the assumption that all legislation on conservation is vicious. Unfortunately, certain companies are willing to sacrifice all for huge profits. Legislation controlling excess profits and certain abuses, if reasonable in application, may be highly desirable.

Some Effects of Ruthless Competition. Probably the greatest enemy to conservation in the metal-mining industries is the lack of cooperative effort. This is not always the fault of members of the industry itself, but, in the main, of anti-trust laws which prevent such cooperation. An anti-trust law may be necessary to prevent corporations from monopolizing the control of an industry; yet it also prevents corporations from regulating their industries in the interests of the principle of conservation. Competition in some aspects is unquestionably highly desirable, but in the metal world it leads to almost everything that is bad from the standpoint of conservation. Unregulated or non-cooperative control leads directly to a slowing down of technologic and scientific processes, encourages waste, brings about periodic overproduction and consequent retrenchments, encourages great fluctuation in prices, activity, and employment; in short, it multiplies the hazards in the way of an orderly development, limits the growth and employment of technical knowledge, and favors the short-term at the expense of the long-term view.

Such a chaotic state within the industry is not the result of ignorance of ultimate effects. A large-scale mining operation is laid out with due consideration for the life of the mine, the cost of production, and a certain price level as parts of the plan. Could the hazards of fluctuating prices be eliminated, a plan for each grade of ore could be drawn up and a technologic attack on ore reserves initiated. But when one of two companies equally favored practices "selective mining" and price cutting, the other is helpless in its attempt to conserve its leaner ores. As a result, certain parts of the mines may be closed, with the result that pillars then crumble and stopes cave in, haulways break down, waters collect, and, in a relatively few years, the accumulated effects may be so bad that the life hazards alone may make the reopening highly questionable. All this demands its toll from the entire industry and must ultimately be reflected in the price level. Since the recent upset in copper-mining conditions, the actual grade of copper-bearing ore which it has been necessary to mine to meet the market has been more than twice as rich as that recovered under normal conditions.[1]

Expendable and Non-expendable Minerals. In the conservation of metals, a sharp distinction must be kept in mind between those which are destroyed—expendable—and those which can be used again and again—non-expendable. After the ores have been mined without undue waste and the metals extracted efficiently, then the ideal is to put the expendable metals to non-expendable uses. In a sense, all minerals by use are ultimately expendable. The wear even in handling gold is a distinct item and must be accounted for in shipments or indeed in the treasury vault. Wherever possible, however, the metals should be shifted to less and less expendable uses. One of the most serious onslaughts on zinc and lead is in their use for pigments. The discoverer of a serviceable non-metallic base for a white paint would be a benefactor to mankind. Zinc also is dissipated in the making of corrugated sheet metal and fencing. Tin used in making tin plate for tin cans is somewhat slowly but just as surely depleting the total tin reserves of the world. The modern tendency in the United States to put almost everything into "tins" may be helpful to the tin plate and can manufacturer, but the effect is just the opposite to the principle of conservation. The present German tendency to use aluminum-coated steel as a tin substitute is a move in the right direction as is also the growth of the use of aluminum rolled cans by the Norwegian fish-canning industry. Cans of aluminum may be salvaged and the metal be made non-expendable. If and when the time comes that a satisfac-

[1] C. K. Leith, *Second Report of the Science Advisory Board,* September 1, 1935, Washington, D. C., p. 364.

tory, non-metallic covering of iron or a cheap, rustless steel is available, then the principle of conservation in iron will be tremendously furthered.

In some metals, the expendable part assumes large proportions; in others it may be fairly negligible, but never unimportant. Iron and steel are outstanding examples of the first group. The iron that goes into a great suspension bridge is, in large part, in storage or non-expendable if preserved from the weather; expendable in part if neglected and allowed to disintegrate. The human energy that has gone into the building of the bridge is so great that it is most profitable to keep the structure protected by a covering. Enormous quantities of iron also go into farm and ranch fencing. Practically all this is expendable. It starts out with a coating of zinc but this is very thin; in handling, cracks develop and some of the zinc even chips off with the result that the iron wire is attacked by the weather, the rusted wires soon break, and the fence is replaced by new fencing. The old, rusty wires are too bulky for scrap, and the "junk man" will not even handle the bulky mass for the taking. The wire is dumped into erosion ravines, or into waste places to suffer the same fate of ultimate disintegration as the tin can on the city dump. Only at the expense of the exploitation of the human element can such material be saved from its fate.

The Use of Scrap Metals. Conservation in yet another group of activities offers growing possibilities. The increasing use of scrap is developing to such huge proportions that the mining industry is viewing the trend with much interest and even, in some instances, with some apprehension. This is, nevertheless, one of the brighter aspects of the conservation of our metal treasures. The amount of "scrap metal" annually entering the industry is almost beyond relief. Unfortunately, reliable statistics are not always available, but certain excellent studies have been made. Our national copper scrap pile has well been called "the largest copper mine in the world." The amount, as for all metals, which annually enters the industry is dependent very much on the price. With low prices it may not seem worth while to sell the scrap; and it accumulates, and much is wasted. In times of high prices, the scraps are carefully taken care of and old dumps are gone over. For 1934 it has been estimated that, for every pound of primary copper produced in the United States, 1.62 pounds reentered industry from secondary sources.[1] The use of secondary copper is a

[1] Kenneth Leith and Donald M. Liddell, *The Mineral Reserves of the United States and Its Capacity for Production,* National Resources Committee, Washington, D. C., 1936, p. 65.

real industry and one of the oldest of this type. The great brass industry of the United States was founded in Connecticut on scrap copper from ship sheeting, old stills, and the copper bottoms of ships. Not only did the brass, bronze, and other copper-alloy industry develop from copper scrap but, as the industry grew, it became a pioneer in the search for primary copper in the West to supply its needs. At present 60 per cent of the total furnace metal produced comes from scrap in the form of clippings, shavings, trimmings, and the like. Copper is refined so readily that broken telegraph and telephone wires are commonly replaced with new to expedite the service and the old wires are sent to the refinery and rerun into wires.

The scrap iron and steel industry is an outstanding example of the use of scrap of the cheaper metals. This to a degree is possible only because of the tremendous amounts of iron doing constant duty in a wide variety of lines. Besides, steels are produced and used in much the largest amounts of any metal alloy. In 1929 the production in the United States reached the enormous total of 63,000,000 tons of steel ingots. Were it not for the re-use of some of this material, the iron situation in this country might become serious in the relatively near future. To the casual reader, it may seem strange that, although steel is made from pig iron, nevertheless our steel production normally is some 12,000,000 tons greater than that of pig iron, in spite of the fact that much pig iron never gets into the form of steel but is used in foundaries in making cast-iron products. The explanation, of course, is that enormous quantities of scrap iron and steel go directly into the making of steel. The difference between pig-iron and steel tonnages would be much greater still were it not for the large ocean tonnages of scrap going to foreign countries without iron, such as Italy and Japan. For coalless and ironless countries the importation of scrap is most assuredly the best way to build up an industrial steel unit. The fabrication of iron goods from scrap calls for less fuel than from iron ore. Contrary to well-established belief, the huge tonnages of scrap do not come through the country or alley junkman but from industry itself, and consist of such items as worn-out rails, mill parts, scrapped machines, motor cars, and locomotives. The annual world total is probably around 100,000,000 tons.

In view of the large tonnages of primary iron entering regularly into active use, it would seem reasonable to assume that the world's supply of pig iron and steel should be growing by leaps and bounds. Unfortunately, this is not so, for iron and steel have many enemies. The figures for the expendable loss each year, were they known, would be staggering. The statement has been made that each year the amount lost from rusting alone equals the total output of thirty years before.[1] Naturally, with an accumulation of stocks, the amounts dissipated are likely to increase rather than decrease. The many ways in which iron may be lost without recovery are made evident to anyone through his daily activities. The greatest hope lies in cheapening the processes for making a more rust-resistant steel.

DEVELOPING A CONSERVATION ATTITUDE

Changing Attitudes Regarding Conservation. Attitudes change, and we may expect the point of view toward conservation to alter from time to time. Already changes are to be noted in this country. With an abundance, little appreciation of values was shown. Why worry about a small patch of ground when "Uncle Sam is rich enough to give us all a farm"? This is largely the attitude of the pioneer, of the adventurer. Why take thought of the morrow when each day's evil is sufficient unto itself? This attitude is well expressed in the frontiersman's motto attributed to Dean Davenport:[2] "Here's a fine animal, let's kill it. Here's a big tree, let's cut it down. Here's a thick sod, let's plow it up." There is enough of this adventurous spirit in the average American for such a motto to make a strong appeal; it is no more clearly demonstrated than in the attitude of many if not most sportsmen toward wildlife. However, there was not added to the pioneer's motto, "Here's a rich ore deposit, let's destroy it," for the adventurous spirit without serious purpose does not make a prospector or a miner. The American people have seen too many surpluses turned to deficits, too many resources willfully wasted and the consequent need felt in a short lifetime or even a short score of years not to see another side too. Especially can it be said of those acquainted with minerals that a part of their background of thinking is the realization that the accumulations of eons of time are being exhausted as though in a day without a thought for the morrow.

Whatever ideal is held relative to the exploitation of mineral resources in the possession of backward nations, it is too much to expect all nations to act as does the best citizenry of any one nation. Attitudes toward the inviolability of the rights of people change with conditions, and nations handicapped in their development may be expected to try to make that deficiency good. They have many precedents of the past to justify their course. With the discovery of Amer-

[1] "Mineral Economics," *A.I.M.E. Series,* Brookings Institution lectures, 1932, p. 166.

[2] J. Russell Smith, *North America,* Harcourt, Brace, 1925, p. 26.

ica, the Pope dd not hesitate to divide the new world into two parts, one for Spain and the other for Portugal, although these new lands were already in the possession of native peoples. Ignoring the Pope's decree, other European nations also began deliberately to exploit the new world, whether in the interest of the natives or not. The Colonies and later the Union did not scruple to take away even the livelihood of the true possessors of the land. England built up a great navy to defend her right to exploit people the world over and to attach their lands to her Empire. Other nations aided Great Britain in parceling out all Africa until only a small, independent element in the hills surrounded largely by deserts was left, and now Ethiopia has lost its identity also.

Naturally, American policies followed the ideals of the times to a great degree. Little reluctance was shown in waging war on Mexico and taking some of her territory. Captain A. T. Mahon, an American naval expert of the last century, did not hesitate to advocate the policy of bringing backward people into the line of progressive nations by force, but even advocated this as a duty of the more powerful nations. This type of thinking unquestionably led to our so-called intervention policy. In the Spanish War, we did not shrink from taking over Puerto Rico as booty without the consent of the island people. Probably more by President Wilson than any other have the American people been educated in a measure to the inviolability of nations. At the close of the war, Wilson's pronouncement that national boundaries should be ethnic ones gave rise to a rabid nationalism that swept the world. More recently Japan and Italy have reverted to the older type of thinking. A main incentive for present-day aggressions in one form or another is the desire for control of the mineral resources irrespective of the rights of the nations involved.

Two Points of View Regarding Exploitation of Mineral Deposits. There are thus today two points of view in regard to minerals. One view, highly nationalistic, would protect all minerals in the homeland for future use. The other takes an international point of view, according to which the best safeguard to a nation is not in holding minerals as reserves, as a line of national defense, but in the exploitation of all minerals to the fullest degree wherever they may be. George Otis Smith, a former director of the United States Geological Survey, says: "The principle that title to territory justly rests upon its best use should win the recognition in international equity."[1] He believes that this is analogous to the current trend toward a contraction

[1] George Otis Smith, *The Strategy of Minerals*, Appleton, 1919, p. 316.

of private property rights in the interests of the larger group, the public. He concludes that "We are to grow nationally by our generosity internationally."

These points of view—whichever will ultimately dominate is hard to predict—raise important questions in conservation, together with a host of others. What is the greatest thing in the use of the world's treasures? Have all people an equal right to mineral deposits no matter what the political control? Should there be a pooling of all mineral resources? Is it a privilege or even a duty, for the more aggressive nation to enter the domain of the less aggressive in order to force the exploitation of its mineral resources for the good of the world? Has an individual or a corporation the right to do what it will with its own irrespective of the larger good? Does this also apply to nations? In the exploitation of minerals, what considerations of the future, which is uncertain, should outweigh the facts of the present, which is real? To what extent is the exploitation of the present human element justifiable for a future contingency? Since no two people will agree unreservedly on the answers to these questions, it may be that there is no one answer. May it not be that as times change the answers also will change? The mass of the people believe as they have been taught to believe. The highest ideals in conservation can survive and expand into a fuller being only through education. Education is the salvation of the world, and especially in the conservation of our mineral treasures. The teachers, however, must have a sound philosophy which reaches beyond home territory.

A Need of a Unified Philosophy of Conservation. A unified philosophy on conservation of our metals must become wide-spread among thinking people if conservation is ever to become effective. Conservation necessarily involves the weighing of the advantages of the present which are real against the claims of the future which, frequently, have an element of doubt. To the elementary mind the present is preeminent, but with cultural advance there is an increasing attention to the future. This future, unfortunately however, does not, in the present stage of our cultural development, extend much beyond a second or third generation. Another element in this philosophy must be that the human being of the present is just as important as the one who may come in the distant future. Metals are here to be used in an orderly fashion for the good of all peoples. The human element must not be exploited for the sake of conserving something for the generations which are to come. Cultural advance justifies the full use of the metal world. Another element must be that ownership must not be thought of as full possession with right to destroy at will, but as a trust in a long sequence of ownerships from generation to generation for the good of the whole human race for all time. Another element which this philosophy must cover is related to the unequal distribution of mineral resources. A part of the white race through a fortunate combination of circumstances, not of their own making, is in possession of the premier mineral deposits of the world, favorably placed. The control of these resources is of a purely accidental nature, and they must be considered as held in trust for the good of all. It is equally fundamental that all mineral deposits be held inviolable by all nations. The philosophy that might makes right and that nations are the products of the survival of the fittest in a struggle for existence must inevitably lead to cultural extinction. The only real hope for a great cultural future based on metal resources lies in an enlarged concept of their meaning in cultural advance, and in a vigorous support of conservational activities designed to secure to society the maximum benefit from those resources.

CHAPTER XVII

THE MINERAL FUELS

By Nels A. Bengtson

University of Nebraska

INTRODUCTION

Fear of want because of lack of ability to produce the necessities of life has been banished from the minds of thinking people. Formerly, thoughtful men were fearful that waning productivity in a world growing old would result in serious scarcity and eventually end in starvation of the human race. For many centuries man gradually placed virgin soils under cultivation only to find that productivity, at first high, soon began to decline and then dropped so low that abandonment of the land became inevitable. Since the total amount of cultivable land was a fixed quantity, it seemed only a question of time until it would all be used up and then would come the end of human existence. Not a cheery picture, 'twas true, but to many it seemed to represent inevitable reality.

During the past century or so the picture has changed. Something profound has occurred. No longer do we hear prophets of gloom point to a world starving because of lack of production. Some people ascribe our present economic and social ills to overproduction, others to unbalanced production, and still others to unequal distribution of the benefits of production, but none claim that there is lack of ability to provide all that is needed for comfortable living. What has caused this change in outlook? As in most questions of wide range or importance, no single factor furnishes a complete explanation, but certainly one of the basic causes, perhaps the foremost one, is the use of sources of energy previously untapped.

Formerly man depended upon his own muscular strength, supplemented somewhat by that of domestic animals and to a slight extent by water power, to do the work needed to produce crops and other goods. This had been the situation for centuries, and productive progress had been slow indeed. The productive capacity per man was probably nearly as high in the days of Grecian greatness as it was during colonial times in America. Then came the use of steam power, with coal as the source of energy. The changes resulting came slowly at first. During the latter part of the eighteenth century and early part of the nineteenth, man had not learned how to utilize this new-found source of energy on a big scale, and hence progress was slow. However, by the middle of the nineteenth century, inventive genius had responded with machines of rapidly increasing efficiency. By means of steam engines and power-driven machinery, the energy latent in coal could then be utilized readily. Soon other sources of energy were discovered in the forms of petroleum and natural gas, electricity made water power more practicable, and thus the modern industrial era sprang into vigorous being. Within a few decades greater mechanical changes occurred than had taken place during several preceding centuries.

The sources of energy which have activated the industrial progress of the past century have been chiefly coal, petroleum, and natural gas. Stores of these mineral fuels had existed throughout the period of human history, but they had remained untouched by man. These stores are the heritage from geological ages past; in terms of centuries they are fixed and irreplaceable; when once used they cannot be restored. They have been drawn upon at an ever-increasing rate since the dawn of the industrial era, prior to which time they were practically unused. Is it not, therefore, incumbent upon us to recognize the extent to which modern industry depends upon the mineral fuels for its sources of power, and that these sources are irreplaceable? Is it not our obligation to use these resources with the highest efficiency and the minimum of waste? Conservation of minerals connotes wise and careful utilization; it does not imply lack of use.

COAL

Early Recognition of Mineral Fuels. It is significant that among the earliest forms of manifestation of mineral fuels was that of the mysterious eternal fires. Burning jets of escaping gas along valley sides in Mesopotamia and ancient Persia were so striking and mysterious that they early became the objects of religious symbolism, a distinction which they still hold. Seeps of petroleum were found to have soothing value as ointment, something much needed by people who walked barefoot along stone-cluttered paths and on rocky lands. Coal also was found, particularly in the Balkan peninsula and to some extent in Italy, and it was used on a small scale. But since wood was then not scarce and methods of coal mining were crude, not much progress was made in the utilization of this fuel. The demand for fuel was not great because during most of the year the weather was warm. Furthermore, the coal was of low grade and it occurred under such structural conditions that mining was difficult, factors which also were important in retarding development.

Coal mining on a large scale first became important in northwest Europe, particularly in Belgium and England. As population increased and wood for fuel became scarce near the cities, the "black rock" which was found along some valley sides was discovered to be a highly satisfactory fuel. Although, compared with present operations, the mining of coal in England prior to the middle of the eighteenth century was on a small scale, it caused the gradual development of a technique in mining which was of great importance later when steam power sprang into prominence in factory operations. Thus, when Watt first gave impetus to the steam engine as an industrial power machine, England had a fairly well-developed coal-mining industry to supply the fuel, whereas in the settled portions of the New World wood was still so abundant that there had been little incentive to begin using coal.

Early Uses of Coal in the United States. It seems hardly believable that coal mining was unknown in this country during all the colonial period, yet such seems to be the verdict of history. Some coal is reported to have been mined in the Triassic Basin near Richmond, Virginia, as early as 1787; the quality was poor and the amount insignificant when compared with present-day production in the more important fields. Shortly after 1800, coal mining for local use evidently began in several places in Pennsylvania and adjacent districts, but prior to 1810 no accurate records were kept. Statistically, the American coal industry began in 1814 with an output of twenty long tons. It is an interesting coincidence, nothing more, that the first complete cotton goods factory was constructed in the same year at Waltham, Massachusetts. Water power was utilized for factory operations, whereas coal was then used merely for heating purposes.

Coal Utilization and Industrial Development in the United States. In order to understand the gradual development of the coal industry in the United States, it may be well to summarize the steps of industrial progress which immediately preceded the initial stages of that development and then became contemporaneous with it. During colonial days the factories were mostly of the handicraft type, the principal exceptions being the sawmills and gristmills operated by direct use of water power. After the War for Independence this condition continued during some years because capital for the erection of larger establishments was lacking, credit was poor, and the limited amount of capital available for investment found quick and profitable use in connection with shipping interests. Progress was slow until after the second war with England. Beginning with 1814 the changes were rapid. During the following decade and a half the modern mechanical factory system became firmly established and the handicraft system lost its position of leadership. Water power through direct transmission by water wheels was dominant, but steam was rapidly threatening its supremacy. The stationary engine had demonstrated its worth, and by 1830 the steam locomotive had won its place at the head of the transportation procession. Nevertheless, the abundance of wood for fuel had postponed the day of coal; the engines were operated solely by steam from wood-burning boilers.

Coal and Steam. The three decades following 1830 witnessed the greatest changes ever experienced in the operations of factories and in the construction of railways. The number of persons employed in industrial manufactures increased from an insignificant figure to such prominence as to include directly and indirectly nearly one-third of the American people in 1860. At the beginning of the period canal transportation was the leading method of long-distance haulage of commodities; at its close the steam railroad held first place. In the early part of the period wood was the fuel most commonly used for generating steam; at its close coal was the unchallenged sovereign. By 1860 coal and steam had vanquished their industrial predecessors and become supreme in the realm of industrial power. They had made possible an industrial revolution in the United States during the same period in which there occurred the greatest agricultural expansion that the world has ever experienced, an expansion in which railway building played a prominent rôle. It seems clear, therefore, that coal and steam were the unrivaled keys to the industrial development in America during the period from 1830 to 1860. During that period coal became a front-rank commodity in the United States, a position it promises to hold far into the future.

Origin and Kinds of Coal. Quite naturally there is almost universal interest in coal, the commodity which is the source of more energy than any other for industrial purposes, and which also outranks all other commodities in physical bulk of output. Coal is not only the foremost freight commodity, but it is also the foremost source of power for the transportation of goods and people alike. This commodity, which has been so important in the transformation of our industrial life from laborious handicrafts to mechanized efficiency, is a form of preserved sunlight from ages past. The theory of origin now almost universally accepted holds that coal is the fossilized residue of decayed vegetation which, millions of years ago, flourished profusely over extensive areas of the world.

Nature furnishes many classes of coal, each one of which represents a particular stage of the primary decomposition and following transformation of the vegetable débris of primeval forests and swamps. The process of decomposition has continued throughout many geological periods and, so far as its original stage is concerned, it is still being repeated in peat bogs and at the mouths of large rivers where enormous masses of water-logged vegetable material are decomposing under the influence of bacteria.

The significance of the theory of the origin of coal is admirably stated by Hoar:

> When reflecting on the formation of coal fields, two conclusions are inevitable: The enormous subsidence of the original surface and the lapse of time essential in forming a series of strata with their coal seams, in all several thousand feet thick. Estimates as to the time necessary for this operation of nature vary greatly. One is that it takes 100 years to form one foot of peat and that three feet of peat are essential to the formation of one foot of coal; also that 20 feet of the original decayed vegetable material are required to make one foot of coal. . . . These hypotheses emphasize the fact that once our coal fields are exhausted there can be no hope of renewal, and that, consequently, conservation becomes vitally important.
>
> The transition from vegetable matter to coal is so gradual that the characteristics in one stage of the process of metamorphism are often similar to those of another. . . . [This makes] a definite classification of each rank or grade rather difficult. . . . However, as the chief heat-producing element in coal is carbon, a classification adopted by American geologists is that based on their chemical composition and, consequently, on their calorific value. This is ascertained through analyses which indicate the percentage of fixed carbon, volatile matter, moisture, and ash constituting each. On this basis the various steps in the development from vegetable matter up to the highest form of coal are: (1) Peat, (2) lignite, (3) subbituminous, (4) bituminous, (5) semibituminous and semianthracite, (6) anthracite.[1]

The Important Constituents of Coal. The heat value of coal depends upon its relative percentages of fixed carbon, hydrocarbons,

[1] H. M. Hoar: *The Coal Industry of the World,* Trade Promotion Series, No. 105, Bureau of Foreign and Domestic Commerce, Washington, D. C., 1930.

moisture, and ash. The first two are positive factors whereas the second two are negative.

Since coal is of plant origin, it is but natural that carbon should be one of the chief constituents, because it is one of the principal products of the partial oxidation of woody matter. Carbon gives coal its black color, and it burns with little flame, high heat, and almost no smoke. Coals which are rich in fixed carbon usually have small amounts of impurities which reduce heat value; therefore the percentage of fixed carbon is widely accepted as indicative of the quality of any particular kind of coal.

The hydrocarbons consist of carbon and hydrogen united chemically in various proportions. These compounds have even higher heat values than has fixed carbon. The hottest coals are those which are rich in hydrocarbons and fixed carbon, and therefore they are in demand for steam-generating purposes.

Moisture in coal is of two principal kinds, namely, extraneous and inherent. The former is water in contact with coal particles, filling or partly filling the little spaces between them; such moisture will evaporate under ordinary storage conditions. Inherent moisture, on the other hand, is chemically combined and does not evaporate to any great extent upon exposure to the air.

The ash, of course, is incombustible and therefore of no heat value. It is derived from two sources, namely, from the mineral matter which occurs generally to greater or less degree in all woody fibers, and from the earthy materials which were carried into the ancient swamps and marshes where the coal-forming vegetation grew. Invariably it is a diluting constituent. One per cent of ash is equivalent to 20 pounds to a short ton; that means it is an economic factor to be considered in storage, handling, and transportation. Some coals have as much as 12 to 15 per cent ash; others, less than 5 per cent. Steamship operators desire bunker coals with low ash content because of the business necessity to use all cargo space and tonnage to the best advantage. Ash is not economic cargo.

Kinds of Coal. The coal series as classified by Campbell and others is not only practical in business usage but also scientifically sound and hence has won wide recognition in the United States. The basis of classification used is twofold, fixed carbon content and coherence; and the series includes the various kinds from peat to anthracite.

Ordinarily *peat* is not recognized as coal, although it may be regarded as the lowest stage in the conversion of vegetable matter into coal. As it comes from the bog its water content is so high that drying is necessary before it can be used as a fuel. The largest known deposits occur in the glaciated areas of the northern hemisphere, notably in north-central United States and in Canada. Because of its low heating power, peat is rarely used in its natural form where coal is procurable at reasonable prices.

Lignite is the lowest member of the coal series proper. Its color ranges from cinnamon brown to nearly black, and its structure is distinctly woody. Chemically it represents a stage intermediate between wood and coal. Its heat value is four or five times as great as that of peat but only 30 to 50 per cent that of bituminous coals. When it is freshly mined the moisture content may be 30 to 45 per cent of its weight. The fixed carbon content ranges from 30 to 55 per cent of the dry weight, the smaller value being much more common than the larger. Lignite crumbles badly in handling and in storage, and with prolonged storage there is danger of serious combustion. These characteristics render it an uneconomical fuel except for local use.

In the United States extensive deposits of lignite occur in North Dakota, northwestern South Dakota, and eastern Montana. Lignite is known to be present also in large areas of the Gulf Coastal Plain from Texas to Alabama. In Europe the most extensive beds are in the north German lowland where they are mined on a large scale for both domestic and industrial purposes.

Sub-bituminous coal is black and some of it quite lustrous. Its moisture content, from 15 to 25 per cent, is much less than that of lignite, but even so it is a handicap in handling; the coal checks and crumbles badly upon drying. The fixed carbon content ranges from 35 to 60 per cent, the structure is compact, and its heating value from 15 to 50 per cent higher than that of lignite. Upon being burned in locomotive fireboxes or in other furnaces with strong drafts, sub-bituminous coal is likely to cause eruptions of sparks which are a fire menace to the vicinity.

Most of the sub-bituminous coal deposits of the United States occur west of the one-hundredth meridian and are found in great abundance in Wyoming, New Mexico, Colorado, Montana, Idaho, Utah, Arizona, and Washington. Lesser quantities occur in Oregon and California.

Although the lignite and the sub-bituminous coal of the northern Great Plains and the Rockies are now used for railroad fuel and for local purposes, the exploitation is on a relatively small scale. The near future promises no important change in this respect. In the more distant future, probably within a very few decades, when petroleum is less plentiful than it is now, the utilization of these fuel resources seems likely to expand greatly. Their high hydrocarbon content makes them available for the manufacture of gas and liquid fuel. The liquefaction of coal, which now is chemically possible but economically impractical, may develop into an industry of major importance. The relatively low cost of mining, if all-year operation can be maintained, and the economy of transportation of liquid fuels, are factors which some day may lead to extensive exploitation of the enormous quantities of sub-bituminous coal known to exist in the Great Plains and the Rocky Mountains. The time may come when those reserves will become the foremost sources of industrial and motive power in this country.

Bituminous coals differ from the sub-bituminous in that they do not slack on exposure to the air and in that they have a much lower moisture content. Their fixed carbon content ranges from 48 to 73 per cent. They are comparatively brittle, of deep black color, and they burn readily with a smoky flame. Since they break down more slowly upon exposure to the air than lower-grade coals, they may be kept in open storage for months with little deterioration. The coals in the upper part of this class are among the best in the United States; they are excellent for steam fuels, best adapted for the manufacture of coke, and richest in gas and by-products. Bituminous coal is not only a fuel; it is also the industrial source of many essential chemical products, inorganic as well as organic.

Bituminous coal constitutes about 52 per cent of the estimated total world's coal supply. It is the kind most widely used for industrial purposes—the foremost source of industrial power. In the United States the well-known producing districts are in the Appalachian Plateau from western Pennsylvania and eastern Ohio to Alabama, and in the interior plains of Michigan, Indiana, Illinois, and southwestward to Missouri, Kansas, and Oklahoma.

Bituminous coals are broadly classified as coking or non-coking. Inasmuch as coke is the essential fuel in blast furnaces, high-grade coking coals are in great demand in the iron and steel centers of the world. Extensive beds of coal of superior coking quality have long been mined in western Pennsylvania and West Virginia; their exploitation has contributed much to the success and prominence of the industrial centers at Pittsburgh, Youngstown, and Cleveland.

Semibituminous coal has a rich black color and is usually of high luster. Cohesion is generally weak; the coal is brittle and friable, and therefore it tends to crumble into small bits when handled. The fixed carbon content is high, 73 to 83 per cent, and consequently burning is accompanied by little smoke. The moisture content is low; the heat value is high, averaging 10 to 20 per cent above that of most of the bituminous coals although some notable exceptions occur. Its low moisture and ash content and its high heat value make this coal a prized bunker fuel.

Semibituminous coals are found mostly in connection with eastern fields, the best-known districts being near Pocahontas, West Virginia, and in the eastern parts of the Appalachian Plateau region of Maryland and Pennsylvania. Some of the high-grade metamorphosed coals found on the slopes of the Arkansas River Valley and along the flanks of the Ouachita Mountains of Arkansas and Oklahoma belong to this class.

The fixed carbon content of *semianthracite* averages about 10 per cent higher than that of semibituminous coal, and the percentage of volatile matter is correspondingly lower. Semianthracite differs from true anthracite in its friability rather than in its heat value. Coals of this class are likely to break down from lumps into fine coal during the handling necessary in mining and transportation; in order to prevent undue waste, care must be exercised in firing and grates and fireboxes suitably constructed for using fine coal must be provided.

The best-known producing districts have been developed near Bernice, Pennsylvania, and along the flanks of the Ouachita Mountains. Semianthracite coal is a clean-burning fuel, giving but little smoke when properly used, and the heat value is as high as that of anthracite. Because it ignites more readily than anthracite and burns slowly and persistently with almost no smoke or soot, it is very desirable for domestic heating. It is therefore a popular furnace coal throughout a large territory tributary to the Ozark Highlands, especially in the markets north and northwest of St. Louis.

Anthracite is characterized by its jet-black color, high luster, and excellent coherence. It differs from semianthracite particularly in its hardness, that is, in being highly coherent, a property of economic importance because it permits the preparation of sizes adapted to particular needs. This aids in preventing waste. The amount of fixed carbon ranges from 80 to 95 per cent of the total weight. Since there is no danger of spontaneous combustion and virtually no loss by deterioration in storage, consumers find it advantageous to buy part or all of their winter supply during the summer months. This is an important factor in promoting a steady monthly output of anthracite in contrast with the sharply seasonal fluctuations of the demands for bituminous coal.

Although anthracite kindles with difficulty, the fire when started burns without smoke, is remarkably persistent, and can readily be regulated to give much or little heat as conditions may require. These various characteristics—cleanliness, steadiness in burning, splendid storage qualities, and high heat value with a minimum of waste—make anthracite the most popular member of the coal series for the heating of home and business houses.

The most important of the anthracite regions in the United States is located in northeastern Pennsylvania, the well-known Scranton and Wilkes-Barre district. The availability of anthracite from such a near-by source for heating the homes, office buildings, and factories in the great cities of northeastern United States has been of tremendous economic significance. Furthermore, the use of anthracite accounts for the absence of palls of smoke such as often occur where large cities depend upon bituminous coals for heating purposes.

Small quantities of anthracite are known to occur in Gunnison and Routt counties, Colorado, and near Cerillos, New Mexico, but none of these areas appears extensive, and to date none has become of much commercial importance. Rhode Island has a small field.

Coal Reserves of the World. The report of the International Geological Congress held in Toronto, Canada, in 1913 has long been accepted as the most authoritative pronouncement of the coal resources of the world. Although subsequent studies have caused revision of estimates for some countries, and exploitation has continued on a significant scale, the general value of the figures remains unimpaired. The total coal reserves of the world were estimated at 7,389,000,000,000 metric tons. Of this quantity about 52 per cent was listed as bituminous, 7 per cent as anthracite, and 41 per cent as consisting of subbituminous and lignite coals.

ESTIMATED COAL RESOURCES OF THE WORLD[1]

Continent	*Metric Tons*
North America	5,073,431,000,000
Asia	1,279,586,000,000
Europe	784,190,000,000
Oceania	170,410,000,000
Africa	57,839,000,000
South America	32,097,000,000
Grand Total	7,397,553,000,000

[1] H. M. Hoar, *The Coal Industry of the World,* Trade Promotion Series No. 105, Bureau of Foreign and Domestic Commerce, Washington, D. C.

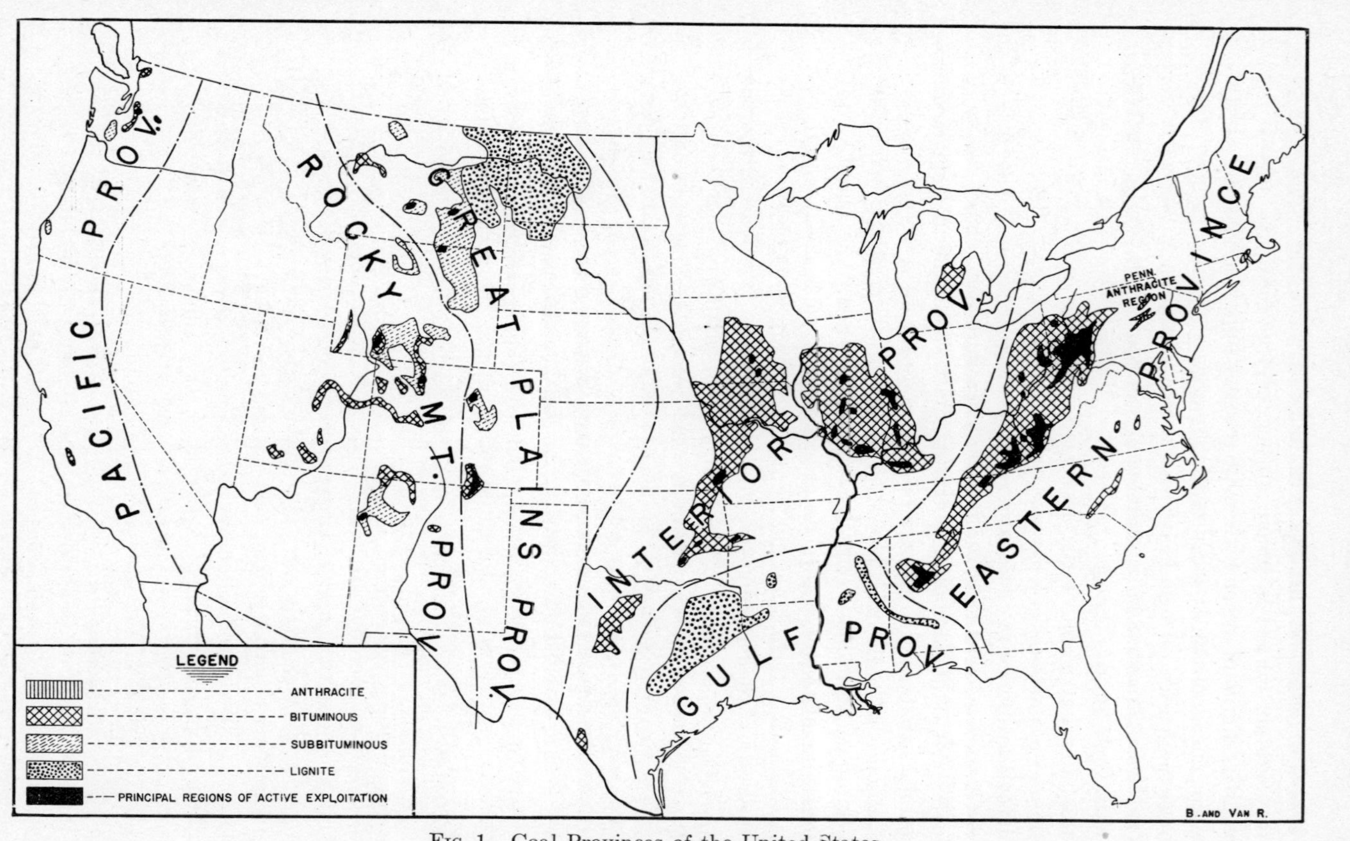

FIG. 1. Coal Provinces of the United States.

The industrial and economic importance of the extensive deposits of bituminous coal from western Pennsylvania to eastern Kansas can hardly be overstated.

It will be observed that the great bulk of the world's coal reserves are in the northern hemisphere, owing in large measure of course to the extensive land masses there found compared with those of the southern hemisphere. Another striking feature is the high rank of North America, credited with nearly five-sevenths of the coal reserves of the world. Asia ranks second with about 17 per cent of the total; this continent, however, has the advantage of leading in reserves of anthracite, China alone being credited with stores far in excess of those of all other countries combined.

Even though the reserves for the world as a whole are so large that there need be no fear of shortage for many centuries to come, we should bear in mind that complete winning of the coal underground is impossible, and that the expense of mining becomes greater as deeper-lying beds or those less favorably situated must be drawn upon. Furthermore, the nations which have pushed forward most rapidly along industrial lines are the ones which may suffer earliest through depletion of their readily available supplies. In similar manner, since the industrial districts within countries have generally developed in close proximity to coal, this power resource is being drawn upon there at a rate far in excess of any general averages. The problems of conservation are therefore not only world wide and national; they are local as well.

Distribution of Coal in the United States. The accompanying map, Fig. 1, reveals more clearly than words could express the general distribution of coal within the limits of continental United States. The principal districts of active exploitation within the several provinces are shown in black. However, no map can show adequately the enormous stores of coal which occur in the northern Great Plains and the Rocky Mountain provinces. In their reserves of unmined coal these two provinces are credited with 60 per cent of the total for the entire country, whereas the eastern province contains but 13 per cent and the interior province but 12 per cent of the total.

In general the coal of the eastern and the interior provinces is of higher quality than that in the other four provinces. This is of particular interest because the exploitation from fields within these two provinces has long been on a scale far greater than in any other. While depletion of the estimated original tonnage of coal within the United States is probably less than 1 per cent, it is estimated that the anthracite fields of Pennsylvania are 29 per cent exhausted. In the eastern province, though reserves of bituminous coal are still huge, the best beds, such as the well-known Big Vein, Pocahontas, New River, and the Pittsburgh, have been so vigorously mined that depletion is well advanced. Since the highest-grade coal and most accessible beds are naturally mined first, as exploitation continues they are the first to be exhausted. This stage then is followed by producing from other beds at greater costs. Waste in any form during the early stages of exploitation inevitably brings the penalty of higher production costs at a date earlier than necessary.

Geographic Significance of the Distribution of Coal in the United States. Among the nations, the United States ranks foremost in known reserves. M. R. Campbell estimated that at the close of 1928 the unmined reserves amounted to the huge total of 3,189,381,368,000 short tons. The nation is fortunate not only in the quantity of its reserves but also in their distribution—every section of the country is within relatively easy reach of some coal field.

Two outstanding economic effects of the geographic distribution of the coal fields deserve emphasis. First, most of the coal deposits of eastern United States are more than 200 miles from tidewater; in contrast with this is the short land transportation in Great Britain where haulage from mine to ship rarely exceeds 20 miles. The rugged country which characterizes much of the distance from coal mines of the Appalachian Plateau to the Atlantic seaboard adds to the expense of railway haulage and therefore increases the cost of the coal at the ports. This is a handicap to the development of a large export trade because of the difficulty of competing on a price basis with the European coals, especially those from Germany and England, mined near tidewater where land transportation costs are slight. Secondly, the wide distribution of coal in the interior has furnished the sources of power to stimulate industrial and agricultural development on a scale far beyond that of the interior of any other continent. The transcontinental railroad systems have natural refueling stations at relatively convenient intervals throughout their routes. Had there been no coal in the interior, the costs of hauling agricultural products to seaboard markets would have been prohibitive and agricultural prosperity could not have been achieved. Without agricultural prosperity, industrial growth in the interior would have been impossible. Without the great markets of the Middle West and the country beyond, the industrial progress of the East would have been seriously curtailed. Although, of course, other factors also are involved, credit must be given to the coal fields of the interior—from Ohio to Colorado—for much of the energy and industrial progress of the United States. The wide-spread distribution of this great power resource is a geographic factor of major importance in accounting for the high agricultural and industrial achievement of the empire beyond the Alleghenies.

The Consumption of Coal. At the outset we stated that the use of mineral fuels was a relatively recent development in this country; the total amount of coal mined to the end of 1845 was only 27,700,000 tons. The annual production increased slowly but persistently and first reached the 10,000,000-ton figure in 1853. The rate of increase during the four decades prior to 1890 was such that the output doubled every ten years. The 100,000,000-ton yearly output was first reached in 1882, the 200,000,000-ton figure in 1897. Nearly as much coal was mined during the first decade of the present century as had been produced in all the previous decades. The increase in output per capita was none the less startling; during the decade 1840-1850 the average annual output of coal per capita was 0.27 ton whereas during the first decade of the present century it was 5.11 tons. The all-time record of annual production was made in 1918 with a total of 678,212,000 tons; this figure, however, was not greatly in excess of the production which was reached in 1920, 1923, and 1926. During the decade following 1926 the curve of production has been irregular and on a somewhat lower level, but still at a rate which would have been deemed enormous if judged by nineteenth-century standards. It is quite evident that, great as our reserves of coal are, the rate of extraction is such that exhaustion of the available supplies is but a question of a few centuries at most[1] (Fig. 2).

Conservation Problems. Since coal is an irreplaceable resource, quite literally a product of geologic ages in the making, should we not appreciate the importance of using it with care and wisdom? Are we not hopeful that our race shall have a future counted not in decades, nor even in centuries, but in tens or hundreds of thousands of years? As civilized human beings our vision should encompass our responsibility to succeeding generations. In order to prolong to the utmost our stores of mineral fuels, we must recognize and eliminate all wasteful practices.

Waste in Mining. In the past, when the prevailing practices in coal mining were designed to obtain maximum immediate returns, the waste was excessive, in many cases ranging from 50 to 150 per cent of the coal marketed. During the past few decades mining practices have been considerably improved and the wastage in most mines has been materially reduced. Even so, there still is room for much improve-

[1] One of our great coal authorities estimates that our resources at the present rate of recovery will last 2500 to 4000 years. (EDITORS.)

ment, and a sound conservation program should be inaugurated to eliminate wasteful practices in the extraction of coal.[1]

In many places the room-and-pillar plan of mining is followed and numerous large pillars are left to hold up the roof. Complete removal of pillars is not practicable because of the prohibitive expense of providing artificial supports, but even so there is no question that the

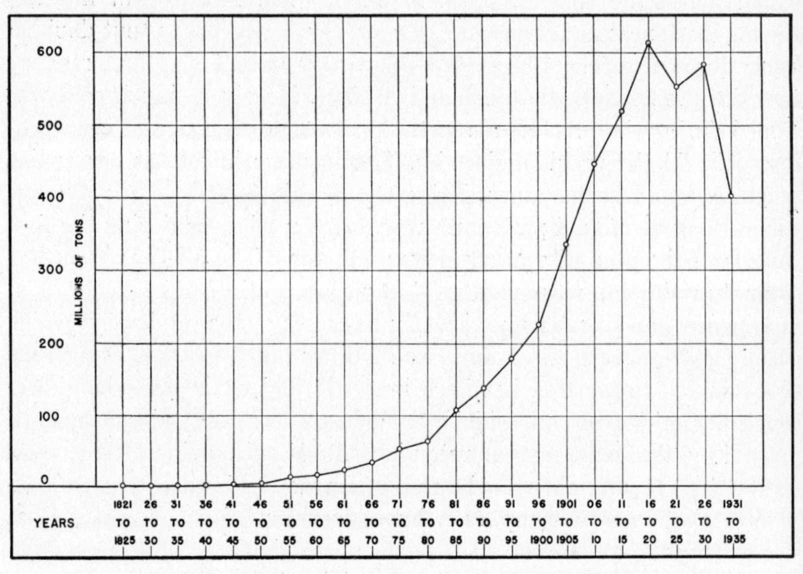

FIG. 2. Production of Coal in the United States.

Since 1821, by five-year periods. Note the slow rate of increase of production until 1880, followed by rapid acceleration for forty years. The sharp decrease during the period since 1930 was primarily a result of the industrial depression.

amount of coal left can be greatly reduced by careful methods of mining. Furthermore, in many mines now operated on the room-and-pillar plan the long-wall system could be used, and, in such instances, practically all the coal could be extracted.

Some coal beds consist of two or more seams separated by layers of shale. In such beds oftentimes the thinner seam is not mined because to do so would necessitate the handling of the shale. This practice may lead to leaving 25 per cent or more of the coal in the ground—a loss that is permanent because the thinner unmined coal seam cannot be extracted after the major workings are abandoned.

[1] In 1923, the United States Coal Commission estimated that the loss was 35 per cent, of which 20 per cent was considered avoidable. The basic cause—overproduction and cut-throat competition—should in some way be eliminated. There are too many mines in operation and too many miners. (EDITORS.)

Where several beds of coal occur in vertical series, as they frequently do, the topmost or upper beds should be mined first. If the lower beds are first extracted the resulting settling of the roof and layers above generally renders the extraction of the upper layers permanently impossible. Too many operators have begun mining the bed of most desirable quality or the one whose mining conditions rendered extraction easiest and cheapest, a practice which usually is induced by the necessity of meeting strenuous and unregulated competition. Such instances are not rare, and they are convincing illustrations of how the goal of immediate gain may obscure that of lasting prosperity. Coal in the ground has no active value; its value is entirely potential, and whenever man acts in such manner that the coal in any given bed must permanently remain underground he destroys even its potential value. Such destruction will inevitably render more difficult the opportunity for creation of wealth in the future.

Another type of waste associated with coal mining is the production of an undue amount of very fine coal, commonly referred to as waste or culm. Careless methods of mining and of handling are responsible for this type of waste. Of course, even where mining is most carefully and scientifically carried on there will be some fine coal, but if modern practices of machine mining are followed the percentage of such sizes need not be greater than the market can absorb.

Wasteful Practices in Coke Manufacture. Coke is the hard residue obtained from heating coals in the absence of air.[1] The percentage of coke obtained from coal varies from about 50 to 80 per cent, with 65 to 70 the percentages commonly derived. The by-products which may be obtained in the process of coke making are so numerous that many students look upon coal as raw material for a great chemical industry. These by-products consist of gas, gas liquor, and tar which may be used with little change for such purposes as fuel gas or briquet-binder. They may also be refined and treated chemically and thus made to yield hundreds of products varying from delicate perfumes and dyestuffs to roofing pitch or pavement filler. These valuable by-products are wasted in the beehive coking oven, whereas they are virtually all saved by use of the modern by-product ovens.

Fortunately great strides in this respect have been made during the last quarter century. In 1893 the production of by-product coke in the United States was only 12,850 tons, whereas beehive coke accounted for 9,464,730 tons. In 1900 by-product coke was only about 5 per cent of the total. Since then the increase has been marked, the output of by-

[1] Elwood S. Moore, *Coal,* p. 315, John Wiley & Sons.

product coke reaching 17 per cent in 1910, 60 per cent in 1920, and above 96 per cent in 1933. This phase of the coal conservation program is, happily, well advanced.

Waste by Imperfect Combustion. The black smoke which may often be seen pouring forth from stacks and chimneys is direct evidence of huge quantities of coal being blown into the air. This not only involves loss of coal; it also causes damage to property and is a hazard to health. Estimates vary as to the extent of loss and damage from the smoke nuisance, some claiming that the loss from this source in Chicago alone is at least $500,000,000 per year. Be that as it may, all students of the subject agree that the losses for the country as a whole reach staggering totals, and that in large measure such losses are avoidable. In the large heating plants where mechanical stokers of modern design have been installed the losses due to faulty combustion have been reduced by 50 to 70 per cent. In all plants, large and small, industrial and domestic, the waste can be reduced to small proportions by more careful firing and more efficient use and arrangement of drafts.

Lessening Waste Through Increasing Efficiency of Boilers and Engines. It is well known that on the basis of work done in ratio to energy used the steam engine can hardly be rated as an efficient machine. Nevertheless, improvement is possible and substantial advances in efficiency are being made. According to the Bureau of Statistics of the Interstate Commerce Commission the coal consumption of the Class I railways of the United States has been reduced materially on a load-distance haulage basis during the past decade and a half. In 1921, the freight service consumed 162 pounds of coal per 1,000 gross ton-mile, whereas in 1935 the corresponding figure was only 119 pounds. In 1921, the Class I steam railways used 18.8 pounds of coal per passenger-train car-mile, including locomotive; in 1935 only 15.3 pounds of coal were so used. These figures, showing decreased coal consumption of 18 to 27 per cent to the unit of load-distance, indicate the substantial progress being made in increasing the efficiency of steam haulage in this country. Much still remains to be achieved, and that further substantial progress will be made is to be expected as well as to be desired.

Outlook for the Future. During the period of rapid expansion of the coal industry various students indicated feelings of alarm at the probability of early exhaustion of our coal reserves. In 1908, Mr. Henry Gannett estimated that if the rate of increase in coal extraction should continue as it had during the preceding decades, the readily available reserves would be exhausted in about 120 years, and all the reserves at depths less than 3,000 feet would be mined by the year 2050. However, he also doubted that such rate of increase of mining would continue; subsequent events have fully justified this opinion then expressed by Mr. Gannett.

As previously stated, the actual peak of annual coal output in the United States was reached in 1918 with a total of 678,212,000 short tons. The 600,000,000-ton mark has been reached subsequently only three other years, namely, 1920, 1923, and 1929. The annual consumption per capita mounted steadily to an average of 5.47 tons during the decade 1910-1920, the highest annual average yet reached during any ten-year period. Since 1926 the average per capita consumption has declined considerably, dropping to 2.77 tons in 1932, but rising to 3.31 tons in 1935. It now seems doubtful that in the near future the consumption of coal per capita in this country will again reach the figures of 1918 or 1920.

Probable Developments. Improvements in the use of coal seem to indicate a lower tonnage demand during the years immediately ahead. Smelters and blast furnaces of improved design have cut the fuel consumption in ore reduction from 10 to 35 per cent since 1900. The change from beehive coke ovens to by-product plants has increased the efficiency of coke manufacture in similar degree, and it will probably be but a few years until most of the remaining beehive ovens will have been displaced.

The increase in efficiency of stokers and fireboxes as well as improved boiler construction for steam power plants may be expected to attain much higher levels in the near future, and of course increased plant efficiency reduces the amount of coal needed to generate a given load of steam. The demand for coal will be lessened also by the expansion of water-power development. Whatever may be said in criticism of water-power development subsidized by the government, the fact remains that water power once lost by lack of use cannot be regained, whereas coal not used remains an asset available in the future.

Another development which seems to be imminent is the transforming of coal at the mine to some form of power more easily transported than the bulky commodity coal. Superpower plants for the conversion of coal to electric power have already been planned on large scale, to be constructed at or near the mines; for many purposes it is feasible and more economical than to transport the equivalent amount of coal by rail. Conversion of coal to fixed gases which may be transported by pipe lines is already an accomplished fact, and further improvements which will lead to extension of this practice seem likely.

Still another method of utilizing coal which promises to lead to important developments in the near future is *hydrogenation*. By this process coal may be converted into liquids which may be used as crude oils or refined into high-grade gasolines and naphthas. This process is already in successful operation in some European countries, notably Germany. In the United States several large experimental plants are in operation and successful commercial operation is assured at price levels only moderately higher than now prevail for the products of petroleum.

In Conclusion. The improved techniques which have recently been introduced into the practices of mining, transporting, and utilizing coal are representative of true conservation ideals. Great strides forward have been made during the past quarter of a century, and partly because of them the curve of increasing drain of our coal reserves has been flattened—temporarily it has ceased to climb. The recent decline in use of coal, however, represents but a temporary tendency, one that seems certain to be reversed within the next few decades. The present abundance of natural petroleum with its accompanying ridiculously low prices will not last long; the best water-power sites will soon have been developed; and then the increasing demand for power resources will, in all probability, again be focused upon coal.

Coal should be recognized for what it is: the greatest store of energy we have and also a material yielding an abundance of varied raw materials which may be converted into hundreds of useful products. The necessities of our daily lives, as well as the comforts and conveniences to which we have become accustomed, depend in large measure upon its availability as a source of power. Notwithstanding the power resources now competitive with coal, we know of no substance which can replace it. In the best scientific light of our times we can discern no substitute for it. Countless generations will need it in the future as we need it now. Is it not clearly, then, the duty of intelligent citizenship today to emphasize the obligation to use this resource with the minimum of waste? In the abundance of the present the tendency to waste is great, but we must recognize that waste soon converts abundance into scarcity. Such waste constitutes an unforgivable sin.

PETROLEUM

The "drama of oil" is perhaps the most intriguing, the most interest-captivating subject of recent times. In the short space of three-quarters of a century petroleum has emerged from the realm of mystery and superstition and has become an industrial giant. Although it has long been known as a liquid which oozed out of the ground, its properties as a mineral resource were not recognized until near the middle of the nineteenth century, and its industrial possibilities were given but little consideration until after Colonel Drake's momentous discovery well was brought in by mechanical drilling in 1859. Drake's success in finding oil by drilling through solid rock layers opened wide the doors to the exploitation of a great fuel resource which had lain dormant during the preceding, almost countless, ages of time. Thus another of nature's irreplaceable gifts became available for man's use.

What Is Petroleum? The term, petroleum, is recognized as having been derived from the Greek, and means literally *rock oil.* Oil was known long before its commercial exploitation, because of seepages found in Persia, Mesopotamia, and along the shores of the Caspian Sea near Baku. Since these seepages came from rock, the name applied to the substance was quite fitting.

Petroleum has been concisely defined by Emmons as "an inflammable mixture of oily hydrocarbons that exudes from the earth or is pumped up."[1] Hydrocarbons are substances which consist essentially of hydrogen and carbon chemically united in various proportions. Petroleum as found in different localities consists of such a variety of mixtures of liquids and gases that the abilities of chemists are tested to the utmost to identify each and to separate any one of them from the others.

Petroleum is broadly classified according to its specific gravity and according to the residue left upon refining. As a matter of convenience, in commercial practice the specific gravity is translated into Baumé readings; 10° Baumé represents the specific gravity, 1.0, of pure water at a temperature of 4° Centigrade. Since practically all crude oil is lighter than water, the hydrometer graded on the Baumé scale reads progressively higher as the liquids are lighter. In general, crude oils which test 20° Baumé or lower are classified as *heavy,* whereas those which test about 30° are known as *light* oils. Ordinarily, light oils are more desirable for refinery runs than heavy oils, and therefore they command higher market prices.

The residue left when all the lighter ingredients have been driven off by heating is the other basis of classification. Some crudes yield paraffine as a residue; others yield asphalt; and still others, a mixture

[1] W. H. Emmons, *Geology of Petroleum,* Chapter I, McGraw-Hill Book Company, New York, 1922.

of both. For this reason they are known to the industry as paraffine-base, asphalt-base, or mixed-base oils, respectively. In the United States, the crudes found east of the Mississippi are mostly paraffine-base oils, those found along the Gulf Coast are mostly asphaltic, and those of the Mid-continent and the western fields are mixed-base or asphaltic.

Distribution of Petroleum in the United States. A glance at the map (Fig. 3) will reveal that the known oil fields are grouped into eight great regions or provinces. These are: Appalachian, Ohio-Indiana (often called Lima-Indiana), Michigan, Illinois, Mid-continent, Gulf Coast, Rocky Mountain, and California provinces.

The *Appalachian Province* includes the productive districts of the Appalachian Plateau from southern New York to Tennessee. This vast area, comprising a large number of local fields, was the seat of the earliest developments of the American petroleum industry. Near Titusville, Pennsylvania, along the banks of Oil Creek, Colonel E. L. Drake rigged up his crude derrick and string of tools to demonstrate the practicability of mechanically penetrating hard rock; his method of drilling was an application of the principle of crushing the rock by successively raising and dropping a heavy iron rod equipped at its lower end with a sharp bit. By this triphammer method, in spite of delays, accidents, and discouragements, he drilled his well to a depth of sixty-nine feet, and obtained a yield of twenty-five barrels of light oil a day (Fig. 3).

Following Drake's discovery well came a veritable frenzy of activities in the search for petroleum. For many years drilling locations were chosen in a haphazard manner. Failures were numerous and discouraging, but success was attended by such substantial rewards that the search for the "black gold" continued unabated. New producing areas were discovered in northwestern Ohio and in far-off California. Drilling methods were improved rapidly, greater skill was attained in refinery operations, pipe lines were constructed for the transportation of the crude, and tank cars were built for railway haulage of refined products. Within two decades petroleum had given rise to one of the greatest lines of business in the nation. During these early developments the Appalachian Province held undisputed supremacy in the growing industry.

Maximum production in this province was reached in 1891 with an output of 33,000,000 barrels.[1] Since that time there has been a slow

[1] A barrel of petroleum, as used statistically, means 42 gallons.

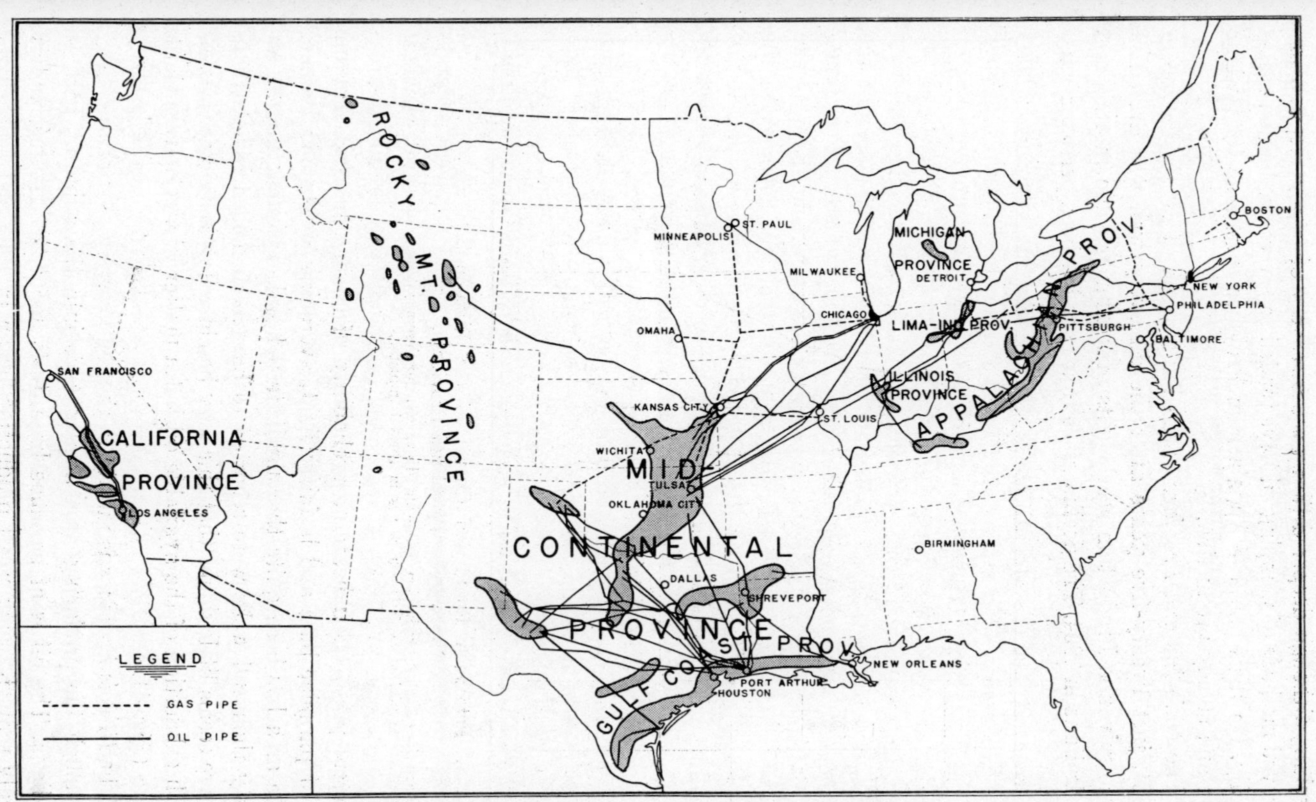

FIG. 3. Petroleum Provinces of the United States.
The major pipe lines used for transportation of crude oil, natural gas, and gasoline are shown. The gas line symbol includes both the natural gas and gasoline lines.

decline, although deeper drilling, the discovery of new pools, and improved methods of pumping oil have tended to revive production materially. On the whole the Appalachian Province is notable for its long life and steady production.

The *Ohio-Indiana Province* entered the arena of oil production in 1884, just twenty-five years after the discovery well was drilled in Pennsylvania. Production reached its maximum in Ohio in 1896 and in Indiana in 1904. The decline since that time has been persistent, and

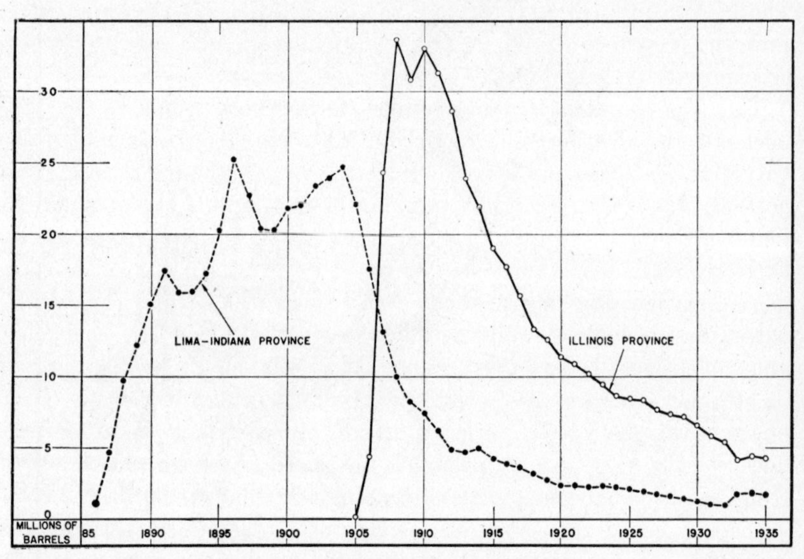

FIG. 4. Petroleum Production Curves of the Lima-Indiana and the Illinois Petroleum Provinces.

Sharp increase of production following discovery, maximum yearly output, and the gradual decline are typical of exploitation curves in the oil industry.

present prospects indicate no probability of change in trend. The oil is of paraffine base and is fairly light, averaging 30° to 35° Baumé. The area has been quite thoroughly tested and exploited; more than sixty thousand wells were reported to have been drilled before 1931. There seems little doubt that this may be classed as a dying province, with exhaustion of the available oil but a matter of a relatively short time (Fig. 4).

The *Illinois Province* is mostly in the southeastern part of the state, although the producing area also extends into the adjacent part of Indiana. The oil is of paraffine base, tests about 30° Baumé, and is easily refined. Commercial production began in 1905 and reached its maximum in 1910, since which time there has been persistent decline to less than 20 per cent of the maximum. The outlook gives no promise of change in trend, and thus its record exemplifies the inevitable decline which will characterize the other oil regions as well, some of which are now in their flush periods of youth.

Michigan is the most recent addition to the oil provinces of the United States. It is not listed separately in the statistical records until 1925, although there had been some production many years earlier. The province is still undeveloped, and exploitation is increasing; however, the present prospects do not give promise of such high production as characterizes some of the other major provinces.

The *Mid-continent Province*, taken as a whole, ranks as the premier oil-producing territory in the world. It extends from near Kansas City across Kansas and Oklahoma into Texas, southern Arkansas, and northern Louisiana. To date no region of comparable extent has been found to embrace so many petroliferous areas, so many different oil horizons, and such a variety of kinds of petroleum. Large-scale commercial production began about 1906, since which time the annual output has mounted steadily with but few interruptions. It seems probable that several years must elapse before maximum production will be attained. The province is noted for its diversity in practically every phase of the petroleum industry; crude of nearly all grades is produced; wells vary in depth from a few hundred to several thousand feet, and from modest pumpers yielding less than a barrel a day to gushers spouting thousands of barrels during their flush periods. Diversity of capital interests likewise is a prominent characteristic. In addition to the hundreds of small operating corporations, practically every large petroleum company in the United States has important holdings in this inland empire of oil. Contrary to popular opinion, competition is keen in all phases of the business, a competition and rivalry so intense that orderly development is rendered difficult. Overproduction and wasteful practices are the results; yet attempts to correct these abuses by law in order to conserve the resources of oil and gas have encountered most bitter opposition, and at best have met with but moderate success. Here again is an illustration of how the abundance which characterizes the present may blind us to the realization that sooner or later these non-replaceable stores will be gone, and that scarcity will follow these days of plenty.

The *Gulf Coast Province* includes the oil-producing areas of the coastal plains of Texas and Louisiana, together with such potential areas as may extend farther east. Production was begun in 1900, after which it rose sharply for five or six years; since 1916 the general trend has been upward, but it has been marked by periodic declines and sharp revivals. It now seems probable that the peak of annual output may be some years in the future. The oil is heavy, of asphaltic base, and therefore less valuable for refining than the lighter paraffine- or mixed-base oils produced farther north. Much of the crude is sold for fuel purposes; the demand for bunker fuels on gulf and ocean steamships provides an important market outlet. Some of the crude contains excellent bases for the manufacture of cold-test lubricants, and its value depends largely upon this quality rather than upon its gasoline possibilities.

The *Rocky Mountain Province* embraces all the fields within or near the mountains from Canada to the Rio Grande. In magnitude of output the most important states are Wyoming, New Mexico, and Montana. Diversity of structures, of drilling conditions, and of qualities of crude is to be expected. In general, however, the oils of the Rocky Mountain Province belong to the light density group, but there are some notable pools of heavy asphaltic crude. Although, except in New Mexico, recent years have been marked by declining production, the area involved is so great, structure conditions so varied, and the exploratory work so incomplete that the future trend is necessarily uncertain. It is quite within the realm of probability that discoveries of important producing fields will yet be made.

The *California Province* ranks second in output in the United States, being exceeded only by the Mid-continent Province. There are two principal producing areas, the southern part of the San Joaquin Valley and the Los Angeles basin. Commercial exploitation began about 1884, but development was relatively slow until after the turn of the century. Then large-scale production soon placed California at the front; from 1903 to 1915 the state ranked first in petroleum output. Since 1915, first place has always been held by one of the three states, California, Oklahoma, or Texas.

The known and potential reserves of California are such that large output seems assured for many years. If exploitation is kept within reasonable limits and wells are not allowed to run wild, the outlook is good for steady, long-time production. Many of the producing districts are characterized by heavy gas pressure and therefore by huge initial production; under such conditions the temptation to take large initial returns rather than more moderate prolonged returns is ever present and not easy to withstand. Therein lies the danger from a conservation point of view. It must be kept in mind, and operators and the public alike must be taught, that gas pressure is essential to the flow of the oil; if such pressure is permitted to decline, the total amount of oil which can be obtained will be materially reduced. The waste of gas is in itself reprehensible, but loss of gas means also a permanent loss in the amount of recoverable oil. This is particularly true in regions where gas pressure is pronounced, and therefore it applies emphatically to most of the producing districts of California.

Origin and Occurrence of Petroleum. The theory of organic origin of petroleum is now generally accepted in scientific circles. There seems to be little reason to doubt that the supplies of oil which are found today in the interstices of sedimentary rocks are the results of natural distillation of organic materials of past ages. Slow migrations

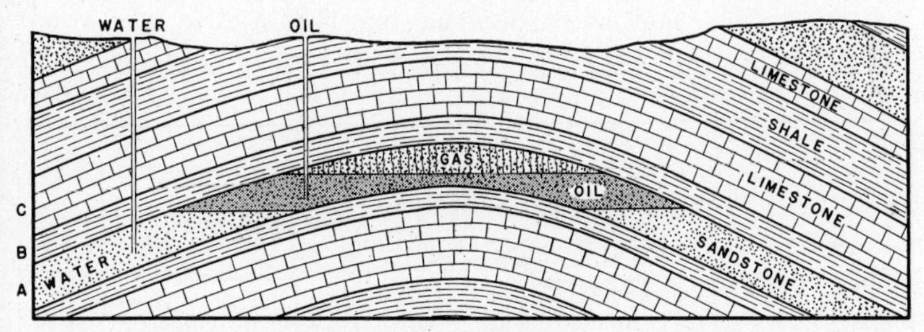

FIG. 5. Diagram Showing Structural Relations of Gas, Oil, and Water in a Symmetrical Anticline.

Oil and gas have been formed by natural distillation of organic materials in the underlying rocks, and, being lighter than water, they have been forced to migrate upward. The sandstone layer, *A*, being overlaid by a close-textured shale, *B*, and a heavy limestone, *C*, is the reservoir zone where gas in the apex and petroleum along the flanks of the anticline have displaced the water from the interstices of the sandstone. Thus the oil is under water and gas pressure; a well drilled at the apex of the structure would be a gasser, whereas wells along the upper walls would yield oil and would probably be flowing wells.

of the minute droplets have led to accumulation of these stores of oil in places where further migration was stopped or seriously impeded by structural conditions. Natural distillation and the migration of the resulting products have necessarily been exceedingly slow processes, so slow that millions of years have been involved in creating the products which we are now tapping at such stupendous rate. Literally, petroleum is a product of the ages; in terms of human existence it is non-replaceable.

Most of the petroleum of the world occurs in sedimentary strata, notably sandstones, conglomerates, and limestones. Open-textured sandstones are perhaps the most common reservoirs, although notable exceptions are found in porous or cavernous limestones, as in western Ohio and in Mexico. Petroleum usually occurs in strata more or less folded or faulted, anticlines being the simplest and best-known structures favorable for its accumulation. In anticlines natural gas may oc-

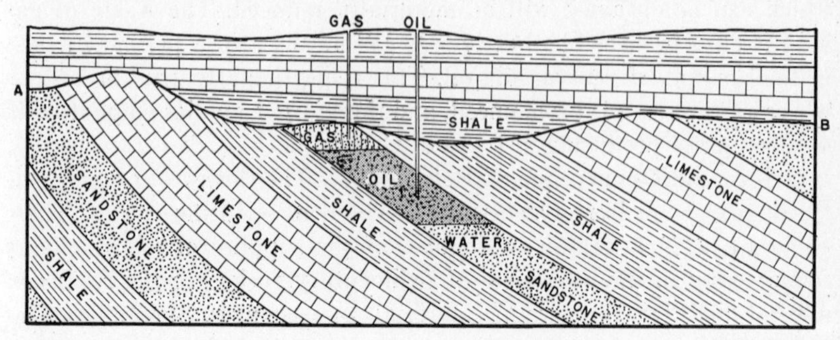

FIG. 6. Diagram Showing Oil and Gas Accumulation in Buried Monoclinal Structures.

Line *A-B* marks a major unconformity. The shale as the lowermost of the horizontal beds serves to seal the oil and gas and thus prevent their escape until man comes along and drills holes at the right locations.

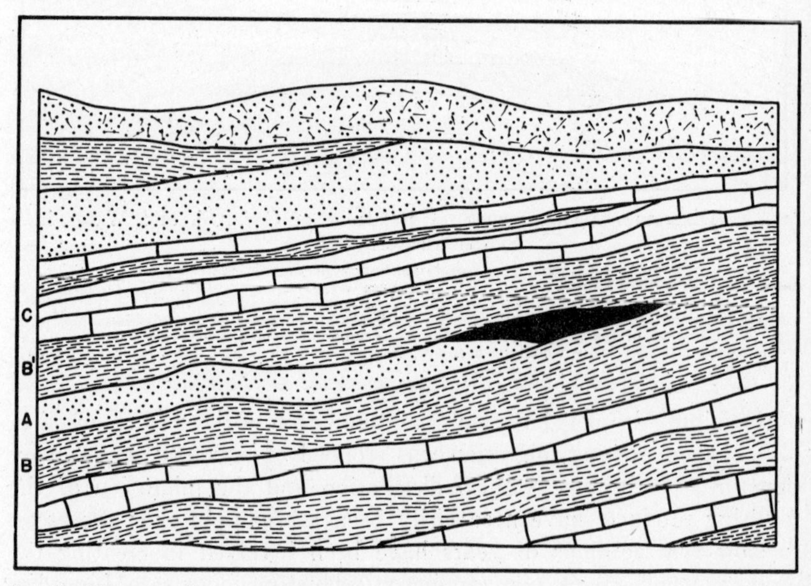

FIG. 7. Diagram Showing Petroleum Accumulation in the Upper Part of a Lens of Sandstone.

B-B' is a shale with an extensive layer, or lens, of interbedded sandstone. The minute droplets of oil, distilled from the shale or other lower rocks, have accumulated by migration in the interstices of the relatively coarse sandstone. The structure is a monocline of low dip. Oil deposits under these conditions and those shown in the preceding diagram are difficult to locate.

cur in the apex of the structure, petroleum along the upper flanks, and water at the lower levels. The same sequence has been observed repeatedly in other types of structures, and in various oil fields of the world wherever studied. It seems clear that, in general, the migration of gas and oil from their sources of origin to their reservoirs of present occurrence has been in accord with pressure and specific gravity of the several substances, because the sequence from higher to lower positions is almost invariably gas, petroleum, and water (Figs. 5, 6, and 7).

Petroleum Products in Modern Industry. Petroleum, like coal, is more than merely something that will burn. While the primary products are the ones with which most of us have almost daily contact in some form or other, the secondary products of refining and manufacture are legion in number. A liquid distilled from coal and known as "coal oil" had reached rather wide-spread use as an illuminant before 1860. It was soon found, however, that a liquid even better suited for use in lamps could be obtained by distilling petroleum, and thus kerosene, often referred to as coal oil, became the first product of petroleum to attain great economic importance. Almost from the outset the refiners exerted themselves to spread the use of kerosene into distant markets and thus provide profitable outlets for the gradually rising tide of petroleum production. The spread of the simple kerosene lamp into nearly all parts of the world in the decades following 1860 brought light which brightened the evenings from jungles to deserts and from the tropics to the polar realms. The kerosene lamp has been aptly termed one of the most important civilizing influences of the second half of the nineteenth century.

Then came the internal-combustion engine and the almost meteoric rise into popularity of the automobile. Gasoline, a drug on the market until shortly before the present century, became the much-sought product of petroleum, whereas kerosene was pushed into the background. In 1899 the production of kerosene amounted to 58 per cent of the number of barrels of crude run to stills; since then the decline has been marked, the percentage dropping to 15.4 in 1919 and to 6.0 in 1934. Were it not for the use of kerosene as a fuel for some forms of automotive activity, notably tractors, the position of kerosene would be even lower.

In 1934, according to the *Minerals Yearbook*, the percentages of the principal refined products in proportion to crude run to refineries were:

Product	Percentage
Gasoline	43.5 per cent
Residual fuel oil	26.8 per cent
Gas oil and distillate fuel	10.6 per cent
Kerosene	6.0 per cent
Lubricants	2.9 per cent

The significance of these products to modern industry can readily be inferred when we study the power situation in the United States. C. R. Daugherty, of the National Automobile Chamber of Commerce, calculated that the motor vehicles of the United States furnished 85 per cent of the total horsepower of the country in 1931. This estimate was based on the number of automobiles in use, their efficiency, and the fuel consumed. This was in sharp contrast to the horsepower estimated for other fields. Steam railroads were credited with 5.56 per cent of the total horsepower of the country, agriculture with 2.95 per cent, electric central stations with 2.58 per cent, and manufacturing with 1.20 per cent. Bearing in mind that fuel and lubricants are both vital to the operation of automotive vehicles we can readily appreciate what a power giant has come into our daily lives. The astounding development of the automobile industry with all its ramifications into the realms of raw material, and to skilled manufactures in related fields, such as paints, rubber, upholstery, and precision tools, could not have occurred without an abundance of low-cost petroleum.

The above statements, striking as they are, do not, however, tell the whole story. The by-products of petroleum available through refining and further manufacture are numerous, varied, and important. They include medicines, ointments, antiseptics, insecticides, alcohols, and a host of other compounds in common use. The possibilities of manufacture in the realm of chemicals are almost limitless. Quite truly may it be said that petroleum compounds contain the raw materials for the manufacture of nearly all organic compounds.

Industrial Relationships of Petroleum. The Drake well inaugurated a new industry, one which was destined to bring about an industrial revolution in the United States whose far-reaching consequences can hardly be overstated. Prior to 1859, petroleum was viewed as somewhat of a curiosity. No technique had been developed in drilling, even Drake's shallow 69-foot well being considered a marvel; now about 20,000 wells are drilled annually, very few of which are less than 1,000 feet deep, and some reach depths exceeding 10,000 feet. There was then no petroleum-refining industry, whereas now more than 600 refineries are in operation (682 in 1935) with a combined total daily capacity of about 4,400,000 barrels. In 1860 the transportation of crude petroleum in large quantities was a problem still to be faced, and heavy wastage occurred during the early years of that decade because adequate means of storage and transportation were lacking. Storage tanks, tank cars, and pipe lines were the answer to the problem, and their construction, operation, and maintenance now comprise one of the great industries of the country. Since 1860 facilities at fields, refineries, and ocean ports have been developed so that crude oil in above-ground storage frequently exceeds 350,000,000 barrels—a larger quantity than was produced in any 10-year period prior to 1895. In the United States, about 240,000 miles of pipe line are used for transporting petroleum, gasoline, and natural gas, with a total investment estimated to exceed $2,500,000,000.

The industrial expansion thus briefly outlined is of course only part of the story; there are scores of industries more or less closely identified with the production, transportation, and refining of petroleum. Among such industries the manufactures of tools, machinery, power equipment, and chemicals hold high rank.

The focal point of the whole industry, however, is automotive transportation on land and sea and in the air. Automobiles, trucks, tractors, Diesel-motored ships, airplanes, and dirigibles all depend upon liquid fuels, particularly the products of petroleum. The low cost of fuel and lubricants has enabled the use of motor vehicles to spread into all hamlets of the United States; without petroleum the present state of development of the great automotive industry could not have been attained.

Rate of Exploitation in the United States. Almost from the beginning of the industry, the exploitation of petroleum has been on a large scale. In 1860, the first full year of production, the output of petroleum exceeded 500,000 barrels, and the production of the following year is officially recorded as 2,113,609 barrels. It is well known that during those two early years more oil was wasted than was used. Lack of markets, lack of storage, and a frenzy of drilling led to a flood of oil almost at the very beginning of successful operations.

Although the production of petroleum thus began on a scale where some millions of barrels became commonplace figures, the rate of increase remained moderate for a number of years. Not until 1874, fifteen years after Drake's discovery, did the annual production exceed 10,000,000 barrels. The total quantity of petroleum which had been produced in the United States by the end of 1900 was 1,006,876,313 barrels, a quantity but slightly larger than the annual production in the years immediately following 1930.

The following table tells its story more effectively than words. Although the original underground stores of petroleum in this country were stupendous, and even though important reserves may yet remain undiscovered, we must face the fact that eventually even such reserves will become depleted. At the increasing rate of extraction now in prog-

PRODUCTION OF CRUDE PETROLEUM IN THE UNITED STATES

(By decades, in barrels of 42 gallons)

Ten-year Periods	*Total Production*
1851–1860	502,000
1861–1870	32,462,279
1871–1880	125,186,842
1881–1890	292,485,842
1891–1900	552,966,659
1901–1910	1,374,240,735
1911–1920	3,052,004,000
1921–1930	7,718,615,000

One-year Periods	*Production*
1931	845,803,454
1932	785,304,403
1933	901,273,323
1934	903,104,233
1935 (estimate)	990,620,775
Total, five years, 1931–1935	4,426,106,188
Grand total, to close of 1935	17,574,569,128 barrels

ress the date of depletion to the point of scarcity cannot be remote—a few years, or at most a few decades seem a distinct probability.

Proved Reserves of Petroleum in the United States. Reserves of petroleum can be considered *proved* only when their existence has been verified by the drill. By scientific methods the structural conditions may be determined as being favorable or unfavorable to oil accumulation in any given locality, and in many places such methods may be conclusive as to the impossibility of oil being present. However, even if the structure is favorable oil may not be present, and therefore the only sure test is to drill (Fig. 8).

In view of the above statement, it is apparent that as long as drilling continues to open up new fields and pools it also serves to augment the proved reserves of oil. Thus, in the earlier years of the industry when the production was small, the proved reserves were likewise small. In 1908, David T. Day, of the United States Geological Survey, computed them to be about 8,100,000,000 barrels. Since that date about 16,500,000,000 barrels of crude oil have been produced and yet the proved reserves are still much larger than those of 1908. The tremendous drilling campaign which has been carried on year after year furnishes the answer to this apparently anomalous situation.

In the autumn of 1935 a committee of experts working under the auspices of the American Petroleum Institute undertook to appraise the petroleum supply of the United States in the light of current knowledge. The committee had the active cooperation of many experts each of whom was familiar with the details of the local situation in some part of the country. The report made by this committee stated that the

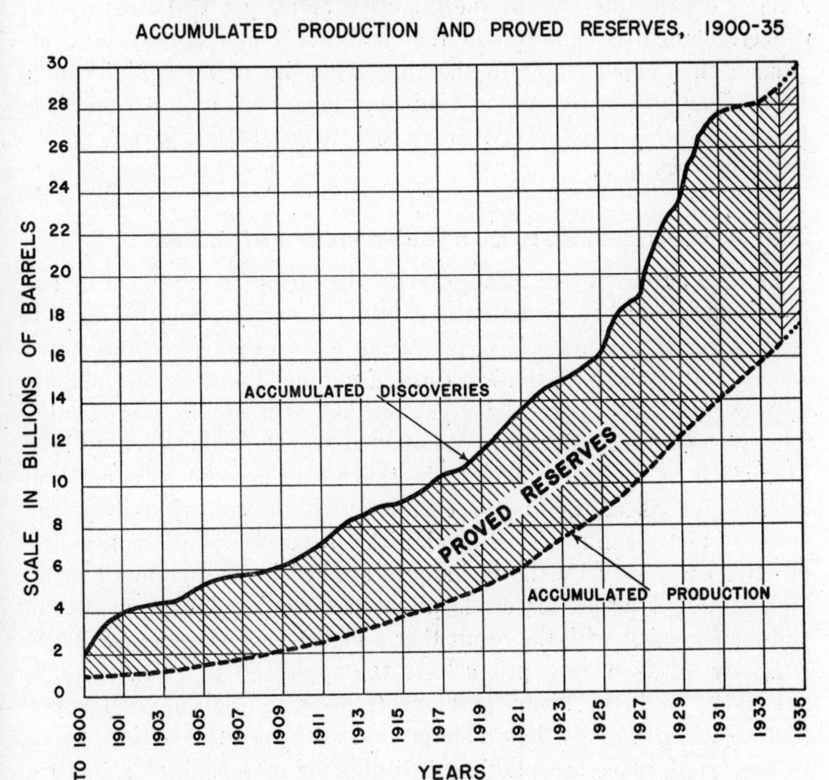

FIG. 8. The Accumulated Discoveries, Production, and Proved Reserves of Petroleum in the United States.

That proved reserves have increased steadily in relation to the mounting annual output is a strong assurance against an early rapid decline in supply. The form of the curve, however, cannot continue so indefinitely, and sooner or later the fact of lower proved reserves must be faced.

proved reserves as of January 1, 1935, were 12,177,000,000 barrels.[1] That figure represented the quantity of petroleum which could be obtained by the ordinary methods of production then in use. During 1935 these reserves were depleted by the production of nearly a billion barrels of crude; this, however, was somewhat offset by the dis-

[1] "Petroleum Production and Supply," *Bulletin of the American Association of Petroleum Geologists,* Tulsa, Oklahoma, January, 1936.

covery of new supplies. Based on the data available and on the report referred to, an estimate that the reserves as of January 1, 1936, were approximately 12,427,000,000 barrels seems justifiable.

It should be kept in mind that the amount of the known reserves is not an indicator of the volume of the future supply, because it does not offer a dependable clue to the quantity of oil yet to be discovered. Nevertheless, it is equally true that with every new discovery we approach that much closer to the time when no new supplies can be found. The proved reserves in 1908 may have been only 8,000,000,000 barrels, but the actual reserves were then 16,000,000,000 barrels greater than they are now.

PETROLEUM CONSERVATION PROBLEMS

Some Factors to Be Recognized. In facing the problem of how petroleum should be exploited and utilized, various realities must be recognized. In the first place, petroleum is an exhaustible natural resource, and its exploitation is a form of mining. The reserves, immense as they originally were and great as they still are in this country, nevertheless are irreplaceable. Whatever natural distillation may be in progress is at a rate too slow to be taken into account as a factor in replenishing them. Secondly, complete withdrawal of underground stores of petroleum is impossible, but the percentage of extraction may be affected greatly by the techniques applied in production. Thirdly, higher market prices for crude promote careful practices in drilling and management with the result that a higher percentage of extraction is finally attained. Low prices have the opposite effect and therefore are likely to bring about permanent losses in that a greater percentage of oil may be left underground without chance of recovery. In the fourth place acceptable substitutes for petroleum as a fuel can much more readily be provided than can substitutes for it as a source of high-grade lubricants.

Unrestricted Competition Often Wasteful. Petroleum, unlike coal or ore, is not a fixed commodity—it moves underground with shifting pressure. Thus oil will move from adjacent areas toward a producing well. If ownership of the land is in many hands and small holdings, economic self-interest is likely to necessitate putting down too many wells, thus leading to production at such a rate that gas pressure is quickly reduced to a low point and the chances for ultimate recovery of oil are seriously lessened. This is in addition to the economic losses which producers may suffer by being forced to sell at times when the market is already flooded with oil. A sound conservation policy implies the development of any pool or field as a unit. Wells should be spaced in accordance with structural conditions and operated so as to utilize to the fullest extent the gas or water pressure, and thus insure the maximum ultimate recovery. Such a policy would prove economically sound in the long run, but occasionally it lessens the immediate returns, and therein is the difficulty of applying it under the theory of rugged individualism.

Methods of Exploration. In the early days of the oil industry the common expression was "oil is where you find it." Well sites were chosen without any scientific basis for the choice; often they were chosen on a "hunch," or by flipping coins, or because of a peculiar dream on the part of the driller. Failures were numerous, but since the successful ventures were richly rewarded the game went on. Gradually, however, the geologic conditions favorable to oil accumulation became better understood, field investigations prior to drilling became the common practice, and the percentage of failures declined. During the past thirty years the petroleum geologist has been an important factor in the exploration for oil, one whose services are in large measure responsible for the success of the industry in supplying the huge quantities of crude demanded in recent years.

The latest advances in the technical realm of exploration are of geophysical nature. By means of methods and equipment brought into play within the past decade or so, subsurface structures can be ascertained with considerable accuracy. Evidence thus obtained makes unnecessary the former practice of blind wildcat drilling in areas where surface evidences of structure are entirely lacking. The further development of techniques of subsurface investigation may be expected to assist effectively in locating petroleum reserves now undiscovered.

Improvement in Drilling Practices. That oil sands may be drilled through without being discovered is well known to oil men, although not generally appreciated by the public. The drilling of oil wells is a technical enterprise. Improvements in that technique have made it possible to penetrate to depths exceeding 12,000 feet (the deepest well as of April, 1936, was 12,786 feet, located in Upton County, Texas), whereas twenty years ago 5,000 feet was believed to be the maximum depth to which drilling might be expected to penetrate successfully. Equally important improvements have been made in adapting methods of drilling to the varying conditions in different fields. There is, however, need for further advances in technique in drilling and also in methods whereby the formations penetrated may be more accurately logged, sampled, and studied in order to reduce errors in interpretation of the underground structures involved.

Control of Flow of Wells. From a conservation point of view, it is highly important that the flow of wells which are producing under heavy gas pressure be carefully controlled. When gushers, capable of producing thousands of barrels a day, are brought in, the temptation is strong to let them flow regardless of market conditions. Even if prices are low, free flowing oil at the rate of thousands of barrels daily is productive of high income at the time, and with many people, particularly small independent producers, maximum immediate income is sought regardless of the ultimate results. In the interest of the general public neither gas wells nor oil wells should be permitted to run wild. If the gas pressure is conserved through control of oil flowage, the life of the well will be prolonged, the total amount of oil which may be obtained without pumping increased, and maximum ultimate recovery facilitated. This conservation factor is one of great importance and needs more consideration than is often given to it.

Storage of Crude. With proved reserves as great as they are in the United States, huge above-ground storage is not only unnecessary, it is distinctly uneconomical. Underground storage in the original reservoirs is the best and cheapest mode of holding reserves ready for action. Excessive quantities in storage tend to depress the market for crude to points so low that owners cannot afford to operate the tens of thousands of wells of small daily production; yet those wells constitute the essential mainstay of the industry. Furthermore, many small producers, if abandoned, cannot again be brought into play and their stores of undelivered oil are permanently lost. In periods of heavy flush production from newly discovered fields the tendency is ever present to flood the market with oil, and to place inexcusably large quantities in storage; the result is that markets decline to the point of actual losses to thousands of producers. In such times the public interest demands that the amounts of flush oil to be produced be sharply checked in order that maximum ultimate recovery from all fields, both new and old, may be promoted.

Refining Technique. The improvements in petroleum refining which have been made during the past decade or two have placed that industry among the leaders in technical efficiency. No longer is it true that "gasoline is gasoline"; there are gradations in quality prepared for specific purposes. Through scientific methods of refining, petroleum can be made to yield not only motor fuels and lubricants but also medicines, dyes, perfumes, and chewing gums. Further improvements will probably result in increasing still further the diversity of products and the efficiency of the manufacturing processes.

Use without Waste. In the use of petroleum products the importance of the obligation which rests upon the motoring public is usually forgotten. One wonders if the ordinary motorist ever considers that in the use of gas and oil he is the beneficiary of wealth produced and accumulated during millions of years past and that the stores of such wealth are limited; waste will deprive those still to come of a heritage which should be theirs to enjoy. Waste in filling gasoline tanks to overflowing is usually merely the subject of levity or wisecracks; it should be met with sharp reprimand. Of course, statistics are not available on this kind of loss, but there is no doubt that the total quantity of gasoline wasted yearly through careless servicing of cars amounts to a gallonage inexcusably large.

John Q. Public—you and I—should feel obligated to watch motor efficiency. To obtain the maximum mileage per gallon of gasoline with a given car is of course to the interest of the owner or driver; moreover, it is in line with public duty, because in this way the fuel supply serves most efficiently and is conserved most truly.

In the use of motor vehicles there result, quite inevitably, quantities of sludge or outworn oil, which must be disposed of. For land vehicles this disposal is not very difficult because even sludge has fuel value and it can be used in heating plants or incinerators. For oil-burning vessels, however, whether small motor boats or ocean liners, the disposal of sludge is a serious problem. The practice of throwing such waste upon the waters has been commonly followed, and, unfortunately, still is. These waste oils spewed out upon the waters of streams, lakes, and ocean shores have raised havoc with wildlife and ruined many places for bathing resorts (discussed in Chapter XIX). The problem of disposal of the sludge from oil-burning boats demands attention, immediate and effective, in order to prevent further ruinous pollution of the waters of streams, lakes, and seacoasts. Conservation of wild life and promotion of human comfort, both of major importance, are the issues at stake.

NATURAL GAS

Value, Distribution, and Use. It is often remarked that natural gas is nature's ideal fuel. It is a product of natural distillation and accumulation under conditions quite similar to those which have given rise to the stores of petroleum. As a fuel for domestic or industrial use it has several distinct advantages over coal, petroleum, or manufactured gas. Its heating value is nearly double that of manufactured gas; in comparison with coal or oil it has the advantages of ease in handling and absence of residue; it requires no storage space; and it obviates the expenditure of large amounts of capital for fuel inventories.

Natural gas is produced in commercial quantities in twenty-one states, namely Arkansas, California, Colorado, Illinois, Indiana, Kansas, Kentucky, Louisiana, Michigan, Mississippi, Missouri, Montana, New Mexico, New York, Ohio, Oklahoma, Pennsylvania, Texas, Utah, West Virginia, and Wyoming. The oldest and still among the most important producing areas are the Appalachian fields extending from western New York southwestwardly into Kentucky. Leadership in natural gas output has passed to Texas, whose production in recent years has been more than 25 per cent of the country's total. California usually holds second place and Oklahoma a close third.

Even though the use of natural gas began in this country almost as early as that of coal, the greatest development has occurred during recent decades. In 1906 the total production, as reported officially, was 338,842,000,000 cubic feet; in 1923, it was 1,008,135,000,000 cubic feet, and ten years later the figure had risen to 1,555,474,000,000 cubic feet. To estimate the reserves of natural gas is even more difficult than to estimate the reserves of petroleum, and therefore to forecast the potential life of the stores of gas still available would be futile. Some students claim that the recently proved fields of the Panhandle of Texas are ample to furnish supplies for the next century at current rates of consumption. More conservative-minded students place the estimates of potential supplies at much lower figures. Whichever may prove to be more nearly correct, it is evident that even the most optimistic estimates are for relatively short periods of time. Natural gas, like the other mineral fuels, is fixed in quantity and irreplaceable.

Avoid Waste. The conservation of natural gas faces problems similar to those which confront the petroleum industry. Perhaps the greatest waste is that which is caused by uncapped wells, or wells improperly capped. A number of gassers have been allowed to run wild where immediate markets for the product were not available, because the operators thus hoped that the wells would later "blow in" as oil producers.

Slow seepages of gas, wherever discovered, should be brought under control. To allow gas wells to burn indefinitely is another form of inexcusable waste, even though the spectacle may be thrilling and the present market value of the gas in some remote district so low that the immediate economic loss appears negligible. It is another example where the obligation to future interests should transcend the whim, fancy, or carelessness of the present.

On the whole, the life of gas wells is so short, the value of the fuel so great, and the supply so definitely limited, that no form of abuse should be tolerated. The permanent public interest demands that prompt action be taken to reduce waste. Whether the wasteful practices be associated with production, transportation, distribution, or utilization of natural gas, such practices should be promptly eliminated. Public interest demands that they be stamped as unsound both socially and economically.

GENERAL SUMMARY

The modern industrial world is dependent in large measure upon mineral fuels for the energy to furnish the power necessary for the maintenance of the present high rate of productivity. Never before has the average production per capita been so great as it is now, and even greater possibilities seem assured of attainment. Inasmuch as high production is the first essential for high standards of living, it is vital that such potential productive capacity be safeguarded.

The mineral fuels are abundant, but nevertheless they are irreplaceable and definitely limited in quantity.

No substitute for coal as a store of energy available for conversion into power is known. Fortunately our stores of coal are large; yet as extraction progresses costs necessarily increase. Economic shortage of this commodity will be felt before actual physical shortage occurs.

Increasing efficiency in methods of exploration, exploitation, and utilization will serve to prolong the life of our petroleum reserves. The recognition of this fact should not, however, make us indifferent to waste in any form.

Heavy flush production of petroleum in some fields when large-scale exploitation is first achieved should never be permitted to depress prices to the extent that production by the many thousands of small wells becomes economically impossible. As of December 31, 1935, there were 332,806 active oil wells in operation in the United States; based on this number, the average daily production per well was 8.15 barrels. The 79,997 active wells of Pennsylvania were credited with an average daily output of but 0.54 barrel for each; the 34,100 active wells of Ohio with 0.33 barrel each. These numerous small wells which are found in all producing states must be protected from extinction in order to insure the maximum ultimate extraction of our petroleum reserves.

Substitutes for natural petroleum are available, and their use in increasing quantities is a development to be expected in the near future. Costs will probably be greater than present prices of petroleum products, but not prohibitively so.

There is no need to fear any shortage of power resources for decades to come unless extravagant waste should become prevalent. Nevertheless, it is the duty of intelligent citizenship to realize that the life of nations, as of civilization, should be projected into centuries or even into millenniums of time. On that basis careful conservation of mineral fuels demands immediate recognition.

In the near future, use of power resources may be expected to increase, and with it per capita production of goods will mount to heights heretofore unrealized; as a normal and desirable result higher standards of living will be made possible and they should be attained.

PART VI

CHAPTER XVIII

CONSERVATION OF NATURAL RESOURCES AND THE MANUFACTURING INDUSTRY

BY HELEN M. STRONG

Soil Conservation Service, U.S.D.A.

THE IMPORTANCE OF MANUFACTURING

The manufacturing industry forms as significant a foundation stone of American progress, prosperity, and well-being as does the agricultural industry. So important did manufacturing bulk in the emerging economic life of the early days of the Republic that one of the two positive measures passed by the patriots of the first Congress was an act "aimed to establish their independence on the basis of the productive industry and laborious arts of the country."[1] It is safe to say that, without manufactures, American pioneers a century ago would not have enjoyed the comforts and profits which came to them in ever-increasing measure. Today, American factories send forth machines and materials which are as necessary to all the various phases of American life as food is for the human body. Furthermore, without these material means and vehicles, the human spirit of achievement and creative thought could not function in arts, science, business, or social endeavor. Wires and cables, telephone switchboards and telegraph keys, steel rails and trains, dynamos and motors, gas and steam engines, and the countless other manufactured products too frequently taken for granted, assume an almost human position as they extend, multiply, and amplify human powers.

THE RELATION OF MANUFACTURING TO RESOURCES

Since the decade 1890-1900, according to United States census statistics, the products of the manufacturing industry of our country have

[1] Edward Everett in an address on American manufacture, delivered in New York in 1831, United States Census, *Report on the Manufactures of the United States, 1880,* Washington, 1883, p. 5.

led all others in value. Expansion of settlement westward, development of new regions, growth of large-scale manufacturing in the East and elsewhere, all have contributed to the rise of the industry. But the demand created by the cumulative interaction of this vigorous expanding economic life was met by American manufacturers only because they could draw upon a wealth of agricultural and mineral resources; because highly developed transportation facilities were available; because there was freedom of trade between the states and territories, and, finally, because the pioneering spirit and vigorous manhood and womanhood were free from inherited and over-conservative ideas.

The close connection between manufacturing and natural resources was recognized early. When Alexander Hamilton in 1791 reported to the House of Representatives on the "manufactories already established," he said that they "were such as would spring up in a new country to supply the immediate necessities of the people, together with those whose materials were most abundant and inviting."[1] Today a list of the leading manufacturing industries, each producing goods exceeding one billion dollars in value, is almost synonymous in its implications with that of our principal natural resources, forests, minerals, and products of the soil.[2] In short, the manufactures of the country, taken as a whole, utilize and depend directly or indirectly upon the natural resources of the country. Our varied resources contribute to our having varied manufactures.

SOME EXAMPLES OF DEPLETED RESOURCES

Since the acquisition of the Louisiana Purchase and the Pacific Northwest, California, and the Rocky Mountain-Great Basin Region, this country has possessed such a wealth of resources in the way of minerals and large areas of productive soil having climates suited to a wide range of agricultural crops—grain, forage, vegetable, and fruit

[1] *Census Reports,* Vol. VII, Twelfth Census of the United States taken in the year 1900, Manufactures, Part I, United States by Industries, Washington, 1902, p. xlix.

[2] Foundry and machine shop products; cotton goods; lumber and timber products; iron and steel—steel works and rolling mills, car and general construction and repairs—steam railroad repair shops; electrical machinery—apparatus and supplies; motor vehicles, motor vehicle bodies and parts; bread and bakery products; women's clothing; printing and publishing book and job, printing and publishing newspaper and periodical; meat packing; cigars and cigarettes; petroleum refining; flour and other grain mill products. *United States Census of Manufactures,* 1930, Vol. III, pp. 35, 36.

—that an abundant never-failing supply of materials for factory fabrication generally is taken for granted.

Such, however, has not always been the case and may be less so in the future. Even in the earliest times, the limited available supplies of bog iron ore in New England felt the pinch of demand. Shipbuilders and lumbermen went farther and farther into New England for tall straight spars for their ships and good logs for lumber. Finally, no more were to be had. Fur-bearing animals were hunted successively farther upstream in New England and the East until they too, disappeared. Before the acquisition of the Louisiana Purchase, the supply of lead was entirely inadequate.

In 1810 iron manufacturers of the country were in serious straits. The eastern states lacked sufficient ore and fuel, situated with reference to each other, for producing the quantities of pig iron needed to supply "the air furnaces, the steel manufactories, rolling and slitting mills, gunsmiths, blacksmiths, triphammers, naileries, cutlers, shipsmiths, and other iron workers" in the East. The developing country with its new settlements and enlarging industries and population called for larger quantities of iron ore. So urgent and critical had the situation become that serious thought was given to admitting coal and pig and bar iron from abroad free of duty, the same as pig copper, block tin, hides and skins, cabinet woods, and other goods for which the domestic supply was inadequate.[1]

Manufacturing has been furnished with a continuous supply of mineral raw materials and agricultural and timber products only through successive development of new sources of supply. Essentially no large manufacturing industry today has, from the beginning, derived its raw materials from the same source. The iron and steel industry has depended successively upon bog iron ore in the East and Middle West, hard ore in the Piedmont, the Blue Ridge, the Appalachian Valley, the Upper Peninsula of Michigan, and finally the open-pit mines at the head of Lake Superior. As the known higher-grade ores diminish in quantity, no doubt other sources of high-grade and low-grade ores will be utilized, but situation, size, location, and other factors determine the availability of an ore deposit. Once used up, ore is gone.

The modern electrical industry during the last half century has brought about a large demand for copper. Eastern ore bodies even

[1] A statement of the Arts and Manufactures of the United States prepared in execution of an instruction of Albert Gallatin, Secretary of the Treasury, in accordance with a resolution of Congress, March 19, 1812, by Tench Coxe, p. 8.

before electrical development were insufficient to meet manufacturing demand, so foreign copper was admitted free of duty. Lake copper from Keweenaw Point in Michigan long controlled the domestic market. Now that from Arizona, Montana, and Utah far exceeds production in any other states. Imported copper supplements large domestic production. The rich Michigan mines have now gone more than a mile beneath the surface and are unable to compete in cost of mining even with many foreign ores. Large production in the southwest today obscures trouble in the famous Butte district.

Supplies of domestic lead and zinc fell far short of requirements in the manufacturing industry until the Louisiana Purchase was acquired. Now lead and zinc depletion in these mines is far advanced, and the geologist finds it hard to tell where the supplies of twenty years hence will be found.

Teeming traffic on our highways and countless filling stations blot from our minds the idle and rotting oil derricks in once busy fields in Pennsylvania, Ohio, Illinois, and Indiana. The Mid-continent Field, then California, and now Texas, successively have led in American production, and have served to keep America at the top as a petroleum-producing country and to supply crude oil for the petroleum refineries. Each new district has, in turn, covered up exhaustion or near exhaustion of its great predecessor pools.

Once the logs of New England, sawed in New England sawmills, provided lumber for most of the wood-using industries of our country. Later the forests of New York state and Pennsylvania on the Allegheny Plateau made this the greatest lumber region of the country and Pittsburgh the lumber metropolis. Now denuded mountain sides in some places covered with small scraggly second- or third-growth timber replace these magnificent forests.

Next the virgin white pine forests of Michigan and Wisconsin supplied lumber to the wood-using industries in Chicago and many smaller cities of the prairie states. For two decades and more these denuded lands have been reverting to the states for taxes. In the Pacific Northwest and northern California magnificent forests of Douglas fir and redwood are going the way of the Michigan white pine and eastern oaks, maples, and pines. Woodworking and wood-using manufacturing industries have gone farther and farther afield, away from the location of the original plants, of labor, and of principal demand to obtain their raw materials.

Coal, the source of power for factories and human activities, light for city and country, and many raw materials for other industries, presents a picture which calls for thought. The Pennsylvania anthracite fields are 29 per cent exhausted, and the industry is increasing its costs. Although there are yet stupendous preserves of bituminous coal, in many of the high-grade seams depletion is far advanced. We yet may face the same situation as England, where high costs of mining because of great depth of working seams already present a problem to her manufacturers.[1]

To consider agriculture as a great industry in which more than 10,000,000 people are engaged presents only a small part of the picture. Products from these farms provide the raw materials for many of our leading industries such as cotton goods, knit goods, bread and bakery products, clothing, meat packing, canning and preserving fruits and vegetables, flour and grain mill products, the chemical industry, and many others. Some of these industries like those depending upon minerals and timber have shifted their centers of production as the crops providing their raw materials have moved from one region to another, or they are paying the high costs of long-distance transportation. Questions of soil erosion and preservation of soil fertility are far from being solely the farmers' or housewives' concern, for they also vitally influence the prosperity and interests of every American manufacturer.

MANUFACTURING A CONSERVATION AGENCY

The evidences of depletion stressed above form one side of the picture of the relation of manufacturing to natural resources and one which requires thoughtful consideration. There is, however, another and a most significant aspect of modern manufacturing, for modern manufacturing is itself, in many ways, an important conservation agency. Chemistry has played a large part in bringing this about. Through chemical research many changes and large opportunities have come to industry. By-products formerly wasted have become valuable raw materials, some of them being more valuable than the product of which they were the waste. Raw materials have been broken down into their component parts, and these combined with others to form new substances, or the resulting residues themselves used, giving rise to new industries. New uses have been found for old materials, and new materials have been discovered for old uses. Food chemistry, the prepara-

[1] These facts as to supply and exhaustion of minerals and timber are taken from *National Resources Board Report,* December, 1934.

tion, preserving, and canning of foods, their long-distance transportation all are elements in the conservation of natural resources.

Anyone who is familiar with the old Pennsylvania or Ohio blast furnaces has seen the long, long piles of slag now covered by grass and trees. Or he may have walked along the southern shore of Lake Michigan near the sand dunes and picked up curious porous "stones" resembling pumice from a volcano—blast-furnace slag, waste from the great steel mills. Today this slag finds an important use, and near the Gary, as well as the other, steel mills, are other great plants coated white with powdery dust, where this slag becomes Portland cement. In fact, it has largely replaced the natural materials for this product, in some sections of our country.

To keep a house warm in winter and cool in summer it is insulated —walls and roof packed with "mineral wool," another product made from blast-furnace slag.

The story of coal, oil, and gasoline is well known, and many living today have worked and played by the light of the coal-oil lamp, knowing gasoline only as a fuel for the summer stove or as a cleaning fluid. Through modern heating and cracking processes the quantity of gasoline obtained from a given quantity of petroleum has been multiplied many times over. In addition, research has made available from crude petroleum more than 2,000 by-products, such as the ingredients for non-freezing dynamite, insecticides, and chemical agents for affecting the ripening of fruits.

Asphalt imported from Trinidad long had been important for pavements, but today nearly all the road-paving material used on roads in the United States comes from coal tar and petroleum residue, and is now available from chemical processes.

During the process of refining petroleum a certain amount of gas becomes a waste product, but it is not permitted to go to waste. In the Texas Panhandle are long sheds, with row on row of flames burning near roofs over which scrapers move back and forth collecting the fine, powdery soot which forms there, the same as it does when a saucer is held over a candle. This is lampblack, the substance which makes our automobile tires black, and is used in printing ink, shoe-polish, phonograph records, typewriter ribbons, carbon papers, paints, and enamels. It is the same carbon black which the Chinese have made for thousands of years; but now the United States, not China, furnishes lampblack for the world.

In 1935 the entire country watched with keen interest a record trip into the stratosphere. Suspended beneath the balloon was a gondola of "Dow metal," light but strong, evolved in the plant of Herbert H. Dow, a gifted chemical engineer, who literally built his plant over some salt beds in Michigan and his business on bromine extracted from these brines. On this spot has evolved a long list of important chemicals from bromine, chlorine, sodium, and magnesium, and he has pioneered in light metal alloys.

Alloys are not new, for bronze, the oldest of them, made by combining tin and copper, became so important that it gave its name to the Bronze Age. Every alloy is in reality a new metal, possessing new qualities, permitting and inviting new uses. Chromium, aluminum, steel, silicon alloys all have significant uses due to their lightness, hardness, rust- or acid-resisting qualities. Without these lighter, stronger, rust-resisting, high-speed alloys the airplane, automobile, and modern train would be impossible. It is estimated that we are now manufacturing more than 10,000 different alloys. (See also the discussion in Chapter XVI.)

When the steel industry turned from charcoal and anthracite coal to coke, all it wanted was coke, and this was produced in the old-fashioned beehive ovens. Everything else in the coal, except at a few plants where gas was used as fuel, went to waste. Now these waste products, conserved in the by-product coke plants, form the basis of great industries. To mention only two derivatives from coal tar: phenol gives us artificial wintergreen, aspirin, the plastic fittings for electric plugs, sockets, etc., and synthetic resins such as Bakelite; benzol is used in motor fuels and in producing rubber cement, plastics, and lacquers, as well as for a solvent for artificial leather.

The manufacture of plastics and lacquers possesses wide significance in several ways from a conservation point of view. They utilize waste by-products and, as finished products, aid in the preservation and utilization of yet other products and by-products. Before the World War, celluloid was the only plastic. In its production nitrocellulose was rendered plastic by camphor, and the solvent used was fusel oil, sometimes commonly called banana oil, a waste product from whisky. Only limited quantities of either could be produced, however, for camphor was high in price, it was produced and marketed by a monopoly, while fusel oil could be obtained only in restricted quantities.

The large war demand for acetone was met by fermenting grain (corn), during which there was left as waste enormous quantities of butanol. In searching for a way to use these accumulated stocks of butanol, it was discovered that butanol possessed solvent properties similar to those of fusel oil, and it could be produced in unlimited quantities. Now many different chemical solvents have replaced fusel oil, and lacquers have been produced which possess wearing qualities unthought-of in the old paints. The solvent in the lacquers evaporates readily, leaving a tough impervious coat of preservative plastic. Lacquers are used in "painting" automobiles and many other metal surfaces. The use of the quick-drying lacquers instead of the slow-drying enamels has greatly speeded up automobile production and reduced the acreage of drying rooms.

Plastics such as Bakelite possess a wide range of present and potential uses. Equipment for the electrical industry can now be made small, compact, and to precision measurements. This was impossible with the old porcelain or hard-rubber mediums. As for lacquers, however, it is now impossible to measure their field of usefulness.

Rayon and cellophane represent use of waste products as well as utilization of what might be a surplus of nitrocellulose should cotton production be increased. Such products as shoe buckles, buttons, book bindings, toilet articles, motion-picture films, explosives, safety glass, flexible glass such as perspex, the scuffless pyroxyline on women's high heels, all originate in the lumber camp or the cotton patch. They were introduced via the chemical research laboratory of the modern manufacturing world.

Until recently all wool came from the coats of sheep and other animals. But the chemist has discovered another source of wool, which will, at the same time, utilize a product hitherto going to waste. He has evolved wool from caseine, the waste from farm and dairy. Consequently, today it no longer can be said that wool is wool, cotton is cotton, or wood is wood.

To look for a moment into the food field: in the earlier days Maine corn growers canned their surplus for shipment to market. Now corn and other vegetables are grown for commercial canneries. Florida and California citrus groves most years furnish a surplus of fruit because it cannot be marketed fresh in the relatively short season for ripe fruit. Instead of allowing this surplus to rot, canned fruits and preserves and fruit juices reach our markets in immense quantities. Canneries are also located near the apple orchards of the Shenandoah Valley, the Yakima district of Washington, the Willamette Valley of Oregon, and the fruit districts of the Great Valley in California, as well as in southern Texas and many other places.

SUMMARY AND CONCLUSION

In short, the manufacturing industry is utilizing in continuously increasing quantities the products of field, forest, and orchard. Some products retain their original character, but others are transformed into a multitude of new products, the manufacture of which requires the use of many otherwise waste products. No other industry, perhaps, occupies in so large measure the dual rôle of conserver and efficient utilizer of resources.[1]

Conservation or effective use of natural resources thus is the intimate concern of every American factory. Conservation is not alone a problem placed remotely in mountain forests and mining camps, out on the wind-swept plains of the West, in farm, and fruit orchard, or on the water-eroded red sand and clay hills of the Coastal Plains and the Piedmont of the South. On the contrary, for example, canning centers in the Willamette Valley, a great aluminum plant in a small town in Tennessee, the many-sided factory industry of northern Illinois, the Cleveland-Pittsburgh district, or of that intensively developed industrial region between Boston and Baltimore, are doing their share in the conservation of natural resources.

Abundance of raw materials, high in quality, must be maintained if manufacturing is to be continued as a flexible, potentially expandable, and adjustable industry, ready to meet the varying demands of the American people. Since manufactured products contribute to and are inextricably united with the American standard of living, conservation of our natural resources forms the keystone for sustaining a sound and progressive manufacturing industry and a progressive American life. Should these resources be wasted through self-interested or *laissez-faire* procedure, American manufacturers will be burdened with high costs, and their growth will be limited. As a result they may crystallize and become static, and American society which uses their products can hardly help reflecting this condition in a less vigorous national life.

Thus the general statement in the Foreword of the *National Resources Board Report* for December, 1934, assumes a deep significance: "The natural resources of America are the heritage of the whole nation and should be conserved and utilized for the benefit of all our people."[2]

[1] For fuller discussion see: Williams Haynes, *Men, Money, and Molecules,* Doubleday, Doran and Company, Garden City, New York, 1936.

C. M. A. Stine, *Change Rules the Rails,* and other publications of the Chemical Foundation, New York.

[2] *National Resources Board Report,* December, 1934, p. v.

PART VII

CHAPTER XIX

CONSERVATION OF WILDLIFE

By V. E. Shelford

University of Illinois

INTRODUCTION

Definition of Terms. The people who have colonized the American continent, beginning about 1600, have demanded the freedom of the land and its wildlife for nearly three centuries practically without any check; this came only after our most spectacular ungulate, the bison, was nearly exterminated, the passenger pigeon gone, and other species at a very low ebb. With the beginning of the conservation movement, various rather ineffective restraints were set up and wildlife management began, but owing to lack of a general background of knowledge such as grows up out of experience, and lack of scientific attention to the larger animals, numerous mistakes were made. The result has been a great many failures, but also the acquisition of much valuable knowledge, even now too frequently not transmitted to those charged with the care of so-called wildlife.

If any word was ever used in such a graded scale of meanings by different persons and interests as to render a maximum amount of confusion it is "conservation" in reference to wildlife and other so-called renewable resources. As applied to non-living and sometimes to living resources, the word means to foster and promote while utilizing. It further implies, frequently, that the resource may eventually be exhausted. As a result of this fact some have attempted to divide resources into renewable and non-renewable, with the tacit assumption that all living resources are renewable.[1]

It is impracticable to pass to further discussion without defining several terms, including "wildlife." The sportsman and his agent, the state

[1] A. N. Pack, "A Plan for Conservation," *Nature Magazine,* Vol. XXVII, p. 169, 1936.

or provincial conservation commissioner, commonly apply the term only to the larger animals which they divide into (*a*) *wildlife* (that is, game) and (*b*) *vermin* or *pests* and predators, including those which may take, or are alleged to take, what the hunter himself desires to shoot or trap. In this chapter, however, wildlife means all uncultivated plants and undomesticated animals native to our continent, regardless of size, form, attributes, or uses. The classifications into *noxious* and *beneficial*, *game* and *vermin*, or the like, are almost never in complete accord with the facts and result from measurement with reference to some single economic or human interest. However, probably no animal is wholly good or wholly bad from the human standpoint.

The degree of renewability of wildlife (including plant life) resources must be clearly in mind if one is to understand wildlife problems. At the outset everyone will doubtless admit that the remnants of original biotic communities of which our plant and animal wildlife resources were a part would not be the same if we were to vacate the continent for a thousand years and let the processes of succession restore them to something like their former size. Furthermore, everyone will more quickly recognize that if the effects of man had remained essentially the same from 1600 to 1936 the communities would not have remained the same. The stress of drought, flood, and frost would have changed them. The present small relics usually have lost some of their species;[1] these lost species are actually not renewable, and their re-establishment with other related species or varieties is doubtful. The original vegetation, if in any but the very early stages of community development, is not even approximately renewable in any reasonable length of time, say fifty years. Thus in general it will readily be granted that primeval biotic communities are not *renewable resources*.

Wild animal life, its maintenance in a primeval state, and its management in reservations and on public lands are inseparably tied up with the land, the waters, and the vegetation. A few game managers have very recently come to adopt this view, although it has been held by animal ecologists for thirty years. This has been brought home most forcefully by the quail studies of Stoddard,[2] who controls production, enemies, etc., on the Georgia estates which he manages, almost entirely by the control of the environment as expressed in the amount or kinds of cover. The tardy acceptance of this view may be seen in the small

[1] V. E. Shelford, *Naturalist's Guide to the Americas,* Classification of National Parks, pp. 86, 175, etc., Baltimore, 1926.

[2] H. L. Stoddard, *The Bobwhite Quail,* New York, 1931.

amount of land controlled by the United States Biological Survey, which, if it were to function properly in the maintenance of the birds and mammals with which it is concerned, should have supervision of large areas of land. The maintenance of original biotic communities must be on a hands-off basis. It must be *preservation* in the strict sense, and although "preservation" on a hands-off basis may be implied in conservation, it can hardly be said to have been the practice. *Fostering* and *promotion* by management have characterized the work bearing the conservation label. A standing committee of the Ecological Society of America entitled Committee on the Preservation of Natural Conditions was established in 1917 and has been urging the non-management or hands-off policy for national parks and reservations of all types in order that they may be left as nearly primeval as possible.

The difference between preservation and the practices commonly followed is well illustrated in a recent publication by Wright, Dixon, and Thompson,[1] who advocate the preservation of the birds and mammals in national parks. They point out the importance of dead timber to various birds and mammals. The need of such timber for numerous invertebrates might well be added. Conservation as usually practiced removes dead and mature timber, whereas preservation lets nature take its course.

Classification of Wildlife. Wildlife is divisible into habitat types: terrestrial and aquatic, and the latter into marine and fresh-water. From the standpoint of management, fresh-water animal communities are closely related to the land within which they lie, and except for the very large lakes, such as Lake Superior and others, must be classed with the land. For convenience even these large lakes may be discussed with the small bodies of water. If treated in a comprehensive manner, marine wildlife must be discussed separately. The fresh-water and terrestrial wildlife must be evaluated as to land use and general purpose.

Considering the matter from a more restricted view, the Report of the Senate Committee on the Conservation of Wildlife[2] states:

Game land is of two kinds:

(A) That which is cheap enough for the public to buy and manage; and

(B) That which is too expensive for the public to buy in quantity,

[1] G. M. Wright, J. S. Dixon, and B. Thompson, "Fauna of the National Parks of the United States," *Contribution of Wild Life Survey,* Fauna Series 1.

[2] F. C. Walcott, "Wild Life Conservation," 71st Congress, 3rd Sess., 1931.

and which therefore must be managed by the present owners or not at all.

Game is of four classes:

I. Farm game, which inhabits class B land. It thrives best on farms with suitable cover.

II. Forest and range game, which inhabits class A land. It thrives best on land partially farmed.

III. Wilderness game, which inhabits very cheap class A land. It is excluded by farming, or other economic uses.

IV. Migratory game, which inhabits both classes of land. It thrives on farms if marshlands are left undrained.

PUBLIC OPINION AND ACTION

To understand the wildlife problems of North America, it is necessary to realize that Europeans have for thousands of years regarded the wolf, coyote (jackal), puma (panther, chita), bobcat (wildcat), and lynx as personal enemies and enemies of domestic animals, and to be killed on sight. Coupled with this has been the use of game animals for food and the skins of both for clothing. This has resulted in a wholly unscientific and prejudiced approach to wildlife problems. In the early Colonial days, there was little study or even record of the habits of these unpopular types, and various subspecies were exterminated before being described (described later from skulls).

It is also necessary to know that the general policy of all the various state and federal agencies, having wildlife in charge, looked to the extermination of these unpopular animals as late as five to fifteen years ago, the date depending on the bureau, its functions, and its personnel at the time.

Attitude of Settlers. From 1600 right down to the present, the belief that all exploitable areas should be settled and developed has been almost a national religion. Settlement of the continent went on without any classification or control of land with reference to use, the tendency being to exploit all areas according to preconceived ideas, many actually ill-suited to the eastern deciduous forest area in which they had been tried. Surveys were made in arid regions based on the assumption that the land would support a population similar to that of Virginia, and many areas have been partially settled and abandoned repeatedly, to the detriment of the land, the settler, and the country at large. Here, as in the more moist area, the settlers perhaps lived for a time by exploiting wildlife and such timber as occurred, but finally abandoned their land. A few settlers went to grazing livestock, a business which attracted prospectors, trappers, and adventurers of all kinds. The stockmen, in practice, believed that the herbage of the forest as well as of the glassland was for cattle to eat away completely each year, because it died down and disappeared each winter: they forgot the necessity for seed plants. As the range was depleted there was an increase of grass-eating rodents due to the destruction of the predatory animals. They undertook the reduction of both rodents and predators, securing help from the states for ten or more years; finally in 1916 the federal government came into the field with appropriations to control predators in order to reduce losses of the stock-raising group of the West. These appropriations have been continued until the present.

Attitude of Federal Agencies. In 1927 the attitude of the federal bureau in charge is well-expressed in the following quotation from Cameron:

> It is now pretty generally agreed that the end of the wolf is in sight. His known casualties, accounted for by hides and heads, had reached a total of about six thousand by 1926, and practically all of the most notorious stock-killers had been accounted for. In a general way, similar comment may be said to apply to the cougar (or mountain lion), the lynx, and the bobcat. Their depredations have been controlled, and their ultimate elimination, though not so apparently imminent as that of the wolf, is only a matter of time. The coyote has been definitely checked but still exists in numbers, and his complete extermination, it is safe to say, lies a long way in the future.[1]

This attitude on the part of the government bureau was bitterly assailed by the American Society of Mammalogists[2] and others in 1930 with slight favorable results, but Table 1 should be studied for a comparison of the government kills of 1927 with 1935.[3]

TABLE 1

	Wolves	*Coyotes*	*Bobcats Lynxes*	*Mountain Lions*	*Bears*
1927	201	37,887	3,718	246	186
1935*	1,332	59,289	5,380	349	305

* "The largest ever taken in one year by the Bureau and its cooperating agencies."

This indicates increasing vigor in the attack on the wolf and mountain lion. Public sentiment in 1935 is little different from that expressed

[1] J. Cameron, *The Bureau of Biological Survey,* Brookings Institution, Mon. U. S. Gov., No. 54, 1929.

[2] *Symposium on Predatory Animal Control, Jour. Mammal.,* Vol. XI, p. 325, 1931.

[3] J. R. Darling, *Report of Chief of Biological Survey,* 1935.

in the quotation above. There was little or no indication of any material change at the large game conference held in Washington in February, 1936.

Industry and Wildlife. With the introduction of poison as a means of insect and mammal control, manufacturers of chemicals have taken a very active part in advertising and propagandizing for the use of poisons, oils, etc. They have given funds for experimental work, and they have published and freely distributed manuals for the use of chemicals in the eradication of pests. This is not the only point at which profits and advertising have been brought into the field. Long ago the manufacturers advertised firearms to shoot vermin and finally the manufacturing interests have advertised hunting and trapping equipment on a large scale so that hunting is constantly played up before youth as well as manhood. Various study projects have been financed by gifts from these industries, which, as will readily be seen, is not the best method to finance scientific work.

Upland game birds such as ruffed grouse, heath hen, prairie chicken, and quail have been on the decline. Through contributions from the arms and ammunition manufacturers in the form of fellowship, studies have been made which have supplied information, the application of which has accomplished much to increase their numbers.

Effects of Swamp Drainage. Federal, state, and private agencies stimulated by profit in the sale of land have drained or otherwise destroyed shallow swamp waters of river bottoms, upland lakes, and marshes which constituted the feeding and breeding grounds of myriads of ducks, geese, crane, and other water birds. Notable among these areas are the drained marshes of the Dakotas and the upper Mississippi, Illinois, and Missouri River "bottoms" and the numerous glacial lakes of the northern part of the United States and the southern ends of the Canadian provinces. These originally constituted the chief duck breeding grounds of North America. This drainage has been going on steadily for seventy-five years, and water birds have been undergoing a steady decline in numbers until the recent drought period brought the matter sharply to attention.

Conflicting Uses of Streams. Pollution has greatly reduced the productivity of waters, having destroyed uncounted numbers of fishes, water fowl, and other aquatic resources. Migratory fishes like the salmon and shad are those which leave the hatching place in lakes and streams while young, go to sea to grow to maturity and fatten, and return again to spawn. Since 1797 these fisheries have received little or no consideration when dams were to be built.[1] Several such dams are in progress now: two of them endanger Columbia River salmon. So long as the local population profit through the irrigation of land to which they hold title, so long as machinery and materials are used and contracts let, wildlife has little chance for protection.

Lack of International Cooperation. Originally the North Atlantic right whale was abundant in the Gulf of Maine, the gray whales rolled in the mud of the small bays of the Pacific, and many others occupied the open sea. These great whales have largely become a thing of the past through greed and exploitation. There has been concern that they may be exterminated, and organized attempts have been made to save them. The seals and walruses have likewise suffered severe depletion and are the subject of international treaties; in general, this type of wildlife has suffered almost incomprehensible reductions. Many fishes, shellfish, and edible crustaceans (crabs and shrimps) have suffered severe depletion, especially from pollution. This menace was increased everywhere by the coming of oil-burning boats.

Lack of Trained Men. The lack of training of those in charge of game is noteworthy, especially in relation to predatory animals. Quantitative concepts have made very little progress. Game managers and conservation directors have no data on which to evaluate the different predatory animals with reference to the amount of game which they destroy. Therefore, the fact that a bald eagle was known to take certain game birds put it in the class with predatory animals without regard to any definite idea of the degree of damage it really does the country over.

Influence of American Political System. In this connection the American system of politics cannot be forgotten. It results in the dictation of legislative policy by organized and often unrepresentative minorities. The extensive destruction of predatory animals has intimate relations to our system of politics. For example, some organizer approaches a few ranchers and promises them to get more grazing, goes forward and sets up a plan for killing predatory animals, affiliates with other leaders, and urges a certain drastic program. Candidates run for office on such a program and bid high in the hope that the "killingest" wins, as he usually does. Poland has 5,000 wolves and has done nothing about it simply because she has not a thoroughly good vote-getting system of politics such as characterizes the North American continent. The unusual discourteous senatorial treatment of the scien-

[1] V. E. Shelford, "Fortunes in Wastes and Fortunes in Fish," *Sci. Mo.*, Vol. 9, pp. 97-124.

tists who protested, at a hearing on a bill to appropriate $1,300,000 per year for ten years, for mammal control, probably grew out of a fear of losing or hope of gaining votes rather than anything else. The promise of more grass and less predators is a lure to stock-raisers' votes; and the promise of more game and more fish is a lure for the votes of sportsmen and of men who hope for jobs as wardens. But few states and provinces have risen above the latter system although some have done fairly good work in spite of it.

PRESENT CONDITION OF WILDLIFE

Wildlife in National Parks and Other Complete Sanctuaries. In the United States the act which set up the Yellowstone National Park was to: "provide for the *preservation*, from injury or spoliation, of all timber, mineral deposits, natural curiosities or wonders, within the park, and their retention in their natural condition." Unfortunately wildlife did not come into the picture, and some hunting was allowed in the early days. The National Park Act of 1916 changed the terminology and the "purpose is to *conserve* the scenery and the natural and historic objects and the wildlife therein and to provide for the enjoyment of the same in such manner and by such means as will leave them unimpaired for the enjoyment of future generations." Further, the Secretary of the Interior may cut timber to control attacks of insects and disease, and "he may also provide in his discretion for the destruction of such animals and of such plant life as may be detrimental to the use of any of the said parks."

There is said to have been doubt as to the legality of the removal of animals, etc., but under the new act, authority was given for work already accomplished in the destruction of predators. No doubt most of the officials regarded the park as a game refuge in which the "pure" animals might be seen by visitors. Even the naturalist, Bailey, held this view:

> With persistent hunting and trapping during the spring (1916) this band of wolves was broken up, and apparently most of those not procured were driven out of the park. Evidently a few remain, however, and, as they breed rapidly, constant care must be exercised to prevent their becoming reestablished in numbers to do serious damage to the *game*. In 1927, *Nature Notes* reported that over two hundred coyotes were killed annually but that the species was still numerous in the park.
>
> At present mountain lions are few and far between. The *last* one killed was treed and *shot by chief ranger* Woodring in November,

1924. . . . They are so secretive[1] in their habits that they add *little of interest* to the animal life of the park to compensate for their destructive habits.[2]

Thus in the few months preceding the 1916 enactment, the large wolf was hunted, breeding dens found, and adults and young destroyed, although in the face of these flesh-eating animals the mountain buffalo herd had increased from 25 to 37 between 1901 and 1912. With the destruction of the wolf, the coyote increased as in all cases.

The report of the Brookings Institution[3] prepared about 1920 indicates the trend of public opinion and of action by the park officials at that time:

> The park rangers are continually on the lookout for poachers. Predatory animals, such as wolves, coyotes, and mountain lions are also hunted by the rangers, and efforts looking to their *extermination* are constantly going on.
>
> In severe winters feeding of elk, buffalo, and antelope becomes necessary. Hay is grown and cured in the Yellowstone for winter feeding, the work being done on contract. An expert of this bureau vaccinates the tame buffalo herd of the Yellowstone each year.
>
> All of the parks are bird refuges, and birds are *protected* from hunters and predatory animals while in the parks just as are the game herds. . . . Fishing with hook and line is permitted in the parks under regulations. . . . The Bureau of Fisheries maintains three hatcheries in Yellowstone Park and one in Glacier.

Exotic species were thus introduced into the parks!

The quotations and remarks are not introduced to cast aspersions on the present excellent National Park Service or its personnel, but rather to make clear to the reader the background against which the present officers must work since they have undertaken to make the preservation of all forms of life a part of their program. In the first publication of their wildlife division, Wright, Dixon, and Thompson make the following statement:

> Every species shall be left to carry on its struggle for existence unaided, as being to its greatest ultimate good, unless there is real cause to believe that it will perish if unassisted. No native predator shall be destroyed on account of its normal utilization of any other park animal, excepting if that animal is in immediate danger of extermination, and then only if the predator is not itself a vanishing form.

The Park Service has reduced control measures to a minimum, and

[1] May be treed by dogs to show to those interested.
[2] Bailey, Vernon, *Animal Life in Yellowstone Park,* p. 131.
[3] J. Cameron, *The National Park Service,* Brookings Institution, 1922.

decries the use of poison as non-selective and generally detrimental. However, it must be borne in mind that the views represented in the quotations from Cameron are those still held by a large body of the public, such as sportsmen, guides, stockmen, many officials of the United States Department of Agriculture, and state officials concerned with agriculture and "conservation." Such officials usually ignore native species as possible subjects for domestication and import some animal from another continent. The introduction of the reindeer into Alaska has led to an unfortunate condition for one national park.

Murie states that reindeer herds maintained in close contact with caribou during migration suffer frequent losses through strays. Already the domestic reindeer are mingling with the *caribou herd of Mt.*

FIG. 1. Wolf Pups in a European National Park.

McKinley National Park with inevitable hybridization. "Such a possibility would be regrettable in interior Alaska, which has produced a splendid type of wild caribou, coming near at least to being the largest on the continent."[1]

The state of animal life in the national parks of the United States is a sad one. No wolves are known to exist in any of the parks in the territory of the United States; Olson, however, maintains that they are a benefit even in game preserves (Fig. 1). The wolverine, bobcat, and cougar are at a very low ebb; the grizzly bear is on the decline and must have protection or it will become extinct. The bison, elk, and antelope suffer from lack of space or winter range or both; the elk and bison are fed in winter, and the latter essentially *domesticated.* Nonnative trout have been introduced into practically all streams. Many of the parks had lost important species; many were over-grazed; and in

[1] O. J. Murie, "Alaska-Yukon Caribou," U.S.D.A. Biological Survey, *N. A. Fauna,* No. 54, p. 93.

some, timber had been or was removed under pre-existing rights before the areas became parks. A few dams have been built; only vigorous efforts have prevented the building of others; and there are plans to drain off floodwaters from Yellowstone Lake with detriment to animal and plant life.

The conditions are probably due primarily to the past attitude, training, and lack of interest of biological scientists in the United States. For many years the evolution and morphology of organisms small enough to be studied in fingerbowls held attention almost altogether. (See Summer, 1921; Adams, 1929, Appendix.)

Wildlife in Large Forest and Game Preserves. In the United States there are more than 133,000,000 acres of nationally owned forest in tracts of considerable size; these areas are supplemented by several state forests of notable size, especially in Pennsylvania and a few other eastern states. (See maps in Chapter XX.) In Canada the national lands were very recently turned over to the provinces. They have not developed a system of national control, but the end result as regards wildlife is essentially the same under their system as in the United States. In general in the United States the game in the national forests belongs to the state. The states have set up game preserves within the national forests and have attempted, as a rule, to control hunting, trapping, and fishing through officers appointed in return for political work during the last campaign—men all too commonly without scientific training or rules for work other than the dictates of prejudice. The usual result has been the destruction of predatory animals, and increase in deer and excessive damage to forage. In one state, trappers were allowed to take beaver illicitly from a national forest to pay for their warden services. In the Kaibab, where the predatory animals were destroyed over a period of twenty or more years, cyclic increase in deer led to the destruction of 40 per cent of the winter browse and the carrying capacity was reduced in proportion, fifty or more years being required for recovery. The destruction of predatory animals has been carried on in these areas by bounty and by hired hunters, employed by state conservation departments, stockmen's associations, and the United States Biological Survey, which a few years ago maintained fifteen or more hunters to one scientific investigator. Some hunting of puma was carried on by men who charged tourists large sums to accompany the hunt and see the puma.

Riley describes his experience with local wardens as follows:

> It is true that the present state game warden, dealing in generalities, has expressed himself in favor of the destruction of all

fur animals because he claims that they prey upon game birds. . . . Game birds were plentiful in the Shoshone National Forest fifteen years ago . . . at a time when fur animals were much more numerous than they are now. Food and seasonable weather have far more to do with the prevalence of game birds.[1]

The drain on wildlife in the national forests of western United States has been enormous.

The annual fish and game report for the Manti Forest (72,000 acres) for 1928 shows some interesting facts. The estimate shows there are 6,500 deer, 1,005 elk, 96 bears, 85 lions, and 1,330 coyotes on the Forest. During the past open hunting season, 460 deer and 42 elk were killed. Also 426 deer and 6 elk have been killed by predatory animals or have died from other causes. Nine bears, 10 lions, 485 coyotes, 105 bobcats, 51 badgers, and 1,366 porcupines have been killed within the Forest during the past season. Representatives of the Biological Survey have killed most of the bobcats, coyotes, badgers, and more than one-third of the porcupines. For four of the Ranger Districts, the cattle owners are asking for an open season on female deer. The numbers have increased to such an extent during the last few years, that they now seriously compete with the domestic stock for the forage. On these districts the elk have also reached such numbers that they are destroying some of the range used for spring grazing by cattle. (From the Mount Pleasant Pyramid.)

This process of destruction has gone on until in 1935 the Utah Academy of Science has become alarmed at the almost certain elimination of the wolf, bear, bobcat, puma, and other flesh eaters, from the forest adjacent to the Great Basin.

Management of wildlife in forest is based fundamentally on prejudice and the raising of stock. Pearson and Marsh discuss this question:

It is reasonable to conclude that the killing of carnivora which normally live on mice, chipmunks, squirrels, and porcupines, not to say large browsing animals, is detrimental to the forest. Where the control of predatory animals is deemed necessary in the interest of the live-stock industry, it should be accompanied by equally intensive control of the enemies of the forest. . . . The most common rodents of the forest are seed eaters, and for this reason they are usually regarded as forest enemies.[2]

The authors enumerate seven types of rodents, stating that the burrowers do much good to the soil. They continue:

[1] Smith Riley, "Some Observations on Beaver Culture with Reference to the National Forests," *Jour. Mammal.*, Vol. 2, p. 206.

[2] G. A. Pearson and R. E. Marsh, "Timber Growing and Logging Practice in the Southwest and the Black Hills Region," *Tech. Bull.*, 480, U.S.D.A., 1935.

> Tree squirrels are active seed-eaters, but are placed in a different class because of their esthetic and economic value. . . . The Abert squirrel should not be exterminated, but his numbers should be limited. . . . Perhaps the most harmful of all rodents in the forest is the porcupine. He begins eating the bark of pine seedlings when they are six inches high and continues through the life of the tree.

Taylor has pointed out that the porcupine injury is a result of overgrazing by stock, especially of the porcupine's favorite herbs. These quotations lack conclusiveness from the standpoint of wildlife as a whole but indicate the encouraging attitude of forest investigators.

Wildlife on Public Lands in Uninhabited Areas. Uninhabited areas of North America are principally desert in territorial United States and great stretches of spruce bogs and tundra in Alaska and Canada. These areas are essentially wilderness areas with scattered groups of North American natives and an occasional trading post. The pioneer trader usually buys furs or native handiwork, and pays in firearms, traps, provisions, etc. There is a natural tendency to sell firearms, which enable the natives to kill too much game; ultimately this has a tendency to increase the sale of provisions. A trapper friend of the author says that the caribou is doomed to practical extermination by the sale of high-power firearms to natives who are encouraged to use them to excess. Predators are killed by trappers for their skins and sometimes for the bounty, too frequently with poison. At times a great source of animal destruction is the use of poison commonly mixed with tallow scented with fish and put on the end of a stick bored out to receive it. These are placed at intervals, and foxes, wolves, and other flesh eaters are killed and picked up and skinned at the next round. This is done chiefly by newcomers from Europe. The beginning of the depression was marked by the entrance of such "trappers" in uninhabited areas which ruined the trapping in certain localities. The destruction was large and the dead animal often not recovered.

Areas in the far north have suffered from the decrease of the muskox and caribou and the introduction of the reindeer, the latter being a type of political economic venture all too common on our continent. Murie says:

> The caribou's greatest menace is not the wolf, nor the hunter, but man's economic developments, principally the raising of reindeer. Wherever reindeer herds are introduced, caribou must of course disappear, for both cannot occupy the same range. The disappearance of the caribou along the Bering Sea and Arctic coasts, while regrettable, was unavoidable *in view of the development of reindeer herding* in this section, which is ideal for the purpose. In considering

eastern Alaska, however, a different viewpoint is permissible. This region is less suitable for effective handling of reindeer, and the ranges are already occupied by thriving herds of caribou, numbering many thousands, a public resource of considerable proportions and a boon to the prospector and traveler. Since reindeer and caribou cannot exist together—it is wise to designate certain areas in which each may develop—one part of the Territory in which the reindeer industry may develop its possibilities and another part in which the caribou herds may be maintained as a public resource. Both are of incalculable value to Alaska, and neither should be sacrificed in any misguided attempt to combine them.[1]

Wildlife on Grazing Lands. The grassland of our western states should be one of our greatest resources. However, far too much of it has been plowed, the remainder over-grazed, until it is a spectacle of incompetent and unscientific management which exceeds that of the destruction of our forests. At the outset that portion which would have been better not plowed probably supported fifteen to twenty million bison and fully as many antelope. There were doubtless reasons why those east of the hundredth meridian should be destroyed, but on the open western plains there was no good reason.

Originally the carnivores held the rodents in check. The carnivores of the plains were ferrets, weasels, badgers, kit foxes, all of which are harmless to agriculture if the poultry were properly housed. In addition the coyote is useful rather than detrimental, but the wolf could probably not be tolerated. Unfortunately no experiment was ever set up to see whether it would be possible to maintain the balance between the jack rabbits, prairie dogs, and ground squirrels, and these flesh eaters. It is entirely possible that success could have been attained on cattle ranges if the experiment had been tried. However, the carnivores were reduced and the rodents increased and since then have been repeatedly poisoned, finally on the Santa Rita Federal Reserve Area.[2]

Wildlife on Farms and Abandoned Farm Lands. This includes the small fur-bearers, rabbits, squirrels, raccoons, and opossums and upland game birds such as quail, heath hen (now extinct), ruffed grouse, sage grouse, prairie chicken, wild turkey and others. In the case of the quail, Leopold enumerates the following conditions for success:

In bobwhite quail, for example, in the northern half of the United States, feeding places are usually adequate except during winter

[1] O. J. Murie, "Alaska-Yukon Caribou," *N. A. Fauna,* No. 54, Biological Survey, U.S.D.A.

[2] C. T. Vorhies, "Wild Life Aspects of Range Rehabilitation," *Hoofs and Horns.* Vol. V, No. 8, pp. 6-7; No. 9, pp. 10-11, 1936.

snow or sleet storms. Under these conditions a cornshock, or a patch of seed-bearing ragweed protruding above the snow, is a requirement for survival, *i. e.,* the critical element in the food factor for northern bobwhites.

Places to hide are likewise usually adequate except during winter, when the white snow buries the understory of grass and leaves and renders every bird visible to predators. Under such conditions the mechanical protection offered by a thorny bush like osage, or a dense tangle of grapevines, represents the quail's only chance to dodge his enemies.

As nearly as we know, almost any ground will do for resting purposes, except during winter snows, when there must be a hiding place near at hand in which the birds may seek refuge from sudden attack.

For a sleeping place quail require at all seasons a rather open and preferably elevated spot, from which, if attacked at night, they may successfully take wing without striking mechanical obstacles.

If the quail requires a special place for play, we have no knowledge of it. For nesting, quail require moderately thin grass or brush on a well-drained spot, with bare ground nearby on which the young may dry out after rain. Stoddard thinks this accounts for the frequency with which nests are found near paths and on roadsides.

Quail are commonly believed to require grit. If they do, then ledges of rock or gravel, or windfalls bearing gravelly soil, are necessary during snows.[1]

In recent years the condition of the habitat has been discovered to be more important than predation and enemies. In attempting to build up conditions for game on farms, Leopold was shocked at the happenings and described his experience as follows:

It required the open money-bags of 1933, however, to demonstrate what a disparity still exists between this paper ideal and the actual performance of a field-foreman turned loose with a crew and a circular of instructions on how to do some one particular kind of conservation work. There was, for example, the road crew cutting a grade along a clay bank so as permanently to roil the troutstream which another crew was improving with dams and shelters; the silvicultural crew felling the "wolf trees" and border shrubbery needed for game food; the roadside-cleanup crew burning all the down oak fuel wood available to the fireplaces being built by the recreation-ground crew; the planting crew setting pines all over the only open clover-patch available to the deer and partridges; the fire-line crew burning up all the hollow snags on a wild-life refuge, or worse yet, felling the gnarled veterans which were about the only scenic thing along a "scenic road." In short, the ecological and esthetic limitations of "scientific" technology were revealed in all their nakedness.

Such crossed wires were frequent, even in the CCC camps where crews were directed by brainy young technicians, many of them fresh

[1] Aldo Leopold, *Game Management,* New York, 1933.

from conservation schools, but each schooled only in his particular "specialty." What atrocities prevailed in the more ephemeral organizations like the CWA, he who runs may read. The instructive part of this experience is not that the cub foreman should lack omniscience in integrating conservation, but that the high-ups (of which I was one) *did not anticipate* these conflicts of interest, sometimes did not see them when they occurred, and were ill-prepared to adjust them when seen. The plain lesson is that to be a practitioner of conservation on a piece of land takes more brains, and a wider range of sympathy, forethought, and experience, than to be a specialized forester, game manager, range manager, or erosion expert in a college or a conservation bureau. Integration is easy on paper, but a lot more important and more difficult in the field than any of us foresaw. None of us had ever had enough volume and variety of field labor simultaneously at work to be fully aware of either its pitfalls or its possibilities. If the *accouchement* of conservation in 1933 bore no other fruits, this sobering experience would alone be worth its pains and cost.[1]

Vanishing and Endangered Species. After five years of depression accompanied in the United States (*a*) by the use of emergency funds for the destruction of predatory animals and rodents with the extensive use of poisons and a greater kill in 1935 than hitherto reported; (*b*) by an increase in hunting by the unemployed in many localities; (*c*) by the extreme drought of 1934 in which waterfowl suffered heavily; and (*d*) by the driving out of caribou in parts of Alaska and introduction of the reindeer and hybridization with the caribou of Mount McKinley National Park, it is safe to say that the future of no species is reassuring. It is disheartening to learn also that Canada's national parks are undergoing their first predatory animal control campaign and a wide-awake Canadian naturalist states that barren ground and woodland caribou, muskox, lynx, marten, fisher, and otter are in need of protection or are in a serious position. At the Wild Life Conference called at Washington by the President of the United States, on February 3-7, 1936, there was much discussion of wildlife for shotguns, for profits to makers of munitions and sporting goods, a list of vanished game species was presented, but little or no mention was made of the predators.

The National Parks Fauna No. 2 indicates that the grizzly bears are at their last stand. The wolves of all species have probably disappeared from the national parks, and where they have been reduced coyotes have increased. Cougar have almost disappeared. The fisher and wol-

[1] Aldo Leopold, "Conservation Economics," *Jour. For.*, Vol. 32, pp. 537-544.

verine are in desperate condition, and they are fur-bearers. With this condition inside the park there is little hope outside.

The peccary, badger, Allen jack rabbit, and various kangaroo rats may well be in danger from the extensive use of poison. Many of our ungulates are reduced to small remnants held in parks and reserves, in some of which they are under doubtful management and are no longer really wild animals. Of the birds, the passenger pigeon, heath hen, Labrador duck, Eskimo curlew, and Carolina paroquet are gone, and the whooping crane, trumpeter swan, and several ducks are nearly gone. Leopold[1] discusses several extinct species: the giant mink, the heath hen, etc.

Introduced Species. Of these we have plenty: many insects, mice, rats of two species, and the English sparrow and starling, both successfully introduced after dozens of failures, and both serious competitors of our small native birds. The excrement of the starling sometimes kills the trees of rookery groves. We also have the carp in our waters, where it sometimes clears out most of the native fishes. The introduction of reindeer into the tundra has already been mentioned.

We have three introduced game birds, the Hugarian partridge and the ringneck and the golden pheasant, each of which is locally detrimental to native birds. We also have the horse, African ass, European cow, Mediterranean sheep, the Asiatic goat, Indian wild fowl, the African guinea fowl, the Mexican turkey, the Asiatic cat, the European wolf, the Asiatic jackal, and the European wild hog, nearly all of which were domesticated in the Eastern Hemisphere and most of which have gone wild at one time or another on our continent. Wild cats, dogs, hogs, asses, and horses are or have been of considerable significance in some localities.

The presence of domestic species is important on account of the psychological effect of their presence. The moment an estate owner puts pheasants out on his land, he wants to kill everything that injures or is *alleged* to injure pheasants. This is the exact attitude of cultivators of all the other animals.

Destruction of Vermin. Any animal that kills or is alleged to kill that which a sportsman wishes to shoot is called a vermin. Vermin-killing campaigns have characterized the work of various state conservation commissions for many years, and are still in progress under the pressure from sportsmen's organizations and manufacturers of firearms and poisons.

[1] Aldo Leopold, "Threatened Species," *Amer. For.*, Vol. 42, pp. 116-119.

As Reese points out, many animals not of positive economic value are of great interest to nature lovers, and these non-killing nature lovers have as much right to enjoy animals alive as the sportsmen have to enjoy them dead. Most organized sportsmen do not know it, but there is difference of opinion as to the actual part taken by predatory animals in the reduction of game. There are other factors of greater significance.

As chairman of the West Virginia Biological Survey, Reese has been collecting the reports of the vermin-destruction contests held in 1935 in 40 of the 55 counties of the state. He states:[1]

> In these contests, local merchants and other persons offer substantial prizes to those killing the greatest number of the animals on the "vermin" list.
>
> In the Biennial Report of the Conservation Commission of West Virginia for 1933-35, a list of "Vermin" killed in the fiscal year 1933-34 was published (see Table 2). Only 26 counties held contests during this year.

TABLE 2

1933–34	*Pieces of Vermin*
Hawks	3,007
Hunting house cats*	1,892
Snakes	79,481
Water dogs	13,497
Crows	9,438
Weasels	1,430
Grey fox	1,451
Turtles	15,370
Kingfishers	1,030
Rats and mice*	34,475
Garfish	87
Terrapins	4,417
Mink	321
German carp*	59
Red squirrels	399
Chipmunks	18,089
Owls	954
Starlings*	3,985
Wild cats	311
Timber wolf	1
English sparrow*	1,907
Total	191,511

*Those starred are introduced.

[1] A. M. Reese, "The Destruction of Vermin," *Science*, Vol. 82, pp. 593-594.

The report continues:

"During the fiscal year 1934-35 forty counties have sponsored and conducted vermin control contests. This is an increase of fourteen contests over the previous year.

"While the actual results are not available at this time, information in our possession, based on partial reports, indicates the results will greatly exceed the previous year's showing. A conservative estimate will show a grand total of three hundred thousand predatory animals, birds and snakes disposed of by these beneficial contests."

If 300,000 animals are destroyed in a single season in a small state like West Virginia, what would be the total for the entire country if these "beneficial" campaigns were held everywhere?

Of course, there are several animals of this list that might well be exterminated, but there are more which are not only of general interest but are of actual benefit to man.

The introduced species (*) in the list are true vermin and should be reduced in numbers. In other states the eagle, raccoon, and various other animals have been considered vermin.

Wildlife of Waters and Swamps. The most prized fresh-water fishes and mollusks are dependent upon clean bottoms, abundant vegetation, and a good flow of water in dry seasons—conditions which characterized our streams in primeval times. Clearing of timber has modified stream flow, stream margin shade, etc., detrimentally. Household and industrial effluent dilution has modified the character of the water and covered the bottoms with filth, to the destruction or injury of fishes and their associates.

In the settlement and early development of our country, fish were very important. Shad, salmon, trout, bass, alewives, eels, and many other kinds were available to the eastern colonists. They furnished a plentiful supply of healthful food, easily attainable, until the forests could be hewn down and crops raised. Shad was the most important variety and was abundant in all Atlantic coast rivers. Shad and salmon are now greatly reduced or exterminated in our Atlantic coast streams.

The whitefish of the Great Lakes, which served as bread, meat, and vegetable to the early explorers and settlers, was once abundant. In the Illinois River years ago the buffalo fish afforded the chief marketable species. In recent years it has constituted less than 8 per cent of the total fish catch.

Ruthless catching has been followed by sewage, and sewage by industrial wastes. Lead works, zinc works, tanneries, paper mills, and gas plants turned extremely poisonous substances into the streams and lakes and often extirpated the fishes.

For the proper protection of fishes and mussels, fishways, fish elevators, etc., are needed in connection with river improvements. In the north branch of the Susquehanna, in Pennsylvania, "the shad industry was wholly abolished by the erection of dams to feed canals (early in the last century), and thousands of dollars of capital invested in the business was instantly swept out of existence." The canals have long since been abandoned.

The best type of fishway is the stream itself, and the aim should be to reproduce stream conditions so far as current is concerned.

It is doubtful if any salmon stream should ever be dammed without a fishway costing the full annual value of the fish, if necessary. Salmon were exterminated in the Connecticut River by a dam built in 1798. This also shut out shad and alewives. The value of the shad fisheries of the Delaware about this time was $200,000 per year. With salmon and alewives included, the Connecticut fisheries should have more than double this. At an expenditure of 10 per cent of the annual value of the fisheries a fishway quite adequate for all the fish could have been constructed. The very large one in the Susquehanna built in 1873 cost only $11,053. Not only are the swamps and marshes valuable for waterfowl, but those near the large cities produce quantities of frogs. Fifteen thousand dollars' worth are secured annually from the margins of Oneida Lake, New York.

North America possesses about two hundred species of game birds which are associated with water courses, lakes, swamps, and the seashore. This number includes seventy-four species of edible web-footed fowl. Sixteen of these have been shown to feed upon wild rice, wild celery, and pond weeds. These three plants supply an average of 25 per cent of their food, more than half of which consists of pond weeds which grow well in waters not too badly polluted. These birds are all closely dependent upon water for breeding. Ducks eat quantities of grasshoppers, locusts, cutworms, and marsh caterpillars. The rails and coots have similar habits and relations. All are useful to the farmer. There are some sixty species of long-legged, slender billed birds, the so-called shore birds, which devour quantities of mosquitoes, horseflies, etc., both adult and larval. Nearly all these birds are very fond of grasshoppers, and many feed on weevils, wireworms, leaf beetles, and other pests of the field.

The breeding grounds of the waterfowl have probably been reduced to 1 per cent of their original area in the upper Mississippi Valley and Lake states. The fowl have decreased from almost untold myriads to a mere handful. Their value for food was entirely forgotten when a machine capable of draining the grounds was invented and investments which would make large profits to the landowners were at stake. This extensive drainage has increased the flood hazard, and has thereby endangered fishes and mussels and the wildlife of the river bottoms farther down the streams.

PRINCIPLES, PLANS, AND REMEDIES

Objectives of Preservation-Conservation. The objects of a preservation-conservation plan are:

1. To provide and maintain representative natural areas from each extensive biotic community, to be used for preservation of the primitive in plant and animal life, as check areas in scientific study of modified biotic communities, and for continuous observation of cyclic phenomena.

2. To provide hunting, fishing, and trapping for fur-bearers on lands devoted to tree growing and recreation, and on the streams and lakes associated with such lands. To maintain wildlife on public lands ill-suited to white race occupancy; and to afford opportunities for scientific study of problems arising in connection with these and other land uses.

3. To provide game and fur-bearing animals on agricultural lands and abandoned farm lands, and fish in waters associated therewith.

4. To provide breeding grounds, winter grounds, and protection for migratory fowls.

It is probably the desire of nearly all persons that representatives of all the larger animals be preserved to posterity. Considerable differences in viewpoint among scientists and laymen as to methods of accomplishing this are also evident, and these views fall into two groups. (*a*) The view that predatory animals may be preserved in small numbers throughout grazing and other agricultural areas. This is perhaps the taxonomic rather than the ecological and interaction view. (*b*) The view that they can be saved only in buffered areas set aside for that purpose, which may provide numbers suitable for ecological study.

The persistent hunting and trapping and poisoning of the several wolves, cougar, badger, kit-fox, and wolverine, their extirpation over most of their range, and the extremely low ebb of their populations indicate the failure of the first plan.

A few years ago an intensive fight was carried on against federal appropriations of $1,300,000 per year to control or exterminate predatory animals and rodents. However, in the year 1934-1935 a larger sum has actually been spent for these purposes and many of the smaller species are in jeopardy.

The Buffer Zone of Partial Protection. The national parks of Europe were almost without exception proposed and fostered by scientists, especially biologists, and are set aside for educational and scientific purposes, but most of them are small.[1] Probably the nearest approach to this method on our continent has been obtained in the

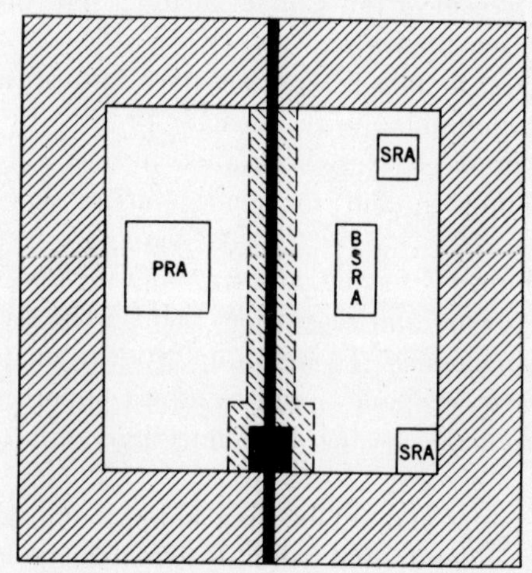

Fig. 2. Diagram of Buffering and Subdivision (after Wright, et al., 1935), Prepared by the National Park Service.

Black: Road and development area.
Dotted: Indefinite extent of human influence modifying wilderness conditions somewhat along roads and development center.
Hatched: Buffer area surrounding the park.
PRA: Permanent research area.
BSRA: Biotic succession research area.
SRA: Specific research area.
White: Primitive area—rest of the park.

province of Ontario. The roads, recreation features, and hotels of the national parks of North America, especially the United States, have shocked Europeans. The larger parks of North America as a rule are large enough to support some of the recreational features and often contain biological features of great value, in spite of the fact that they were commonly selected on a scenic basis.

One of the important principles applied to the European national parks is the buffer zone of partial protection which surrounds many of the parks. This zone may be used for tree growing, fishing, and recreation, but also for protection for wildlife. The central reserve or

[1] H. M. Hall, "European Reservations for the Protection of Natural Conditions," *Jour. For.*, Vol. 27, pp. 667-683.

park proper is used largely or exclusively for educational and research purposes.

A little progress in this direction has been made in America as the National Park Service of the United States has set aside research areas selected for their special value in the study of mature or developing biotic communities. Figure 2 shows these in relation to human occupancy. In addition, for the larger animals, buffer zones of large size are necessary, especially for animals which wander far from home or which

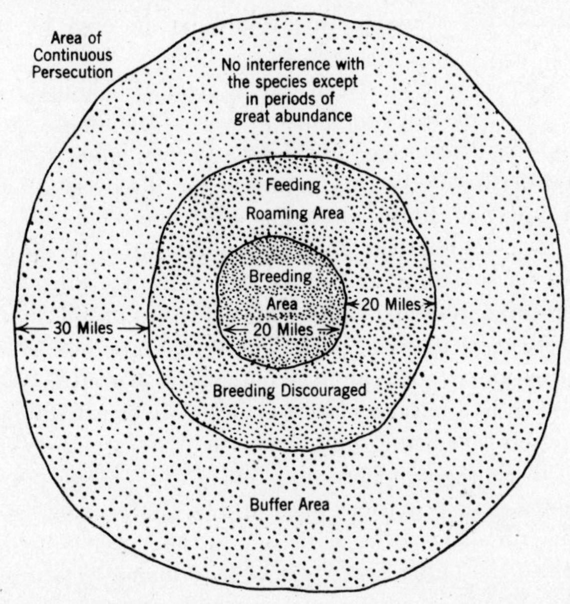

Fig. 3. Diagram Illustrating Buffering and Subdivision of Territory, Based on a Carnivore with a Fifty-mile Home Range.

migrate from higher to lower altitudes with the seasons. The extent of the buffer zone must depend upon the wandering or migrating range of the species, and its relation to industry, hunting, and recreation, in and outside the buffer zone. The large wolf of central North America no longer exists in any of the territorial national parks of the United States; the small number left in the parks when the custodians began protecting them have wandered across boundaries and been destroyed.

The method of buffering may be illustrated by a diagram, Fig. 3. The wolf is a difficult animal to manage but may serve to illustrate the general principles. Naturalists state that wolves den in an area after mating, presumably for life, and range about fifty miles from home.

No doubt when mates are killed, dens destroyed, and food scarce, they may travel farther, but this would not often happen in a park. A series of four concentric circles, therefore, may illustrate the method of buffering for the wolf. First a breeding area twenty miles in diameter—an area containing natural caves suitable for breeding as well as the possibility for excavating them—is necessary. Surrounding this is a ring twenty miles wide which would constitute the principal roaming and feeding area. Surrounding this is another ring thirty miles wide in which no interference of the species would take place except in times of great abundance. Outside this would be an area of continuous persecution.

Various naturalists have stated that a good wolf hunter is one who finds the dens and destroys the pups as well as the adults. Accordingly breeding could be discouraged in the area twenty miles wide surrounding the breeding area. By this is meant the discovering of breeding dens, the trapping of adults alive, and the removal of the families to the central area, if practicable, and the obliteration of natural caves, etc., suitable for breeding, as fast as they have been discovered. The combined breeding area and feeding area thirty miles in diameter may lie in or constitute a national park. The thirty-mile buffer area might well be in a national forest, and the outer zone of continuous persecution may also be in a national forest or in public or private lands. This scheme is purely academic, but serves to illustrate the principle of buffering, of discouraging of breeding, etc.

On a national scale provisions must also be made for both winter and summer range for such species as the elk in the Yellowstone Park. The size or width of the buffer areas will be determined by the ranges and habits of the species concerned, and the buffer territory may be used for recreation, tree growing, and restricted hunting of prolific species. The question of management of the animal life should be simple and free from political pressure, for national parks such as are here contemplated are not amusement areas or game preserves though these functions are inherent in the arrangement. The grave difficulties of management arise from fluctuations in abundance of the life being guarded. Custodians have in the past viewed all fluctuations with alarm and have called for immediate remedial measures—nobody has had the courage to let nature run its course.

Balance in Nature. The doctrine held by the older naturalists was to the effect that in undisturbed nature there is a uniform amount of life running forward through long periods of time. Biologists are now arriving at the conclusion that there never was any such a balance but that the abundance of life fluctuates markedly. It is necessary to conceive of the total population, particularly animals (also herbs, tree seedlings, etc.), of any area as being similar to a lake. The total amount of water fluctuates from time to time probably with some degree of periodic regularity. The total amount of life is comparable to the height of the lake surface. On top of this there is a wave movement characterized by very large difference between crest and trough comparable to the cyclic changes in abundance of single large species. Furthermore, in the surface of the waves there are many minor waves and irregularities; each of these corresponds to some minor change in abundance of some one small species. A good many of the attacks upon predatory animals have been started at the low point for other wildlife on the assumption that predators are responsible for the general low point.

In the short-lived animals there may be sharp fluctuations in numbers within brief periods. The outbreaks of insect pests, rodents, and coyotes receive a large amount of attention, and a great deal of money is expended in carrying out control measures. If these control measures begin when the insects and other pests are at their maximum abundance, the results attained may be *artifacts* as the funds may have been expended to kill animals which would never reproduce.[1] Among the longer-lived animals, these fluctuations take place in the same way, but the crests and troughs of abundance extend over a much longer period, thence efforts to increase or decrease this or that type of animal may be entirely erroneous even here. It becomes a serious question as to when remedies should be applied with reference to fluctuations in abundance of either so-called useful or noxious species.

Check Areas in Wildlife Investigations. Wildlife management has rarely been conducted in a thoroughly scientific manner. There have been no check areas. An agriculturist operates two areas: one which he fertilizes and one which he does not fertilize; one which he cultivates and one which he does not cultivate. However, the game manager or the student of biotic interaction rarely has an undisturbed area on which to check cycles and biotic balance, and it is difficult to judge the validity of the results obtained. Check areas in general are the greatest needs of animal ecology and of wildlife and game management.

Figure 4 shows a series of national and provincial parks, national monuments (United States), areas in process of acquirement as

[1] F. S. Bodenheimer, "Theoretical Considerations on the Evaluation of Control Measures," *Hadar,* Vol. 3, pp. 3-14.

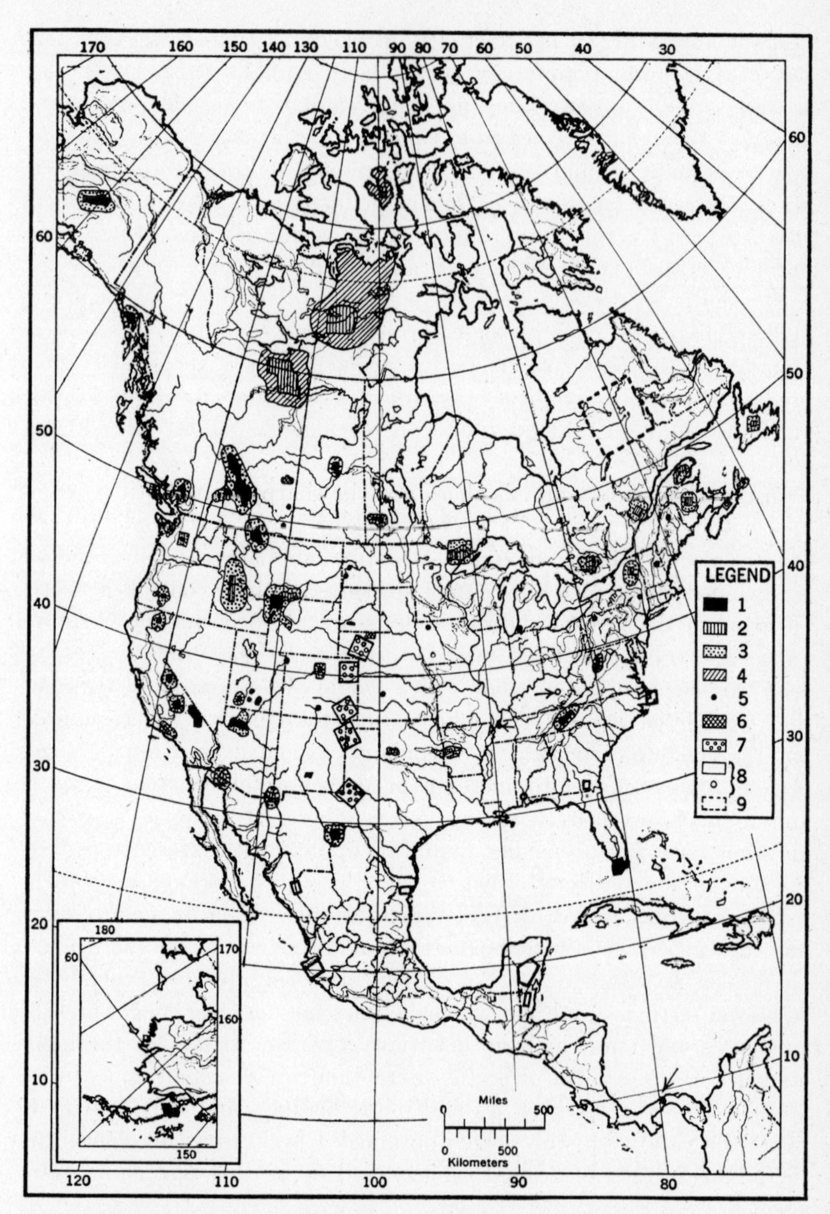

FIG. 4. Map Showing the Distribution of Existing and Essential Sanctuaries and Reservations and Suggested Buffer Zones.

(1) National Parks and Monuments, actual and in process of acquirement. (2) Areas suggested as nature sanctuaries. (3) Buffer areas suggested for existing and proposed sanctuaries. (4) Buffer areas from which trading-posts should be completely excluded. (5) Small but important publicly owned remnants of important biotic communities. (6) Experimental game reserves, existing and suggested. (7) Proposed plains fauna restoration reserve. One of the five areas should be selected. (8) Reserves proposed to perpetuate certain types of biotic community not yet provided for. (9) Natural reserves.

parks, etc., with suggested buffer zones. Many of them are in the main managed on a "let nature take its course" basis except for minor reductions of certain carnivores. The management of these can be greatly improved by adding the suggested buffer areas which will give protection to roaming species such as the elk, grizzly bear, wolf, and wolverine. A number of additional sanctuaries are necessary and are suggested in the legend and description. The setting aside of a park somewhat larger than Yellowstone National Park is suggested by five optional areas of the map (Fig. 4) all lying in the range areas of the Great Plains, one of which should be selected.

The following areas in the National Park System of the United States are believed to be the ones which operate most effectively as wildlife sanctuaries: Yellowstone, Mount McKinley, Glacier, Yosemite, Grand Canyon, Sequoia, and Great Smoky Mountains National Parks, and Death Valley, Glacier Bay, and Katmai National Monuments. All are badly in need of buffer zones. Katmai and Glacier Bay in Alaska, in addition to their value as preserves of extraordinary ecological relationships, also provide sanctuary for the Alaska brown bear. The native biota of Katmai has been studied by Griggs.[1]

The proposed national parks and monuments which would serve as effective wildlife sanctuaries and should be supported by the public are the following:

	Approximate Area in Square Miles
Proposed Mount Olympus National Park, Wash.	512.88
Proposed Kings Canyon National Park, Calif.	900.00
Proposed Everglades National Park, Florida	2,031.25
Proposed Big Bend National Park, Texas	1,150.00
Proposed Green River National Monument, Colorado and Utah	681.00
Proposed Escalante National Monument, Utah	6,845.25
Proposed Organ Pipe Cactus National Monument, Ariz.	564.00
Proposed Kofa Mountains National Monument, Ariz.	1,260.00

The proposed Mount Olympus National Park should provide protection of a considerable proportion of the all-year range for several thousand Roosevelt elk. It is to be hoped that the area will be acquired and provide better protection for the Oregon cougar, bobcat, Pacific marten, Pacific fisher, Pacific mink, Olympic Mount beaver and various other native forms the populations of which are exceedingly small.

The proposed Kings Canyon National Park should provide addi-

[1] R. F. Griggs, "The Edge of the Forest in Alaska and the Reasons for Its Position," *Ecology,* Vol. 15, pp. 80-96.

tional protection for the Sierra bighorn, the southern wolverine, and Pacific fisher, all of which are in precarious status at present.

The proposed Big Bend National Park in southern Texas is now a state park project. The area has been authorized by Congress for national park status if and when sufficient lands have been donated to the federal government. It will provide additional protection for mountain lion, bear, Mexican muledeer, Sonora deer, javelina or peccary, Texas raccoon, ringtailed cat, Rio Grande spotted skunk, long-tailed Texas skunk, hog-nosed skunk, Mexican badger, and small-toothed coyote.

The proposed Green River National Monument, if established contiguously to the proposed Lodore Game Refuge, will provide protection for Rocky Mountain bighorn and Rocky Mountain muledeer.

The proposed Organ Pipe Cactus National Monument in Arizona is designed primarily to protect the organ pipe cactus and the other native desert vegetation. It would also provide sanctuary for native fauna, such as Galliard bighorn, deer, possibly both burro deer and Mexican muledeer, antelope, possibly both the Mexican and plains varieties, and Sonoran peccary. The Biological Survey is proposing a bighorn refuge with an area of perhaps 2,000 square miles contiguous to the proposed monument.

The proposed Kofa Mountains National Monument in Arizona has for its purpose the protection of native palms. It would also provide sanctuary for native fauna, such as Galliard bighorn, desert muledeer, and American pronghorn antelope. The Biological Survey is proposing a bighorn refuge of approximately 3,000 square miles surrounding the proposed monument.

The proposed Escalante National Monument in Utah, because of its unusually large area, is believed to have excellent potentialities as a range for antelope and bighorn particularly, as well as other native fauna.

As Skinner[1] points out, Canada and Mexico have been much less inclined to destroy their wildlife than has the United States. The Canadian national parks have been in better condition than those of the United States, as they were acquired before being over-grazed and exploited. The first reduction of predatory animals is reported recently. The fact that the forest lands surrounding these parks were ceded to the provinces may interfere with the establishment of buffer zones as the management of the buffer is governed by the needs of the sanc-

[1] M. P. Skinner, "The Predatory and Furbearing Animals of Yellowstone Park," *Roosevelt Wild Life Bulletin,* Vol. 4, pp. 164-284.

tuary. The Canadian National Park System has not been expanding as rapidly as that of the country to the south, but it is to be hoped that it may be extended to include large areas in the tundra.

One of the most difficult types of preserve is the floodplain of the Mississippi River. Only a few small areas about Reelfoot Lake, Tennessee, are state owned, but poorly cared for. Some reserves in the tropics are suggested by outlines and are located on the map (Fig. 4) merely with reference to the type of vegetation.

Natural Areas and Buffer Zones. The United States Forest Service has set aside sample areas of various types of natural forest vegetation called *natural areas*. These afford some protection to small animals, but are not free from control measures; they are subject to trapping, and most of them are too small to cover the home range of even the smallest animals. The United States Forest Service has been urged to set aside some large buffered sanctuaries in the Idaho primitive area and elsewhere (Fig. 4).

The national monuments should also be buffered with lands in partial use; the system should include important types of biotic community such as cypress swamps, lowland deciduous forest, grassland of various types, chaparral, etc. Where not surrounded with public land they should be buffered by the states by means of state forests, parks, etc. State parks should also be buffered as even deer, foxes, and raccoons need a zone of protection when in small areas. This applies to the small 50- to 100-acre holdings of the universities.

The estabishment of buffer zones about the national parks of the United States will require the removal of scattered ranches and perhaps the cancelation of grazing rights in the surrounding national forests. This may require appropriations to remunerate ranch owners, and perhaps special legislation. The establishment of sanctuaries in the United States national forests presents similar difficulties. The problems in Canada are similar. Local opposition seems inevitable, making necessary the carrying out of plans to preserve remnants of complete biotic communities very largely a matter for national action.

In the northern coniferous forest and tundra, attempts to set up sanctuaries are beset by some of the most difficult and primitive of game problems. Nature sanctuaries are difficult to establish and maintain because of the natives and the traders. Natives in general are conservative in their trapping and hunting, but the trader is out to make profits and usually has a decided influence in the direction of excessive killing and ill-seasoned destruction of game of all kinds. It is probably necessary that all trading posts be removed as far as practicable from northern sanctuaries and native trapper activities restricted by a process of zoning.

The principle of buffering is extremely important, especially for small areas; fur-bearers range outside their nesting territory in search of food and are often treed by dogs and killed, so that small areas set aside for farm-game studies in which natural balance is to be considered must be both buffered and guarded. Hardly any other line of research will be of so much benefit to humanity in general as carefully controlled studies of *cycles*. The data on receipts of furs by dealers cannot be relied upon because in times of low prices trappers often store and hold skins awaiting better prices.

Some Requirements. Restoration of wildlife involves restoration of habitats. For aquatic animals, suitable waters must be re-established; for terrestrial animals the first requirement is cover and the second is food. Cover must often be maintained because the best cover may represent only the early stages of succession or development of forest and, therefore, may pass into a different and less suitable phase within a short period.

The setting-up of these physical and biological conditions meets with significant difficulties growing out of public prejudices and lack of information. The latter calls for research of all kinds. When the correct course has been found through investigation it will be necessary to correct the difficulties growing out of legal rights, ownership, and conflicting interests by cooperation and legislation, but to secure this the public must be given the facts through agencies which can put them into popular terms.

Hawes, writing from the point of view of the sportsman, states that the major part of game and wildlife research in the United States has been done in the universities, in a comparatively few state game organizations, and in the United States Biological Survey, with little or no mechanism for translating the full results of this work into beneficial activity for the wildlife, particularly game.

Recently the United States Biological Survey has sought and secured appropriations from Congress enabling it to help finance cooperative research and instruction programs in some one college in each of several states. Nine such programs were set up in 1935-1936.

In research and demonstration work these nine stations are doing three things: (1) carrying on original research or modifying the practices of others to fit local conditions; (2) demonstrating, in practice, the application of research results to game restoration; and (3) putting information into the extension system already established in the land-grant colleges and the Department of Agriculture in such form as to enable the extension workers to carry it to the public. Hawes has said, "For the first time we are attempting to gear game conservation and restoration program into an existing agency."[1] It is the belief of sportsmen that this should be extended to all the states.

The instruction plan involves the conducting of research under supervision as thesis material for post-graduate students. The restriction of the entire game and wildlife instruction to the post-graduate field will bring best results, for game management is not simple as sportsmen and politicians believe, but involves very complicated fields of ecological science in which knowledge is only at its beginning. It is to be hoped that undergraduate courses leading to the bachelor's degree in game and wildlife management will not be instituted. Those in charge of game work should have strong training in biology and ecology followed by specialization in the field of wildlife.

RESTORATION OF GAME

Terrestrial Game Restoration. The buffered sanctuaries will serve various purposes, but among other things as reservoirs of big game which overflow into the surrounding territory for sportsmen who should support such a program. The large size of the proposed areas, the presence of predators and normal interactions give the best possible assurance of perpetuation of game for all time. The overflow from these areas can favorably affect surroundings—forests, range, abandoned farm lands, and farm areas.

The Biological Survey has called attention to the following facts. In the eastern forest area the removal of the forest during the Colonial and post-Colonial period caused a dense new growth to spring up, affording far more food and cover for game than originally existed. The larger predatory animals had been eliminated early. Marginal or submarginal lands, as in many sections of the Appalachian Mountain region in half a dozen states and in the Ozark Mountains of southern Missouri and northern Arkansas, are relatively barren of game except for limited areas. The dense second growth has thus been prepared for the restoration of deer, bears, grouse, and wild turkeys on a scale far exceeding the game populations of the same areas in the pre-Colonial period. If these areas were restocked and properly administered, the annual game products that could be taken would go far to relieve the present unfortunate condition of a portion of the population. The suc-

[1] H. B. Hawes, "Four Vital Factors of Wild Life Conservation." A separate, pp. 1-16.

cess of forest-game restoration in cut-over areas in Pennsylvania, New York, Michigan, and other states is indicative of what could be done in similar sections elsewhere.

Conditions in the West differ materially from those in the East, as the western forests have been cut over only in part—domestic stock grazing is a more important factor to be reckoned with, and large predatory animals, especially coyotes, are still numerous. There have been remarkable increases in game, especially deer and elk, in recent years.

Game Refuges Are Needed. We quote the Biological Survey on this subject:

> The importance of establishing more refuges, Federal, State, municipal, and private, as a part of a comprehensive program of wildlife management, is becoming more generally recognized; but these must be suitably located and properly administered to achieve their highest usefulness.
>
> "Wildlife refuges of one kind or another are under the jurisdiction of several departments of the Federal Government, their varied situations being largely due to expedience, as the control of wildlife tends to run concurrently with that of the land (or water) it inhabits. (See *Report of Natural Resources Board*, Part 9, pp. 71-81.)

The refuges on the national forests under the Forest Service, and hundreds of refuges, mainly for birds but including a few big game ranges, under the Bureau of Biological Survey, are too scattered, especially in the center of the continent, to be as effective as desired. With a few noteworthy exceptions the state game preserves are too small, unstable, and badly conducted to deserve much consideration from the wildlife standpoint.

The protection of marine mammals, notably the northern fur seal, which breeds on the Pribilof Islands, and the sea otter, is entrusted to the Bureau of Fisheries, Department of Commerce.

Specialized Refuges Are Needed for Upland Game. The Biological Survey points out the following facts:

> The ideal upland game refuge is a protected area that will favor the rapid increase of game within its borders and from which the surplus may readily spread to suitable surrounding territory that may be open to hunting. It need not necessarily be very large, but alone or in conjunction with neighboring refuge units should provide year-long range, ample forage, water, and cover for resident game. This is the type of refuge that has succeeded so admirably in building up the game supply in the State forests of Pennsylvania and other Eastern States, and on Federal and State refuges on the national forests, mainly in the West. Wherever game thrives, a game

crop may reasonably be expected. It can be removed by hunters, or allowed to die of starvation or disease. Game management, therefore, calls not only for adequate protection but the disposal of surplus.

The remaining public domain of the United States is now or probably soon will be under administration under the Taylor Grazing Act. These lands have been abused for years, and are badly over-grazed. There are many complicating factors in first restoring them and then wisely allocating them to their best uses. Gabrielson,[1] of the Biological Survey, points out various features in the West as follows:

> Grazing these lands is essential to the welfare and in some cases the very existence of small communities in most of the western states. In many cases the major values of these lands to the nation are in livestock production. On the other hand, this public domain is the natural habitat of the antelope and the sage grouse—largest and most stately of our native grouse, and a host of other beautiful, interesting, and useful game and other species.
>
> These are public lands, a fact that some radical livestock raisers might wish to forget, and as a public resource wildlife is entitled to provision for its needs in their administration. Several areas of the public domain in which some preference is given to wildlife have been or are in process of being set aside by Executive order.

This is a distinct gain for wildlife. The disturbing fact is the wild furor of opposition that was stirred up among certain elements in the livestock industry when the request was made, not that livestock be excluded, but that the needs of wild species be recognized on less than 10 per cent of the total area of the public domain.

Such protests do not represent the feeling of all or even a majority of livestock operators, many of whom are now and have been for years protecting wildlife on their own holdings at considerable trouble and expense to themselves. There are stockmen to whom those interested in wildlife are greatly indebted. Without the personal interest and care of these stockmen many of the present herds of game and coveys of birds would long ago have passed out of the picture. Such men are not as much against the conservation of wildlife on the public domain as some politicians would have us believe.[2]

Hawes[3] has pointed out the federal, state, sportsman, and farmer factors in wildlife conservation. The farmer and the landowner hold

[1] I. N. Gabrielson, "A National Program of Wild Life Restoration," *Amer. For.*, Vol. 42, p. 104.

[2] From Gabrielson's address before the American Wildlife Conference, Washington, D. C., February, 1936. (Mimeographed.)

[3] H. B. Hawes, "Four Vital Factors of Wild Life Conservation." A separate.

the key to the restoration of game on farms. Without an understanding between the sportsman and the farmer, preservation and restoration cannot succeed. The farmer must be convinced that game is a valuable by-product of the farm and learn how to produce it, and the sportsman must assist in the task and not expect the farmer to contribute to his pleasure without compensation. The farmer has usually labored to secure his land, and the sportsman must expect to bear his part of the cost of game production. The farmer's land does or could provide ample food and cover for upland game birds and many of our smaller game animals. No plan for the restoration of wildlife in the eastern half of closely populated North America can be successful without the inclusion of the farmer as the first vital factor. When the farmer can make enough from game at least to pay his taxes, as has been done in many of the southern states where shooting privileges are leased, game becomes a matter of interest to him.

Aquatic Game Restoration. The fishes, frogs, and purely aquatic animals have suffered from over-catch by all kinds of methods including the use of poisons, dynamite, traps, and snares, but worse than any of these is pollution. This is destructive not only of fishes, but also of waterfowl, their food, nesting materials, etc. Oil often finds its way onto the surface of duck waters, and is fatal to birds.

It is a fact that a certain amount of purely household sewage added to water increases nitrogen and hence acts as a fertilizer, producing more food for fish and other aquatic animals. Certain European towns run their sewage into ponds where the yield of carp is increased through the increase of fish food.

In America there is no such thing as purely household sewage; even in the smallest town the garage runs oil and gasoline into the sewers, the creamery adds milk wastes, or the gas plant adds quantities of deadly poison, until there is really no certainty that the process of breaking down the organic matter of the household sewage presents into nitrogen available for fish food will go on. In addition, washings from roads surfaced with various tars and oils complicate matters and kill the fish. This subject has received careful attention in England.

How much sewage can be used advantageously as fertilizer? The amount that can be used for carp is detrimental to most aquatic resources, because carp are more resistant than almost any American food fish. When is a stream self-purified? The sanitary chemist and bacteriologist have criteria, but they fail for important aquatic organisms. A large number of questions demand investigation. Tests of the toxicity of sewage and industrial wastes and other poisons introduced into the water must be made, as a basis for rendering them harmless. The question, often asked, as to whether or not a given substance will injure fishes, in general cannot be answered. First of all, the resistance of different species, and of different stages of the same species, differs as much as a hundredfold for the same poison.

Conditions in streams and other bodies of water vary. The summer low-water conditions are dangerous because of little flow, of concen-

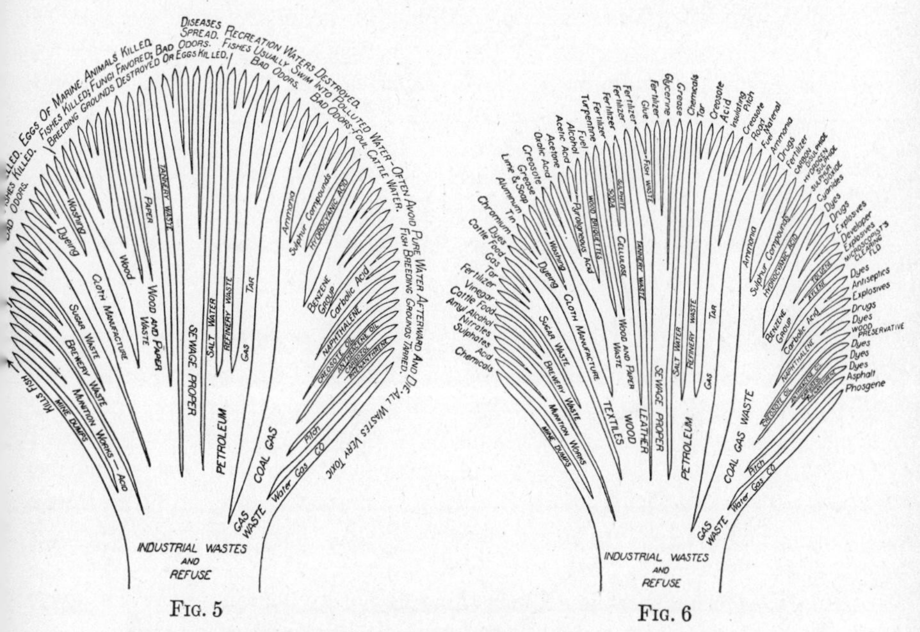

Fig. 5. Diagram Indicating the Damage Done by Pollution.
Fig. 6. Diagram Indicating the Useful Products Recovered from Polluting Substances.

tration of polluting substances, and of high temperature, which increase toxicity; the winter low-water conditions are dangerous because of slow flow and because of the presence of ice, which prevents aeration.

There are various new methods of treating sewage. It is true that plants for the recovery of sewage materials by the older processes have failed to pay profits. It is possible that methods, old or new, pay only when the damages which result from pollution are taken into account. The damages must include a value on all resources represented by a stream or other body of water. Sewage contains much nitrogen needed to maintain soil fertility. It is recovered and put into form suitable to return to the land with doubtful success at the present time, but that is largely because of the lack of adequate effort. A study of the two diagrams, Fig. 5 and 6, will indicate the damage that the various types of pollution do and the use of products which may be obtained from polluting substances.

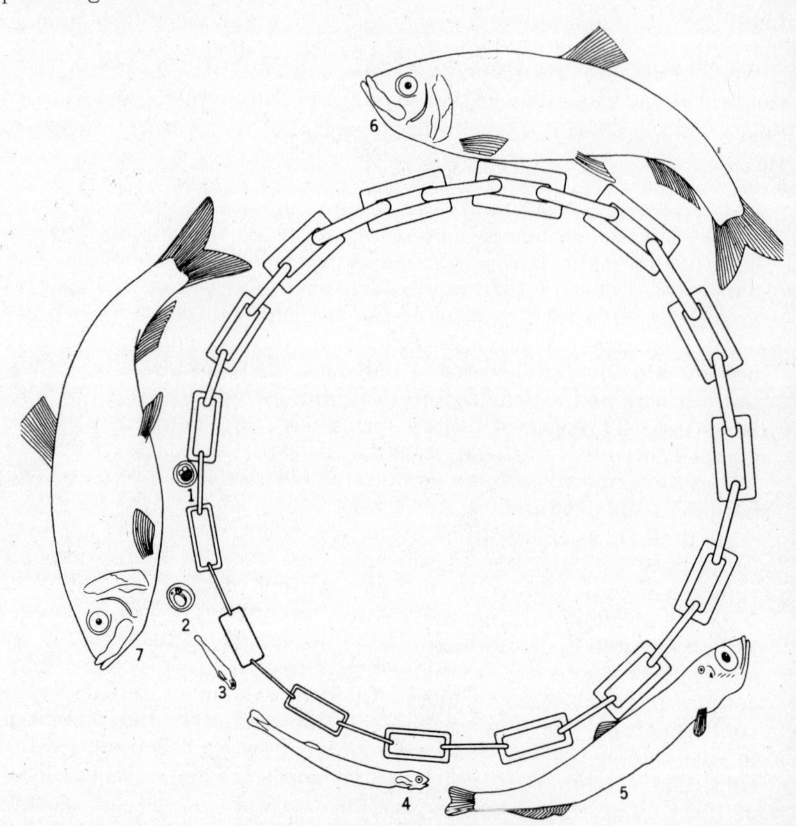

Fig. 7. Showing the Sensitive Stage in the Life History of an Aquatic Animal as Illustrated by the Herring.

The effect of pollution on fishes is often misjudged because very resistant adults are used for tests. The life history is a chain with its weakest link in the young stages (Fig. 7). Hence, for short-time tests of the suitability of water, young of game fishes should be used.

Fur-bearers will probably increase rapidly with the restoration of their habitats. The waterfowl, on the other hand, has suffered an enormous depletion due to over-shooting and the drainage of land, much of which was ill-advised. The more southerly breeding water birds have gradually been forced north in their breeding through the drainage of land and the utilization of land for agriculture in northern United States until nearly all ducks and geese breed in Canada. The Canada goose, for example, once bred freely as far south as south central Illinois. Mallard commonly nested in prairie sloughs of Illinois.[1]

An effort is now being made to restore these birds through cooperation with the Canadian government. Concerning this the Biological Survey prepared the following statement for the Natural Resources Board:

> The present program of acquisition of migratory-bird refuges by the Federal Government has as its objective two major purposes. The predominant purpose is the acquisition of all possible areas which by reason of their present natural environment will attract migratory birds in the nesting season, or which through development or by restoration to primeval conditions may be made attractive to nesting waterfowl. The second objective contemplates the acquisition of more or less extensive resting and feeding areas in the flight lanes used by migratory birds spring and fall, in order that they may be provided with conveniently situated sanctuaries furnishing water, food, and cover in an unmolested environment, protected from both man and predators.
>
> At present, as pointed out by Salyer, the major efforts are being concentrated on the breeding-ground phase of this migratory-bird-refuge restoration program, but not entirely to the exclusion of efforts for providing resting and feeding grounds. The size of refuges to be so acquired should as a rule be not less than 10,000 acres, but single units where the environmental elements are favorable might comprise 50,000 acres or more. An ideal system of refuges would contemplate a series of major projects approximately 300 miles apart in each one of the four major waterfowl flyways described by Lincoln, that extend from the Canadian border to the southern limits of the United States, and in proximity to most, if not all, of these might well be created groups of refuges smaller in size that would be beneficial in the wildlife restoration and conservation program.

The statement further brings out the fact that the accomplishment of the object will be largely dependent upon availability of funds and upon a cessation of ill-advised drainage of land and of ill-advised use of water in futile reclamation projects.

Pirnie discusses the sanctuary problem in the following terms:

> The primary function of refuges is to save game for breeding stock, not to make it easier to kill more. Another justifiable use,

[1] E. W. Nelson, "Birds of Northeastern Illinois," *Bull. Essex Inst.*, Vol. 8, pp. 90-155, 1877.

under conditions of plenty, is to hold game on areas which ordinarily would be "burned out" by a few days' shooting. Assuming that refuges serve primarily to reduce the kill from shooting, the need for refuge protection will vary according to the total of all other safeguards which are applied (predator control, game law restrictions, etc.) provided shooting is a major mortality factor; and the gun is not always equally destructive to all game species. In theory at least, refuge needs are least under closed seasons and greatest under long open seasons and high bag limits, and with many shooters afield. No sound refuge program can afford to ignore the probable trend and development of future state and federal regulations and policies as to seasons and bag limits. Large gatherings of waterfowl in refuges are not guaranteed by decoys and baiting or by refuge posters. Proximity to the principal flyways or to fall and winter concentrations counts for even more than attractive feeding and resting places or large flocks of decoys. To create an adequate system of refuges along the principal routes of migration and at points of greatest concentration is desirable but will take a long time and will cost much money. Worthwhile refuges are bound to interfere to some extent with boating and fishing and may lessen local shooting. To be truly effective, any system of refuges should harbor throughout the open season our most important waterfowl species in shooting areas. That a few, widely scattered refuges actually save but few birds is indicated by the reported kill of black ducks banded at several Michigan sanctuaries. Refuges and sanctuaries have many excellent opportunities to stimulate public interest in better wildlife management.

Refuges offer many chances for wildlife studies dealing with feeding and breeding habits, diseases, migration, mortality from natural causes, and as to relations with other animals or to the plant life of these areas. Although absence of gunning is essential to certain studies, a continuation of regular shooting seasons is essential to the study of how refuges function in saving waterfowl. Such seasons need not be long. It is more important that regulations be kept as uniform as possible from year to year to avoid introducing new factors which prevent good analyses of population trends among the waterfowl. Refuges are but part of the whole management program to improve conditions for wildlife and to stimulate and make possible wider use of our potential game resources. Refuges go hand in hand with, but do not take the place of, other valid shooting restrictions; neither do they lessen the need for restoring and cresting additional feeding ranges and nesting or breeding grounds for certain species, when such programs can be afforded. A sound waterfowl program will not include refuges as a matter of course, but rather only when and where local conditions and needs so indicate. The probable cost of creating and maintaining any sanctuary must be weighed against the expected or actual benefits, since the need for economy pertains to sports and recreation when public rather than private funds are being expended.

The much-discussed duck foods do not appear to have the significance which interest in the subject would lead the public to expect. Ducks eat large numbers of terrestrial insects during grasshopper outbreaks, and some have been found with 200 or more of these insects in their stomachs. Pirnie further states that

> the Michigan duck foods investigations have shown that many of the better known and most advertised duck food plants are already widely distributed and often very abundant. There is little evidence of a general food shortage in that state [Michigan], for the animal life of streams and lakes contributes far more food for wild ducks than is usually recognized. Most waterfowl enjoy varied diets rather than restricting their feeding to one or two items such as rice or celery. Local food shortages are by no means the only reason for duck scarcity, for many excellent weed beds and good grain fields are without ducks during most of the fall flight. To a limited extent it is true that the better feeding grounds attract, and, to some extent, hold waterfowl, but it would be absurd to expect feeding conditions to overcome such potent influences as migration and flocking instincts and habits, or the effect of hunting season disturbances.

Pirnie[1] has pointed out the following general principles regarding regulations related to waterfowl conservation:

> Regardless of how successful all new refuge and breeding grounds programs may be, there is need for a continuation of some sort of legal protection, and it is now up to someone to decide as to what sort of restrictions should be adopted. Two principal aims must be kept in mind, (*a*) the increasing of waterfowl, and (*b*) the preservation of all possible opportunities for reasonable field sports, and here is where many differences arise. . . . Rest days are but an excuse or substitute for that far more valuable conservation measure, a shorter season, and for that very reason they are likely to be in greater favor. Similarly, shorter seasons are but an application of the refuge system on a large scale and without the attendant costs of refuge operation. . . . Evidently seasons longer than five or six weeks will result in too great a kill of most kinds of ducks under present conditions of waterfowl concentrations and under existing hunting methods. . . . No waterfowl conservation plans can afford to neglect the evident value of short seasons in helping to secure real waterfowl increases without putting a complete stop to shooting. . . . If waterfowl are steadily decreasing, past protection must have failed of its purpose. If shooting has been too severe, additional restrictions may possibly solve the problem of how to get more ducks and geese; but if unknown factors are primarily responsible for this possible decrease, added shooting restrictions may avail little. The reported kill of leg-banded black ducks and mallards indicates that the gun

[1] M. D. Pirnie, "Michigan Waterfowl Management," *Department of Conservation, Game Division,* Lansing, 1935.

is responsible for too heavy losses; and in all probability few if any kinds of game ducks are exempt from the danger of over-shooting. Since it is possible that most species of waterfowl are diminishing it seems only sensible to continue with game law protection, at least until such action has been proved unnecessary. Regardless of the merits of "constructive" management (marsh restoration and the improvement of feeding grounds), attention should not be diverted away from the evident value of "restrictive" management. To duck populations it matters little when or where each bird is shot, whether in the air or on the water; but the total kill does matter, and that evidently is in need of reduction. With or without decoys and baiting, the hunter's conduct (whether as a true sportsman or a poacher) depends on himself as well as on the game laws laid down for him by others. Evidence piles up in favor of restrictions which affect all alike, namely the shorter season accompanied by low bag limits instead of tinkering as to how many shells a gun holds or at what angle the shooter holds it when he pulls the trigger. So long as waterfowl shooting is permitted, so it seems, care should be taken to perpetuate those methods which help to distribute hunting opportunities, as well as to conserve waterfowl.

Control of Predators. This type of management has so commonly been conducted in an ill-advised manner and without check areas that its status must be determined experimentally by comparison of treated areas with untreated check areas.

Pirnie states the case relative to birds as follows:

> The chief function of useful predator control is to discover when and where any wild animals are doing sufficient damage to crops or wildlife to justify remedial measures. Control work should employ only those practices which of themselves are decidedly less destructive to wildlife or crops than the predators which are condemned. Wasteful poisoning campaigns or careless trapping cannot be justified in the name of predator control if done without specific reason or merely on general principles.

This is generally applicable at all times and in all places.

Poison probably has been used to control noxious and undesirable animals since early times. It has been in general use for many years for killing introduced rats and mice. However, doubtless so long as relatively primitive people lived in one locality they sought to conserve even the noxious animals because they provided skins. Sedentary people also conserved game as our American natives orginally did and in some localities still do. It is mainly in the past 35 years that poison has come into use in natural habitats to reduce wild species. It began in the grassland areas of western Kansas and other parts of the great plains where prairie dogs and jack rabbits had become very abundant.

In 1903 the Kansas Agricultural College used two tons of strychnine in a campaign, in charge of the late D. E. Lantz, against prairie dogs and jack rabbits. A number of men claim the honor of being the first poisoners.

The chief criticism of the use of poison is that it is non-selective in killing the animals sought and at the same time getting many others such as fur-bearers, song and game birds, and even occasionally human beings. Quail and other game birds have commonly suffered, sometimes to the point of extirpation. There has been criticism of the methods employed in noting stomach contents, bait having frequently been listed as the normal food.

Land Ownership and Public Education. The most fundamental requirement of wildlife preservation and conservation is the control of the land on which the animals are found—a control of areas sufficiently extensive to retain individuals of the species concerned which reside in a central portion of the sanctuary. The control of the land by the federal government and of the game and other wildlife by the state in which the land and game are found is an absurdity. The control of land by the Forest Service and the game by the Biological Survey is also incongruous. The weakness of the United States Biological Survey in the past is traceable in part to its lack of land to control. It has not been possible for it to conduct experimental studies. The recent destruction of the mammal material on which the Survey was working on the long-time project on lands controlled by the Forest Service is an example of failure of divided responsibility. Again the fact that, in certain areas, much game must be produced on farms, if at all, introduces a similar principle. The farmer must be responsible for the land, protect the game, and put out the coverts, but he has no means for securing a return for his labors except by the leasing of hunting rights, which is quite a proper procedure. But the difficulty of guarding individual farms is great, so that this has to be carried out as a large-scale cooperation between farmers and sportsmen's organizations. The acquirement of proper land control will go forward only at a rate comparable to public education in the game and wildlife fields. There is a large body of accepted land-use practice which is the outgrowth of extreme individualism and the development of separate branches of science. These accepted views will have to be remoulded to fit wise *general land use* plans before progress can become extensive. Besides these modern adverse tendencies there are a thousand prejudices relative to wildlife, *for* this species and *against* that one, which can be overcome only by research followed by popular education based upon facts.

SUMMARY

1. Wildlife management is tied up with land use. Lands devoted to wildlife are divisible into:

(*a*) *Preservation* areas managed on a "let nature take its course" basis.

(*b*) Conservation areas in which there is an attempt to manage wildlife for some particular purpose.

These are subdivisible into several types.

2. Preservation areas are chiefly the national parks of Canada and the national parks and monuments of the United States. All these must be buffered if they are to function to save threatened species now in or near them; many additional areas are needed to save samples of original biotic communities. The buffer zones must be controlled primarily with reference to the needs of the sanctuary. These sanctuaries and their communities are not renewable resources.

3. Conservation areas contain modified biotic communities which are in a considerable measure renewable resources to be managed in the interest of game, fishes, and recreation. The science of management is at its beginning, and the field is characterized by ignorance, prejudice, and politics. To correct these conditions will require much research and education of the public.

4. The control of the land occupied by wildlife is ordinarily the first essential of proper management. Lands are best subdivided on the basis of the use of the plow. Areas *not* characterized by the general use of the plow cannot be wisely operated in accord with agricultural practice.

PART VIII

CHAPTER XX

RECREATIONAL RESOURCES

By Edward C. Prophet

Michigan State College

THE RECREATIONAL MOVEMENT

During the last twenty years the attention of the general public has been directed to recreation, and especially to outdoor recreation. The back-to-the-wilds movement has been strong, vigorous, and cumulative in its effect. The movement is stronger today than at any time in the past, and it appears that it will gain momentum. Millions of acres of land, most of it not utilizable at present for other economic purposes, have been put to use in providing recreation grounds for the American people. The movement is now so vigorous that some land-utilization specialists, as well as laymen interested in land affairs, are pointing to the recreational use of land as the panacea that will settle many or most of our idle-land problems. This is unfortunate, as land may be submarginal for recreational use, just as land is submarginal for agriculture, forestry, etc. The old law of supply and demand must certainly be considered in discussing recreational resources and in determining whether the areas are marginal or submarginal. What today is submarginal may in a few years be in great demand. Accordingly, then, one phase of the conservation of recreational resources is to see that areas not now in economic use are not materially disturbed but are left in their present condition until the future demands for this type of resource may be properly and fairly evaluated.

What Are Recreational Resources? At the outset, it is frankly admitted that no two students of recreational affairs have fully the same viewpoint and so their definitions will vary. This general field is a new one, so that its limits have not been established and it overlaps a number of other fields of research. For the purposes of this discussion only the phases of the recreational industry that deal with land will be considered. Land is here used in the sense in which the geographer-economist employs it, meaning not only land surface but also all natural resources such as climate, water, vegetation, etc. To give the reader some idea of the wide range of recreational resources the following may be listed: mountains, forests, rivers, lakes, ravines and glens, hilly belts, landscaped parks, ocean shores, areas with hot climate in winter, areas with cool temperatures in summer, and even cut-over forest lands for hunting. This list is not all-inclusive but merely suggestive.

Forests as Recreational Land. A report[1] of the Forest Service made in the spring of 1933 shows that 250,000,000 man-days of recreational use of forest lands were taking place yearly with an expenditure by the recreationalist of more than $1,740,000,000. This measures only the recreationalists' utilization of forested areas. If other phases of the recreation industry are considered, the total number of man-days spent in outdoor recreation and the expenditures made by the participants will be several times the figures given.

The rapid increase in utilization of forested lands by recreationalists in recent years is exhibited, in part, by the attendance figures for the national forests and the national parks. In 1917, 300,000 people visited the national parks and 3,000,000 the national forests; in 1931 the attendance figures rose to 3,000,000 for the national parks and 32,000,000 for the national forests.[2]

In this same report[3] the Forest Service makes the following estimate of the total area of forested lands needed for recreational uses in the United States:

Superlative areas	3,000,000 acres
Primitive "	9,500,000 "
Wilderness "	10,000,000 "
Roadside "	4,000,000 "
Residence "	6,000,000 "
Campsite "	1,500,000 "
Outing "	11,000,000 "
Total	45,000,000 acres

This total includes 11,000,000 acres now withdrawn from forest uses. The definitions given the adjectives used in the tabulation are quoted as they identify many of the special types of recreational land uses. *Superlative areas* are "localities with unique scenic values, so sur-

[1] *The Forest Service of the Agricultural Department, A National Plan for American Forestry,* Senate Document 12, Seventy-third Congress, 1st Session, pp. 29 and 30, United States Government Printing Office, 1933.

[2] *Ibid.,* pp. 29 and 30.

[3] *Ibid.,* pp. 1544-1546.

passing and stupendous in their beauty as to affect almost everyone who sees them." *Primitive areas* are those "tracts of old-growth timber in which human activities have never upset the normal processes of nature." *Wilderness areas* are those "regions which contain no permanent inhabitants, possess no means of mechanical conveyance, and are sufficiently spacious that a person may spend at least a week or two of travel in them without crossing his own tracks." *Roadside areas* are those "timbered strips adjoining the more important roads." *Campsite areas* are "forest land set aside for camping." *Residence areas* are "forest land set aside for private homes, hotels, resorts, group camps, sanitaria, and stores and services of one sort or another." And finally, *outing areas* are "tracts of land on which one can get away from the sounds of the highway and which have not been severely injured scenically."

Some of the lands described above are to be found in our national forests, some in the national parks, some in state parks and forests, and some under private ownership. In the pages which follow, the discussion of recreational lands and their utilization is arranged according to the basis of the ownership of the land and the uses to which it is put.

HUNTING AND FISHING LANDS

If area used is the basis of measurement, hunting and fishing are the most important recreational uses of land. If the number of people involved, or better still, man-days of use, is the basis, hunting and fishing lands would still rank with the foremost recreational lands. Only if we consider the amount of investment in recreational resources and the expenditures of the recreationalists would this phase of the recreation industry take a secondary position.

Need of Public-owned Lands. In the past it has not been necessary for the hunter or fisherman to own the land that he hunts or fishes on. In the United States we have a heritage that hunting and fishing are free to all men, but we have had to modify that by license laws as the amount of game and fish has become more limited. For the last few years we have also faced the problem of trespass in order to hunt or fish. This problem has become sufficiently acute that a demand for public-owned hunting grounds has resulted in the setting aside of such tracts.

Changes in Number of Animals. The damage done to our wildlife by the destruction of its original habitat and the destruction accomplished by unregulated hunting and fishing has been covered in a previous section (Part VII) and will not be repeated here. The results accruing from the application of fair principles of conservation of game and fish and their propagation and protection by societies and commissions in various states are more than gratifying. In spite of a change in habitat, due to lumbering, that at first was thought to be very damaging, it is found that as large or even larger game populations are present in some areas than existed before the lumbering operations. Members of the Game Division of the Department of Conservation of Michigan state that the deer population of the state is as large today as ever in the past and that some sections are actually overpopulated. This latter fact is causing some very perplexing problems. It seems that with the removal of the forest there is far more summer forage than in the days before these areas were cut over. However, the amount of winter forage—cedar swamps—is limited so that with an increasing number of deer, in some sections, winter feeding has been necessary and overcrowding resulting in congestion has aggravated some diseases common to the herds. However, such results have been attained only where strict enforcement of the game laws is in effect and where the hunters make a reasonable effort to cooperate with the game management and propagation organizations. Damage has been done to our game resources, but it may be undone, at least for some species, by the application of fair conservation measures.

Hunting and Fishing Lands Classified. Game exists on areas exhibiting two distinctly different settlement patterns, in the sparsely populated areas made up of forest, cut-over, and abandoned lands, and secondly, in more densely settled farm areas. Small game predominates in the latter. Woodlots, fence rows, and uncultivated fields provide cover and some food, and the cultivated fields provide the rest. Far more people hunt small game in the farming section than attempt to hunt in the sparsely settled areas for larger game. In 1935 more than 390,000 small game hunting licenses were sold in Michigan while 95,000 deer licenses were sold.[1] In our southern states small game hunting is indulged in by a large part of the residents of rural areas.

Since hunting and fishing take place on most of our land and waters, it might be said that for practical purposes the entire area of the United States should be included as part of this recreational resource. For the purposes of this discussion hunting and fishing lands are discussed under three topics, namely: private ownership of the land

[1] Statistics furnished by the Education Division of the Department of Conservation, Lansing, Michigan.

by hunters or fishermen, governmental ownership, and uncontested trespass.

Private Hunting and Fishing Lands. In some states, Michigan for example, private ownership of hunting lands has been encouraged. Groups of hunters form a club, purchase or lease cut-over land, and post it, closing it to other hunters. Some of the clubs have been very instrumental in increasing the deer population in their territory by enforcing even stricter game laws on their members than those imposed by the state. There are 220 such hunting and fishing clubs in the northern half of the Lower Peninsula of Michigan.[1] One has an area of 18,000 acres, two have more than 10,000 acres each, and there are 32 in all owning more than 1,000 acres each. These 32 clubs have under management and reserve to their members exclusive hunting on 122,000 acres. Additional clubs exist in the Northern Peninsula, but statistical data have not been gathered or tabulated for that section. One fishing club in the Upper Peninsula of Michigan owns an entire surveyor's township. This club is made up of the members of six families, who keep the property as a private wilderness park. Almost half the area is composed of lakes well stocked with fish. The club maintains its own force of wardens to prohibit trespassers from fishing in these lakes. Statistics are not available on the total area of privately owned hunting and fishing land in the United States. Privately owned hunting or fishing land is defined here as land that is owned for that specific purpose rather than the hunting and fishing being an incidental use as it is on farm lands. The total area, however, is much larger than is generally realized.

Government Hunting and Fishing Lands. Under government-owned hunting and fishing lands, the national forests, some of the national parks, waterfowl refuges and public hunting areas adjoining them, state-owned game refuges and hunting grounds, as well as state forests, should be included. Most of the national parks allow fishing but prohibit hunting. States have had to purchase lands for public hunting as privately owned lands have been closed to the public by their owners. The demand for more and larger areas of public hunting land is very pressing in several states, among them Michigan, Pennsylvania, and New York. The usual procedure is to establish a game preserve in the center of a tract of state-owned land and allow public hunting on the remainder of the tract. In Michigan a definite sum is

[1] Wilbur O. Hedrick, "Recreational Uses of Northern Michigan Cut-over Lands," *Special Bulletin* 247, p. 26, Agricultural Experiment Station, Michigan State College, 1934.

set aside from each deer license fee to purchase such lands. There are about 170,000,000 acres of land under federal, state, county, or municipal ownership that either are or may be utilized as game cover and public hunting and fishing grounds.[1]

Uncontested Trespass Lands. Today most hunting is done on privately owned land where trespass by hunters is not contested. Hunting in the farm sections takes this form except when the hunting is done by the farmer and his family on his own farm. Farmers object to the depredations done to their property by many hunters, but it is difficult to keep them off the property even when it is posted. Cutover lands, held by absentee owners, are more or less free hunting areas, but as this land is sold out to governmental agencies or acquired by hunting clubs it is closed to the public. The land-acquisition activities of several branches of the federal government during the last two years have added several million acres of hunting lands to those held by governmental agencies. If this trend continues and the farmers become more effective in prohibiting trespass the hunter will be faced with the situation that he can hunt only on public lands or lands that he owns for that purpose. Uncontested trespass is rapidly becoming a thing of the past. If the American public is to have ready access to hunting land, then public agencies must acquire far more land than they now control in order to provide for the demand. Fortunately, hunting does not conflict with the use of the land for forests and other conservation projects so that little conflict arises in utilizing the land for more than one purpose as far as hunting is concerned.

THE USE OF NATIONAL FORESTS FOR RECREATIONAL PURPOSES

The national forests constitute the largest area of potential recreation land in the United States. Their location, however, is not to the best interest of the majority of the recreationalists. The center of population is in eastern United States while most of the large national forests are in the western part of the country. In 1933 the national forests contained 162,000,000 acres of land. Their recreational use has just begun (Fig. 1).

Why Recreational Use Is Now Secondary. The *Use Book* of the Forest Service definitely gives recreationalists rights and privileges

[1] Data for federal, state, county and municipal forest lands are combined. *The Forest Service of the Agricultural Department, a National Plan for American Forestry,* Senate Document 12, Seventy-third Congress, 1st Session, p. 1552, United States Government Printing Office, 1933.

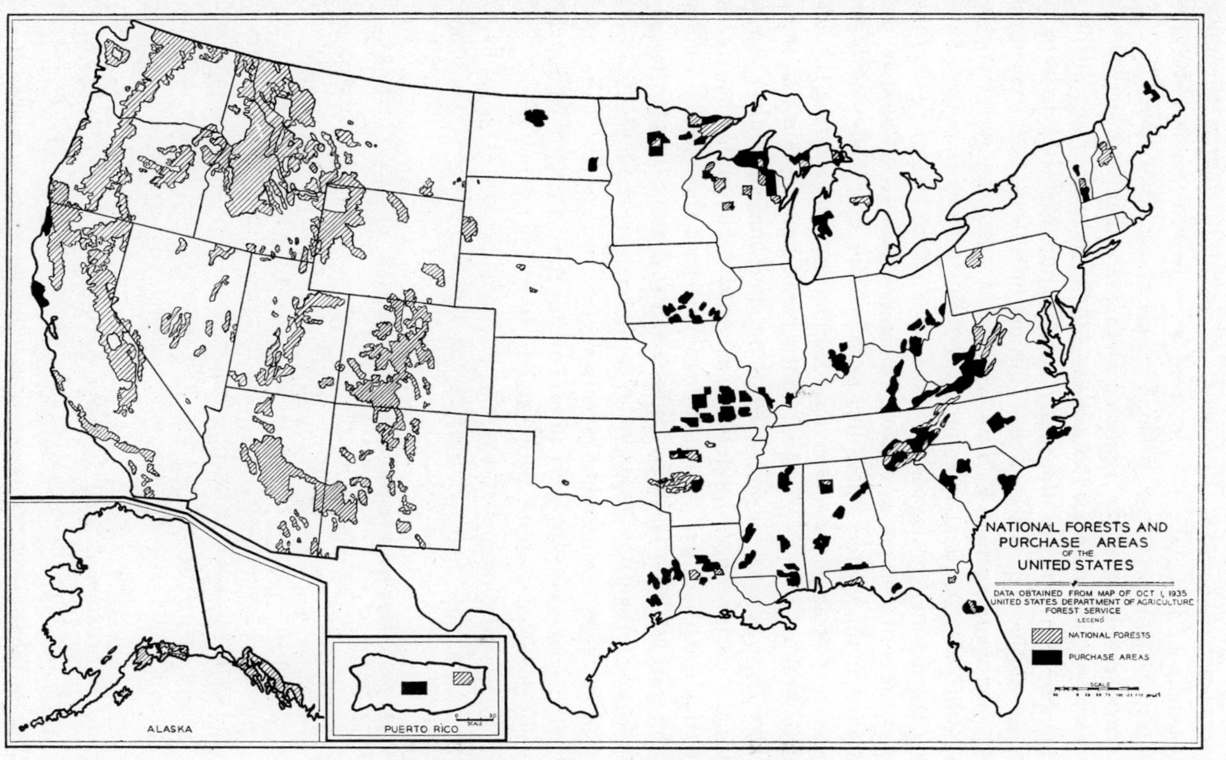

Fig. 1. National Forests and Purchase Areas.

in the forests, but in most areas the recreational use is secondary and subservient to that of the forest use. It is natural, but unfortunate, that this is so. In most areas, more fires are caused directly by carelessness or malicious intent by man than by any other single means. In some areas man is the cause of more fires than all other causes put together (see Part III). Accordingly, the forester is not anxious to increase the hazards of fire by encouraging visitors into remote sections of the forests, especially during the fire season. Except in designated spots camp fires are not allowed unless a special permit has been issued. Selected spots of limited area are set aside for camps along the main roads traversing the forests where fires may be controlled easily if they start and where some check can be kept of the activities of the visitors. Care has been used to select spots that are attractive and are near either good fishing or hunting areas. Unless the visitor is interested in fishing, hunting, or hiking there is not much to keep him entertained while camping in a national forest. As a result the campers usually stay for a limited time only. Camp sites along main state or national highways that pass through the forests are the most used, but enough visitors wish to get away from the beaten path to make the camp sites on the lesser used forest highways justifiable. Undoubtedly it will be necessary to provide more of these.

The average recreationalist has to travel a long distance to reach the larger national forests that have virgin timber. Unless he is primarily interested in hunting or fishing he can as easily go to a national park where the entertainment features are more plentiful, and where better facilities are arranged to take care of him. This is the main reason why the national forests have not attracted a much larger number of visitors than they now do. As stated in the introduction, in 1931, 32,000,000 people visited our national forests for recreational purposes, and special rangers are employed in some forests to take care of the recreationalist. This is a drain on the operation funds set aside for forest management.

How Some Forests Are Used. As an example of the fact that intensity of use depends on distance from populated centers, we cite the Angeles National Forest which lies just to the north of the Los Angeles metropolitan area. It is only a short drive from this population center to this forest. Picnickers visit it on week-ends and holidays. A number of private camps have been allowed within the forest which provide entertainment of various sorts. Traffic patrols have to be maintained on the main roads in this forest to regulate traffic and keep a safe speed limit. Steep grades, sharp curves, hard surfaced roads, and visitors just released from the limitations of city driving set up a traffic problem that is hard to control. Throwing of lighted tobacco from cars is also a serious problem. An effort is made to prohibit smoking except at designated camp sites, private camps, or sight-seeing grounds. These prohibitions have not discouraged the volume of traffic. The majority of the visitors confine their activities to motoring through sections of the forest to enjoy the altitude, coolness, and beautiful scenery. It is used more like a large city park than the other national forests.

Leased Building Sites in National Forests. The national forests grant leases and permits for the erection of cottages and permanent camps. These are usually in selected areas where danger of fire is not great or where it can be controlled easily. In southern California the demand for this type of permit in the forest is great. People wish to spend part of the year at a higher elevation than where they live near the sea, or else they are driven to the higher elevations by the summer heat. In most parts of the country, however, the demand for summer cottage sites in the national forests has not been as pressing as one might expect. The lack of national forests in the east, or the recentness of their acquisition there, has not led to big summer colonies as yet, but the movement is under way. In 1931 when the Hiawatha National Forest located in the Upper Peninsula of Michigan was dedicated, and before even a reasonable amount of land had been acquired, demands began to pour in for leases of cottage sites. By the end of 1931 more than three hundred such requests had been received by the forester in charge. Since at that time less than 25 per cent of the acreage within the purchase area had been acquired and management had just begun, leases for cottage sites were held up until the foresters could find out what they really had within the forest and to determine a satisfactory management scheme. This is just an example that shows the volume of recreational use that may be made of some of our eastern national forests.

More National Forests in East Needed. During the last three years impetus has been given to the acquisition of lands for national forests in eastern United States by the desire of the government to retire submarginal farm land from agricultural uses and to put under forest management large areas of cut-over and burnt-over lands. Purchase of areas for national forests has been declared in most of the states east of the 100° meridian with a concentration in the Lake states, the Gulf states, and the southern Appalachians. (See Fig. 1.) With national forests occupying most of the wild land areas in the

East we can anticipate a greater use by resorters of the national forests in the future.

More hunters and fishermen use the national forests than any other type of recreationalist, and it appears that this will continue to be the case in the future. The areas that are being put into national forests in the eastern part of the country have been used for some time by hunters, and unless they are kept out they will continue to use these same areas. The cut-over lands provide very good forage for deer and various kinds of small game, as previously pointed out. As more land is closed to trespass, as is the trend now, we will see more hunters turning to the national forests for their hunting.

A Change in Forest Management in Eastern United States. The new national forests are located within a few hours' driving distance from large cities and densely settled agricultural regions so their attractiveness as recreation sites will improve as the land comes under proper forest management. This will provide a real opportunity for most of the people in this country to make use of the national forests as recreation areas. It may be that recreational uses will need to be given first consideration and forestry uses secondary consideration in many of these eastern forests. The danger is that some foresters consciously or unconsciously think of recreation as just one of the secondary and more or less unimportant uses of forest areas, and unless broad-minded foresters with a very broad training are put in charge of these new forests, recreational uses may be stifled. The seriousness of this danger can be realized when one considers that most foresters are trained to manage forests and not recreationalists. Often, in a forest area, the needs of the forest and of the recreationalist conflict, and in the western national forests the practice has been, and rightly so, to give the forest use first choice. In the East, on the other hand, it may be necessary for a really enlightened forest policy to give recreation first choice. If the forester will follow the principle of producing what timber and pulp he can in spite of the amount of space he must turn over to recreationalists, without reducing materially the supply of forage for game, and doing all he can to aid the recreationalist in having a pleasant time during his stay on the forest, he will have done a really fine piece of work in promoting the welfare of the national forests. He will be selling the idea of conservation to millions of visitors and making them staunch supporters of the national forest system. He can continue without interference to make forestry the primary objective in the more inaccessible forests.

The national forests are serving the recreationalist in several ways;

providing hunting and fishing lands, camp grounds, resort sites, and pleasant and beautiful drives.

THE NATIONAL PARKS AS RECREATIONAL GROUNDS

Why National Parks Were Founded. The national parks are our recreational grounds par excellence. The facilities for handling the visitor are as fine as any, better than most, and are set in a background of unique scenic splendor. The two main purposes underlying the founding of the national parks were: (1) to set aside areas having unusual natural features that they may be kept undisturbed for all time, and (2) to allow ready access to these areas to all citizens and keep these areas from being exploited for private gain. Some of the incidental results, which are of great importance from the standpoint of recreation conservation, that have resulted from setting aside the lands included in the national parks are: exploitation of minerals, game, and forests has been prohibited in these areas; first-class fire protection has been provided for areas otherwise more or less unprotected; game preserves have been set up, protecting and proving a permanent home for some species that were facing extinction (bison, Rocky Mountain goats, antelope, etc.); and the opportunity has been provided to educate millions of people on sound conservation policies. This last item is of the utmost importance. The ranger-naturalists have been doing a very effective service in spreading the gospel of conservation in an unoffensive way, and under conditions in which the pupil is very receptive. The real effectiveness of this work may be understood when one realizes that about 3,000,000 people visit the national parks annually.

The Need of Parks in Eastern United States. With the exception of a few parks which were recently created, most of the national parks are located in the western states, too distant from the residences of the majority of our people for regular use by them. This is unfortunate, but efforts to remedy this situation have been made in recent years. The year 1919 saw the opening of Acadia National Park in Maine, and 1931 the opening of Great Smoky Mountains National Park in the southern Appalachians. There are now three proposed park areas in the eastern states: Shenandoah in Virginia, Mammoth Cave in Kentucky, and Isle Royale in Michigan. Each of these areas has been declared a national park project by Congress, and as soon as sufficient acreage is purchased and deeded to the federal government, parks will be set up. Work toward this end has progressed rapidly during the last three years, but it may take a number of years more to obtain control of the entire acreage needed for these parks.

Most national monuments are similar in function to the national parks, but smaller in area, and the facilities for taking care of visitors are more limited. Battlefields, historic spots, and national cemeteries in the eastern states also serve as tourist attractions, but details of their use as recreation centers are omitted in this discussion as the general function is much the same as that of the national parks.

In 1932 there were twenty-two national parks, having a total area of 8,417,000 acres[1] (Fig. 1). There were thirty-six national monuments, comprising 4,166,000 acres, administered by the National Park Service, fifteen national monuments comprising 358,000 acres, administered by the Department of Agriculture, fifteen national monuments, comprising 1,197,000 acres, administered by the War Department, and twelve national military and other parks, comprising 13,000 acres, administered by the War Department.

In acquiring lands east of the Rocky Mountains a question of basic policy has been raised. The purpose of the national parks is to preserve for present and future use some natural feature or features of great interest and rarity so that it will not be damaged or exploited for private gain, as well as to provide recreational grounds for visitors. Originally the latter was of secondary importance as some of the parks were little used owing to inaccessibility. Now the matter of serving the public has or is becoming uppermost. Accordingly, pressure is being exerted by local residents to have national parks created near their communities whether the natural features are worthy of such a project or not. The reason is that the prestige of a national park is a fine advertising asset to any locality serving tourists, and there is danger that the original concept may be destroyed by attempting to create national parks wherever the local residents desire them. The National Park Board has fought against this, but Congress has an ear to local demands. The solution to this problem may be another type of park, under federal control but differentiated from the present national parks at least in name. A movement along this line is now under way and will be discussed later.

Intensive Use of Parks Near Large Population Centers. The parks in the East have shown very excellent attendance records, even

[1] United States Department of the Interior, *Annual Report of the Director of the National Park Service for 1932,* pp. 71-83, United States Government Printing Office.

if they lack the grandeur of many of the western ones. Acadia in Maine records a steadily increasing attendance, from 64,000 in 1919 to 237,000 in 1932.[1] Since then new records in attendance have been set. Great Smoky Mountains National Park attracted 150,000 the first year that a road was opened into it (1931) and doubled this number in 1932. Since then the number of visitors has steadily increased. We may expect that the limited number of eastern parks will soon attract more visitors each year than all the western ones.

Yosemite, located near the greatest concentration of people in the West, shows a yearly attendance of about 500,000 now.[2] In 1917 only 34,000 visited it. Since then the gain has been steady. It affords a refuge to many Californians from the heat in the Great Valley and the Coastal Ranges during the summer. Actually it is a summer resort in many respects. It appears that most of the visitors are interested in the entertainment features and the relief from the heat rather than the opportunity to observe and enjoy natural phenomena. The number of visitors desiring the use of camp sites is so great that limited camping privileges are granted in order that no one may monopolize the facilities provided by the government, and so that they are made available to more individuals. During the peak of the season (July) in 1935 more than 8,000 people encamped in an area of a few square miles in the main valley where most of the facilities for campers are located. In most of the other parks the visitor is attracted by unique natural features which were the reasons for the setting aside of the park area.

Accommodations for and Care of Visitors. In the majority of the larger parks accommodations of four kinds are provided to take care of the visitors: (1) hotels, (2) cabin camps, (3) tourist cabins, and (4) tourist camping grounds.

Hotels were established as the first step in opening the parks to visitors. They were first served by horse-drawn stages, and now by motor buses or stages cooperating with the railroads. The hotels and the stages are operated as concessions from the government, and a certain amount of regulation is imposed so that the service is good and the safety of visitors is assured. Elaborate hotels exist in many parks which are utilized mainly by visitors coming by rail and stage. The cabin camps are operated on the same basis, providing accommodations at a lower price than the hotels. These cabin camps usually consist of elaborate rustic buildings devoted to lounges, dining rooms,

[1] *Ibid.*, p. 85.
[2] *Ibid.*, p. 85.

and entertainment halls, and the visitors are put up for the night in individual cabins clustered around the main building.

The tourist cabins are a new feature, having made their appearance in the last few years. Since many travelers utilize cabins in traveling by automobile and do not carry camping equipment, but desire accommodations at a nominal price where they can prepare their own meals and have comfortable sleeping quarters, it has been necessary to provide that type of accommodation in the national parks. During the summer of 1935 this type of accommodation was at a premium in the western parks. This type of service is being expanded rapidly but not rapidly enough to meet the demand.

The tourist camp grounds have been a familiar sight in the parks for a long time. The majority of the visitors utilize them. Travel by automobile, camping en route, and at the parks is the most inexpensive way to visit the national parks and is within the means of the majority of the people of this country. Some of the parks furnish free wood for camp fires and about the only expense is the entry fee into the park, which is very low (with two exceptions it is $1.00 an automobile in the western parks). Cabin trailers are coming into vogue, but still the majority just pack their equipment in and around their car and start off. The national parks are a focus for such travelers.

The government provides services of various kinds to visitors; free guide service to the main features of the park, maps of the park, police protection, camp fire programs, lectures on natural science, and museums. All these services are free and are given in a cordial and pleasant manner by the rangers.

Creating a Sentiment for Conservation. The ranger naturalists direct the visitors' attention not only to the special geological features of the park, but also to the animal life, the plants, the flowers, and the trees that occur there. Many of the rangers are college teachers of geology, zoology, botany, and allied subjects. The visitor is taught to appreciate all phases of nature in a way that is absolutely painless, and he hardly realizes that he is being taught anything while he is vacationing. A real interest in natural phenomena is developed, and at the same time the visitor is shown why man should not exploit them. Some of the most effective work in getting the public to realize the true value and importance of conservation is being done in our national parks.

The national parks have established themselves so well with the American people and are so well protected by the laws that created them that there is little or no danger of their being exploited or spoiled in the future. Any efforts to change these laws so as to endanger the national parks as they now exist would be resisted so strongly by public opinion that no Congress is likely to have the hardihood to make the attempt. The national parks are one phase of the conservation movement that has really sold itself to the American public.

STATE PARKS

Their Function. State parks during the last twenty years have come to be recreation areas of very great importance. Their primary purpose is to provide outing places for city dwellers and densely settled rural areas. Some are small, being only picnic grounds with an area of as little as three or four acres; others are large, like Ludington State Park, in Michigan, with more than 3,000 acres. These parks may well be divided into two groups: (1) the picnic areas near big cities, and (2) parks having natural features of special interest which may be located in wild land areas (Fig. 2).

County parks and state forests are utilized by recreationalists in the same manner as the state parks and the national forests, so will not be given separate consideration here.

The small picnic parks serve more people than the larger state parks. On week-ends and holidays having favorable weather conditions, there is actually hardly any standing room at most of the parks in the vicinity of Detroit, Michigan (Fig. 2). They are so intensely used as to be overcrowded in southeastern Michigan around Detroit. Additional areas are being set aside as parks since the problem of finding even standing room in them is actually acute (Fig. 3).

The larger parks might be considered miniature national parks. Some of them have been located so as to preserve special natural features and provide camp grounds, playground equipment, picnic equipment, and nature trails. Caretakers not only attempt to keep the parks clean but act as police officers and nature guides if they have the time.

The State Park Movement. Thirty-four states now have state parks, but some have very few.[1] Three of the states have only one park each, three others have just two parks each, and three others have three or four parks each. Five states have more than thirty-five parks each. These are Connecticut with thirty-six, California with thirty-seven, Iowa with thirty-seven, New York with fifty, and Mich-

[1] A map with data printed on its back compiled and drawn by John J. Black, *Recreational Areas of the United States,* Department of the Interior, 1933.

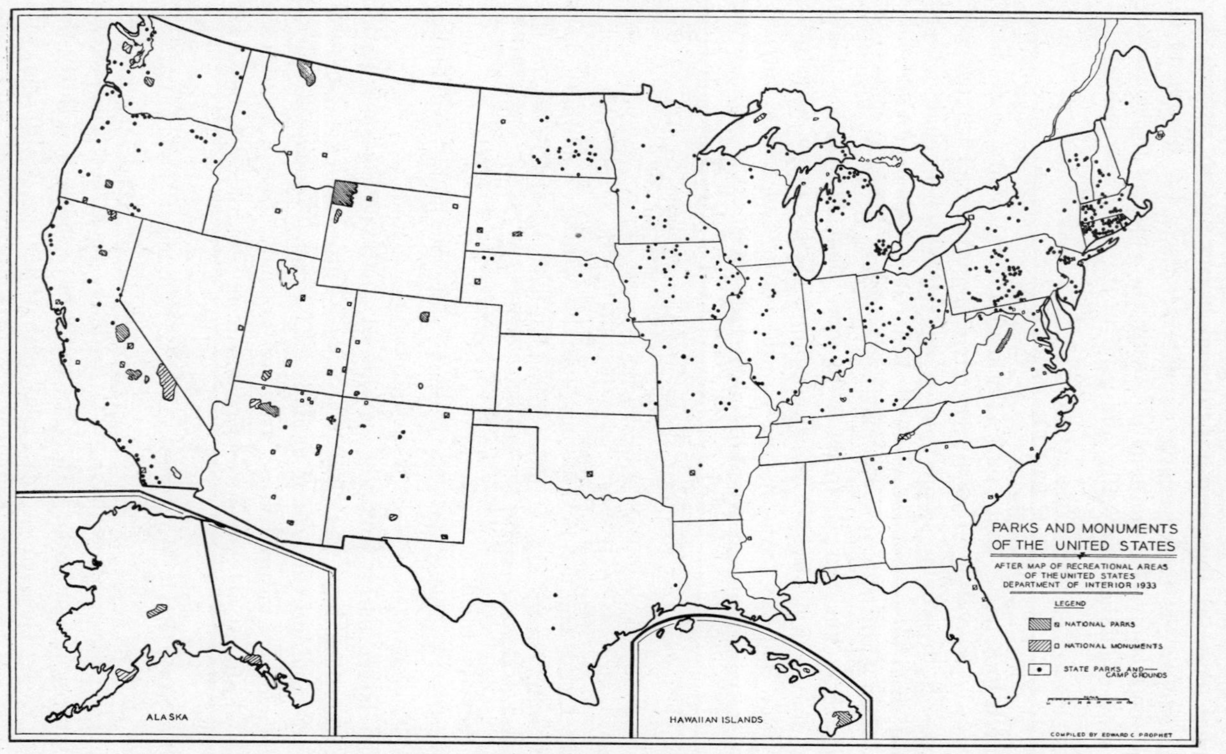

Fig. 2. National Parks, State Parks, etc.

igan with sixty-six. This tabulation does not include camp grounds provided in state forests or state historical monuments. It appears that Michigan has done more in the way of setting up a state park program and carrying it out than any other state. It pioneered in this work and has been enthusiastically supported by the public.

Fig. 3. Michigan, Showing State Parks, Forests and Main Cities.

Now there is need for many more, or at least much larger, state park areas in the southeastern part of the state, as indicated above. The director of parks in this state has had two objectives in picking out sites: (1) to serve the largest number of people, and to have the parks spaced at a reasonable distance apart and scattered over the state to serve tourists; and (2) to try to include samples of each type of topography, vegetation, and animal life that occurs within the state. In other words, the idea in part is that followed in the national parks.

Fig. 2, showing state parks, indicates that the Pacific Coast states, the Middle West, the Lake states, and the Northeastern states are the ones where state parks are most numerous and where they are best supported. There is a decided lack of state parks in the South, in the prairie states, and the mountain and intermountain states. However, in the mountain states there are adequate vacation grounds in the national forests and national parks.

During the season of 1934 the attendance at the Michigan state parks totaled 8,561,016, of which 150,000 were campers.[1] These figures show that the real function of the state parks is as picnic grounds and one-day outing sites. The following attendance figures (1934) for individual parks show how intensively some of them are used:

Grand Haven	1,642,000
Bay City	910,000
Walter Hayes	672,000
Island City	526,000
Bloomer #2	433,000

Except for Grand Haven, all these are within easy reach of metropolitan Detroit.

Utilization of state parks by the public has shown a steady and healthy growth.[2] In 1925, 2,540,000 people visited the parks in Michigan, and a steady gain was shown until 1931 with a total attendance of 9,634,000. A slight decrease is recorded for 1932 and 1933, and a drop of about 10 per cent for 1934, to a total of 8,561,000. Considering the intensity of the financial depression, especially in industrial areas like southern Michigan, the reduction in attendance at the state parks is not serious. With 10 to 40 per cent of the population on relief in most industrial counties the large attendance at the parks is really surprising. One could safely hazard a guess as to the number of people who would make use of state parks or other free recreation grounds located near centers of population if they were provided throughout eastern United States. The need for parks near cities is clearly demonstrated by the above examples, and it is to be hoped that this need will be provided for in the near future.

The Administration of State Parks. During the last two years California has charged a fee of fifty cents a night for camping in the

[1] *Seventh Biennial Report,* Michigan State Department of Conservation, Statistical insert at end of report by the Division of Parks. 1934

[2] *Ibid.*

state parks. This has had an adverse effect on the number of campers or potential campers. Innumerable camping parties in the national parks located in California stated in the summer of 1935 that they usually utilized the state parks, but since the fee has been charged have crowded into the national parks. That was one cause of the congestion in Yosemite National Park in 1935.

Though in no way questioning the right or justification of the states to charge camping fees in their parks, it must be regretted in that it tends to discourage people from using them and also encourages campers to camp along the roads, in out-of-the-way places, on private lands causing numerous trespass problems, to create hazards to the forests in the form of fires, and hazards to health due to lack of sanitary camp sites. In some sections the cost of fighting fires and protecting water supply is greater than the cost of maintaining the state parks without charging a camping fee. It is better to have the campers concentrated where they can do little damage by fire, and where protective measures may be put in force with the minimum cost, than to force the campers to scatter to out-of-the-way places where they may do considerable damage.

The state appears to be the best administrative unit for parks that serve local needs. The state can locate parks in the areas where needed throughout its area, can administer them all with a trained staff, can avoid local politics, and it runs into fewer legal barriers in acquiring land than smaller governmental units do when they go beyond their own legal limits. Also, in most state budgets the funds needed to maintain the parks are not a large percentage of the total budget, while the reverse may be true in smaller governmental units.

"RECREATION OR OUTING" PARKS

A new type of park is being created and will be opened to the public within two or three years. It will be a mixture of "Coney Island" and a national park. It resembles the former in that special features are to be installed to entertain properly the visitor from either city or farm while he is getting an outing. It resembles a national park in its size and the fact that the federal government is providing the funds to create it. Three such projects were under way in Michigan in 1936. One, the Waterloo Area, is roughly delimited in Fig. 3. The other two are also in the southern part of the state; one, the Yankee Springs project, is located in the southwestern part about 100 miles from Chicago by automobile, and the second, the Allegan project, is located about 30 miles southwest of Grand Rapids and is easily reached from Chicago. These three projects are within 350 miles of more than 28,000,000 people, most of whom are living in areas with poor facilities for outdoor recreation in forested areas. The fundamental purpose is to provide a suitable and attractive park for an outing as well as over-night accommodations.

Parks of this type may be started in other sections of the United States. These parks should not be confused in any way with the national parks, and so another name is needed. Suggested names are either "recreation parks" or "outing parks."

A park of this type will not eliminate the need for state parks or locally owned parks nearer the big cities where people may come without having to drive as far as most will to one of these "outing parks."

ESTHETIC AND OTHER USES OF LAND

Recreational Areas for Nature Lovers and Others. By esthetic uses of land is meant the use of land by the sightseer who enjoys the beauties of the landscape but who does not tamper with or destroy the resource. The national parks fall under this category, but they have already been covered at some length as a separate type of land use. Wilderness areas, scenic areas, canoe trip routes, hiking trails, and riding trails make up the basic resource for recreation in this case.

Many Americans are learning that it is as much or even more enjoyable to hunt with a camera as with a gun. They desire places where game and other wild animals may be observed in their natural habitat undisturbed by man. Such areas are becoming a real attraction to tourists and are a real resource as far as the recreation industry is concerned. Nature trails are also popular. On these the visitor may observe, or have pointed out for his observation, various natural phenomena which he does not have an opportunity to see at home. Experiments have been tried in some of the state parks, and such trails are very popular in the national parks. No great effort has been directed along this line elsewhere, but it is bound to come. Possibly, special areas may have to be set aside near the centers of population for this type of park, but up to now, only limited areas have been devoted exclusively to this use. One example of this is Wilderness State Park in Michigan.

Accommodating "Hikers." Hiking trails need not involve the ownership of much property. During the last two years a series of inns have been established in southern New England to accommodate hikers. Public roads and by-ways are used for the routes which pass through areas of beautiful scenery. The operators of these inns report a successful season during 1935, which shows that many of our citizens desire this type of facility and use it when it is provided. The popularity of hiking in the Austrian and Bavarian Alps shows how this phase of the recreation activities may be developed in this country. Accommodations need to be very moderately priced to attract vacationists. A vacation of this sort is not costly; it is very enjoyable to those who like to walk but do not care to be dodging automobiles on the highways all the time, and it gives the individual a chance really to observe the scenery. It may be necessary to locate these trails on government-owned property in order to construct trails that are away from highways and that cannot be closed on account of trespassing on private property. Inns are not provided on the trails in our national forests for they are too far away for the majority of our people to make use of them. These trails should be located near population centers if good scenery exists there. The nearer they are to where people live the more use will be made of them. It may be necessary to purchase land for this purpose as the demand becomes greater. The New England experiment shows that it pays from a purely business standpoint.

Short hiking trails may be constructed along river banks actually within city limits if our river beautification plans are carried out. Such resources are today largely overlooked and wasted.

Meeting the Demands of Equestrians. Riding trails are in much the same category as the hiking trails in the East since they do not exist except as short bridal paths in some of our city parks. Our present scheme of highway and road layout makes it inadvisable for a rider to utilize them even in farming sections. Also, accommodations spaced one day's journey apart for riders and mounts are not available in the more settled areas. This again is a recreational resource that we have passed by. Camping parties utilizing horses are not uncommon in the mountainous areas of the West, but facilities for this type of travel are not provided in the eastern part of the country except in a few sections of the southern Appalachians where the local residents travel horseback.

The dude ranches of the west are really capitalizing on this idea.

Some now gain most of their income from the visitors rather than from the ranching activities, and in these instances the land use may well be considered as recreational rather than grazing.

Canoe trip routes could be put to more use if canoe liveries were provided at suitable points on our better canoe waters. These liveries are lacking on most of the better routes except in New England. Temporary subsidization of commercial liveries by local interests can very soon demonstrate where such liveries will pay, and thereafter no subsidy will be needed.

Ownership of Esthetic Lands. No extensive areas need be owned outright by the public in order to make use of the esthetic values that they contain. The total amount of land owned for this use is not large, but its utilization in terms of the enjoyment it yields to the public is great. Public agencies need not even own the lands through which scenic highways pass, but they really constitute the resource which causes the road to be used by tourists. It is possible to make this resource available to the public in some places where it is not now available by merely rerouting some of our main highways or constructing branches that may be used by the visitor who desires scenery and let the through traffic continue on the present more direct routes. The cost of such roads is largely the cost of construction and the purchase of the land on which the highway actually rests.

An All-purpose Park. The Adirondack Mountain Project, in New York, is in some respects a mammoth "recreation park" under state ownership. However, it also carries out the functions of a game preserve and wilderness park. It is large enough so that these various uses do not conflict, as they can be isolated from one another. The primary object has been to provide an area where the esthetic uses are given first consideration.

RESORTS

Summer, winter, and health resorts are among our most-valued and best-appreciated recreational land uses. Under this category are included resort subdivisions, colonies of cottages, seasonal hotels, clubs, and health centers. The placing of health centers in this list might be questioned as they represent an organized business, but except on public lands, most phases of the recreational use of land are organized business enterprises. The health center is exploiting a natural resource just as much as the owner of a cottage or the owner of hunting land.

Recreation at Health Centers. The health centers individually occupy large acreage, but taken as a group do not utilize enough land to warrant an attempt to estimate the area. A few outstanding health resorts are French Lick, Indiana; Hot Springs, Arkansas; Saratoga Springs, New York; Excelsior Springs, Missouri; and Asheville, North Carolina. In each instance, an entire city has been built up to take advantage of either a mineral spring or a comfortable climate. Entertainment, especially outdoor exercise, is provided in order to keep the patients' time occupied and to aid in the cure. The larger hotels provide golf courses, riding stables and bridle paths, swimming pools, spacious lawns, and woodland trails for hiking. An individual establishment may have upwards of a thousand acres or more, but the total number of such establishments throughout the country is limited. Recreational facilities of such excellent quality have been provided that many people come to these health resorts to make use of them rather than for the medical services provided.

Resort Subdivisions. Resort subdivisions occupy at least a million acres in the United States. There are no accurate figures for the country as a whole, or for that matter, for any one state. The author has made investigations and tabulations for some counties in Michigan, and on the basis of these surveys conservatively estimates the figure given above. A thorough tabulation and check is more likely to show double that acreage. In Michigan alone more than 80,000 acres are included within resort subdivisions. Wisconsin, Minnesota, Maine, California, and Florida are a few of the other states in which this type of subdivision is popular. Much more land is subdvided into resort plats in Wisconsin or Minnesota than in Michigan. Just how much of the Florida subdividing and real estate promoting should be charged to recreational use of land is a moot question, but a vast area should certainly be included irrespective of how limited the definition of a resort subdivision is that serves as the criterion of classification.

It is true that the majority of these lots that have been platted for resort use have not had cottages built on them, but many have. In Roscommon County, Michigan, there were more than a thousand cottages in the summer of 1929.[1] About a hundred have been built since that time. Around three lakes, isolated in the center of the northern half of the Lower Peninsula of the state, there are over 1,100 cottages. In 1931 there were more than 2,100 cottages in the

[1] Data obtained from surveys made by the author. Reports of these surveys are on file with several Michigan state commissions, but are not in published form.

Upper Peninsula of Michigan. Unfortunately there are no accurate figures for the total number of cottages in the state, but a conservative estimate will place the number at 20,000. The larger colonies of summer cottages are located along the shores of Lake Michigan, the inland lakes in the southwestern part of the state, inland lakes within 60 miles of Detroit, and on the shores of Lake Huron and Lake St. Clair.

The Taxable Value of Resort Subdivisions. From the standpoint of local taxation, the cottage is a valued asset. If an individual can afford to own a cottage he can certainly afford to pay the taxes. On some cut-over lands this is the most important source of local taxation.[1] In West Traverse Township, Emmet County, Michigan, recreation facilities are assessed 86.5 per cent of the total property tax. In Denton Township, Roscommon County, Michigan, they are assessed 85 per cent of the tax. There are seventeen townships in the northern part of the Lower Peninsula of Michigan where over 50 per cent of the total tax burden is borne by recreational facilities, largely cottages and resort hotels. These figures are presented to show how important recreation may be to a locality even in terms of its tax rolls.

Cottages represent one of the most stable forms of the recreation business. They involve a long-time investment, they bring a definite number of visitors to the area each year, and they help to support the local community by providing a market for goods and services, as well as bearing a fair share of the local taxes. The same can be said for resort hotels.

Some summer colonies are operated as clubs, drawing their members from the same community and strata of society. These developments are very similar to resort associations of cottagers with a central organization which provides certain facilities for the entire membership more economically than can be provided by individuals. Special recreational features are provided at group expense, such as tennis courts, boats, golf courses, and riding stables. In the clubs the members maintain their own cottages and possibly a central club house.

RECREATION CLUBS

The name "recreation club" is here used to connotate a resort and hunting club which in its origin is little more than a real estate

[1] Wilbur O. Hedrick, "Recreational Use of Northern Michigan Cut-over Lands," *Special Bulletin* 247, pp. 51-55, 60, Agricultural Experiment Station, Michigan State College, 1934.

promotion scheme. Enough of them have survived even the nation-wide financial depression to involve several hundred thousand acres of land that might otherwise be either abandoned or be in some governmental project. The basic plan of most of these clubs is for the promoters to acquire several thousand acres of land (usually 10,000 to 20,000) in an undeveloped area, but within one or two days of easy driving from large population centers, and then to organize a club. A club house is constructed and possibly a number of cottages. Memberships are sold, giving privileges to use the club house, the cottages for a week or two each year, to hunt and fish on the club's land, and to buy a lot and have the club build a cottage for that member's exclusive use. Fundamentally, the idea is to sell some of the land at subdivision prices and hold the bulk of the land as a bait to get more members. The original cost of the land is very low, and if enough members join and buy lots, the project may pay the promoters very well. They usually expend some of the dues to provide reasonable fire protection and possibly to stock the streams with fish.

This is one way to keep on the tax rolls large acreages of land and at the same time have private interests maintain good fire protection and forest management policies. However, from the member's standpoint, he could get most of the benefits and privileges he obtains here from the average resort development or in the national forests and not have to pay dues or membership fees.

With more normal business conditions in the United States, this type of development is likely to become more important. The idea of having limited rights on several thousands of acres of land, as well as owning outright a cottage in a club where membership is supposed to be exclusive, has a great appeal to many of our citizens. Even in the midst of the depression, one such club in Michigan has been promoted and has succeeded fairly well. At any rate, it is a going concern today. Individuals acquainted with land affairs can name several such clubs in a number of our states. More of these clubs are bound to develop as business reaches an equilibrium. It is conçeivable that as much as 2,000,000 or 3,000,000 acres may be held by such clubs by 1950.

ORGANIZED CAMPS

Organized camps require the same general resources that summer cottages and hotels do. The use of the land is the same as in any resort areas. They act as a force encouraging outdoor recreation, as the youth of the country is being trained in these camps to appreciate outdoor recreation. They are doing much to build up a future demand for recreational resources. Look over the advertisements of some of these camps in the monthly periodicals like *Harper's* or *Cosmopolitan*. Some people may be astonished at the number of camps that can afford to advertise in magazines with a national circulation. Most of the directors of physical education in our high schools operate summer camps. Y.M.C.A.'s, Y.W.C.A.'s, luncheon clubs, chambers of commerce, scout troups, and numerous other organizations sponsor summer camps. The total number of such organized camps and the number of youths that they serve is really astounding. No estimate is available of the total investment in such properties or the area of land involved, but it is sufficiently large that it must be given consideration in evaluating the recreational use of land.

TOURIST CAMPS FOR RECREATIONALISTS

Mention should be made of types of land use that are minor in area, but very important in some phases of the recreation industry. These are tourist camps, roadside picnic grounds, lodging houses, and tourist inns. None of these involve a large area of land, either for the individual establishments or in total, but they are necessary facilities for some classes of recreationalists.

The tourist camp has exhibited a marvelous transformation in the last fifteen years. At that time no community was complete without a public camp ground where visitors could pitch their tents. Today, the majority of these camp grounds have either been abandoned or are no longer kept up since the traveling recreationalist demands another type of accommodation. The overnight cabin is rapidly displacing the camp grounds but the present developing fad of cabin trailers is causing a renewed demand for camping grounds. How strong this will be no one can foresee. On the West Coast many people in the tourist business expect the fad to run its course within a few years and are not putting in accommodations to take care of cabin trailers. In the South they are very popular and special camp grounds are being set aside to accommodate them. In the Middle West some interest is now being exhibited in them, but as yet they are not sufficiently popular to be counted except as a fad. They are a fine substitute for a tent and are popular in localities where camping has been important, but in areas where an adequate number of overnight cabins are available they lose their appeal.

The overnight cabin has become the choice of the nation on touring trips. The investment in the individual cabin may not be great, but the total number of cabins in the country is large and is increasing rapidly so that the total investment runs into several million dollars. A safe estimate would place upwards of 100,000 acres of land devoted to this use. The fact that the visitor is able to cook his meals as well as obtain a night's lodging in a cabin has encouraged this type of travel and has made it more important than tourist camps where a tent must be pitched and extra luggage must be carried on the automobile. The cabin is more desirable than the lodging house as meals can be prepared and this saves expense in traveling. The overnight cabin is a type of accommodation that has come to stay unless the architectural extremists carry the designs to even more grotesque types than appear now, with the result that possible tenants may actually be scared away by the architectural monstrosities that face them.

Roadside picnic grounds do not account for any real amount of acreage and usually utilize small strips of land adjoining the road right-of-way that had to be purchased at the time the right-of-way was acquired. Their value lies in alleviating the trespass problem by providing a comfortable and attractive place for picnickers to stop. Their location is too public for most people so that they have not been greatly utilized.

Lodging houses should be mentioned here, but they are really beyond the scope of this discussion since they represent a partial use of land and buildings ordinarily used as residences. The overnight cabin is replacing the need of lodging houses in many sections of the country. In industrial sections they may be considered as one evidence of the financial depression. These lodging houses will disappear as recovery is more wide-spread.

GOLF COURSES FOR RECREATIONALISTS

Although all the golf courses in the country do not occupy a large acreage as compared to national forests or national parks, still they utilize a large enough area to be included in any discussion of recreation from the land-utilization standpoint. There is a possibility that more than a million acres may be devoted to golf courses by 1950. From the standpoint of man-days of use, golf courses deserve a high rank among our recreational lands. Also, most courses pay their own way as private clubs, contributing taxes for the support of the local governments. The fundamental idea of recreation land is human enjoyment, and judged on this basis, golf courses should be ranked at present as one of the most important types of this land use.

URBAN PARKS

Establishment of a Belated Movement. Practically all the cities of 100,000 population or above have park facilities, but, with the exception of a very few cities, these facilities are not adequate. Even where there is an adequate area in parks, the parks are not well located to serve the people. All our cities are relatively young, and in most of them their great growth has come since 1900. If the American people had been alert to the fundamental need for recreational space, it would have been possible to have set aside adequate, well-located park space then. Unfortunately, the real demand for park areas on the part of the public has come only in the last twenty or twenty-five years, after the more desirable sites had been given over to other uses. A few notable examples of foresight in regard to recreation sites would include: Lincoln Park and the Midway, in Chicago; Central Park, in New York City; Audubon Park, in New Orleans; and the Zoological Park, in St. Louis.

There are very few cities in the United States of 100,000 population or above which are not located either on a river or lake, but either industry or transportation has been given first choice on the better recreational sites, and has now been entrenched there so long that it is next to impossible to recover them for their badly needed recreational use. Polution of waters with industrial wastes and city sewage made rivers undesirable for recreation, and railroads found easy routes along their banks. Industry occupied the sites undesirable for homes or business along the lowlands near the rivers which were especially desirable for industry because they were near the transportation routes. The public callously stood by, or actually encouraged the industrial use of this land, not realizing that it was giving its birthright away. Any foresighted individual objecting to the utilization of the water frontage for transportation or industry, and foolish enough to raise a protest, was looked upon as a menace to the city's progress and was ridiculed and condemned.

Almost any American city that the reader can mention is an example of this principle of giving transportation and industry the first choice of the water frontage. A few random examples would include Seattle; Portland, Oregon; San Francisco; New Orleans; Tampa; St.

Louis; Kansas City; Denver; Minneapolis; Duluth; Detroit; Buffalo; Pittsburgh; New York; and Philadelphia.

The few exceptions to this rule are found in non-industrial cities like Miami, St. Petersburg, and Atlantic City. In each city listed, the main business is catering to recreationalists, and ready access to the water is desired.

Lake and River Front Parks. At great expense and with much labor Chicago has provided itself with a lake front park in the heart of the city. This has been accomplished by creating a new shore line by filling in part of Lake Michigan. The new land lies between the railroad lines and the lake, and has brought into being several thousand acres of land now used as a park, and several miles of lake frontage. Most cities have neither the physical sites to permit such a project nor the financial resources to pay for it. The other recourse to obtain frontage put to other use than recreation is to buy it, but that involves costs beyond the means of most corporate bodies. In addition, the question is raised of the practicability of devoting vast sums of public money to a use the results of which cannot be measured directly in dollars and cents.

Urban Marginal Parks. The general practice in our larger cities is to acquire large acreages for park purposes at their outskirts where land can be purchased at a nominal cost and where structures do not have to be removed. Some cities have even gone beyond their corporate limits in acquiring park lands. Chicago has a number of forest preserves located in Cook County, outside the city limits; Detroit has a zoological park and a golf course located in an adjoining county, as well as the large new River Rouge Park, extending for several miles along its western border. Several other cities, including San Francisco, New Orleans, and St. Louis, have new parks on their outskirts. These large parks usually provide several types of facilities: golf courses, tennis courts, baseball diamonds, football fields, bridle paths, and outdoor theatres, as well as expanses of lawn, shrubbery, and forest.

The Urban Playgrounds. Another type of recreational use of land in the cities is the playground, usually located adjoining the school. As individual playgrounds only a few acres are involved, but taken as a group they embrace many thousands of acres. Unfortunately, most of them are too small and should be enlarged, but the high cost of land and the buildings on it that would have to be razed practically prohibits much expansion in area. Here, again, appears to be a fine example of our short-sightedness. Sooner or later most of these playgrounds will need to be enlarged, for children need to be kept off the streets, and as these playgrounds are located in the neighborhoods in which the children live, they will be used fully.

The Problem of Golf Courses in Urban Parks. The demand for public golf courses has further complicated the urban parks problem since a golf course takes a relatively large acreage. These have either been constructed in large existing parks or in new parks at the outskirts of the city. Lansing, in central Michigan, has three public golf courses, one of them an eighteen-hole course that will compare favorably with the better private clubs anywhere in the United States. In addition, three privately owned courses are open to the public at very low green fees. Here is a city of 80,000 people, the majority of whom are factory workers and their families, supporting six golf courses by very nominal green fees. In addition, there are two private clubs taking care of the class who desire club membership and more privacy. This example shows the number of golf courses that can be supported by an industrial population of this size. There is a decided lack of such facilities in most of our cities. Many more public or quasi-public courses are needed throughout the country. No record is available of the total acreage now involved in golf courses, either public or private, but it runs upward of a half million acres. If an adequate number of public links are provided the total acreage may reach a million acres.

Inadequacy of Urban Recreational Facilities. In spite of the splendid efforts made by a few of our large cities to provide a sufficient area in parks and playgrounds during the last ten years, we still are very inadequately supplied. We have turned our best recreation sites, those that are well located in the urban areas, over to other uses and in some instances damaged them beyond repair. The misuse of a natural resource stands out vividly in this case. Today we have the need of these resources, but are in a poor position to make them available to the public except at unjustifiably great expense. We can provide parks, but they are not located where they will receive the maximum use or serve the public best. Drives are regularly staged to clean up the river fronts or lake fronts of our cities, but usually the efforts fall far short of their objectives. Possibly the best example of success along this line is a portion of the river bank at Minneapolis. It is hoped that these periodic drives to clean up what is left of the river frontage in many of our cities will not only be continued, but will yield real results as the public becomes better informed and demands real action. There is still enough frontage within city limits to be worth saving, and it is hoped that it will become worthwhile recreational grounds instead of an eyesore as it is now.

CONCLUSION

In the foregoing pages an effort has been made to show the main ways in which recreational use of land takes place. This classification of the different types of recreational lands is not intended to be all-inclusive but suggestive to the reader. The comments are made with the hope of stimulating further interest in this phase of conservation affairs and of showing the magnitude and importance of outdoor recreation in our society. It is impossible to estimate the actual amount of damage already done to recreational lands by mismanagement or utter failure to manage the land. However, we still have adequate resources for the recreational need of our people except in the cities and more densely settled rural areas. The really big need is to make the existing resources available to the people. In the last twenty years great progress has been made along that line, and it must continue at an accelerating rate if lands now available for recreation are not put to other uses before the demand for their proper utilization fully manifests itself.

The student of land affairs may find numerous suggestions for research problems in the foregoing pages. Accurate detailed information is lacking for nearly every topic discussed. Until more information of an inventory nature is assembled, we will not know fully the extent of our present utilized recreational resources or the real needs of the future along this line. It is hoped that, from this sketchy discussion of recreational lands and their use, some students of land affairs will be encouraged in gathering more complete and reliable data.

The present trend for shorter hours of labor in industry and business and a limited number of years of work for most of our citizens is forcing leisure time on many people so that they will have more time to indulge in outdoor recreation. The demands on our recreational lands have just begun to be made. Adequate plans for the future need to be formulated now while we still have vast resources in the form of reserve recreational lands that have not been put to other uses.

PART IX

CHAPTER XXI

THE CONSERVATION OF MAN

By Ellsworth Huntington

Yale University

THE VALUE OF OUR HUMAN RESOURCES

The greatest of America's resources is in many ways the most neglected and most poorly developed. This chapter illustrates the matter. It is scarcely more than an afterthought planned by a far-sighted editor who realized that the human resources of America are more important than any others, even though this fact is commonly overlooked. By the time they reach their first birthday, the two million or more babies born each year in the United States have cost the country nearly as much as the new automobiles. The annual cost incurred for the entire forty-five million children from eighteen years of age downward is vastly greater. It amounts to approximately $25,000,000,000 a year. This is three times as much as the value of all farm products in 1929, and three-fourths as much as the value added to raw materials by manufacturing. A third of our total annual income is spent in raising children.

Capitalizing these figures, it appears that all the children of the United States up to the age of eighteen years represent an investment of more than $200,000,000,000. This is nearly three times the value of all the country's farm land, farm buildings, farm machinery, and livestock, even at the inflated values of 1920. The capitalized value of the entire population rises still higher, to $800,000,000,000. This is enormously more than the total value of all the property of every kind in the entire United States. In 1925 when the estimates of human values here set forth were made, the total national wealth, as estimated by the Census Bureau and the National Industrial Conference Board, was $362,000,000,000. At the inflated prices of 1920 it mounted to $449,-000,000,000, and at the low values of 1932 it dropped to only $247,-

000,000,000. Thus the people of the United States are worth twice as much as all their property.

The foregoing statements are based on the very careful estimates made by two life insurance statisticians, Dr. L. I. Dublin and Dr. A. J. Lotka, in *The Money Value of a Man.* In this book the authors very carefully estimate the average cost of bringing up a child to the age of eighteen. Then for each later year they estimate the investment that would be required to produce the earnings that are normally to be expected in the future, but with a deduction to allow for the cost of living. Thus we have an estimate not only of what it costs to bring up a child to the age of eighteen years, but also of the loss borne by society in general through the death of an average individual at any stage in his life. Knowing the number of people at each age we can compute the value of the whole population. No questions of sentiment or of subjective value enter into the matter. Drs. Dublin and Lotka have simply used all the available statistics, and from these have computed how much a person at each age is worth.

To begin with the value of the baby crop, each year in the United States, even at the low birth rates which have prevailed of late, some two million babies are born. Of these approximately 55 per thousand die during the first year of life. This leaves almost exactly 2,000,000 survivors as the average for the years 1928-1932. In *The Money Value of a Man* the authors put the cost of being born at $250 for the average child; other sums paid out on behalf of the child during its first year of life raise the cost to $560 at the end of the first year. This is for a family in which the maximum earnings of the father will at some time reach the level of $2,500. It includes not only the sums actually paid by the parents or by the public for doctors, nurses, medicines, food, clothing, and the like, but also the child's share of the family rent, insurance, and other household expenses. To this must be added $32 per child, which represents the cost of the children who die. Another $15 represents interest at 3½ per cent on the amounts paid out for the child's maintenance. This makes a total of $607.

At this rate the 2,190,000 children under one year of age in the United States at the census of 1930 cost the country approximately $1,325,000,000. In 1929 the wheat crop of the country had a value of $839,000,000, the oats $410,000,000, and the barley $141,000,000. Thus the baby crop cost the country approximately as much as the value of these three farm products. In the second year of life, according to Dublin and Lotka, the cost per child ($368) is less than in the first year, since the expenses of birth are eliminated. Thereafter the demands of education and recreation, as well as the greater expense of food and clothing, cause the annual cost to rise until it amounts to $866 at the age of eighteen.

The allowances for children who die and for insurance perhaps need explanation. They are based on the assumption that 128 out of every thousand die before reaching their eighteenth birthday. The cost of these children is included in the final cost of the living children, just as the grocer must include the price of decayed oranges in the price of those that he sells. An allowance for interest at the low rate of 3½ per cent per annum is included because the investment of the parents and the public in children yields little return in productivity until the age of sixteen or even twenty.

The final result, then, is the following table which seems to be a fair estimate of what it actually costs to bring up a child to the age of eighteen years.

TABLE 1

COST OF BRINGING UP A CHILD TO ADOLESCENCE

1. Cost of being born	$ 250
2. Food	2,755
3. Clothing and shelter	3,333
4. Education, minor items met by the individual family purse	50
5. Education, major items, cost of schooling provided by the community—$1,100	
6. Health	283
7. Recreation	130
8. Insurance	54
9. Sundries	570
10. Premature death	211
11. Interest at 3½ per cent	2,849
Total	$10,485

It will be noticed that in this table the cost of education provided by the community ($1,100) is not included. Nor is any allowance made for the time spent by the mother in caring for the children. If her time were capitalized at its full value the figures here given would be much larger. This omission is balanced, however, by the fact that the table is based on a maximum income of $2,500, whereas a vast number of families never see much more than $1,000 a year of real income. The average income per worker in the United States, not including the mothers, was estimated as $1,719 in 1929, but only $793 in 1932 at the worst of the depression. On an average there are about one and a half workers to the family. Hence a *maximum* income of $2,500 per family at some time during life does not seem unduly high when allowance is made for the value of the unpaid work of the mothers.

Let us next see how Dublin and Lotka estimate the value of people who have passed the age of eighteen and become self-supporting. In order to be conservative we will assume that the average maximum income of all the individuals in the country is $1,000. This is distinctly below the normal, for even in the five years from 1929 to 1933 the average, according to the National Industrial Conference Board, was $1,174, but we are here assuming a maximum of only $1,000 at any period of life. Thus, if we have overestimated the cost of bringing up children, we are here underestimating their earnings after they become productive. According to Dublin and Lotka the present worth of the net future earnings of persons whose maximum incomes will stand at various levels is indicated in Table 2, provided we allow for normal mortality and a discount of 3½ per cent a year.

TABLE 2

PRESENT WORTH OF NET FUTURE EARNINGS

Calculated on the basis of normal mortality and a discount of 3½% per annum
Income classes $1,000 to $10,000 per annum

Age	$1,000	$1,500	$2,000	$2,500	$5,000	$10,000
20.........	10,050	17,200	23,850	30,200	37,450	62,900
30.........	10,550	17,750	24,450	30,950	48,450	86,500
40.........	8,700	14,750	20,350	25,800	45,550	90,500
50.........	5,700	9,900	13,800	17,450	30,200	60,150
60.........	2,450	4,700	6,700	8,500	10,250	20,000

In other words, if a person whose maximum earnings will be $1,000 a year dies at the age of twenty after having cost the country $7,425 for his upbringing, or $10,485 if we allow for deaths and interest, the actual loss so far as future earnings are concerned is $10,050. If the maximum income will be $1,500 the corresponding loss is $17,200, and so on until the person whose maximum income is $10,000 represents a loss of $62,900 over and above what he might have spent for living expenses.

From the full table of this kind in *The Money Value of a Man* we have calculated the total value of all the people in the United States in 1930. We have assumed that the value of a woman is the same as that of a man. On this basis the children up to the age of eighteen have a value of $208,000,000,000, while the adults represent a capital value of $593,000,000,000. This, then, is the basis of our statement that the net value of all the people in the United States is twice as great as that of all the country's material possessions of every description. If this fact could once be realized by all classes of society our whole attitude toward the conservation of man would change. We should realize that instead of leaving so much of human development to pure chance the human material should be guarded, conserved, and improved far more carefully than any other resource.

WHERE OUR HUMAN RESOURCES ARE PRODUCED

Let us now see where this human material is produced. A map of the number of children born each year to the thousand population shows at once that the main area of high birth rate is in the South. There the birthrate per thousand inhabitants runs from 20 to 25, although Florida and Tennessee drop a little lower. At first thought the tendency is to ascribe this to the presence of large numbers of Negroes, but West Virginia with only a few Negroes stands second only to North Carolina. Moreover, Maine, North Dakota, and a belt of Rocky Mountain states from Idaho through Utah to Arizona and New Mexico also stand above 20. On the other hand, a belt of industrial and farming country from southern New England to Colorado has less than 18 births per thousand population each year, while on the Pacific coast the rate drops close to 14.

The actual birth rate is far less important than the rate by which the birth rate exceeds the death rate. This survival rate is modified by the fact that in general the death rate is low where the birth rate is high. The matter is complicated by the fact that some parts of the country have a large percentage of old people, young children, or persons of the ages fitted for reproduction. Therefore, in order to get the truest possible picture of what is happening we need to know how many children there are per thousand women of child-bearing age (20-44 years), and how this number compares with the number needed to replace the persons who die. Calculations of this sort have been made by Lorimer and Osborn in *Dynamics of Population*, and are used in Fig. 1. There 1.00 means that among the native whites there are exactly children enough to replace those who die, thus maintaining a stationary population. Figures above or below 1.00 mean that the population is reproducing at such a rate that its numbers change from generation to generation. In Maine the rate is such that 100 native white persons today will be represented by 122 a generation hence.

Connecticut is declining, for, unless there is immigration or some other change, 100 native whites today will be represented by only 84 a generation hence.

From Fig. 1 it is evident that the human material which will determine the character of the United States a generation or two hence is coming in very different proportions from different parts of the country. The South is still vigorously increasing its population. West Virginia (1.61 in Fig. 1) actually has 61 per cent more children than it needs to maintain its population, and even Florida (1.17) and Texas

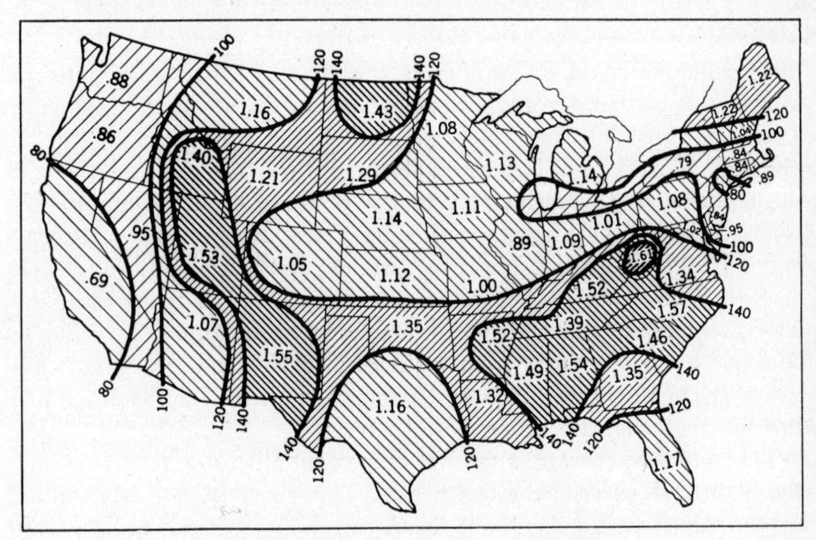

Fig. 1. Index of Net Reproduction per Generation among Native Whites in 1930.

1.00 = Trend toward Stationary Population. Lorimer and Osborn, *Dynamics of Population*, p. 358.

(1.16) are increasing somewhat, although not rapidly. The same is true of the Rocky Mountain states, North Dakota, and northern New England. The great agricultural states from Pennsylvania to Colorado and Minnesota are just barely maintaining themselves. On the other hand, the North Atlantic coast and the Great Lakes have definitely dropped below the level where the population is maintained by natural increase. Unless the population is recruited heavily from elsewhere it will rapidly decline. A similar situation prevails still more emphatically on the Pacific coast, especially in California.

The full significance of a figure such as that of California (.69) can best be appreciated by considering what it means over long periods. Suppose that the Californians maintain their present rate of reproduction for the next three generations. In that event each thousand of the present inhabitants will be represented by only about 330 descendants. If the population of California should double during the century, five persons out of every six would be derived from some outside source. As things now stand, the main source will have to be either foreign countries or the states of this country where the reproduction rate as shown in Fig. 1 is 1.20 or more. West Virginia, for example, at its present rate of 1.61 would not only double its population in a century but in the last generation of the century would have 2,150 persons to send out for every thousand now living there. This would mean 3,700,000 people, but this large number is less than 60 per cent of the 6,400,000 who would be needed in the third generation merely to maintain the population of New York state at its present level.

From all this it is evident that the quality of the population a generation or two hence in all parts of the country depends in high degree upon the children born in the South, the Rocky Mountain states, and the more northerly central and eastern states. Either those states or foreign countries are now supplying the population which fills up the voids arising from the low birth rates in the industrial regions and on the Pacific coast. The quality of the children in these places, whatever it may be, is bound to be reflected in the quality of the inhabitants of the heavier shaded areas of Fig. 1, a generation or two hence.

The contrast between the human productivity of rural districts and of cities is much like the contrast between the South and the Northeast. Our annual crop of human beings is supplied in unusually large proportions by rural districts in contrast to cities. This is true not only in the geographical sections where the birth rate is low, but also in the South and other regions where it is high. All over the country the tendency is for cities to have a high death rate and a low birth rate compared with the rural regions around them. In the United States as a whole from 1928 to 1932 the death rate in cities of 10,000 or more averaged 12.6, whereas the rate for the rest of the country was 10.6. In the highly rural state of North Dakota the contrast appears to be still greater. From 1928 to 1932 the city death rate there was reported as 14.3 and that of the rest of the state as 7.1. This contrast applies to all ages. According to that invaluable little publication, the *Statistical Bulletin* of the Metropolitan Life Insurance Company, the urban deaths for every hundred rural deaths in the country as a whole from 1929 to 1931 were as follows:

Age	*Male*	*Female*	*Age*	*Male*	*Female*
0 years.........	126	125	40 years.........	139	133
10 years.........	171	161	50 years.........	162	149
20 years.........	109	110	60 years.........	163	146
30 years.........	105	113	70 years.........	136	124

The contrast in urban and rural birth rates becomes clear only when allowance is made for the number of women of child-bearing age in each type of environment. From 1928 to 1932 the average birth rate per thousand inhabitants in the cities of the United States with a population above 10,000 was 18.46; in the remainder of the country it was 18.14. This looks as if the cities were reproducing themselves more rapidly than the rest of the population, but that is by no means true. The cities contain an unusually large proportion of women in the reproductive ages from 20 to 44 years. In the cities of over 10,000 such women form 42.3 per cent of all the females, whereas in the rest of the country they form only 33.6 per cent. When allowance is made for this, the birth rate in proportion to the number of women of child-bearing age is found to be 21 per cent greater in the rural districts than in the cities. The big cities are much more extreme in this respect than the smaller ones. For example, in New York state in 1928, a typical year, the births per thousand women aged 20-44 years were as follows:

New York City	79.8
Other cities of over 100,000	94.7
Cities of 25,000–100,000	99.4
Cities of 10,000–25,000	108.8

In Iowa, although the cities are small and relatively rural, those with more than 10,000 inhabitants had only 92 births per thousand women aged 20-44 in 1928, whereas the rest of the state had 100. In similar fashion the census publication entitled *Ratio of Children to Women* shows that in 1920 the conditions in every state in the Union were essentially like those of Pennsylvania as given below in Table 3. In other words, the number of children in proportion to the number of women increases systematically from a low figure in large cities to a high figure on the farms. This is equally true of native- and foreign-born whites and of Negroes.

TABLE 3

Children under 5 Years of Age per 1,000 Women 20 to 44 Years of Age in Pennsylvania

	Native White	*Foreign Born*	*Negro*
Philadelphia	370	737	259
Other cities 100,000 and over	396	902	288
Cities 25,000 to 100,000	429	1,048	352
Cities 10,000 to 25,000	484	1,160	430
Cities 2,500 to 10,000	515	1,211	406
Rural	671	1,336	491

When one considers the enormous sums spent in the cities for sanitation, physicians, vacations, and other means of improving health, the high urban death rates and low birth rates become still more surprising. If left to themselves the large cities would steadily and rapidly decline in population.

The extent to which the cities recruit their numbers from the rural districts may be judged from the relative growth of the two types of areas. Between 1920 and 1930 the native white population of the cities increased by 12,000,000—that is, from 40,000,000 to 52,000,000. The corresponding farm population decreased by nearly a million, dropping to less than 24,000,000. The rural non-farm, or village, population increased by only 3,000,000, and in 1930 was under 20,000,000. All this means that among the native white population, with which alone we are for the moment concerned, at least 10,000,000 people, or 1,000,000 every year, came to the cities from the rural districts, and especially from the farms. One person out of five in our cities is a gift, so to speak, received from the villages and farms during a period of only ten years. The financial depression which began with the crash of 1929 checked and even reversed the cityward tide for a while, but even in 1934 the old tendency was again dominant.

In order to understand where our human resources come from, the population must be divided not only geographically and according to the degree of urbanization, but also according to occupation. The situation in this respect may be summed up by saying that in a general way the more intellectual occupations have few children, whereas the non-intellectual occupations have many. The following table shows the approximate size of completed families as estimated from the records published by the Census Bureau. Only a few of the many occupations there mentioned are given, but these are enough to show the steady decline from intellectual groups like lawyers and teachers through less intellectual types, such as policemen and barbers, to the least intellectual, such as day laborers and miners. The families of the last group are more than twice as large as those of the first.

Summing the situation up, then, we may say that the vastly valuable human material which forms by far the greatest resource of America is produced most abundantly under three main conditions: (1) in the states of the South, Rocky Mountains, and far north where farming is the dominant occupation; (2) in rural districts; and (3) among the less intelligent types of people, such as farm laborers and miners. It is produced least abundantly under three other sets of conditions: (1) in the urban and industrialized regions of the northern

TABLE 4*

Occupations of Fathers	*Estimated Number of Children Ever Born in Completed Families*
Physicians	2.4
Bankers	2.5
Teachers	2.6
Factory officials	2.7
Real estate agents	3.0
Electricians	3.2
Policemen	3.5
Machinists and mechanics	3.6
Gardeners	3.8
Barbers	3.9
Janitors	4.1
Draymen	4.3
Factory laborers	4.6
Farm laborers	5.1
Coal miners	5.3

* From *The Builders of America*, by E. Huntington and L. F. Whitney, New York, William Morrow and Company, 1927.

states and the Pacific coast; (2) in the great cities; and (3) among the most intellectual types of people.

MEASURES TAKEN FOR THE CONSERVATION OF HUMAN RESOURCES

The next step is to see how much is being done for the conservation of our human resources. In certain respects great progress has been made along this line and excellent methods are in use. One of the best means of human conservation is the guarding of health. The story of the marvelous improvement in the cure and prevention of disease is well known. A classic example is the reduction of the tuberculosis death rate from about 200 per 100,000 persons each year in 1900 to less than 60 in 1933. So far has this process gone that there are not enough patients to fill the beds in our tuberculosis sanatoriums. If this continues, some of these institutions will be available for other uses.

Equally good is the record as to education. There is, to be sure, much criticism of the way in which children are trained; and there are certainly enormous possibilities of improvement. Nevertheless, it seems to be true that children are trained more wisely now than in the old days of severe repression and constant physical punishment. Their psychological reactions are understood and appreciated. We recognize that the child passes through distinct stages, each of which needs its own particular form of training and direction. Easy though it is to find fault with the present system, there can be little doubt that our achievements in education represent one of the most creditable phases of the progress of human culture.

Other methods of conserving our human resources are found in such activities as the clearance of slums, the spread of social welfare work, the improvement of government, the ministrations of religion, the institutional care of defectives, the movement to do away with war, and the spread of saner ideas as to diet and exercise. All together these activities and others indicate that the problem of human conservation receives a great deal of attention. Nevertheless, the efforts put forth along this line lose much of their effectiveness because they are concentrated in the very places where they are least needed from the standpoint of the future.

DEFECTS IN OUR SYSTEM OF HUMAN CONSERVATION

This serious defect in our system of human conservation is well illustrated by both education and health. Figure 2 shows that, where

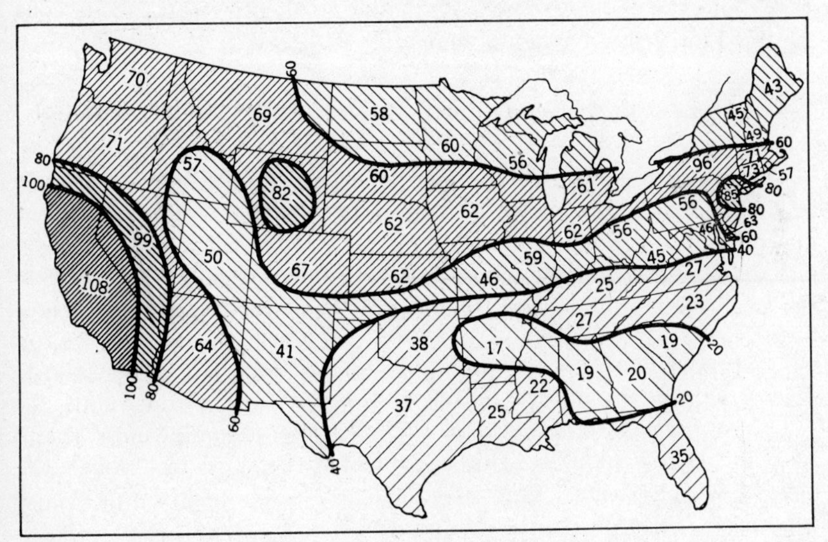

FIG. 2. Expenses for Teaching Children, Aged 5-14 Years (Dollars per Capita), 1931-1932.

children are born in greatest proportion, the expenditures for education are at a minimum. Compare Fig. 2 with Fig. 1. In Fig. 2 we find that the amount spent per year upon the average child for education is very low in the South, only about $20 in much of the section where

Fig. 1 shows a reproductive index above 1.40. Relatively low expenditures for education also prevail in the northern and Rocky Mountain areas of rapid reproduction. The amount spent per child rises fairly high in the great central area of high agricultural productivity, where the number of children is just barely sufficient to maintain the population. And it rises highest around New York City and in the Pacific states, especially in California. These are exactly the places where children are least numerous. In other words, there is a complete reversal: where children are fewest the largest sum is spent per child. California spends five or six times as much to the child as Alabama,

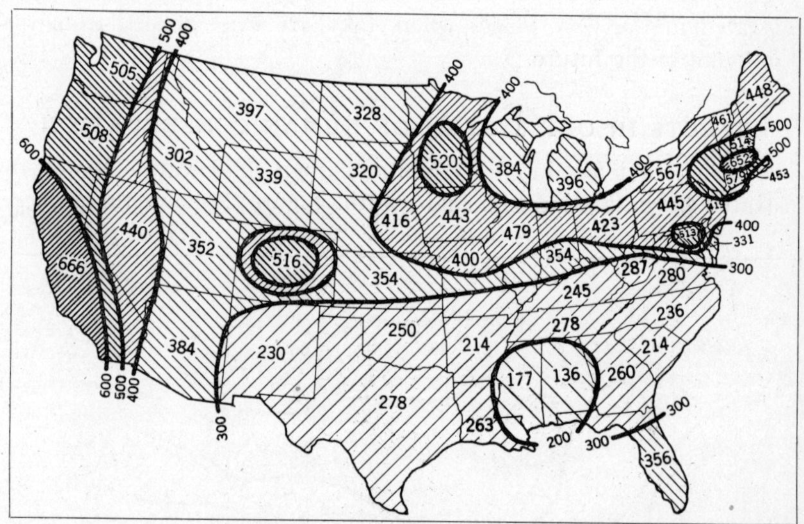

Fig. 3. Number of Physicians, Dentists, and Nurses per 100,000 Persons, 1930.

but in proportion to its population it has less than half as many children, even though only the native whites are taken into account.

The care of health and general welfare shows a similar unfavorable geographical distribution. This is evident in Fig. 3, which shows the number of physicians, dentists, and nurses per hundred thousand population. Here, just as before, we find that the South, which is producing many children, and which spends least per capita for education, is also the region where there is the least care for health. Even when dentists and nurses, as well as physicians, are included, Alabama has only one person to take care of people's health where Massachusetts and California have five.

Although the inverse correlation between rate of reproduction and number of people whose duty it is to take care of health is strong, it is rendered imperfect by many accidental circumstances, as appears in Fig. 4. There the fine dotted line shows the reproductive rate of the states named at the top. In inverted form this same line appears as the comparatively regular solid line. The other two lines show the

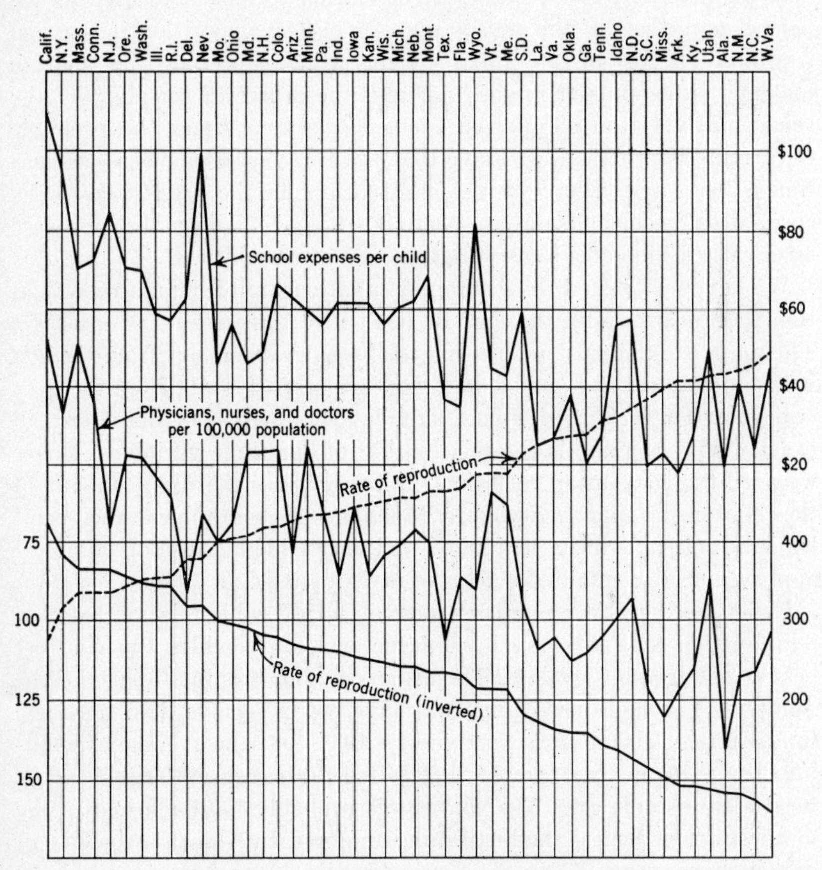

FIG. 4. Rate of Reproduction by States Compared with School Expenses and Number of Doctors, Dentists, and Nurses.

school expenses per child and the number of physicians, dentists, and nurses per hundred thousand inhabitants. Certain states such as Colorado, North Dakota, and Utah stand consistently higher than one would expect from their rate of reproduction. They are central or northern agricultural states. Certain others, on the contrary—for example, Texas, Louisiana, Mississippi, and Alabama—stand even lower than would be expected even on the basis of their high rates of reproduction. Nevertheless, the general trend of both school expenses and care for health is obviously opposed to the trend of reproduction.

Expressed in the form of correlation coefficients, the relationship of reproduction to school expenses is -0.58 ± 0.065, and to people who care for health -0.52 ± 0.071. A correlation coefficient of 1.00 means perfect agreement if the sign is plus, or perfect opposition if the sign is minus. The size of the probable error, which is preceded by the sign meaning either plus or minus, indicates the degree of certainty of the relationship. If the correlation coefficient is four times the probable error there is practical certainty that the two variables whose correlation is being tested have a real relationship. In the present cases the correlation coefficients are respectively 9 and 7 times the probable error, which indicates a very high degree of certainty.

We have now tested the geographic relationship of human reproduction to education and the care of health by three standard methods. The maps are the most interesting to the geographer, but from them it is not easy to see at a glance how far each state departs from the general rule. The graph of Fig. 4 supplies this need, but does not tell exactly how intimate is the relationship of our three variables. Hence we need the correlation coefficients which express the total amount of the relationship in a single figure. Much of our geographical and sociological thinking is hazy, indefinite, and unreliable because of failure to apply a sufficient number of tests of diverse kinds.

Urban and rural communities show an unfavorable relation between reproduction and the care of children which resembles the contrast between geographic sections. The urban communities in all parts of the country spend more per capita and have better schools than the rural communities. During the school year of 1931-1932 the average expenditure per pupil in the cities of the United States was $109 and in the rural sections only $64. The contrast is probably most marked in the southern states, where the birth rate is highest. In Alabama the city of Birmingham spends $39 a year on instruction alone for each child enrolled in the public schools, whereas in the rest of the state the amount falls to $18. Even in the most progressive states there is a similar discrepancy, but not so great. In Wisconsin, for example, Milwaukee spends $71, whereas the rest of the state spends $52.

The situation is rendered still worse by the fact that the expenditures for health and education differ socially in the same unfavorable way as geographically. The intellectual classes, which have very small families, spend large sums on the health and training of their children.

A professional family with an income of $5,000 to $10,000 a year frequently sends two or three children to college at an expense of $1,000 or $1,500 apiece for each of four years. The total cost of educating three children if they go to the public schools, but attend private colleges, may easily run to $20,000 or $25,000. Additional expenses are often incurred for kindgartens, summer camps, and dancing schools. The children who receive this expensive type of education are also taken on trips to places which are interesting historically, economically, or otherwise. In addition to this, their health is very carefully guarded. They go to the dentist twice a year; their teeth are straightened; any defects are carefully investigated and corrected. The child upon whom $10,000 is spent for education may cost $2,000 or $3,000 more from the point of view of health.

The contrast between this and the amount spent on the children of the miner or the poor farmer need scarcely be pointed out. In many instances the cost of education to the laborer with six children may be not more than $100 for each child. The children leave school long before they have finished even the eighth grade. Practically no educational books or toys are furnished them at home. Their doctor's bills are very slight, and their teeth are neglected. Practically nothing is done for them except to keep them alive and take care of them when they are seriously ill.

SUMMARY AND CONCLUSIONS

The gist of the whole thing, then, is this: The human material of America is overwhelmingly the greatest of its assets. This material, we fondly believe, is fundamentally good. It is produced in very uneven amounts in different geographic regions, and also under different social conditions. Almost invariably the tendency is for the largest supply to be produced where the geographic and social conditions are least favorable. The contrast between this and our procedure in respect to farming is extraordinary. We recognize that corn should be produced where the climate is well adapted to it and where grain of high quality can be raised. We also appreciate the fact that the larger the amount produced, the more essential it is that the best methods of production should be employed. In addition to all this, we recognize that the best seed should be used; the more valuable the crop, the more important it is to have good seed. In respect to human material we pursue the opposite course, for we have not yet learned the most elementary lesson of human conservation. The regions which produce the largest crop of children are the very ones where the conditions of health, education, and social betterment are least favorable. Yet from these less-favorable regions a million poorly trained young people pour into the cities each year to fill the places left vacant in the cities and in the more prosperous parts of the country because the supply of human beings is too small. For their own sake, if for no other reason, it would seem as if the cities ought to show far more interest in improving the rural and less-favored regions from which they draw so much of their human material.

PART X

CHAPTER XXII

STATE AND LOCAL PLANNING

By Loyal Durand, Jr.

University of Wisconsin

INTRODUCTION

Geography as a subject, and geographers as individuals and as a group, have long been interested in various aspects of planning. This is largely the result of geography's interest in regions as areas of the earth's surface, and of the fact that much of planning has to do with areas of the surface. Thus, very naturally, some members of the field of knowledge that deals with area have been drawn into planning. There has arisen, however, a technical profession of city planning, manned by professional city planners, some of whom entered the planning field after preliminary work in engineering and others of whom were directly trained for the planning of cities. At the present time many city planners have stepped into the more recently developed field of regional planning, while individuals are also being trained for the expanded field of national regional planning, one to be described in a subsequent chapter.

THE PLANNING REGION

The City a Unit. The region that is the subject for planning may be of almost any size. Perhaps an example of a small region which is the subject of planning is the city subdivision, although as a matter of fact every lot is the subject of a plan, and even the house and landscaping adjuncts to the lot are planned. The whole neighborhood of a city may very properly be the subject of a plan, for it usually includes several subdivisions, and as a result creates problems of wider interest than those of a given subdivision.

Planning for the entire village, town, or city is a natural outgrowth of smaller plans. Thus there has arisen the need of a broad, well-conceived city plan to care for both present and expanding needs of the metropolitan area. This is one phase of local planning that is well understood and permanently rooted. The ancients had city plans. Medieval castles and their adjacent villages were planned, although an adequate defense of the area from outside attack was the prime object of the plan. Many of our American cities were planned from the start, excellent examples being Philadelphia, Washington, Detroit, and Salt Lake City. Others of our cities, objects of intensive planning at present, grew rather aimlessly from small centers, or grew in mushroom fashion by the continued additions of subdivisions, each subdivision being perhaps planned by itself, but the entire area not co-ordinated into a well-thought-out whole.

The Metropolitan Area a Unit. The metropolitan area or the county plan were outgrowths of city planning. The formulation of plans for a wider region than the city itself was the result of continued urban growth. Suburbs were growing rapidly and had many interests in common with the main city. However, political separation of the suburbs from the city made it impossible to apply the city plan to them, for that kind of plan must halt at the city borders on account of political exigencies. Planning regions for these urban and urban-rural areas larger than the city itself have primarily assumed two forms: (1) the metropolitan district, and (2) the county. In the former the entire metropolitan area is the subject for the plan. This type of planning region includes the city and its satellite suburbs, the surrounding rural and rural-urban districts, and it commonly crosses county and even state lines. Thus the New York regional plan includes portions of New York state, New Jersey, and Connecticut; the Philadelphia Tri-State plan crosses from Pennsylvania to New Jersey and Delaware; and a broad plan for the Chicago metropolitan region included surveys and suggestions for portions of Illinois, Indiana, and Wisconsin.

The County as a Unit. The second type of larger area surrounding a city is the county, and many of the planning organizations and commissions of the United States have been organized on this political basis. Examples of a county planning region are furnished by some of the New Jersey counties, by Monroe County, New York, the larger area for the city of Rochester, and by Milwaukee County, Wisconsin. The county planning region of this type functions best when the city is near the center of a county so that the county and the metropolitan region become essentially synonymous. It has advantages in that the planning is made for but one or two units of government, thus often circumventing difficulties offered by different and sometimes conflicting governmental administrations when county and state lines are crossed.

The State or Region a Unit. Two additional regions, both larger in area than all those previously mentioned, are areas subject to planning. One is the state itself, and the other a large entity crossing state lines, larger than counties or metropolitan regions, and comprising all the territory within an arbitrary limit. Any one of the forty-eight states, of course, is an example of the first. The Tennessee Valley Authority set up as one of the "new deal" projects of President Franklin D. Roosevelt is an example of the second type of larger region, the arbitrary borders of which were furnished by the watershed of the Tennessee River. A group-of-states arrangement can also be used as the subject of a plan, such as the six New England states, or the Pacific northwest region, which comprises Washington, Oregon, and Idaho. The larger-than-state regions, and the regions of considerable area that cross state lines, are, however, primarily sub-national units, and as such are practical subdivisions of national planning rather than state planning. Consequently they will be treated more fully in the section on national planning.

For many reasons the state is an ideal unit for planning, primarily as a result of its political unity. For many planning purposes the state is the geographic unit, the master region. The major natural resources of the state can be studied and inventoried, conservation problems can be approached from a statewide basis, and the geographic distribution of the resources and problems can be adequately recorded and catalogued within the limits of the state. Uniformity and similarity of government, from both practice and personnel, within the state also permit considerable uniformity of approach to the planning problem. The collection of basic data, the formulation of a plan, and the eventual carrying of the plan into practice are also facilitated by state arrangements.

It must ever be kept in mind, however, that, even though the state is for many purposes the geographic unit for planning there are regional diversities involved. The regional concept, the breaking down of the master state region into subregions, is essential. A planned attack on any of the problems of an American state forces recognition of the regional diversities within state boundaries, just exactly as national planning involves breakdown of the nation's territory into sub-national regions.

The state is also a good region for planning because of several inherent American qualities. Among these is the theory of state's rights, an idea which has been very strong at several different periods of our history, which has been dormant and quiescent at other periods, but which is ever present, may at any time come to vital life, and which is a major factor of both our state and national life. In addition the state, under our American form of government, has certain functions to perform, functions not expressly delegated to the national government. The question of planned land use, water use, highways, and other features is one within the states that ranks to the forefront of state problems. The people of a state may accomplish much toward realization of a fuller life in their regional planning.

How State Planning and Conservation Are Related. Intelligent conservation of natural resources involves knowing the resources, and involves problems of inventory, preservation, efficient utilization, and renewal. Thus state planning in every sense, and on all sides and aspects of its philosophy, strikes at the essence of modern conservation in its broadest interpretation.

The major natural resources of the United States are located, of course, within the borders of the several states. Many of these resources are of utmost significance to state and nation. The state as an entity is interested in planning for continuation of these resources so that the state may profit from their existence, perhaps directly in the form of taxes or indirectly through the welfare of the citizens most immediately concerned with the resource. No state wants its soil depleted by needless soil erosion. Intelligent planning and active conservation will save the soil. Wise and efficient use of minerals will bring the greatest good to the greatest number, even though the mineral may be exhausted at some future time. A wise and planned use of the forests of the state, coupled with intelligent reforestation, will permit the continuation of industries dependent upon forest raw materials, and save the state from possible loss of manufacturing plants, impoverishment of workers, and the stranding of inhabitants in the formerly forested areas. Examples of the type of the three just cited might be multiplied at length. The need for state planning is evident. It is necessary to correct mistakes of the past, to help with present problems, and to serve as a guide to wiser utilization of resources in the future.

EXTENT AND NUMBER OF PLANNING REGIONS

Planning regions of all the types previously listed exist in the United States. In addition, the entire country may be considered a single planning region, the subject of national planning projects.

City Plans. The National Planning Board in 1934 undertook a survey of the planning commissions engaged in city and town planning within the United States.[1] Their survey and report indicated a total of 739 city and town planning agencies in existence at that time, not including 121 cities previously recorded as having a planning commission but from which no replies were received in this particular survey. Also in May, 1934, were 1,244 cities that possessed zoning regulations and approximately 218 cities that had either general or comprehensive city plans.

Metropolitan Plans. Metropolitan and county plans have been developed in numerous places within the United States. The Boston metropolitan area was among the first to be organized for planning, especially for its water, sewer, and park system.[2] New York City and its environs have been the subject of one of the largest metropolitan plans set up in the country.[3] Some dozen or more large and major metropolitan regions have been organized for planning, among them the regions surrounding such cities as Philadelphia, Chicago, St. Louis, Washington, and Los Angeles.

County Plans. More than 250 counties have been organized for regional planning, and the total is growing constantly. In some of these planning units the county is used as the political basis of a metropolitan-area plan, as previously explained. In others, and by far the larger number, the county is a unit for county planning in the rural sense, that is, the county itself is the basis of the planning and reason for the planning, and is not used as synonymous with a metropolitan area. Mercer County, New Jersey, Los Angeles County, California, and Monroe County, New York, are examples of "county-metropolitan" planning. Counties organized for rural regional planning in 1935 were primarily those within Wisconsin and California. Each of these states has an enabling law permitting the county to be the subject of land zoning and permitting the county board to enact a rural zoning law designating various types of land use within the area of the county. Not all the counties of either state have taken advantage of the enabling act. Counties possessing much "problem" land within their borders, such as counties in the northern cut-over region of Wisconsin, have, however, taken advantage of the act of 1923, and sixteen of the nineteen northern counties primarily affected by the problem of cut-

[1] "State Planning: A Review of Activities and Progress," National Resources Board, Washington, June, 1935, p. 3.

[2] *Ibid.*, p. 3.

[3] Regional Plan of New York and Its Environs, Russell Sage Foundation, 1931.

over land have enacted rural zoning ordinances. There is, consequently, a wide discrepancy in numbers today between the total counties that are organized for planning, and the total number of counties that have actually instigated a plan and have passed zoning ordinances to put the plan into effect.

State Plans. State planning organizations at the close of 1935 were located in 46 of the 48 American states. The state planning movement received tremendous impetus between 1933 and 1935 as a result of federal assistance, and the large percentage of the United States subjected to state planning in 1936 reflects the rapid spread of the regional planning movement as an aid to problems of conservation, orderly development, and a fuller life.

STATE PLANNING

What Is State Planning? The National Resources Board has defined state planning as "the systematic, continuous, far-sighted application of the best intelligence available, to programs and problems of State development and organization, in order to provide higher standards of living and greater security for the people of the state. Planning is the use of scientific and technical skills, coupled with imagination, to determine and influence trends or changes which can be helpful to this larger purpose."[1] State planning thus consists of gathering all necessary data about the state, of recording and analyzing these data, and of bringing all possible intelligence to the study of the data with a view to discovering trends so that the eventual plan will be more accurate and have more chance of success.

The Need for State Planning. The need for state planning is evident. Previous chapters have discussed usage of the individual resources, and examples of unplanned land use, water use, forest use, and others have been given and are well known to every intelligent citizen. One basic need for state planning is thus to correct the mistakes of the past, or to help correct them as far as possible. A second need for planning is to help with present state problems. A third need is the service that planning can perform for a wiser utilization of resources in the future.

The planners can serve to collect the data, take inventories, analyze data, suggest changes, guide legislation, and correlate isolated plans suggested by individual state administrative departments.

The state itself is a natural planning unit for problems within its

[1] National Resources Board, "State Planning," *op. cit.*, p. 4.

borders. Different states are affected in dissimilar ways by similar problems, for conditions are not constant in all American commonwealths. The states are the most important framework of the nation. As such, each state as an individual unit cannot help being vitally interested in planning for its own welfare. One of the basic needs for planning is the result of the fact that our nation consists of forty-eight commonwealths. Each state must thus plan for itself and for resource utilization within its area. The correlation of individual state plans and common action on these plans lies either with a group-of-states arrangement or with national planning organizations.

Development of State Planning. State planning grew naturally, the result of its need. Preliminary growth was slow but sure, and growth after 1933 was aided by federal assistance. Nevertheless, planning evolved as a necessary function, and the impetus state planning received after 1933 pushed it more quickly to the forefront.

State planning in a sense has been going forward ever since formation of the states themselves. State governments were planning before the term "state planning" had arisen, and when most individuals who called themselves "planners" were engaged in city planning.

In the 1890's planning movements were instigated for the preservation of historic and scenic sites, and a great deal of public interest was aroused. Forest and game planning followed about 1900, and was an important factor in the formation of several state conservation commissions as units of state government. Health problems, city water supply problems, and allied fields of planning led to organization of state health departments. The advent of the automobile led to the movement for good highways, and resulted in the formation of highway commissions. These bodies undertook the planning for highway needs of the state. State governments today are replete with various departments and commissions, each of which is a planning agency for some particular function of the government.

State planning as respecting land grew apace during the 1920's, for particularly in that decade there arose the need for planning for "land problem" areas within the several states. It had been previously supposed that most of the land surface of the country, other than very rough land or dry lands, would eventually be devoted to agricultural land use. That had been the preceding history throughout most of the eastern United States—the passage of area from forest land to farm land. Gradually the realization came that such changes were not occurring in the Laurentian Upland portions of the Lake states. Northern Minnesota, northern Wisconsin, northern Michigan, and the Adirondack region of New York had not passed through the cycle from forest to farm, but had been left as cut-over land, burned-over land, and land covered with poor second-growth timber. But few farmers had followed the lumberman in the region. As long as lumber and real estate companies held this cut-over land in the hope of selling it to future settlers, the problem was not serious, for the companies paid taxes on the land and consequently local and state governments received an income from it. As soon as the companies allowed large areas of their former holdings to become tax delinquent, and eventually to pass to county or state ownership, with resulting removal from the tax rolls, the problem became acute. People gradually came to realize that a new era had set in, that much of the northern type of glaciated, stony land located in a region of short growing season was not potential agricultural land, and that plans for the wisest use of this marginal and submarginal land would have to be developed.

The New England states and New York were faced with the problem of abandoned hill farms. Vermont and New Hampshire had literally been moving downhill.[1] In New York the hill farms of the southern plateau counties had been abandoned in large numbers, and population had been moving toward the lowlands of the Hudson-Mohawk valleys and the Lake Ontario plain. The study of the New York state situation resulted in a 1926 report by the New York State Commission of Housing and Regional Planning, considered by many authorities to be the first comprehensive state planning report in the United States.[2]

The large areas of cut-over tax-delinquent lands in the northern portions of the Great Lakes states of Michigan, Wisconsin, and Minnesota became serious problems for these individual states. The land problem of the north finally precipitated investigations, field studies, and administrative control in these states, and each in turn developed planned efforts to meet the problem, such as the detailed inventory studies of the Michigan Land Economic Survey, the Land Economic Inventory of the state of Wisconsin, and the county studies of the Wisconsin College of Agriculture.

The need for planning that resulted in various functional surveys was well recognized. The stage was now well set for inclusive state planning projects, involving several functions of the state. This last stage, the fostering of a more rapid development of state planning, re-

[1] J. W. Goldthwait, "A Town That Has Gone Downhill," *Geog. Rev.*, Vol. 17, 1927, pp. 527-552. See also H. F. Wilson, "The Roads of Windsor," *Geog. Rev.*, Vol. 21, 1931, pp. 379-397.

[2] National Resources Board, "State Planning," *op. cit.*, p. 4.

ceived prime impetus under the National Planning Board in 1933 and its successors, the National Resources Board in 1934 and the National Resources Committee, in the years immediately following.

The National Planning Board conducted preliminary surveys of the planning bodies in the United States and aided in having planning boards organized in states that did not possess them. To the state planning boards the National Planning Board assigned regional planning consultants, men actively engaged in the planning profession, and capable of guiding the newly organized state committees and planning boards in the field of planning. The immediate result was the taking of the preliminary state inventories and the issuance of preliminary reports. These activities, fostered by federal aid to the states, gave state planning rapid momentum, and resulted in the awakening and quickening of planning interest within the states.

The National Resources Board, organized in 1934, continued the policies of the National Planning Board, which it superseded, and fostered state planning. The professional planners continued services to the state planning boards, the results of which were embodied in final state planning reports, primarily inventories of the resources of the states, but also containing preliminary recommendations for wiser and fuller use of the natural and human assets of the respective areas. The National Resources Board also undertook study of the land resources, the mineral resources, water resources, and other basic resources of the United States in order to correlate the separate state work into a nation-wide inventory and report. To this end additional consultants were assigned, each charged with special detailed investigation of a single resource. Completion of the preliminary studies of these basic resources of the individual states, and correlation in Washington of the separate reports, resulted in the National Resources Board report to the president in December, 1934, the most complete inventory and study of the United States undertaken to date. State planning in each state was thus capped by a national inventory. State planning boards continued intensive work and made recommendations within their respective states, and at the same time the nation received a national inventory as a result of a combination of work by state, state-federal, and federal agencies. The National Resources Committee succeeded the National Resources Board in 1935 and has continued the policies of its predecessor as regards the aiding and fostering of state planning.

The rapid rise of state planning within the last ten years has been significant in the United States, and planning has been carried to the forefront of state projects. The New York state planning report in

1926, the establishment in Wisconsin of the State Regional Planning Committee in 1931, the sponsoring of Illinois planning work by the State Chamber of Commerce, and early regional plans in several other states were significant starts. However, despite these notable state exceptions, it remained for the national bodies to furnish the impetus to carry state planning to a total of forty-six states within a brief period.

Fields of State Planning Work. State planning in the United States covers a wide range of subjects. The regional aspect of the United States is one of the factors largely responsible for this, since obviously one of the western intermontane states is most interested in the water resource from the standpoint of storage and control for irrigation, while a lower Mississippi Valley state approaches primarily the flood-control aspect of the water resource, and a densely peopled eastern state is primarily concerned with reservoir storage facilities for city water supplies and the control of stream pollution. In still other states the water-power aspect of the water resource may be the most critical one, and within the geographic regions of any one state all of these water problems singly or in combination may be critical factors. The ensuing discussion of the fields of state planning briefly describes the major problems that have been studied by the various state planning boards of the United States. That these problems are regionally located, both within the country as a whole and within the several states, is recognized. A later section will deal with a few highlights of regional distribution by states.

The National Resources Board in a study of state planning activities fostered by the individual state planning boards and commissions found that a dozen or two major headings form the primary activities and interests of the state organizations.[1] Among these fields are: (1) population studies, involving present population distribution, and forecasts of the human resource at some future date, and future population trends; (2) basic mapping of the state, including topographic, aerial, soil maps, cover maps, and others; (3) planning the land resources of the state in all its various aspects; (4) water resources; (5) minerals and mineral land planning; (6) power resources and projects; (7) transportation planning, including highways, airways, railroads, waterways, and other types of transportation; (8) housing programs and studies of existing housing conditions; (9) recreation; (10) conservation of natural resources; (11) distribution of industry; (12) fiscal programming; (13) unemployment; (14) relief; (15) education;

[1] National Resources Board, "State Planning," 1935, pp. 5-7, 111-289.

(16) public works programming; (17) governmental reorganization; and (18) governmental relationships. Other conceivable subjects also enter the realm of the state planning organizations, and not all the boards within the several states have studied all the above subjects. Certain federal governmental projects, however, such as the long-time program of public works, have been cleared through existing state planning organizations. Consequently studies and plans of the boards to date have had both a markedly direct and indirect effect with the individual states possessing state planning organizations.

The Kinds of Things Inventoried in a State as the Basis of a State Plan. A few of the many physical, economic, and human resources that are important as a basis for state planning and that must be inventoried are as follows: land, water, power, minerals, forests, transportation lines, and population. These resources in turn may be broken down into component units. Land, for example, may be agricultural land, forest land, pasture land, urban land, or it may be put into certain uses such as an Indian reservation that must be considered in a plan. Water resources, in turn, may be most significant in certain regions of a state for water power, elsewhere within a state the problem may be one of flood control, and a third region may have a serious problem of stream pollution. Thus the planner in planning for a state must have before him an adequate and detailed picture of present natural and human resource conditions before he can analyze data and before he can formulate a state plan for the future. It cannot be too strongly emphasized that the existence of adequate basic data is essential to the formulation of a regional plan. It is in the collection and interpretation of these data that the geographer is primarily interested.

How State Planning Is Carried Out. State planning consists of at least four significant stages. They are:

1. A statewide inventory of regional assets and endowments. This includes an inventory survey of both physical features (features of natural earth) and cultural features (man-made features). Included within the survey should be as complete a study as possible of the human resources of the state, for after all it is man that is using the state's natural resources, and it is man himself for whom the plan is made and for whom it is eventually to be put into effect.

2. Analysis of the data collected in the surveys. This second stage is most important, but cannot be carried to complete fruition without adequate preliminary data.

3. Planning proper. The National Resources Board defines this as

something "to suggest measures, tools, new ways of doing things which may promote orderly development and fuller use of our resources."[1]

4. The administrative carrying out of the plan.

The state planning boards in their preliminary reports in 1934 and 1935 investigated primarily the first point in order to have an effective groundwork for an intelligent analysis. In other words, they have collected a great body of inventory and survey material during the past few years and have laid the groundwork for effective state planning, a process which is well under way in the individual states. The plans have reached an advanced stage of development, and the public has awakened to the need of wiser utilization of our physical, economic, and human assets.

Rural Land Zoning. Regional planning involves the making of a plan, the transference of the plan from paper to the region, whether the plan be for water, land, or people, and finally the administration of the plan by existing state agencies or duly created administrators. Rural zoning has proved an effective means of transferring land plans from paper into actuality, and as such it deserves a place in modern American thinking.

Zoning of rural territory is in reality a method for achieving the objectives in planning. Zoning has been called "the use of the police power to bring the utilization of privately owned land into harmony with public purposes."[2] Wisconsin and California permit zoning in rural areas under general state enabling acts; some other states have extended the zoning power to counties under individual or special acts. Oneida County in northern Wisconsin is considered to have passed the first rural zoning ordinance in the United States. The typical rural zoning law is not related to metropolitan planning, but has as its objective the zoning of land for agriculture, forestry, and recreation. Zoning permits enforcement of the land uses through the police power and consequently is more than merely classification of land.

Successful zoning, as in Wisconsin, has come about through state direction and supervision combined with local classification of the lands for zoning purposes. The procedure has usually been for the county board to recommend the instigation of a study leading to the eventual passage of a zoning ordinance. Township meetings are held after this declaration of intent, and the inhabitants of the local government units actually zone the land within their political divisions. This comes about through township discussion of problems in town zoning

[1] "State Planning," *op. cit.*, p. 4.
[2] Wisconsin Regional Plan Report, 1934, p. 271.

meetings. After all townships have zoned their land the county board takes final action, passes the zoning ordinance, and issues an official land-use map of the county. In many respects the practices followed in rural zoning are thus quite similar to urban zoning, the major differences being only in types and classifications of land use. The strength of the rural zoning movement to date has been in the local township meetings, the final zoning ordinance being the summation of local knowledge. Rural zoning has thus "come up from below," and has not been spread as a mantle from higher governmental authorities, a practice often leading to local dissatisfaction.

Human resource planning of necessity accompanies land zoning. The setting up of forest districts, for example, may remove land from agricultural use and may result in movement of the population from the forest district. This fact involves readjustments in local governments, readjustments in roads, schools, and school districts, and perhaps even a change in the community pattern. A change in one major land use thus commonly promotes a series of succeeding changes. Under an ideal arrangement agricultural zones in a territory such as northern Wisconsin, Michigan, or Minnesota should consist of well-blocked lands of fair to good quality located on good roads in a "going" community, and near markets, schools, churches, and community centers. Resettlement of scattered population in the forest zones may be necessary if the entire population is not able to obtain employment in the forests. These resettled people should be concentrated on farm lands in existing communities, a practice permitted to Wisconsin counties if the settler is willing. Planning for the region may also involve major changes in political units, may result in consolidation of school districts or townships, the dissolution of small districts, the abandonment of unnecessary roads, changes in rural mail routes, and a host of other changes. The ramifications of planning are numerous and diverse, but extremely critical and necessary. Changes are essential in many areas, and rural land zoning has been proved one of the effective ways of transferring a plan from its preliminary inventory stage to its final fruition.

Regional Aspects of Regional Planning in the State. The regional point of view places emphasis upon regions of the earth's surface. A region is an areal convenience selected for a purpose. Various purposes require regions of unlike definition, and since nature seldom creates areas of any great size that are uniform throughout, and that have sharp boundaries, it is necessary to limit many areas arbitrarily. The region, however transitional it may become toward its margins, may nevertheless be recognized by the nature of its central complex or core, about which it is defined. Many regions, especially those of subnational character, as previously noted, transcend state boundaries, while numerous regions are entirely within the political borders of one state or else are state units for state planning purposes.

The regional aspect of regional planning is important in the several states. Land resources and land planning have received regionally different treatments within the country. Some state planning boards have made land ownership surveys. In some of the western corn belt states, where corporations frequently hold large blocks of land, the state planning boards have studied effects of this type of ownership. In Idaho a harmonized state reclamation program had an important place in the land studies. In the eastern and midwestern states the problem of submarginal agricultural land is critical. Iowa, a prime agricultural state, studied the land resource as one of its primary endeavors, a good example of a regional interest. In Maine, on the other hand, the planning board studies correlated the land with the state's recreational problems. Wisconsin and Michigan, faced with the cut-over submarginal land problem, interested themselves in inventory and zoning to take stock of the land problem and to attempt to solve it.

Regional aspects of the water problem have been cited in another connection in the present chapter. Flood control and water conservation are paramount in the southwestern United States; flood control and stream pollution in the lower Mississippi and the Ohio valleys; watershed examination, both for public water supplies and for danger from industrial wastes, are critical items of water resource planning in densely peopled Connecticut, Massachusetts, and parts of New York and Pennsylvania; hydroelectric power is an important item for planning in Maine; irrigation problems interest Nevada; and water diversion, storage, and irrigation are fundamental in Colorado.

Practically all the individual items of state planning have been and are being approached regionally within the states. States possessing large cities within their borders have stressed recreational needs, as in the Chicago and New York areas. States with large natural recreational areas, as the Great Lakes section, Missouri with its Ozark Highlands, or Maine with its seacoast and wilderness areas, have stressed private commercial resort planning and public parks planning. Missouri contemplates an Ozark Parkway, New York state believes that about nine million acres, or one-fourth of the land area of the state, might be considered for public ownership, while Maine plans to acquire public beaches, and headlands that may be developed for public use.

Forest land and forest resources have been stressed in practically all states. However, those with large forest areas or with important lumber industries or critical watershed problems have emphasized the subject. New York state wishes reservoirs in all headwater areas, with a proportion of the land in forest.

The New Jersey planning board has instituted a field survey of the larger industries of the state. Connecticut has made very detailed cover maps of the state. These types of planning studies have been carried on in small, densely populated states, obviously with a regional orientation different from that in the western states and with a definite regional consciousness.

Human resources may also be approached from the regional standpoint. Population forecasts, for example, call for intensive regional study at present in order that regional potentialities may be foreseen and possible changes noted.

Regionalism, both on the national and state scale, is critical. A realization of the regional method is necessary for the complete understanding of state planning and is desirable in helping interpret various aspects of the state planning movement within the United States.

LOCAL PLANNING

City and town planning have been rooted for a long period of time. The ancients planned centers of defense, medieval peoples planned their towns and fortresses, and modern peoples have planned many types of areas. City and town planning has been defined as a science and an art concerned with the shaping and guiding of the physical growth and arrangement of towns in harmony with their social and economic needs.[1] City planning as a profession, and as a means to an end, has assumed a major place in the United States, and is accepted by citizens as desirable. The end toward which city planners are working is the existence of a well-balanced city physically in which health, safety, and human welfare are well cared for by the structure of the city.

Major problems in city planning have to do with such subjects as (1) means of communication, including streets, railways, and waterways; (2) housing facilities; (3) recreational and educational needs; (4) the regulation of city land use and of population density through zoning; (5) protection of health; (6) the development of civic centers, civic art, and so on, and a host of additional subjects. It will thus be

[1] Thomas Adams, *Outline of Town and City Planning,* New York, 1935, p. 21.

seen that city planning includes far more than merely the physical alignment of certain features, or the patterns of transportation and sewerage systems. The future development of parks, schools, streets, the relationship of residence districts to commercial and industrial areas, the protection of health, the zoning of land—all involve public improvements. The city planner must be a broadly educated man, able to cope with a variety of problems.

City planning commissions in the United States are often empowered by statute with authority to regulate the location of industries, to regulate the location of buildings designed for specific uses, as for example an apartment house, to regulate the areas of courts or yards, which in effect permits the commission to control the density of population in parts of the city, and to exercise authority for measures that are designed for public health, safety, and welfare. The kind of regulation that may be imposed by the various city planning commissions under general state statutes is not arbitrary, but usually must be based upon a scientific study or inventory of the municipal development, and ordinarily requires several public hearings before adoption. Changing of regulations and of zone districts from time to time is permitted, for a city is constantly in a process of evolution and the plan must be adjusted to changes that it itself may have helped to bring about.

City zoning ordinances, enacted under permissive state statutes, and designed to protect various land uses within the city, have commonly been upheld in the courts when reasonable. The designation of definite land uses for given city areas is well known and accepted by the public. City planning calls for coordination of an entire area into a well-conceived plan. Past planning of American cities has too often been carried on in piecemeal fashion, each subdivision added to the city having been planned by the realtor at the time of its development, but planned perhaps only for the best interest of the operator and not with a thought to a coordinated whole. Modern city planning is consequently not a substitute for no planning at all, but is rather a development of coordinated planning to take the place of unrelated and unregulated scattered planning. City planning has reached its present stage of development as a result of public demand. Residence districts wish to be protected from encroachment by factories. Residents of areas that are devoted to single-family homes want protection of their property from encroachment by large apartment houses. An apartment-hotel district in turn does not wish to be encroached upon by tenements or by industrial plants. Public sentiment is strongly in favor of city zoning ordinances, most of which designate specific land uses to specific areas. Changes in zoning ordinances usually require public hearings and frequently require consent of interested parties. For example, a change of a city block from a single-family unit residence zone to a double- or multiple-family dwelling zone commonly requires consent of the landowners within the block, since they are the interested citizens affected by the change.

Physical aspects of city planning extend beyond the city borders and link city with metropolitan-county planning. The highway system, for example, must connect with important arteries that lead from the city to its surroundings. Bridge approaches, water-supply approaches, such as aqueducts, and dozens of similar items are of utmost significance. The complexity of planning for a large city, and of connections between the city and its surrounding region, is well illustrated by the admirable plan of New York City and environs carried out and published under the auspices of the Russell Sage Foundation.

The human element is an important one in local planning. The human resources of the area are among the reasons for the planning, and a fuller life for the future may be realized if the population characteristics and population trends are known. Educational planning, hospital planning, parks and recreation, for example, are all items that depend upon as accurate future forecasts of population as possible. Population trends, the shift of population within cities, the size of the families, and other pertinent facts that can be obtained in the human inventory are all of significance to the city planner. The environs of the business district may have a large population, for example, but if the largest child population is in the outskirts of the city the result upon educational and school-need planning is profound. On the other hand, the park and recreational needs may be the reverse of the school needs in the instance just cited.

City planning commissions and state planning boards have worked in close cooperation. Both local and state planning appear to be permanently rooted features of the United States.

CHAPTER XXIII

NATIONAL REGIONAL PLANNING IN RESOURCE USE

By George T. Renner

Teachers College, Columbia University

INTRODUCTION

Conservation has been defined as the fullest possible use of resources—their use in such manner as to produce the greatest possible good for the greatest number of people. Simple and easy as this may sound, it can never be realized unless the exploitation, the economic conversion, and perhaps even the ownership of our resources be based upon a definite program. In order to have such a program, however, it is not enough to cultivate proper attitudes on the part of industrial enterprisers, business men, scientists, and citizens in general, nor is the encouragement of desirable group attitudes and public opinions sufficient to achieve proper conservation measures. A program must be deliberately planned and formulated, by individuals who are in position to view intelligently all functions and elements as a related whole, to eliminate selfish and partisan considerations, and to look ahead to desirable social objectives. Planning, therefore, reveals itself as the reverse side of a concept whose obverse side is conservation.

No matter how much intelligence, foresight, and energy be put into planning for conservation, the result is nevertheless only a plan. A plan becomes a program when, and only when, it becomes law and takes on administrative reality. It can assume this status only through political channels. Moreover, a conservation which rests solely upon education and persuasion must fail at almost every point where it comes into conflict with individual interests and property rights. It must rest instead upon public administration and legality. One is led to conclude, therefore, that conservation must, in the main, be planned and administered by government, even though the success of that administration will in large measure rest upon public attitudes and opinions. At this point, therefore, it might be well to raise the question as to what premises should underlie conservation planning.

In approaching the subject of conservation, in the past, our entire thinking has been clouded by a tacit assumption that we were living under an economy of scarcity. The major objectives, therefore, have been to restrict, to limit, and even to withhold and hoard. At times and under certain circumstances, all these are desirable and even necessary, but as a concept, conservation designed merely to save, can have no more than academic interest to a society which at times threatens to suffocate in over-abundance.

This, however, does not mean that conservation is unnecessary. Far from this, it is one of the really pressing needs of both the present and the future. Conservation programs merely need to be based upon somewhat different objectives. The fact is that we in America are living and must for a long time continue to live under an economy of abundance. This abundance springs out of a very rich endowment in natural resources plus a highly developed technology operated by a vigorous and ingenious population. The resultant of these three factors is an amazingly prolific system of economic production, within which it is commonly believed we need fear no immediate major forms of scarcity. There are, to be sure, some isolated resources of which scarcity does threaten, as for example, tin, phosphorus, petroleum, and a few others. For nearly all, however, remedial measures, substitutions, and new discoveries are likely to solve the specific needs and problems. Such a philosophy of abundance does not, unfortunately, solve our major problem. So far, we as a people have shown no convincing proof that we are wise enough to use our modern technology or to operate under an economy of abundance. A system which produces great cities filled with human misery and social problems, which engenders a magnificent scale of production incapable of avoiding disastrous crashes and collapses, which supplants yeoman farmers with tenants, which turns pleasant countrysides into highway slums, which leaves unemployed large portions of the population in the midst of plenty, and which supports an unbelievably complex structure of government by means of crushing taxation—such a system invites a very significant kind of conservation. To conserve human values, to enrich facilities for living, and to devise a plan for the orderly and balanced exploitation of resources—there lies the major challenge.

THE NECESSITY FOR PLANNING

One of the outstanding results of our modern improved technology has been the rapid exploitation of our natural resources. During the last seventy years, we have converted more resources into economic goods than during all the prior span of human history. Concurrently, we have brought about a degree of waste which surpasses that of all preceding generations. Steel plows have been substituted for hoes and wooden plows, thereby enabling man to stir the soil more rapidly and more deeply, so that it has washed away faster. Multiple plows, multiple harrows, and combines have likewise speeded up enormously the processes of soil exhaustion. Power saws, stump pullers, and dynamite have multiplied the effectiveness of man's attack on the forest. The high-powered rifle and the steam trawler have threatened the doom of wild game and fisheries. The compressed-air drill, the steam shovel, the electric tram, and processes for refining low-grade ores have enabled man to extract minerals in wholesale fashion. Hydraulic cement, the power dredge, the high-pressure caisson, the turbine, generator, and dynamo, together with high-frequency electric transmission, have enabled man to tame rivers with impunity.

This is patently a condition out of which society must plan its way, but what is even more significant, there is superimposed upon this secular trend in waste and careless exploitation a cyclical trend of feverish overproduction and economic collapse, the cure for which is not entirely known. It is certain that in the face of the terrible efficiency of our modern economic system the old principles of economics appear to be gone, the old relationships of geography vanished. We are discovering that in technological improvement man has created a juggernaut which crashes its way through the stored riches of the ages, piling up a surplus of goods produced from natural resources, while man may starve in the midst of over-plenty. Periodically, the whole machinery stalls from the sheer weight of this surplusage. Moreover, the individual cannot plan against the emergency of such a situation. During the recent crisis in Germany, for example, even the shrewdest classes—bankers, brokers, and stock-market experts—probably saved little more than 50 per cent of their assets; landowners salvaged perhaps 30 per cent; the small saver and investor rescued an amount between 3 and 5 per cent. The remainder was wiped out in the process of economic collapse. In view of these facts it would seem that society as a whole must evolve a plan for control. The official expression of society is government, the highest form of which is the nation. Upon this latter rests some sort of responsibility for planning for society. National planning of some kind is therefore imperative.

PLANNING UNDER THE "NEW DEAL"

National planning is not a new thing in the United States. Indeed, since its very inception, the national government has carried on certain forms of planning for the development of human and physical resources. Except in times of national emergency, as for instance during the Great War of 1914-1918, this has, however, been short-range, partial planning often without major objective and frequently colored by partisan considerations. The national Committee on Social Trends, set up during the administration of President Hoover, seems to have marked the first attempt to secure a long-range view of the national situation.

After the economic fiasco during and subsequent to 1929, the so-called "New Deal" was conceived and erected as a set of devices for working the nation out of its difficulties. These included the Civilian Conservation Corps, the Civil Works Administration, the National Industrial Recovery Administration, the Agricultural Adjustment Administration, the Petroleum Administrative Board, the National Power Survey of the Federal Power Commission, Rural Electrification Administration, Resettlement Administration, the Federal Surplus Relief Corporation, Federal Emergency Relief Administration, Federal Emergency Administration of Public Works, and several other agencies.

It was soon realized that in order to emerge from the nation's difficulties it would be necessary to plan the way out, and that action without a forward-looking program would probably be unfruitful. As a consequence a planning section or division was attached to each of these new agencies. These planning units were, of course, limited in their scope and often restricted by administrative policies immediately above them. The programs which were devised were, as a result, functional and departmental rather than long-time, continuing, over-all national programs. Such programs in operation unavoidably led to duplication, overlapping, and even conflict in policy.

In 1933, however, the seeds of real national planning were planted, when a small organization known as the National Planning Board was unobtrusively created and enjoined with the following duties:

1. To coordinate federal planning activities.
2. To stimulate state and local planning.
3. To advise the administrator of PWA on the progress and programs of public works.

4. To formulate a plan for national planning.

During the ensuing year the National Planning Board discharged these duties successfully and in addition demonstrated that national planning should be identified with the whole movement for conservation of national resources. Moreover, its accomplishments proved so significant that on June 30, 1934, it was recreated by executive order as an independent agency—the National Resources Board. This organization continued to discharge the four duties of its predecessor, the National Planning Board, and in addition it was directed by the President to make a detailed inventory of, and a general plan for, the use of the nation's resources. In June, 1935, the Board was again recreated by executive order, this time as the National Resources Committee. Since that date, its central staff has continued its efforts toward coordinating federal planning activities, advising on public works programs, and encouraging state and local planning. The Committee has comprised seven planning subcommittees—land, water, minerals, power, transportation, industry, and labor. In addition, from time to time several technical subcommittees have been set up to deal with such problems as regionalism, urbanism, allocation of public works costs, stream pollution, and industrial capacity. In May, 1935, a bill (S 2825) was presented in the Senate by Senator Copeland, to establish a permanent National Planning Board of five members. It is believed by many to be imperative that the nation possess such an agency; that it is needed to bring together materials upon which future programs can be based. Its powers should be broad, but only advisory. It would not be a spending agency nor would it be assigned the duties of initiating proposals for spending. Rather it would seem to be a means of effecting conservation and economy through the elimination of duplication, indirection, and ill-advised development of resources. Such an agency should be an intelligence organ of the executive branch of the national government which has long been needed, and which will become increasingly necessary as society grows more complex and the margin of resource use becomes narrower.

COMPLETE PRODUCTION PLANNING

The activities of the New Deal do not constitute national planning in any complete sense. Planning for the national economy, in order to be complete, would involve the following steps: first, complete inventory and codification of resources, natural and human; second, determination of the consumption capacities of the nation under different standards of living; third, an inventory of the conversion factors and conversion equipment now in existence; fourth, adjusting conversion ratios to consumption needs. This last operation involves three stages of activity: (*a*) deciding upon a desired level of economic consumption, (*b*) creating the proper conversion capacity to supply the population at this consumption level, and (*c*) ear-marking those natural resources to be exploited and used for creating economic goods.

No such planning procedure, however, is possible within our existing socio-economic order. It is a recognized method of solution which would probably work effectively, but which cannot work because it is dictatorial and hence incompatible with the social, economic, and political objectives of the American people. Dictatorships tend to arise during periods of despair or economic collapse, and America seems to be neither in despair nor in collapse. In Russia, where dictatorship is perhaps most complete, there was a breakdown of the whole economic and social system. In the new order which is arising there, planning and government have become synonymous functions with more or less success. In the United States, where the system did not collapse but was merely stalled, the New Deal was the non-revolutionary attempt on the part of the government of the American people to plan its way back to normal on a rather short-time program. Conservation plus long-range planning of some sort, however, would seem to be a more effective answer to such recurring crises, and to constitute the best measure for postponing whatever scarcity may occur in the realm of physical resources.

National planning in America can neither go to the extremes nor employ the methods used in Russia, Germany, Italy, or other countries under dictatorships. Even the American New Deal may be transitory because of its direct intervention into our free economy. To a large degree, it is likely to follow into oblivion the War Industries Board, the War Trade Board, the War Shipping Board, and other devices for emergency planning and control evolved two decades earlier. It is obvious that any permanent national planning in the United States must be of restricted scope unless wide-spread changes, which are not now foreseen, occur. The experience of the national planning agency indicates that the following may be carried on successfully and fruitfully: (1) inventorying of resources and formulation of recommended programs of resource use and conservation; (2) the development of coordinate planning, i.e., the rationalizing and integrating of federal and state development programs; (3) maintenance of an alert attitude which shall forestall waste, rationalize public works improvements, coordinate federal administrative efforts, and consistently attempt to educate the people toward voluntary adoption of desired objectives.

There are some, however, who believe that certain forms of production planning will also eventuate. David Cushman Doyle expresses this in the following words:

> Two kinds of production planning are evidently unavoidable. One is the control and allocation of limited and irreplaceable natural resources. Any sort of economic system which will let the engineers produce what they can produce will soon run up against the limits of certain raw materials, and then conservation will cease to be questionable by anybody. The other field for production planning is in the industries which naturally tend to become monopolies, such as power, communication, transportation, and some others—a list that will perhaps grow with time.[1]

THE PRESENT SCOPE OF NATIONAL PLANNING

In the preceding paragraphs, the case for and against a national planning which would include programming and regulating the entire socio-economic structure has been presented briefly. Regardless of what might be desirable, however, national planning in the United States has been and probably will continue to be largely restricted to physical planning. This is shown clearly both by the work of the National Resources Committee and by the reports of the state planning boards which it has fostered.

State Planning, Its Development. State planning began in an experimental way a good many years ago, but only during the last six years has it assumed definite and organized form. In 1933, the National Resources Committee (then known as the National Planning Board) undertook to encourage and sponsor planning in the states, as stated in the preceding chapter. The response was immediate, and very shortly forty-six planning boards or commissions were in operation. Most of these have prepared and released progress reports and preliminary plans. An examination of the state planning reports which have already appeared shows that planning officials have, so far, engaged in two types of activities: first, the collection of data which deal with functions, trends, and specific areas; second, the formulation of programs and policies wherein improved socio-economic patterns are to replace existing maladjustments. The major items (listed in a different form in the preceding chapter) dealt with may be classified as follows:

[1] David Cushman Coyle, *The Irrepressible Conflict—Business Versus Finance*, 101 Park Ave., New York, 1933, p. 16.

1. Land resources and use.
2. Water resources and use.
3. Mineral resources and use.
4. Manufactural resources and development.
5. Commerce and commercial assets.
6. Transportation facilities and patterns.
7. Urban formations and their problems.
8. Population trends and characteristics.
9. Recreational needs and resources.
10. Social conditions and institutions.
11. Local government and public services.
12. Public works needs and programs.

An analysis of this list of topics serves to show that the planner has been interested in three things: (*a*) the basic resources of the natural environment, (*b*) the pattern of cultural works and constructions, and (*c*) the inherent relationships which exist between the two. Grouped together, these indicate strongly that the programming now under way is largely one of physical planning.

National Planning Leads to Regional Planning. Physical planning is primarily a matter of designing a pattern of human works and constructions which will bear harmonious relations to the underlying resources. Since these resources vary from one part of the country to another, it should be obvious that plans for their fullest and wisest use must also differ from one part of the country to another. Although both existing maladjustments in resource use and proposed readjustments are related to trends and functions, they are even more closely related to specific areas. In other words, over-all programs and policies may be formulated for social and economic functions in general, but detailed physical planning must always produce plans to fit specific areas. If this be so, the nature, extent, and degree of homogeneity of the area over which planning is exercised are of major importance.

At the very outset, it becomes obvious that the physical planning of resource-use cannot be done for the nation as a whole. The national area is too large and too lacking in homogeneity to be viewed from a single vantage point. Moreover, in different parts of the country the inhabitants vary greatly in their sentiments and attitudes toward conservation and planning programs. One of the major concerns of the planner becomes, therefore, a search for a sphere of jurisdiction—a unit of area which will provide both reasonable physical and economic homogeneity, and approximately unity of public opinion.

Approaches to Planning. In searching for a workable approach to planning, a number of avenues have been developed. *First,* there are those which have been developed by the groups interested in a single commodity (wheat, corn, cotton, hogs) or a single industry (textiles, leather manufacture, retail grocery) or a single service (medicine, banking). Group interests founded upon such bases are important directive factors in the modern world and have been given governmental recognition in the formulation of policy, as for example under the AAA and NRA. *Second,* there are those avenues to planning which have been developed by the various departments and bureaus of the federal and state governments. These include the administration and handling of forest and range land, disposal of minerals of the public domain, development of navigable waterways, and many similar functions. Such departmentalized activities require careful and detailed programming and the integration of administrative effort at different levels of government. *Third,* there are those avenues to planning which have been developed by those governmental agencies which perform important scientific functions, the United States Geological Survey, the Bureau of Biological Survey, the Hydrographic Survey, the Weather Bureau, the Federal Board of Surveys and Maps, the Coast and Geodetic Survey, and numerous others. Thus, planning may be and is being approached variously by commodities and industries, by nature-determined functions, and by various levels of organized government. The adoption of a national policy dictated by such single interests frequently creates serious problems of incompatibility and maladjustment. There is, therefore, a fundamental necessity for relating the various interests and their peculiar contributions into a uniform and integrated national program.

When one begins a search for a way in which to accomplish this, he is led directly to the realization that these various factors and interests must be related and integrated areally at their point of occurrence. The implications of this is that detailed planning can be successful only when applied to specific areas, i.e., *when it becomes regional planning.* The planner has, therefore, been led to a search for a subnational unit of area, which will furnish him a wieldy and manageable region. At first thought it may be assumed that such regional units have already been supplied by our existing system of counties and states.

> A long step forward has been taken in the direction of more effective utilization of the natural and human resources of the different states, and if this beginning goes forward at the present rate, we

may reasonably look forward to striking improvements in the organization of affairs of the type with which a state may deal. City planning, county planning, and state planning, taken together, are being developed and coordinated in a manner which cannot fail to promote the advantage of state and local communities.[1]

States Not Satisfactory Units for Planning. In spite of the general fruitfulness of state planning, the states are far from being satisfactory regional units. They are not homogeneous areas, and they do not individually contain most of the larger resource problems needing treatment. Their major virtue lies in the fact that (*a*) they are already existing sub-national units, and (*b*) they possess the sovereign power to plan and carry out planned programs. Resources and resource problems requiring attention, however, are not distributed with any regard for political boundaries and consequently are usually interstate in extent and character. The incidence of such problems is becoming more serious as time passes, and numerous devices such as interstate compact authorities have been devised for dealing with them. Most frequently, the responsibility for the solution of interstate problems has fallen to the federal government. This has happened even where the problems involved have had no direct national significance.

If the problem be of concern to the nation as a whole, as for example the improvement of a large navigable waterway, federal action and responsibility are clearly appropriate. But in many respects the federal government is very limited in its sovereignty, and it is obliged to secure, from the states involved, the power to act, even though none of the states is by itself able to act. Thus there are many physical and social problems which are subnational rather than national, and which cannot, therefore, be acted upon by the federal government, and at the same time they are interstate in their extent and hence cannot be handled by any one state. Such problems may be described as regional rather than state or national. For dealing with interstate regional problems, as, for example, the making of a forest program in the Great Lakes area, the development of water power in the southern Appalachians, or the retirement of poor farm land and the resettlement of population on the Great Plains, there is a marked need for some kind of regional planning unit intermediate between the state and the nation. So generally inadequate for planning purposes are state lines that planners are already seeking other types of regions whose extent will be coincident with the distribution of resources and problems requiring treatment.

[1] National Resources Board, "State Planning—A Review of Activities and Progress," Government Printing Office, June, 1935, Washington, D. C., p. xii.

Psychological Regionalism. In addition to these physical and administrational aspects a second consideration enters into the equation. This has been called psychological regionalism. In spite of the sovereignty of the forty-eight states, and the recent resurrection of the issue of "state rights" by state political interests, social differentiation and larger social and economic loyalties do not follow state lines. Instead, they cut across such boundaries, and emerge as large sections or regions. They are so strong in many instances as to constitute a claim on the part of the people of certain sections such as the Pacific Northwest, New England, and elsewhere, that they must be allowed to do their own planning, and carry out the development of their own resources. Such a spontaneous interest in conservation, planning, and local development is too significant to be ignored and too potentially useful to be neglected. Consequently, the national planner is seeking a division of the country into regional units which will not only provide for an interstate level of action and responsibility, but will also harness and turn to constructive account these larger sectional sentiments and consciousness.

VARIOUS TYPES OF PLANNING REGIONS

As the need for regional planning for the nation has become more and more apparent, various types of regional divisions have been proposed. Such proposals have originated from many different premises, and are of course of varying degrees of usefulness. All of them are aimed at a common objective—to find areal divisions of the country which will encompass the particular combinations of resources and problems requiring unified interstate treatment. Among the many proposals, five types of regions would seem worthy of note: (1) group-of-states arrangements, (2) metropolitan influence, (3) administrative convenience, (4) single-function areas, and (5) composite-function areas.

Group-of-states Units. *Group-of-states arrangements* as planning regions exhibit many of the weaknesses of individual states. Although such regions do bring together parts of problems near their cores, they leave fragmented most of those about their peripheries. Upon examination, therefore, it becomes apparent that there are no single combinations of states which will bring about even a passable segregation of resources. (See Fig. 1.) The only solution on this basis would be to form temporary combinations of states to deal with certain major problems as they arise, and after these problems were treated, the combination would be dissolved and recombinations brought about. Such temporary and multiple participation of states in planning and resources development must in the end serve to destroy all identity of regions as such, and to defeat most of the psychological virtues of regional planning. In spite of these shortcomings, two planning regions have already been set up on this premise—New England and the Pacific Northwest. Moreover, several of the federal

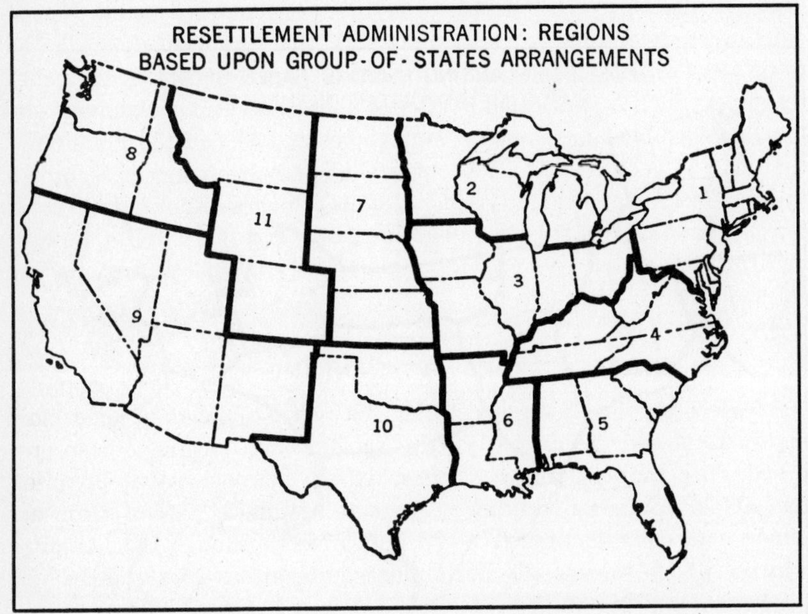

Courtesy National Resources Board

FIG. 1.

bureaus base their field regions on this principle, and the Council of State Governments seems to be thinking in terms of this premise in its projected regional program.

Metropolitan Regions. *Metropolitan influence* is one of the most obvious phenomena in modern society, and therefore to regard cities as the nuclei of regional planning is, indeed, tempting. Figure 2 shows a division of the United States into seventeen regions on the basis of major metropolitan influence. The concept of regions delineated on this basis possesses a certain validity, but it overlooks the fact that not all large cities are actual regional foci, but are more often supra-regional creatures. Even were this not true, regions delineated in terms of metropolises are of dubious value for planning. Cities are social organisms which would seem to be primarily concerned with their own alimentation rather than with the condition of the peoples and resources in their tributary areas. For this reason, regions defined in terms of metropolitanism might not prove to be desirable units for national planning.

Administrative-convenience Units. It has been proposed to create national planning regions by using convenience of administra-

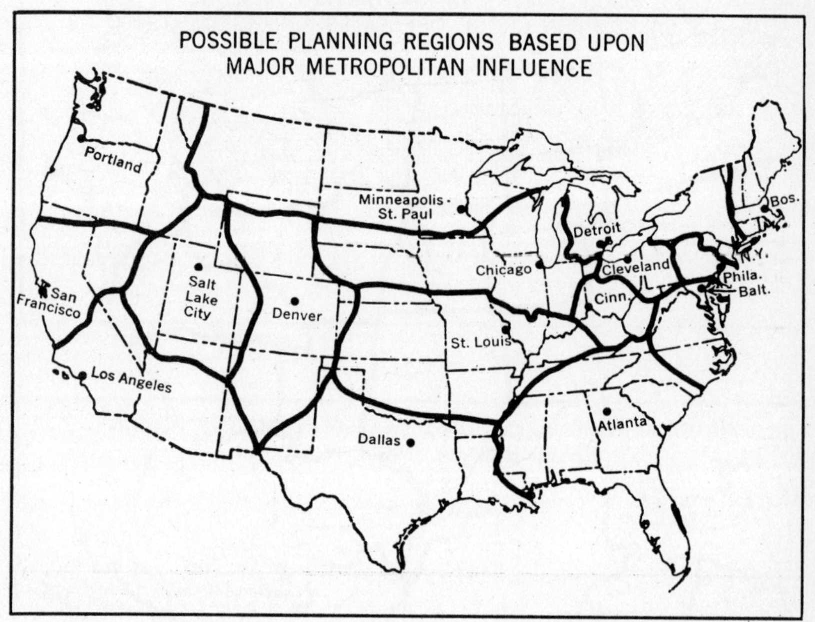

Courtesy National Resources Board

Fig. 2.

tion as a major premise for their delineation. This might be accomplished by selecting, on the basis of administrative convenience, some twenty cities to serve as sub-national planning centers. (See Fig. 3.) These would presumably be chosen by reason of their accessibility by rail, air, and highway, and their possession of libraries, universities, federal field offices, and other conveniences for planners. To each would be assigned arbitrary units of territory for planning jurisdiction. This is the method of regionalization employed by a majority of the federal bureaus in establishing their field offices, but it overlooks the truth that rarely do factors of convenience coincide with the distribution of the elements to be administered.

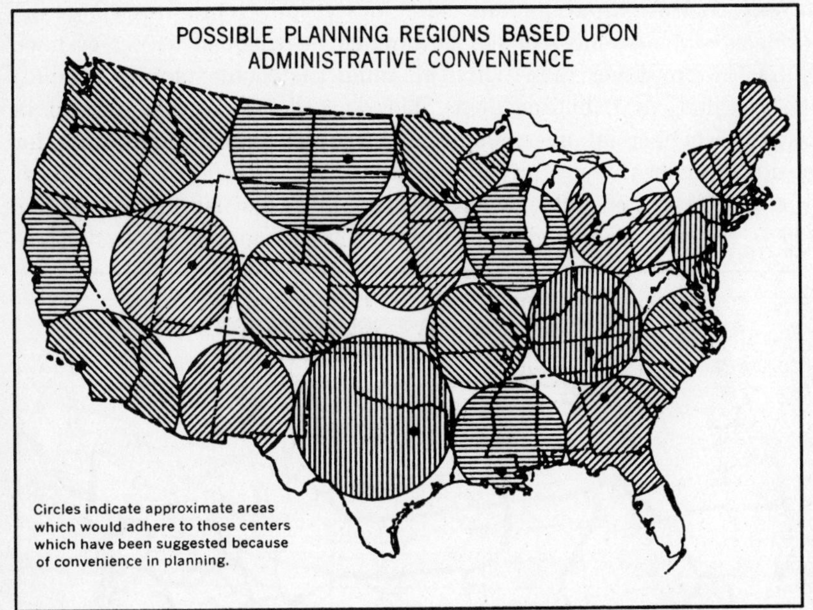

Courtesy National Resources Board

FIG. 3.

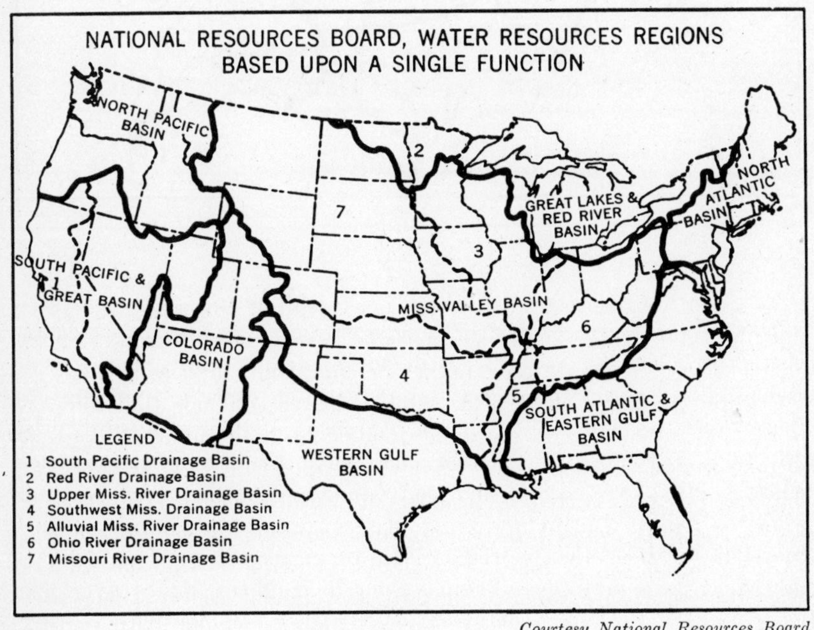

Courtesy National Resources Board

FIG. 4.

Single Function Regions. Regions may be and frequently are delineated on the basis of the areal extent of single *resources* or *functions.* For purposes of national planning the country might logically be divided into hydrographic, floral, pedologic, transportational, faunal, commercial, metropolitan, agricultural, and numerous other types of regions, few if any of which would be coincident. (See Figs. 4 and 5.) This is entirely logical, and would be workable if total plan-

Courtesy National Resources Board

FIG. 5.

ning were to emanate from the national capital. But under a system such as ours, where planning must be decentralized, such a multiplicity of regions could only make for complexity and confusion.

Composite Regional Units. One is led to conclude that, in order to have genuine regional planning, it must be based upon a *composite of factors and elements,* both human and physical. It is at this point that the geographic region becomes a useful concept. This type of region has been defined as an area characterized by general unity in its human ecology. A major geographic principle is that, in an area where resources are roughly uniform throughout, there is permitted the development of a general socio-economic homogeneity. The basis for determining the lineaments of major regionalism within the nation is inherent in such a principle. Indeed, this has to a certain extent already emerged spontaneously, as is revealed by the common use of such terms as the Middle West, the South, the East, the Pacific Northwest, and other endemic regional designations. Such regions, if their outlines be left sufficiently flexible, would seem to be fairly satisfactory sub-national divisions for decentralized national planning. Moreover, they possess added virtues of being readily identifiable, and of

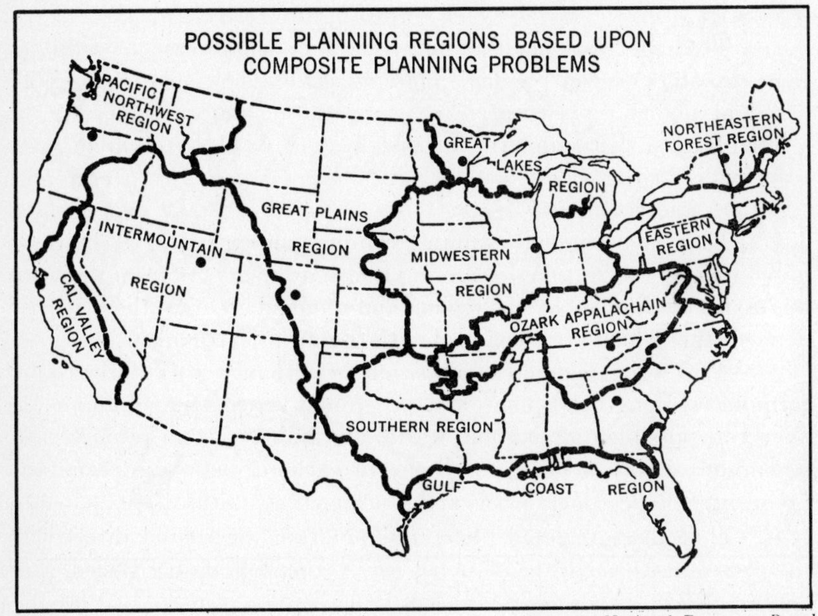

Courtesy National Resources Board

Fig. 6.

expressing already existing regional loyalty and consciousness to which planning can be harnessed. (See Fig. 6.)

ORGANIZATION FOR REGIONAL PLANNING

Early in 1935, the president expressed a desire that the National Resources Committee investigate the possibility of the regional handling of planning and resource development. Accordingly, that agency set up a technical subcommittee, consisting of an engineer, a geographer, and two political scientists, to study the problem and report on ways and means for making national regional planning a reality.[1]

The technical subcommittee made the following recommendations:

(*a*) That there be established a permanent National Planning Board, to act as a part of the presidential staff. The formulation of national policy for submission to the Congress is a presidential function, and hence in order to facilitate the discharge of this function of the president, the Board should be engaged in the evaluation and clarification of the national situation as regards resources and their conservation, public works, and federal policies in relation to the legislative arm.

(*b*) That the National Planning Board be empowered to establish approximately eleven regional planning commissions, with offices located at points representative of each of the major regions of the United States, the boundaries of such regions to be left flexible so as to provide for the widest possible latitude in dealing with overlapping functions and resources.

(*c*) That each regional planning commission consist of a chairman appointed by the National Planning Board, of members from the various states overlapped by the region, and of members from those federal departments which are concerned with resource development.

(*d*) That each regional commission be enjoined with the task of formulating long-time plans and programs, which will eliminate, as nearly as possible, duplication, waste, and indirection in resource use, and improve the facilities for living in each region, these plans and programs to reflect local needs and sentiments as faithfully as possible.

(*e*) That these regional plans and programs be routed directly to the president, through the offices of the National Planning Board, thus insuring that local desires and needs will receive executive and legislative attention without having to flow through political channels as is now the case.

(*f*) That the National Planning Board coordinate and integrate all regional programs and bring them into harmony with the larger issues of national policy.

(*g*) That the various bureaus of the federal government be encouraged to seek some uniformity in field administration instead of continuing to use 108 different sets of regions as at present, and that some

[1] John M. Gaus, Jacob Crane, Marshall E. Dimock, and George T. Renner: "Regional Factors in National Planning and Development," Report of the National Resources Committee, December, 1935, Government Printing Office, Washington, D. C.

attempts be made in the interest of economy and convenience to render such administrative units coincident with whatever national planning regions may be evolved.

From a careful analysis of conservation problems facing the American people, it is obvious that neither a national planning board on the one hand, nor several regional planning commissions on the other, would alone be sufficient. Both are needed in any balanced program. American political philosophy has always recognized that the interests of the whole nation transcend the interests of any group or section. Many of these national interests are not regional at all, but involve balances and controls within the total structure. To deal with these, a national planning board is necessary. Some of the problems to be dealt with by such a national agency would be: the devising of a national conservation policy, the promotion of cooperation between different levels of government within the nation, the formulation of policies governing the division of costs and responsibilities for public works, the consideration of federal subvention for equalization between rich and poor states and cities, the balancing of industry and agriculture, and many others.

Another major premise of our political philosophy is that local policies are best determined locally, a matter which will render necessary several regional planning commissions, "A regional planning organization, whatever its varied form, should not be considered as a new form of sovereignty, even in embryo. It need never to develop to the stage where it would possess elected officers, a legislative body, or the power to tax."[1] "Despite the weakness of an entity without sovereignty, the regional planning commissions can be made strong and useful if they be carefully built and if the federal and state executives are willing to give them preferential treatment."[2]

THE DEVELOPMENT OF NATIONAL RESOURCES

National resources are at present developed through three channels: (1) the initiative of private business, (2) the functional programs of the departments and bureaus of the federal and state governments, and (3) public works at all levels of government. Development bears an obvious relation to planning. Consequently, as society becomes more complex, and as the need for planning increases, resource development, even at the hands of private business, must of necessity be subjected to

[1] National Resources Committee, Report to the President, December, 1935.

[2] David Cushman Coyle, "The Planning of Public Works," memorandum to the National Resources Committee, November, 1935.

increasing regulation. Developmental undertakings under governmental initiative, on the other hand, should originate from and be entirely dependent upon planning. Particularly is this true in regard to large-scale public works which are so often interstate in character. Problems which transcend state boundaries are increasing in number and importance, a circumstance which has necessitated that they be handled in one of two ways: Either interstate compacts and authorities have been set up to deal with them at the state level, or else they have been thrown to the federal government for solution. Since the sovereignty of the federal government is limited, its treatment of most problems has either had to be hung precariously upon premises of national defense or general welfare and carried out by the federal bureaus, or else provided for by specially created corporate authorities.

Federal Corporate Units. The slowness and general weakness of the alternative interstate compact method of dealing with major problems of resource development have made attractive the federal corporate regional authority, as for example the TVA. Consequently, numerous bills have recently been proposed seeking to create, by congressional action, federal regional corporate authorities. A map depicting the areal units for large-scale construction and development so far proposed or in operation (see Fig. 7) reveals that almost without exception they are identified with river drainage basins. In general, this does not appear to be a very satisfactory basis for regional delineation, but it seems to be a result of the fact that Congress possesses authority over all navigable rivers and their tributaries in the United States. Upon such a slender peg can be hung the improvement of navigation, the control of flood waters, the erection of locks and dams, and the generation of electric power. The sale of the resulting cheap power can provide a means of improving living conditions, the encouragement of desirable industrial development, and many other phases of social and economic planning. The control of flood waters would lead into erosion control, reforestation, wild-game protection, forest management, land classification, and land-use planning in general.

Hydrographic Units Not Desirable. Congressional authority over navigable streams thus forms a ready ingress to performing a variety of needed operations, and this has tended to fix the region for development in terms of hydrographic areas in nearly all instances. This is probably not desirable because in the long run, in any planned national program, there will be many needed improvements which cannot be tied to navigable waterways. The map (Fig. 7) shows that, were all the proposals for improvement authorities to become law, more than half of the nation would be put directly under federal improvement authorities. This does not appear to be desirable even in the face of the fact that the temptation for the localities to secure resource development by means of federal monies is very great indeed.

The Federal Government cannot successfully assume the detailed management of all the public affairs of the American people, even if

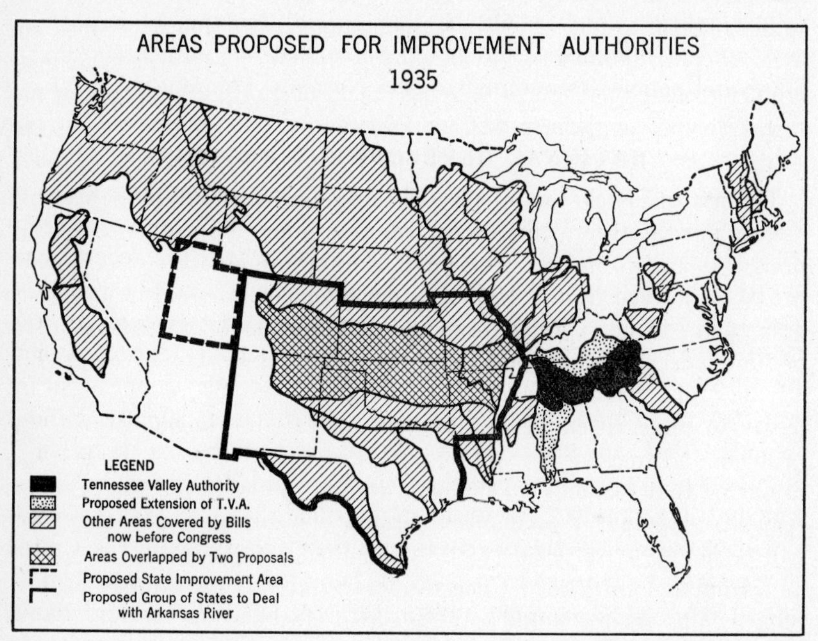

Courtesy National Resources Board

FIG. 7.

it would. State and local governments are necessary, and they should not be left without work to do and responsibility to assume. Federal grants are desirable as a redistribution and equalization measure, and they may also be used to reward a local willingness to cooperate with state and regional plans. But where a project requires a local moral support, it should have a measure of local financial support as a means of giving the local people an interest in its success.[1]

In order to effectuate this there is needed a permanent national development administration, as part of the federal government. It would unite all the desirable functions and powers now residing in the Federal Emergency Administration of Public Works, the Works

[1] David Cushman Coyle, *ibid.*

Progress Administration, the Allotment Committee, the Federal Employment Stabilization Office, and perhaps a few other agencies.[1]

There is needed a clear-cut allocation of responsibility for public works costs which will divide the expenditures for constructions and improvements among the several levels of government. For this reason, the state improvement authority, the interstate compact authority, and possibly a joint federal-state or federal-interstate authority need to be thoroughly explored. In any event, the allocation of costs and responsibilities which would be the especial function of a national development administration should be carried out only according to plans and policies formulated by the National Planning Board.

NATIONAL DEVELOPMENT REGIONS

The natural clustering of physical and human problems demanding developmental treatment almost compels some sort of regional approach to their solution. Certain it is that far greater total benefits are to be derived from a composite development program in any given area than can be expected from the development of its isolated parts or functions. It may be pointed out, however, that "no one can say in advance just what inter-state groupings should be made, until the desire to solve an emergency problem reveals the lineaments of that problem and suggests the appropriate structure."[2] This is another way of saying that regional development should follow rather than precede regional planning. A permanent national development administration, which should be concerned with the detailed administration of policies as formulated in acts of Congress, would greatly expedite such procedure. This agency would establish field offices in the various project areas, whether drainage basins or other types of areal units, undergoing improvement programs. Regional offices of the National Development Administration will not, of course, coincide with those of the National Planning Board, but they should be closely coordinated with them.

CONCLUSION AND SUMMARY

There is very great need of long-term national planning for the use of our physical and human resources. To achieve this, there is needed a permanent national planning board on the one hand, and a national

[1] National Resources Board Report, December, 1934.

[2] Pacific Northwest Regional Planning Commission, *The Columbia Basin Study,* Portland, Oregon, November, 1935, Vol. III, p. 298.

development administration on the other. In order to render national planning really effective, the central planning agency should be located at regional centers where state and local interests can participate in the making of plans and programs.

Regional planning centers should be established in those areas where there occurs a major clustering of related resources coincident with a marked regional consciousness among the inhabitants. At each planning center there should be formulated a plan which when administered will achieve conservation of resources, better facilities for living, and an improved regional economy.

In the end, there will have been formulated for each region:

1. A land-use program, including population resettlement, erosion-control work on marginal and submarginal lands, improved land use, and so forth.
2. A water-use program.
3. A rationalized pattern for transportation.
4. A reforestation, forest management, and forest protection program.
5. A wild-game and fisheries restoration and management program.
6. An electrification program which will coordinate the power facilities so that they will operate as a single system.
7. An industrial program, including relocation of industries and the establishment of new industries.
8. Social and economic improvement programs.

Provision should be made for the channeling of the views and plans of a region directly to the chief executive of the nation, thus removing the obstacles and hurdles of the present political routing. At the same time, the views and attitudes of the federal government should flow directly back to the region. Under our existing constitutional set-up, however, planning and the carrying out of plans cannot coincide. Adequate provision must be made, therefore, for machinery which will carry out faithfully and effectively those regional plans which have been given approval.

Almost as important as the making of regional plans is the need for equalization between rich and poor areas.

> The function of federal taxation in drawing money from rich or creditor areas and bestowing it upon poor or debtor areas is essential to the permanent continuance of uninterrupted flow of trade between the states. In fact, the inadequate performance of that function is the basic cause of the many "quarantines," "buy at home" campaigns, and similar interferences with free trade in debtor areas.

In dealing with federal subsidy programs, the national development agency will be obliged to take cognizance of dying localities where no new constructions should be undertaken. Owing to the political implications of a judgment as to the future of any area, the most careful planning of administrative machinery is needed. Otherwise judgment will be impossible and heavy federal expenditures must be made at places where later events will show them to have been unwise. Ultimately the National Planning Board will need to arrange for a general land-use planning study of the United States. Areas adjudged wholly submarginal will need to be vacated at federal expense—including not only purchase of land but also assumption of public debts. Areas adjudged worth occupying will need to be built up to a tolerable standard of living, primarily by directing industries into those areas by such means as differential railroad rates and cheap power. Federal subsidy, by way of public works, will serve as a definite implement of land-use planning, after such plans are available and have been approved by the Congress.[1]

In conclusion it may be reiterated that

Planning as a system and as to organization should be built up from the bottom. The essential of planning is the dealing with natural resources, and these are best understood in the localities. Any attempt at national planning which leaves the localities behind tends to bring about defeat of the use of the plan when finally adopted. The necessity for decentralization of planning efforts and the building of organization and plans from the bottom toward the top should be stressed at all times. The national planning unit should rely upon the regional planning unit, the regional upon the state, and the state upon the local unit, as largely as can be done. These principles are considered necessary under a democratic system, planning cannot proceed far ahead of public understanding. Progress of the planning movement is dependent upon popular and legislative support. . . . The effective liaison between citizens and governmental agencies is of the essence of planning, it should be developed still further and more closely, so that the leaders in each field of resource development will feel that they are participating with the government in plans for conservation and development. It is also of the essence of sound planning that it should constitute an active working partnership between government and private citizen.[2]

In a period such as the present, it is inevitable that government must expand its functions in many ways not hitherto necessary. It is particularly gratifying to see, along with the expansion of Federal and state government activities, the increasing interest in the very democratic procedure represented by the work of the local planning agencies. It is essentially an organized and continuing effort of

[1] David Cushman Coyle, *ibid.*

[2] Pacific Northwest Regional Planning Commission, *The Columbia Basin Study,* Portland, Oregon, November, 1935, 5 vols., Vol. I, pp. 33-34.

public-spirited citizens and officials in each community to think in terms of the community's best present and future development.[1]

I suppose the way to approach the matter is to consider first just what is a national plan. Do we have such a thing? The answer to that is "yes." There is one in the making. . . . It is a plan whose purpose is to bring better, fuller lives to the people of America. It seeks to conserve the basic resources of the nation, upon a broad scale and with a view to the future. By this means it is intended that the livelihood of this and succeeding generations may be insured. But beyond the conservation, utilization, and development of resources, the plan aims to provide for the progressive improvement of our physical environment, to better the conditions under which all of us live and work and play. Briefly then, the plan that is in the making seeks to guarantee in perpetuity opportunity for all our citizens to make a living, and beyond this, makes provision for the enjoyment of life, for the satisfaction and enrichments which must be added to mere existence to convert it into real living.

So much by way of a hasty sketch of the national plan which is in the making. How is it being developed and by whom? The protection and husbanding of our natural resources—the soil we need for farming, the water for agriculture, for city supply, for navigation and power, our forests, our coal, our minerals—these are the proper province of the federal and state governments. The improvement of community living conditions is, of course, the function of local governments in town, city and county.[2]

[1] Robert H. Randall: "Organization of City and County Planning Boards," address before the National Resources Committee, Southeastern Planning Conference, Savannah, Georgia, December 4, 1935.

[2] Robert H. Randall, "The Part of the Municipalities in the National Plan," in *The Municipality*, Wisconsin Municipal Utilities Association, Madison, Wisconsin, December, 1935, p. 237.

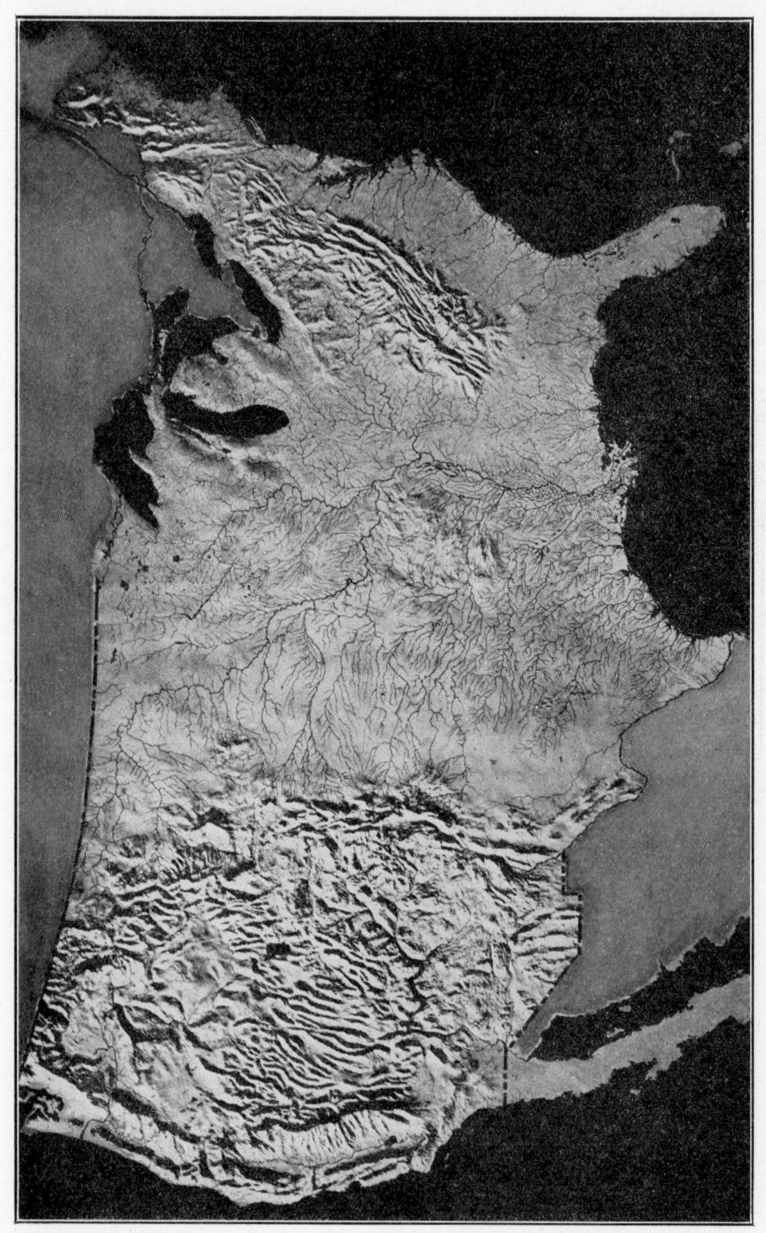

Fig. 1. The United States in Relief—U.S.G.S.

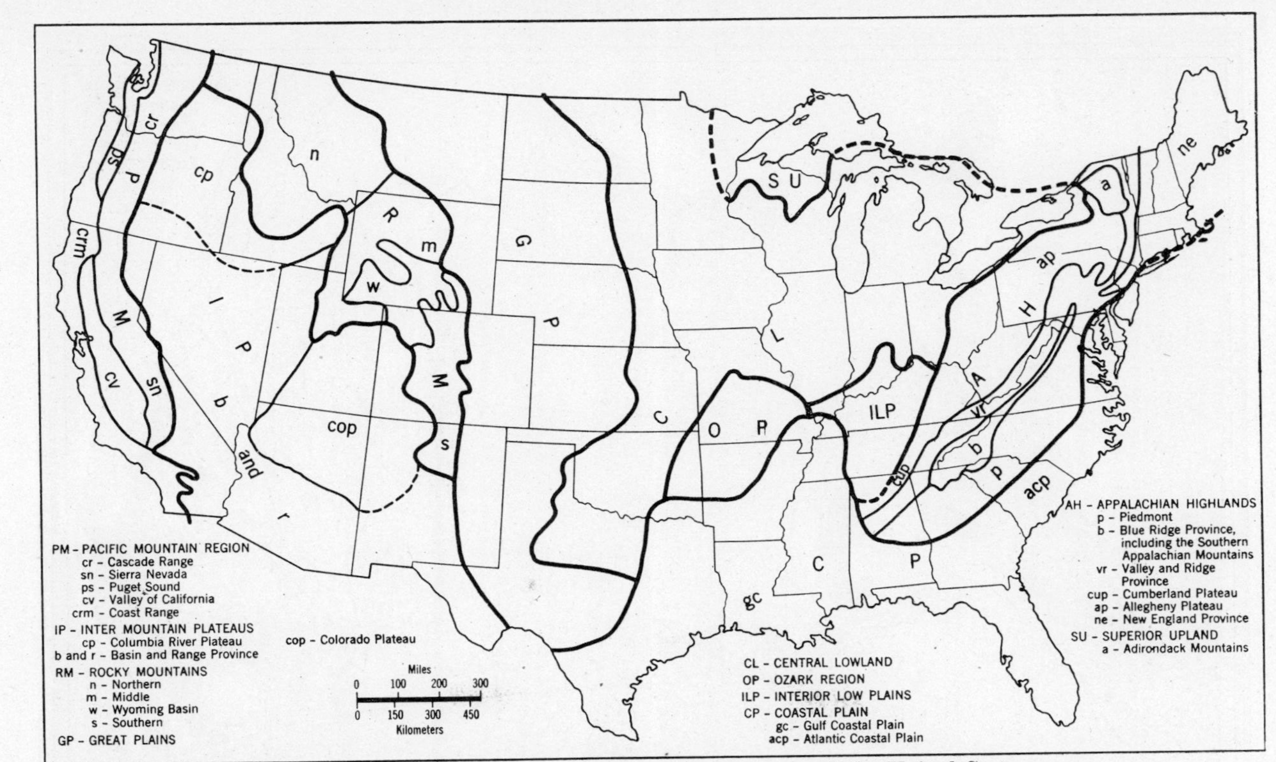

FIG. 2. Boundaries of the Physiographic Provinces of the United States.

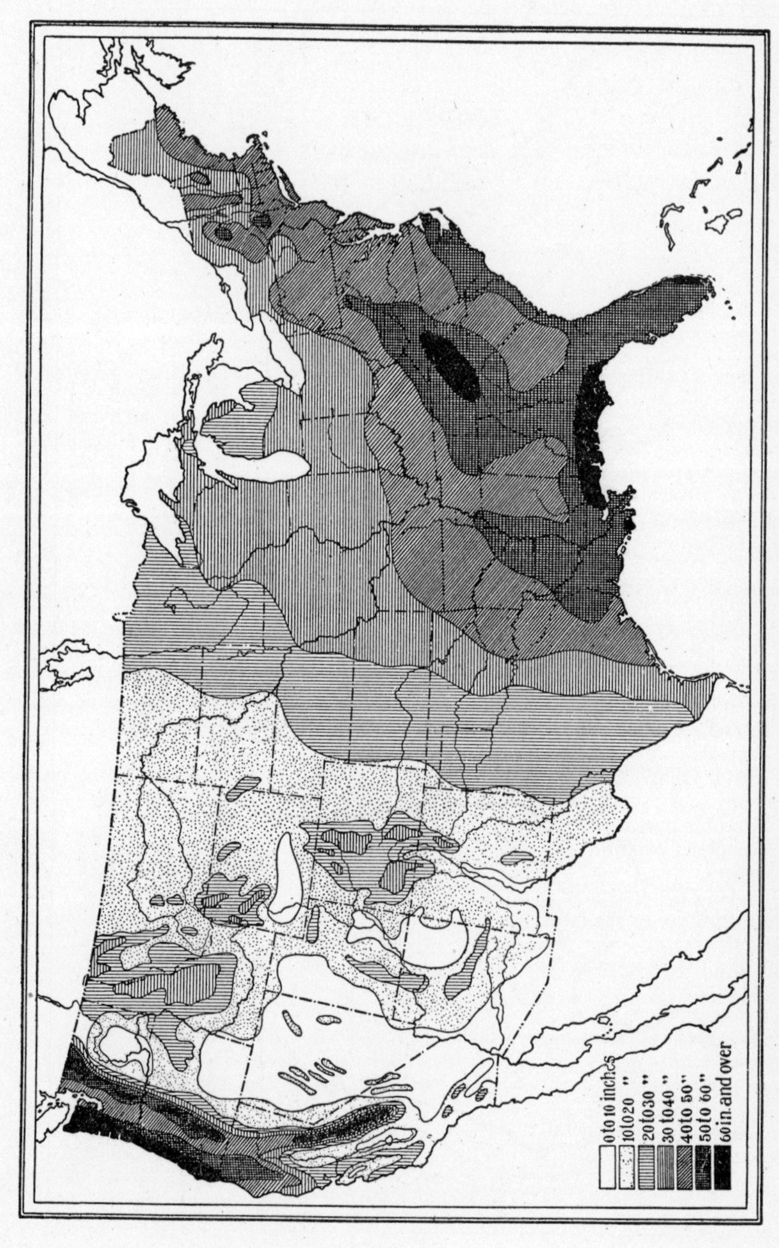

Fig. 3. Mean Annual Rainfall in the United States. (After Gannett, from Data of U. S. Weather Bureau.)

APPENDIX

BASAL DATA RELATED TO THE AGRICULTURAL RESOURCES OF THE UNITED STATES AND THEIR UTILIZATION (1930)

Prepared by A. E. Parkins

(Data from the Census and the *Statistical Abstract*)

Total area of continental United States	3,027,000 square miles or 1,903,217,000 acres
Rural population	53,820,000 (43.8 per cent of total)
Rural-farm population	30,445,000 (24.8 per cent of total)
Rural-nonfarm population	23,663,000
Urban-farm population	287,000
Total number of farms	6,289,000
All land in farms	986,771,000 acres (51.8 per cent of total area)
Cropland	413,236,000 acres
Harvested in 1929	359,242,000
Crop failures in 1929	12,707,000
Idle or fallow	41,287,000
Pasture land	464,156,000
Plowable pasture	109,160,000
Woodland pasture	85,322,000
Others	269,073,000
Woodland not pastured	64,624,000
Average acres to the farm	156.9
Value of all farm property	$57,245,544,000
Land	34,929,845,000
Buildings	12,949,994,000
Implements and machinery	3,301,654,000
Livestock	6,064,051,000
Average value of all farm property to the farm	$9,103
Farms operated by owners	3,568,394 (number)
Operated by tenants	2,664,000

Number Operated in	*By Owners*	*By Tenants*
New England	114,000	7,900
Mid Atlantic	299,000	52,000
E. N. Central	694,000	264,000
W. N. Central	661,000	444,000
So. Atlantic	540,000	510,000
E. So. Central	465,000	594,000
W. So. Central	410,000	687,000
Mountain	179,000	59,000
Pacific	206,000	46,000

Mortgage status:

	Total Number of Farms Free from Mortgage	*Number of Farms Mortgaged*
N. England	59,000	50,000
Mid. Atlantic	164,000	120,000
E. N. Central	342,000	318,000
W. N. Central	271,000	361,000
So. Atlantic	351,000	146,000
E. S. Central	282,000	145,000
W. S. Central	209,000	165,000
Mountain	78,000	85,000
Pacific	89,000	106,600

Trends:

	1850	1870	1890	1910	1930
Number of farms	1,449,000	2,660,000	4,565,000	6,363,000	6,289,000
Number of acres in farms (million acres)	294	408	623	879	987
Per cent of total land area of U. S. in farms	15.6	20.9	32.7	46.2	56.8
Value of farm property (million dollars)	$3,967	$8,945	$16,082	$30,991	$57,246
Gross income from farm products (millions)				$6,643	$9,347
	(1919—$16,935; 1921—$8,928; 1929—$11,911)				
Gainful workers in agriculture (thousands)	2,401	5,922	8,566	12,659	10,472
Gainful workers in manufacturing and mechanical industries	1,596 (combined with minerals)	2,707 (combined with minerals)	5,091	10,659	14,110
Gainful workers in extraction of minerals			387	965	984

Agricultural Export Indexes (quantity and value) Selected Dates to Show Trends

All Exports Except Cotton and Tobacco		*Cotton*		*Tobacco*	
1910–14	100	1910–14	100	1910–14	100
1921	218	1923	62	1922	111
1926	137	1927	108	1926	136
1929	136	1930	77	1928	184
1931	99	1931	81	1931	166

Potential (Ultimate) Uses of the Land Area of the United States*

Crops (extreme physical possibility)	973,000,000 acres
Arid grazing	468,000,000
Forests only	262,000,000
Pasture and forest (not in forest at present)	66,000,000
Cities, roads, farmsteads, transportation land	67,000,000
Waste	67,000,000

* Estimates made by United States Department of Agriculture.

SELECTED BIBLIOGRAPHY

Only a few of the more valuable references are here presented as a guide for further study. The teacher will find an abundance of current material in our general and technical journals and in the daily newspaper. It is by means of current material that conservation may be made a living movement.

Chapter I

Report of the National Conservation Commission, Senate Document 676, 60th Congress, 2nd Session, Washington, Government Printing Office, 1909.

Van Hise, Charles Richard, *The Conservation of Natural Resources in the United States,* Macmillan Co., New York, 1910 and 1921.

Van Hise, C. R., and Havemeyer, Loomis, *Conservation of Our Natural Resources,* Macmillan Co., New York, 1930.

Report of the Committee on the Conservation and Administration of the Public Domain, January, 1931, Government Printing Office.

Wilbur, Ray Lyman, and Du Puy, William Atherton, *Conservation in the Department of the Interior,* Government Printing Office, 1931.

Report of the Land Planning Committee, of the National Resources Board, Government Printing Office, 1935.

American Forests, Anniversary Number, September, 1935, published by the American Forestry Association.

Sears, Paul B., *Deserts on the March,* Univ. of Oklahoma Press, 1935.

Chase, Stuart, *Rich Land, Poor Land,* Whittlesey House, New York, 1936.

Chapter II

Bowman, Isaiah, "The Land of Your Possession," *Science,* Vol. 82, pp. 285-293, September 27, 1935. (Reprinted in Science Advisory Board, Second Report, Washington, D. C., 1935.)

Donaldson, Thomas, *The Public Domain,* Congressional Document, Washington, 1884.

General Land Office, *Reports of the Commissioner,* Washington, D. C., annual.

Hibbard, B. H., *A History of the Public Land Policies,* New York, 1929.

Joerg, W. L. G., "Geography and National Planning," *Geog. Rev.,* Vol. 25, pp. 177-208, 1935. Reprinted in Science Advisory Board, Second Report, 1935.

Nelson, Knute, "Summary of the Most Important Land Laws," *Annals Am. Acad. Pol. and Soc. Sci.,* Vol. 33, pp. 615-617, 1911.

Paullin, C. O., and Wright, J. K., *Atlas of the Historical Geography of the United States,* New York, 1932.

Report of the National Conservation Commission, 3 vols., Washington, D. C., 1909.

SAUER, C. O., "Land Resource, Land Use and Public Policy," Science Advisory Board, First Report, 1934.

U. S. Census, *Statistical Atlas,* 1903, 1914, 1924.

CHAPTER III

BEAR, F. E., *Soil Management,* John Wiley & Sons, 1927.

JESNESS, O. B., NOWELL, R. I., and Associates: *A Program for Land Use in Northern Minnesota,* University of Minnesota Press, 1935.

KELLOGG, C. E.: "Development and Significance of the Great Soil Groups of the United States," U. S. Dept. Agr. Miscel. Publ. 229, 1936.

KELLOGG, C. E., and ABLEITER, J. K.: "A Method of Rural Land Classification," U. S. Dept. Agr. Tech. Bull. 469, 1935.

LYON, T. L., and BUCKMAN, H. O.: *The Nature and Properties of Soils,* The Macmillan Company, 1929.

MARBUT, C. F.: "Soils of the United States," *Atlas of American Agriculture,* pt. 3, Advance Sheets No. 8, 1935.

NATIONAL RESOURCES BOARD: "A Report on National Planning and Public Works in Relation to Natural Resources and Including Land Use and Water Resources, with Findings and Recommendations," Part II, *Report of the Land Planning Committee,* 89-251, Government Printing Office, 1934. Also, Supplementary Reports of the Land Planning Committee to the National Resources Board, 1935.

Proceedings of the National Conference on Land Utilization, Chicago, Illinois, Nov. 19-21, 1931, Government Printing Office, 1932.

ROBINSON, G. W.: *Soils, Their Origin, Constitution and Classification; An Introduction to Pedology,* D. Van Nostrand Co., 1932.

RUSSELL, SIR E. J.: *Soil Conditions and Plant Growth,* Longmans, Green and Co., 1932.

U. S. DEPT. OF AGR.: *Soil Survey Reports,* 1899-1936. These reports, usually issued by counties, comprise the most excellent and detailed studies of the soils of the United States. Each report contains a map and sections describing the area, its climate, agriculture, and soils.

VAN SLYKE, L. L.: *Fertilizers and Crop Production,* Orange Judd Publishing Co., 1932.

WOLFANGER, L. A.: *Major Soil Divisions of the United States, A Pedologic-Geographic Survey,* John Wiley & Sons, 1930.

CHAPTER IV

BENNETT, H. H., "Some Comparisons of the Properties of Humid-Tropical and Humid-Temperate American Soils," *Soil Science,* Vol. 21, No. 5, May, 1926, pp. 349-374.

BENNETT, H. H., and ALLISON, R. V., *The Soils of Cuba,* Tropical Plant Research Foundation (Boyce-Thompson Institute, Yonkers, New York), 1928.

MEHRING, A. L., and SMALLEY, H. R., *A Survey of Plant Food Consumption in the United States for the Year Ending June 30, 1934,* National Fertilizer Association, Washington, D. C., 1935.

Report of the National Resources Board, Washington, D. C., Part II, Section III, December 1, 1934, pp. 173-174.

Soil Survey of Stewart County, Georgia, Field Operations, Bureau of Soils, United States Department of Agriculture, 1913.

Supplementary Report of the Land Planning Committee, Part V, Soil Erosion, 1935.

Chapter V

Smith, J. Russell. *Tree Crops,* Harcourt, Brace, and Company, New York.

Tennessee Valley Authority, Knoxville, Tennessee, Reports of Tree Crop Specialist.

Chapter VI

Baker, O. E., "The Agriculture of the Great Plains Region," *Annals of the Association of American Geographers,* Vol. 13, pp. 109-167, 1923.

Chilcott, E. C., "Some Misconceptions Concerning Dry-farming," *Yearbook, United States Department of Agriculture,* 1911, pp. 247-256, Washington, D. C., 1912.

Haw, John W., and Schmidt, F. E., *Report on Federal Reclamation to the Secretary of the Interior,* by the Committee on Federal Reclamation Policy, December, 1934, Washington, D. C., 1935.

Johnson, Willard D., "The High Plains and Their Utilization," *Twenty-first and Twenty-second Annual Reports of the United States Geological Survey,* 1901-1902.

Lampen, Dorothy, "Economic and Social Aspects of Federal Reclamation," *Bulletin, Johns Hopkins University Studies in Historical and Political Science,* 1934, pp. 13-124.

Osgood, Ernest, S., *The Day of the Cattleman,* University of Minnesota Press, Minneapolis, 1929.

Powell, John W., *Report on the Lands of the Arid Region of the United States,* Government Printing Office, Washington, D. C.

Scofield, Carl S., "The Present Outlook for Irrigation Farming," *Yearbook of the United States Department of Agriculture for 1911,* pp. 371-382, Washington, D. C., 1912.

Webb, Walter Prescott, *The Great Plains,* Ginn and Company, 1931.

Willard, James F., and Goodykoontz, Colin B., "Experiments in Colorado Colonization," *University of Colorado Historical Collections,* Vol. III, 1926.

National Resources Board Report, Parts I and II, 1934, Washington. Fifteenth Census of the United States, 1930, *Irrigation of Agricultural Lands,* United States Department of Commerce, Bureau of the Census, Washington, D. C., 1932.

Chapter VII

Hanson, Herbert C., and Love, L. Dudley, "Effects of Different Systems of Grazing by Cattle upon a Western Wheat-grass Type of Range," *Col. Agr. Exp. Sta. Bull.* p. 377, 1931.

MERRIAM, C. H., "Prairie Dogs of the Great Plains," *Yearbook, United States Department of Agriculture, 1901,* pp. 257-270, 1908.

SAMPSON, HOMER, C., "An Ecological Survey of the Prairie Vegetation of Illinois," *Div. of Nat. Hist. Surv.,* Vol. 13, pp. 523-577, 1921.

SHELFORD, V. E., "The Physical Environment," Chapter 14, *Manual of Social Psychology,* Worcester, Massachusetts, 1935.

SHIMEK, B., "The Prairies," *Bull. Lab. of Nat. Hist., State Univ. of Iowa,* Vol. 6, pp. 169-240.

STEIGER, T. L., "Structure of Prairie Vegetation," *Ecology,* Vol. 11, pp. 170-217, 1930.

VANDENBURG, J., "Reptiles of Western North America," *Occasional Papers, Col. Acad. Sci.,* Vol. 10, pt. 2, pp. 623-1028, 1922.

VORHIES, C. T., "Wild Life Aspects of Range Rehabilitation," *Hoofs and Horns,* Vol. 5, No. 8, pp. 6-7; No. 9, pp. 10-11, 1936.

WEAVER, J. E., and CLEMENTS, F. E., *Plant Ecology,* McGraw-Hill Book Co., 1929.

WEAVER, J. E., and FITZPATRICK, T. J., "The Prairie," *Ecol. Mono.,* Vol. 4, pp. 109-295, 1934.

Second Report of the Science Advisory Board, Washington, D. C., 1935.

CHAPTER VIII

Report National Resources Board, Superintendent of Documents, Washington, D. C., 1934.

Report of the Mississippi Valley Committee of the Public Works Administration. Superintendent of Documents, Washington, D. C., 1934.

BAKER, O. E., and others. "The Utilization of Our Lands for Crops, Pasture, and Forests," *Agriculture Yearbook, 1923,* pp. 415-506, Superintendent of Documents, Washington, D. C.

Drainage of Agricultural Lands, Fifteenth Census of United States, 1930. Superintendent of Documents, Washington, D. C.

TEELE, R. P., *Economics of Land Reclamation in the United States,* McGraw-Hill Book Co., 1927.

State Planning: A Review of Activities and Progress, by the National Resources Board, Superintendent of Documents, Washington, D. C., 1935.

Mississippi River Commission, Box 665, Vicksburg, Mississippi. Many valuable maps are available from the commission.

CHAPTER IX

Report of National Resources Board, Government Printing Office, Washington, December 1934; particularly Part II, Report of the Land Planning Committee.

Report of Committee on Recent Social Trends, McGraw-Hill Book Co., New York, 1933; particularly Chapters I, II, III, V, VI, IX, X, XIII.

LORIMER, FRANK L., and OSBORN, FREDERICK, *The Dynamics of Population,* Macmillan Co., New York, 1934.

THOMPSON, WARREN H., and WHELPTON, P. K., *Population Trends in the United States,* McGraw-Hill Book Co., New York, 1933.

GOODRICH and others, *Migration and Economic Opportunity,* Report of Study of Redistribution of Population, University of Pennsylvania Press, 1936.

BAKER, O. E., "Rural-Urban Migration and the National Welfare," *Annals of the Association of American Geographers,* June, 1933.

Supplementary Report of the Land Planning Committee, National Resources Board, Part I—"General Conditions and Tendencies Influencing the Nation's Land Requirements," Section 1, Government Printing Office, Washington, 1936.

"The Future Need for Farm Land," issued by *Extension Service,* Iowa State College, Ames, Iowa, August, 1934.

"The Outlook for Rural Youth," *Extension Circular* 223, United States Department of Agriculture, 1935 (mimeographed).

BRUNNER and KOLB, *Rural Social Trends,* McGraw-Hill Book Co., New York, 1933.

KIRKPATRICK, E. L., TOUGH, ROSALIND, and COWLES, MAY L., "How Farm Families Meet the Emergency," *Wisc. Agric. Expt. Sta. Res. Bull.* 126, January, 1935.

FREEMAN, RUTH CRAWFORD, "Living Expenditures of a Group of Illinois Farm Families, 1930, 1931, 1932," *Ill. Agric. Expt. Sta. Bull.* 406, September, 1934.

Federal Emergency Relief Administration, "On Relief," Washington, May, 1935.

Bureau of Agricultural Economics, "Crops and Markets," November, 1932, and July, 1927.

HARD, WALTER, "Vermont: A Way of Life," *Survey Graphic,* July 1, 1932, Vol. 68.

CHAPTERS X AND XI

BROWN, NELSON C., *A General Introduction to Forestry in the United States,* John Wiley and Sons, New York, 1935.

CAMERON, JENKS, *The Development of Governmental Forest Control in the United States,* The Johns Hopkins Press, Baltimore, 1928.

FAIRCHILD, F. R., *Forest Taxation in the United States,* Miscellaneous Publication 218, United States Department of Agriculture, Washington, D. C., 1935.

LOWDERMILK, W. C., "The Role of Vegetation in Erosion Control," *Jour. For.,* Vol. 32, pp. 529-536, 1934.

Natural Resources Board Report, December, 1934, pp. 135-143, 206-216. Government Printing Office, Washington, D. C., 1934.

Senate Document 12, 73rd Congress, Ist Sess. "A National Plan for American Forests," Vols. I and II, Government Printing Office, Washington, D. C., 1933.

SHANTZ, H. L., and ZON, RAPHAEL, *Atlas of American Agriculture,* Pt. I, Section E, "Natural Vegetation," Government Printing Office, Washington, D. C., 1924.

CHAPTER XII

General Statistics of Cities, 1915, Part IV, "Municipally Owned Water Supply Systems," Government Printing Office, Washington, D. C., 1916.

NEWELL, F. H., *Water Resources, Present and Future Uses,* Yale University Press, 1920.

BAKER, D. M., and CONKLING, H., *Water Supply and Utilization,* John Wiley & Sons, New York, 1930.

Report of the Mississippi Valley Committee of the Public Works Administration, Oct. 1, 1934, Government Printing Office, Washington, D. C., 1934.

ROSENAU, M. J., *Preventive Medicine and Hygiene,* Fourth Edition, D. Appleton, New York, 1921.

Report on Water Pollution, Special Advisory Committee on Water Pollution. National Resources Committee, 1935.

CHAPTER XIII

Books

BARROWS, H. K., *Water Power Engineering,* Second Edition, McGraw-Hill, New York, 1934.

GILBERT, CHESTER G., and POGUE, JOHN E., *America's Power Resources,* Century Co., New York, 1921.

VOSKUIL, WALTER H., *The Economics of Water Power Development,* A. W. Shaw Co., New York, 1928.

Government Publications

Federal Power Commission, National Power Survey, *Interim Report,* Government Printing Office, Washington, D. C., 1935.

National Resources Committee, *Regional Factors in National Planning,* United States Government Printing Office, Washington, D. C., 1935.

National Resources Board, *State Planning,* U. S. Government Printing Office, Washington, D. C., 1935.

Tenth Census of the United States, Vols. XVI and XVII, *Water Power of the United States, Parts I and II,* Government Printing Office, Washington, D. C., 1885.

Water Supply Paper 579, United States Geological Survey, *Power Capacity and Production in the United States,* Government Printing Office, Washington, D. C., 1928.

Other Sources

Report of the Giant Power Survey Board to the General Assembly of the Commonwealth of Pennsylvania, *Giant Power,* The Telegraph Printing Co., Harrisburg, 1925.

PARKINS, A. E., "The Water Power of the Southern Appalachians," *Jour. Tennessee Academy of Science,* Vol. 6, No. 3, July, 1931.

VOSKUIL, WALTER H., "The Competitive Position of Illinois Coal in the Illinois Market Area, *Bull.* 63, *Illinois State Geol. Survey,* 1936.

CHAPTER XIV

Report of Chief of Engineers, U. S. Army, Government Printing Office, Washington, D. C., Annual.

Annual Report of the Inland Waterways Corporation, Government Printing Office, Washington, D. C.

Port Series, prepared by U. S. Army Engineers and U. S. Shipping Board.

Transportation Series, prepared by U. S. Army Engineers and the Shipping

Board. *Transportation on the Great Lakes. Transportation on the Mississippi and Ohio River Valley.* The second was issued in 1929.

MOULTON, HAROLD GLENN, *Waterways versus Railways,* Riverside Press, Cambridge, Massachusetts.

MOULTON, HAROLD GLENN, *The American Transportation Problem,* Brookings Institution, Washington, D. C., 1933.

MOULTON, HAROLD GLENN, and others, *The St. Lawrence Navigation and Power Project,* The Brookings Institution, Washington, D. C., 1929.

JOHNSON, JULIA E., *St. Lawrence River Ship Canal.* The Reference Shelf, H. W. Wilson Co., New York, 1926.

ANDREWS, ISRAEL D., *On the Trade and Commerce of the British North American Colonies,* B. Tucker, Senate printer, Washington, D. C., 1854.

GREGG, EUGENE STUART, *Great Lakes to Ocean Waterways,* Government Printing Office, Washington, D. C., 1927.

DIXON, FRANK H., *A Traffic History of the Mississippi River System,* Government Printing Office, Washington, D. C., 1909.

Reports of the United States Waterways Experiment Station, Vicksburg, Mississippi.

SWITZER, J. E., "The Completed Ohio River Project," *Proc. Ind. Acad. Sci.,* Vol. 41, 1931-1932.

CHAPTER XV

HENRY, ALFRED J., "The Distribution of Maximum Floods," *Monthly Weather Review,* Vol. 47, 1919, pp. 861-867.

HOYT, W. G., and others, *Studies of Relations of Rainfall and Run-off in the United States,* United States Geological Survey, Water Supply Paper, 772. Washington, D. C., 1936.

HUMPHREYS, ANDREW A., and ABBOTT, HENRY, L., *Report upon the Physics and Hydraulics of the Mississippi River,* War Department, Washington, D. C., 1861.

JARVIS, CLARENCE S., and others, *Floods in the United States,* United States Geological Survey, Water Supply Paper 771, Washington, D. C., 1936.

Mississippi River Commission, Annual reports.

National Resources Board, Part III, *Report of the Water Planning Committee,* Washington, D. C., 1934, pp. 253-388.

Report of the Mississippi Valley Committee of the Public Works Administration, Washington, 1934, 234 pages.

United States Congress, House Committee on Flood Control, *Analysis of Plans of Army Engineers and Mississippi River Commission,* by L. T. BERTHE, Committee Document 11, 70th Congress, 1st Sess., 1928.

ALVORD, J. W., and BURDICK, C. B., *Relief from Floods,* New York, 1918.

BEMAN, L. T., *Flood Control,* New York, 1928.

BOCK, CARL A., *History of the Miami Flood Control Project,* Dayton, Ohio, 1918.

CLINE, I. M., *Floods in the Lower Mississippi Valley,* New Orleans, 1927.

CHAPTER XVI

LEITH, C. K., "Conservation of Minerals," *Science Advisory Board,* second report, Washington, D. C., September 1, 1935, pp. 357-372; also in *Science,* Vol. 82, pp. 109-117, August 9, 1935.

LEITH, C. K., *World Minerals and World Politics,* McGraw-Hill, 1931.

LEITH, C. K., "The World's Iron Ore Supply," reprint of paper read at World Engineering Congress, Tokyo, Japan, 1929.

BAIN, H. FOSTER, "World Mineral Production and Control," *Foreign Affairs,* July, 1933, pp. 706-710.

BAIN, H. FOSTER, "The Third Kingdom: Some Reflections on our Mineral Heritage," *Geog. Rev.,* Vol. 18, pp. 177-195, 1928.

HOLLAND, SIR THOMAS H., *The Mineral Sanction,* Oliver and Boyd, Edinburgh; Tweeddale Court, 1935.

Elements of a National Mineral Policy, prepared by The Mineral Inquiry, 29 West 39th Street, New York, 1933.

"Mineral Economics," *A. I. M. E. Series,* Brookings Institution lectures, McGraw-Hill, 1932.

"Modern Uses of Non-ferrous Metals," *A. I. M. E. Series,* New York, 29 West 39th Street, 1935.

ENEMY, BROOKS, *The Strategy of Raw Materials,* Macmillan, 1934.

VOSKUIL, W. H., *Minerals in Modern Industry,* John Wiley, New York, 1930.

ZIMMERMANN, ERICH W., *World Resources and Industries,* Harper, New York, 1933.

CHAPTER XVII

LEITH, C. K., *World Minerals and World Politics,* New York, 1931.

THOM, W. H., *Petroleum and Coal, the Keys to the Future,* Princeton, 1929.

VOSKUIL, W. H., *Minerals in Modern Industry,* New York, 1930.

World Atlas of Commercial Geology, Parts I and II, United States Geological Survey, Washington, D. C., 1921.

CAMPBELL, M. R., "The Coal Fields of the United States," *Professional Paper* 100, United States Geological Survey, Washington, D. C., 1922.

Coal Resources of the World, 3 volumes and atlas, 12th International Geological Congress, Toronto, 1913.

HOAR, H. M., "The Coal Industry of the World," *Trade Promotion Series,* No. 105, Bureau of Foreign and Domestic Commerce, Washington, D. C., 1930.

MOORE, E. S., *Coal,* John Wiley & Sons, New York, 1922.

National Industrial Conference Board, *Competitive Position of Coal in the United States,* New York, 1931.

EMMONS, W. H., *Geology of Petroleum,* McGraw-Hill, New York, 1921.

GARFIAS, V. R., *Petroleum Resources of the World,* John Wiley & Sons, New York, 1923.

"Refinery Engineering," *Oil and Gas Journal,* Tulsa, Oklahoma, March 19, 1936.

"World Chemical Development, 1934-5," *Trade Information Bulletin* No. 823, United States Department of Commerce.

HOWE, H. E., *Chemistry in Industry,* Chemical Foundation, New York, 1925.

CROWTHER, SAMUEL, *America Self-Contained,* Doubleday, Doran, Garden City, New York, 1933.

CHAPTER XVIII

EAKIN, HENRY M., "Silting of Reservoirs," Soil Conservation Service, *United States Department of Agriculture, Technical Bulletin* 524, July, 1936.

"World Chemical Development in 1935," and similar reports for earlier years. These are *Trade Information Bulletins* of the Chemical Division of Bureau of Foreign and Domestic Commerce, United States Department of Commerce, issued annually for the world and for individual countries.

Proceedings of the First and Second Dearborn Conference of Agriculture, Industry and Science, printed and distributed by the Farm Chemurgic Council, Dearborn, Michigan.

FOSTER, WILLIAM, *The Romance of Chemistry,* Century Co.

HAYNES, WILLIAMS, *Men, Money and Molecules,* Doubleday, Doran.

DAVIS, WATSON, *The Advance of Science,* Doubleday, Doran, 1934.

Chemistry in Industry (Vols. 1 and 2); *Chemistry in Agriculture,* Chemical Foundation.

CHAPTER XIX

ADAMS, C. C., "Relation of Wild Life to the Public in National and State Parks," *Roosevelt Wild Life Bull.,* Vol. 2, pp. 371-401, 1925.

"The Conservation of Predatory Mammals," *Jour. Mammalogy,* Vol. 6, pp. 83-96, 1925.

"Report of the Committee on Wildlife Sanctuaries, Including Provision for Predatory Mammals," *Jour. Mammalogy,* Vol. 9, pp. 354-358, 1928.

"Rational Predatory Animal Control," *Jour. Mammalogy,* Vol. 11, pp. 353-362, 1930.

"The Importance of Establishing Natural History Reservations for Research and Education," *N. Y. State Museum Rep.,* Vol. 24, pp. 71-83, 1931.

ATKINS, C. G., "On Fish-ways," *U. S. Commission of Fish and Fisheries,* Report for 1872-73, Part II, pp. 591-616, 1908.

Biological Survey, "Requirements for Wildlife Areas," Natural Resources Board, *Planning for Wild Life,* Vol. 9, pp. 1-14, 1935.

Federation of Ontario Naturalists, "Sanctuaries and the Preservation of Wild Life in Ontario," Pub. 2.

GRIGGS, R. F., "The Edge of the Forest in Alaska and the Reasons for Its Position," *Ecology,* Vol. 15, pp. 80-96, 1934.

HALL, H. M., "European Reservations for the Protection of Natural Conditions," *Jour. For.,* Vol. 27, pp. 667-683, 1929.

MCATEE, W. L., "Our Vanishing Shorebirds," U. S. Bur. of Bio. Survey, Circular 79.

MARSH, M. C., "The Effect of Some Industrial Wastes on Fishes," United States Geological Survey, Water Supply Paper 192, pp. 337-348.

OBERHOLZER, E. C., "An International Park," *Can. Geog. Jour.,* Vol. 9, pp. 72-80, 1934.

OLSON, S., "The Poison Trail," *Sports-Afield,* December, 1930.

PACK, A. N., "A Plan for Conservation," *Nature Mag.,* Vol. 27, p. 169, 1936.

PEARSON, G. A., and MARSH, R. E., "Timber Growing and Logging Practice in the Southwest and the Black Hills Region," *United States Department of Agriculture, Tech. Bull.* 480, pp. 1-79, 1935.

ROBERTS, P. H., and O'MALLEY, H., "Wild Life a Forest Resource. A National Plan for American Forestry," Senate Document 12, pp. 489-525, 1933.

SHELFORD, V. E., "Animal Communities in Temperate America," *Bull. Geogr. Soc. Chicago,* No. 5, 1913.
"Ways and Means of Measuring the Dangers of Pollution to Fisheries," *Bull. Illinois State Nat. Hist. Survey,* Vol. 13 (2), pp. 25-42, 1918.
Naturalist's Guide to the Americas (V. E. Shelford, Compiler), Baltimore, 1925.
"Nature Sanctuary Plan," *Ecology,* Vol. 14, pp. 241-242, 1932.
"Nature Sanctuaries a Means of Saving Natural Biotic Communities," *Science,* Vol. 77, pp. 281-282, 1932.
"The Physical Environment," *Handbook of Social Psychology,* Chapter 14, Worcester, Massachusetts, 1935.
SUMNER, F. B., "The Responsibility of the Biologist in the Matter of Preserving Natural Conditions," *Science,* Vol. 54, pp. 39-43, 1921.
VORHIES, C. T., "Wild Life Aspect of Range Rehabitation," *Hoofs and Horns,* Vol. 5, No. 8, pp. 6-7; No. 9, pp. 10-11, 1936.
WARD, H. B., "The Elimination of Stream Pollution in New York State," *Trans. Am. Fisheries Soc.,* Vol. 48, pp. 3-25, 1919.
WRIGHT, G. M., and THOMPSON, BEN, "Wild Life Management in the National Parks," *Fauna of the N. D.,* Fauna Series 2, 1934.
WRIGHT, HARRISON, "On the Early Shad Fisheries of the North Branch of the Susquehanna River," *United States Commission of Fish and Fisheries, Report,* pp. 619-642.

CHAPTER XX

Forest Service of the Agricultural Department, A National Plan for American Forestry, Senate Document 12, Seventy-third Congress, 1st Session, United States Printing Office, 1933.
The Director of the National Park Service, *Annual Reports,* United States Department of the Interior.
BLACK, JAMES J., *Map of Recreational Areas of the United States,* Department of the Interior, United States Printing Office, 1933.
Michigan State Department of Conservation, *Biennial Reports,* State of Michigan.
National Park Service, Folders for each National Park, United States Department of the Interior, United States Government Printing Office. Issued annually.
JAMES, HARLEAN, *Land Planning in the United States for City, State and Nation,* The Macmillan Company, 1926.
HEDRICK, WILBUR O., "Recreational Use of Northern Michigan Cut-over Lands," *Special Bulletin* 247, Agricultural Experiment Station, Michigan State College, 1934.
SCHOENMANN, ROY A., "Land Inventory for Rural Planning in Alger County, Michigan," *Papers of the Michigan Academy of Science, Arts and Letters,* Vol. XVI, pp. 329-361, University of Michigan, 1931.
PROPHET, EDWARD C., "Significance of Recreational Development in Roscommon County, Michigan," *Papers of the Michigan Academy of Science, Arts and Letters,* Vol. XVI, pp. 313-327, University of Michigan, 1931.
ELY, RICHARD T., and MOREHOUSE, EDWARD W., *Elements of Land Economics,* The Macmillan Company, 1926.
BRYANT, HAROLD C., and ATWOOD, WALLACE W., JR., *Research and Education in the*

National Parks, United States Department of the Interior, United States Government Printing Office, 1932.

CHAPTER XXI

Bureau of the Census, *Birth, Stillbirth, and Infant Mortality Statistics,* Washington, D. C., 1928 and 1934.

DUBLIN, LOUIS I., and LOTKA, ALFRED J., *The Money Value of a Man,* New York, 1930.

HUNTINGTON, ELLSWORTH, and WHITNEY, LEON F., *The Builders of America,* New York, 1927.

LORIMER, FRANK, and OSBORN, FREDERICK, *Dynamics of Population,* New York, 1934.

METROPOLITAN LIFE INSURANCE COMPANY, *Statistical Bulletin,* 1926, 1934.

THOMPSON, WARREN S., *Ratio of Children to Women, 1920,* Census Monograph, Washington, D. C., 1931.

CHAPTER XXII

ADAMS, THOMAS, *Outline of Town and City Planning,* Russell Sage Foundation, New York, 1935.

AMERICAN CIVIC ASSOCIATION, *American Civic Annual,* edited by Harlean James, 1931-date.

Planning Problems of Town, City and Region, Papers and discussions at the International City and Regional Planning Conference, The Norman, Remington Company, Baltimore, 1925.

Regional Plan of New York and Its Environs, Frederick A. Delano, Chairman, New York, 1931.

United States National Resources Committee, *Status of Organization of Planning Districts and State Planning Boards,* Washington, D. C., 1935.

United States National Resources Board, *A Report on National Planning and Public Works in Relation to Natural Resources and Including Land Use and Water Resources with Findings and Recommendations,* Washington, D. C., 1934.

United States National Resources Board, *State Planning: A Review of Activities and Progress,* Washington, D. C., 1935.

CHAPTER XXIII

A Conference on Regions—articles by ROBERT B. HALL, GEORGE T. RENNER, and ROBERT S. PLATT, in *Ann. Assn. Am. Geog.,* Vol. 25, No. 3, September, 1935.

American Civic Annual, Vol. 5, edited by HARLEAN JAMES, 1934, p. 278, American Civic Association, Washington, D. C., Part II, "Regional Planning," pp. 109-136.

ARONOVICI, C., "Regional Planning versus Sectionalism," *Scholastic Magazine,* p. 3, March 17, 1934.

ASCHER, C. S., "Regionalism Charting the Future," *Survey Graphic,* 2 pp., August 15, 1931.

CLARK, JOHN M., "Economics of Planning Public Works," National Planning

Board (National Resources Committee) 1935, 194 pp., Government Printing Office, Washington, D. C.

Crane, Jacob, and Renner, George T., "Exploratory Survey of a Study of Regionalism in National Development," Report to the National Resources Board, March, 1935, Washington, D. C., 21 pp.

Draper, E. S., "Regional Planning and the Tennessee Valley Authority," lecture before the Harvard School of City Planning, January 14, 1935.

Eliot, Charles W., "Resources Study Begin," *Engineering News-Record*, p. 2, February 7, 1935, New York.

Elliott, Foster F., "Types of Farming in the United States," United States Department of Commerce, Bureau of the Census, 1933, p. 225, Government Printing Office, Washington, D. C.

Gaus, John M., Crane, Jacob, Dimock, Marshall E., and Renner, George T., "Regional Factors in National Planning and Development," December, 1935, National Resources Committee, 215 pp., 47 illustrations, Government Printing Office, Washington, D. C.

Kehr, C., *A Nation Plan*, 210 pp., Oxford Univ. Press, New York, 1926.

McKaye, Benton, *The New Exploration: a Philosophy of Regional Planning*, 235 pp., Harcourt, Brace, New York, 1928.

"New England's Prospect," 1933, edited by John K. Wright, Am. Geog. Soc., 481 pp., New York, 1933.

Woodruff, Joseph T., and Clark, Frederick P., *A Plan for New England*, Boston, 1934.

Woofter, T. J., "Tennessee Valley Regional Plan," *Social Forces*, March, 1934.

INDEX

A

B

C

L

M

N

O

P

R

S

T

U

V

W

Z